Vernice Meye[r]
Wendell Wess[...]
3349 So. Fre[...]
Mpls. Minnesota

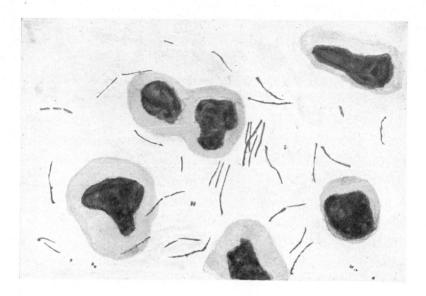

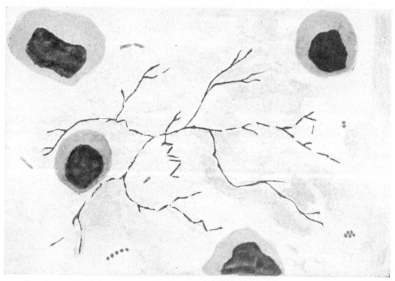

Actinomycetales

The upper drawing shows tubercle bacilli in sputum, stained by Ziehl-Neelsen's method. The lower drawing shows an acidfast Actinomyces (*Proactinomyces asteroides*) in sputum, stained by the same method. Note in the lower drawing the fragmentation of the filaments into bacteria-like segments.

THE
BIOLOGY OF BACTERIA
An Introduction to
GENERAL MICROBIOLOGY
SECOND EDITION

BY

ARTHUR T. HENRICI, M.D.

PROFESSOR OF BACTERIOLOGY
UNIVERSITY OF MINNESOTA

D. C. HEATH AND COMPANY

BOSTON	NEW YORK	CHICAGO
ATLANTA	SAN FRANCISCO	DALLAS
	LONDON	

PRINTED IN THE UNITED STATES OF AMERICA

PREFACE

THIS is a textbook to be used by general or nontechnical students who will take but one course in microbiology; or in introductory courses for other students who will be taught particular applications of the science in advanced courses. It has been my aim to produce a work which would not be too voluminous to be used in a one-semester course, yet sufficiently comprehensive so that the student will gain a clear idea of the scope of the subject. Above all I have tried to present the material as *microbiology*, not as agriculture or hygiene — to stress the pure science aspects rather than the applications. When the student is well grounded in fundamentals, applications will become obvious.

In the preface to the new British *System of Bacteriology* it is stated that "though bacteria are the subject matter of bacteriology, they do not, in and for themselves, constitute its main interest." True enough until recently, this attitude toward bacteriology is rapidly changing. It is commonplace knowledge that, beginning with the investigations of Pasteur, researches upon the activities of bacteria in relation to medicine, agriculture, and industry have almost revolutionized modern life. But such researches are now yielding diminishing returns, and we are beginning to realize that this is due, in part at least, to the fact that we have built upon a poor foundation; while busy studying the activities of economic importance, we have failed to observe the fundamental biological peculiarities of the microbes.

The lower unicellular microörganisms present problems of morphology and taxonomy, of heredity and evolution, of physiology and ecology, which differ not only in degree, but also in kind, from those offered by the higher plants and animals, sufficient to warrant considering microbiology as a separate branch of biologic science, distinct from either botany or zoölogy. And these problems are of fundamental importance. What, for instance, may be the nature of the protoplasm in an organism not much larger than a protein molecule? What is the mechanism of heredity and variation in

iii

organisms which possess no nuclei, no chromosomes? Consider the physiological problems involved in organisms which can grow at a temperature approaching the boiling point of water; in organisms that obtain their energy by burning, not carbon compounds, but sulphur, hydrogen, or ammonia. These are but a few of the biologic problems peculiar to the bacteria.

While not failing to parade the achievements of bacteriology, nor to point out applications in daily life, I have presented the subject entirely as a biologic science, with the applications interpolated in their proper places. Comparative morphology and taxonomy will ever be the firm foundation upon which a knowledge of biologic science, pure or applied, must be built. Although our knowledge of this part of bacteriology is still very incomplete, and is rapidly changing, I believe that it is desirable to stress these aspects of the subject with beginning students.

The bacteriologist, medical or technical, cannot limit his studies to bacteria alone, since important diseases and fermentations are caused by other types of microbes. Moreover, the bacteria gain significance as objects of biological study by comparison and contrast with other kinds of unicellular beings. It is therefore neither possible nor desirable to limit a book of this sort to a discussion of the bacteria. While dealing mainly with bacteria, a considerable part of the work has to do with Protozoa and Fungi, and other forms of microbic life.

The scope of bacteriology has become so extensive that no one person may speak authoritatively on all phases of the science. A work of this sort cannot be considered original save in the selection and arrangement of the subject matter. I have drawn freely from many sources. A number of illustrations have been borrowed from other works. The sources are indicated in the legends. I am very grateful to the various authors and publishers who have granted me permission to reproduce. Much valuable aid and criticism have been received from my colleagues in the department of bacteriology. In particular I wish to express my indebtedness to Mrs. Beryl B. Green, who has kindly read the entire manuscript.

ARTHUR T. HENRICI

The University of Minnesota
December, 1933

PREFACE TO THE SECOND EDITION

Science continues to move on at an ever accelerating pace, and this revision has required deletion, restatement, or amplification of topics in almost every chapter. The nomenclature and classification of bacteria have been changed to conform with the fifth edition of Bergey's *Manual*. Two new chapters have been added, dealing with the effect of environmental factors upon bacteria and with the distribution of bacteria in soil, water, milk, and the human body.

ARTHUR T. HENRICI

The University of Minnesota
December, 1938

TABLE OF CONTENTS

CHAPTER   PAGE

I. A BRIEF HISTORY OF BACTERIOLOGY   1

Early Microscopy. Discovery of Bacteria. Spontaneous Generation. Fermentation and Putrefaction. Putrefaction and Disease. Pasteur. Microbes the Cause of Fermentation. Disproof of Spontaneous Generation. Microbes a Cause of Disease. Need for Pure Cultures. Pleomorphism. Koch. Discovery of Pure Culture Technique. Agar. Koch's Postulates. Many Applications. Cohn. Monomorphism.

II. THE MICROSCOPE AND MICROSCOPY   20

Accommodation. What the Microscope Does. Simple Microscopes. Aberrations. Compound Microscopes. Magnification. Resolving Power. Useful Magnification. Oil Immersion. Use of Condenser. Limitations of Microscopes. The Electronic Microscope. Dark Field Illumination. Observing Bacteria. Wet Preparations. Hanging Drops. Stains. Theories of Staining. Staining Bacteria. Gram's Stain. Significance of Gram's Stain. Theory of Gram's Stain. Negative Staining.

III. A SURVEY OF MICROBIC LIFE: THE PROTOZOA   40

Amoeba. Structure of Amoeba. Nutrition. Reproduction. Amoeba an Animal. Protozoa. Classes of Protozoa. Mastigophora. Structure of Flagellates. Chlorophyll. Subclasses of Flagellates. Nutrition of Flagellates. Reproduction. Colonies. Differentiation. Flagellates a Common Ancestor. Plant or Animal? Unicellular or Multicellular? Sarcodina. Pseudopodia. Tests. Foraminifera. Slime Molds. Sporozoa. Life Cycles of Sporozoa. Ciliata. Paramecium. Structure. Reproduction. Suctoria.

IV. A SURVEY OF MICROBIC LIFE: THE ALGAE   58

Thallophytes. Classes of Algae. Green Algae. Chrysophyceae. Diatoms. Shells of Diatoms. Blue-green Algae. Structure. Reproduction. Relationships of the Algae.

V. A SURVEY OF MICROBIC LIFE: THE FUNGI   67

Mycelium. Reproduction of Saprolegnia. Sexual Reproduction. Classes of Fungi. Slime Molds Again. Structure of Mycelium. Spores. Exogenous Spores. Conidia. Chlamydospores. Sexual Spores. Phycomycetes. Ascomycetes. Basidiomycetes. Fungi Imperfecti. Oidia. Yeasts. Nutrition of Fungi. Relationships of the Fungi.

CHAPTER   PAGE

VI. A SURVEY OF MICROBIC LIFE: THE BACTERIA   82

What Are Bacteria? Size. Structure. Orders of Bacteria. Iron Bacteria. Leptothrix. Nutrition of Iron Bacteria. Chlamydobacteriales. Crenothrix. Sphaerotilus. Caulobacteriales. Gallionella. Sulphur Bacteria. Nutrition of Sulphur Bacteria. Purple and Green Sulphur Bacteria. Nutrition. Types of Red Sulphur Bacteria. Myxobacteriales. Reproduction. Actinomycetales. Actinomycetaceae. Mycobacteriaceae. Proactinomyces. Corynebacteria. Mycobacteria. Eubacteriales. Spirochaetales. Relationships of the Bacteria. The Origin of Life.

VII. A SURVEY OF MICROBIC LIFE: THE ULTRAMICROBES   105

What Is an Individual? Size of Microörganisms. How Small May Organisms Be? Filters. How Filters Work. Filterable Viruses. The Bacteriophage. The Bacteriophage Is Particulate. Cultivation of Viruses. No Free-living Ultramicrobes. Nature of Viruses. The Enzyme Theory. The Life Cycle Theory. Retrograde Evolution. The Ultramicrobe Theory. A Frontier of Science.

VIII. THE FINER STRUCTURE OF BACTERIAL CELLS   117

Cells. Cells of Bacteria. Cell Membrane. Cell Wall. Plasmolysis. Capsules. Capsule Stains. Capsules and Virulence. Sheaths. Flagella. Staining Flagella. Types of Flagellation. Motion of Flagella. Cytoplasm. Reserve Materials. Volutin. Staining of Volutin. Spores. Spore Formation. Staining of Spores. Properties of Spores. Germination of Spores. Nuclei of Bacteria. Theories about Nuclei. No Nucleus. All Nucleus. True Nucleus. Diffuse Nucleus. An Important Problem.

IX. THE GROWTH AND REPRODUCTION OF BACTERIA   138

Cell Division. Cell Groupings. Plasmodesmids. Post-fission Movements. Rate of Growth. The Growth Curve. The Law of Growth. Morphological Changes during Growth. Involution Forms. Cytomorphosis. Pleomorphism. Life Cycles of Bacteria. Branching. Budding. Gonidia. Sexual Reproduction. Symplasm. Filterable Forms.

X. HEREDITY AND VARIATION IN BACTERIA   151

Variation. Hybrids. Mutations. Variations in Lower Organisms. Artificial Selection. Adaptations. Temporary Modifications. Mutation-like Variations. Secondary Colonies. Sectors. Unstable Cultures. Spontaneous and Induced Variations. Microbic Dissociation. Smooth and Rough Variants. Theories. Sex. Cyclostages. True Mutations. Genes in Bacteria.

XI. THE METABOLISM OF BACTERIA   165

Builders and Destroyers. The Work of Bacteria. Bacteriology and

CHAPTER   PAGE
Biochemistry. The Nature of Protoplasm. Metabolism. Energy
Requirements. Autotrophic Metabolism. Chemistry of Autotrophic
Metabolism. Autotrophic Respiration. Heterotrophic Metabolism.
Enzymes. Theories of Enzyme Action. Specificity of Enzymes.
Batteries of Enzymes. Nomenclature of Enzymes. Exoenzymes and
Endoenzymes. Constitutive and Adaptive Enzymes. Carbohydrate
Metabolism. Hydrolysis of Polysaccharides. Hydrolysis of Di-
saccharides. Respiration of Bacteria. Intermolecular Respiration.
Intramolecular Respiration. Three Kinds of Respiration. Oxidation
and Reduction. Induced Reactions in Fermentation. Fermentation.
Fermentation of Monosaccharides. Types of Fermentation. Alco-
holic Fermentation. Other Fermentations. Fermentation in Nature.
The Carbon Cycle. Other Sources of Energy. Protein Metabolism.
Products of Protein Decomposition. Hydrolysis to Amino Acids.
Deaminization. Decarboxylation. Putrefactive Bacteria. Urea.
Ammonification. Nitrification. The Nitrogen Cycle. Denitrifica-
tion. Nitrogen Fixation. Free-living Nitrogen Fixers. Symbiotic
Nitrogen Fixers. Fat Metabolism.

XII. ECOLOGY OF BACTERIA: ENVIRONMENTAL FACTORS   194
Nutrient Requirements of Bacteria. Accessory Growth-promoting
Substances. Carbon Dioxide. Food Supply in Natural Habitats.
Temperature. Reaction. Oxidation and Reduction. Why Cannot
Anaerobic Bacteria Grow in Air? Oxidation-Reduction in Natural
Habitats. Surfaces. Moisture and Osmotic Pressure. Light. The
Living Environment. Bacteria Are Versatile. Niches.

XIII. THE CULTIVATION OF BACTERIA   212
Plating. Streak Plates. Quantitative Plating. Colonies. Dilution
Methods. Single Cell Isolation. Enrichment Cultures. Differential
Media. Conditions Necessary for Cultivating Bacteria. Anaerobic
Methods. Nutrient Media. Broth. Agar. Gelatine. Peptone.
Indol. Potato. Litmus Milk. Carbohydrates in Milk. Proteins
in Milk. Curdling of Milk. Peptonization. Reduction. Sugar
Media. Special Media. Blood Media. Synthetic Media. Steriliza-
tion of Media.

XIV. ECOLOGY OF BACTERIA: HABITATS   229
SOIL. Soil as a Culture Medium. Methods of Studying Soil
Microbes. Distribution of Soil Bacteria. Environmental Factors
in the Soil. Bacteria and Soil Fertility. WATER. Methods for
Studying Water Bacteria. Lakes. Bacteria in Lake Waters. Lake
Bottoms. Kinds of Lake Bacteria. Streams. Self-purification of
Streams. The Sea. MILK. Numbers of Bacteria in Milk. Pasteur-
ization. Normal Fermentation of Milk. Abnormal Fermentations.
Diseases Spread by Milk. THE HUMAN BODY. Where Parasitic
Bacteria Are Found. The Skin. The Mouth. Nose and Throat.

CHAPTER   PAGE

Alimentary Tract. Intestinal Bacteria and Health. Life without Germs.

XV. THE DEATH OF BACTERIA; DISINFECTION   248
The Order of Death. Theories. Bacteria Are Different. Susceptibility of Different Microörganisms. Sterilization and Disinfection. Death by Drying. Light. Heat. Disinfectants. Acids and Alkalies. Oxidizing Agents. Coagulants. The Dyes. Surface Tension Depressants. Standardization of Disinfectants. The Phenol Coefficient. Chemotherapy.

XVI. INFECTION   259
Infection. Parasitic Bacteria. Parasitic Bacteria May Become Pathogenic. Specificity. Factors of Virulence. Invasive Power. Portal of Entry. Resistance of the Bacteria. Local Infections. Spreading Infection. Invasion of the Blood. Septicaemia. Toxins. Toxaemia. Exotoxins. Nature of Exotoxins. Endotoxins. Botulism. Pathogenic Saprophytes. Invasive Power and Toxins. Incubation Period. Variations in Virulence.

XVII. IMMUNITY   271
Vaccination. Other Vaccines. Active Immunization. Antitoxins. Serums. Passive Immunity. Antibacterial Serums. Serum and Vaccine. Phagocytosis. Phagocytosis in Higher Animals. Pus. Different Kinds of Phagocytes. Leucocytosis. Phagocytosis and Immunity. Serum Reactions. Opsonins. Immunology. Antibodies. Antigens. Haptens. Specificity of Serum Reactions. Group Reactions. Antigenic Structure of Bacteria. Applications. Complement. Complement Fixation. Theories of Serum Reactions. Antibody Reactions Are Colloidal Phenomena. Hypersensitivity. Varieties of Hypersensitivity. Anaphylaxis. Serum Sickness. Allergy of Infection. Hypersensitivity and Infection. Skin Tests.

XVIII. BACTERIAL DISEASES OF PLANTS   301
Erwin F. Smith. Plant-Disease Bacteria. Virulence vs. Resistance. Mechanism of Virulence. Resistance of Plants. Portals of Entry. Types of Plant Diseases. Control of Bacterial Plant Diseases.

XIX. CLASSIFICATION OF BACTERIA.   306
Conflicting Aims. A Compromise Is Necessary. Bacteria Require Special Treatment. What Is a Species? Principles to Follow. Discontinuous Variation. Correlated Characters. Early Classifications. Lehmann and Neumann. Migula's Classification. Orla-Jensen's Classification. The S.A.B. Committee.

XX. EUBACTERIALES: NITROBACTERIACEAE, RHIZOBIACEAE, AND AZOTOBACTERIACEAE   319
Bacteria Oxidizing Ammonia and Nitrites. Bacteria Oxidizing

CHAPTER   PAGE

Hydrogen, Methane, and Carbon Monoxide. Bacteria Oxidizing Sulphur. Rhizobiaceae. Rhizobium. Azotobacteriaceae. Azotobacter.

XXI. EUBACTERIALES: ACETOBACTERIACEAE AND PSEUDOMONADACEAE   326
Vinegar Bacteria. Manufacture of Vinegar. Species of Acetobacter. Pseudomonadaceae. Spirilleae. Vibrio. Cholera. Morphology of *Vibrio comma*. Cultural Characters. The "Cholera Red" Reaction. Other Vibrios. Spirillum. *Spirillum volutans*. Pseudomonas. Phytomonas. Protaminobacter. Mycoplana.

XXII. EUBACTERIALES: MICROCOCCACEAE AND NEISSERIACEAE 333
Staphylococcus. Boils. Opsonic Index. Vaccine Treatment. Other Infections with *S. aureus*. Types of *Staphylococcus aureus*. Toxins of *Staphylococcus aureus*. Staphylococcus Food Poisoning. Gaffkya. The Sarcinae. Neisseriaceae. Neisseria. The Meningococcus. Meningococcus Carriers. Types of Meningococci. Serum Treatment. The Gonococcus. *Neisseria catarrhalis*. Veillonella.

XXIII. EUBACTERIALES: STREPTOBACTERIACEAE 343
Streptococceae. The Pneumococcus. Differentiation from Streptococci. Serum Treatment of Pneumonia. Typing of Pneumococci. The Streptococci. Morphology of Streptococci. Classification of Streptococci. Changes Produced in Blood. Sugar Fermentations. Serum Reactions. Key to the Species of Streptococci. *Streptococcus pyogenes*. Scarlet Fever. *Streptococcus mastitidis*. *Streptococcus equi*. Other Haemolytic Streptococci. *Streptococcus salivarius*. Bacterial Endocarditis. Rheumatism. Other Viridans Group Streptococci. *Streptococcus lactis*. *Streptococcus fecalis*. Leuconostoc. Butter Starters. Kefir. Lactobacilleae. Lactobacilli in the Human Body. Lactobacilli in Dairy Products. Propionibacterium.

XXIV. EUBACTERIALES: PARVOBACTERIACEAE, ENTEROBACTERIACEAE, AND BACTERIACEAE 362
Parvobacteriaceae. Pasteurella. Plague. Haemorrhagic Septicaemia. Tularaemia. Malta Fever. Contagious Abortion. Malleomyces. Haemophilus. *Haemophilus influenzae*. *Haemophilus pertussis*. *Haemophilus conjunctivitidis*. *Haemophilus ducreyi*. Dialister. Noguchia. Enterobacteriaceae. Escherichia and Aerobacter. *Escherichia coli*. *Aerobacter aerogenes*. Differentiation of Escherichia and Aerobacter. Sanitary Water Analysis. The Presumptive Test. Isolation of the Gas Formers. Final Identification. Correlated Characters. Intermediate Types. Klebsiella. Erwinia. Serratia. Proteus. Salmonelleae. Typhoid Fever. *Eberthella typhi*. Diagnosis of Typhoid Fever. Protective Vaccination. Salmonella. Paratyphoid Fever. Food Poisoning. Paratyphoids in Lower Animals. Shigella. Bacteriaceae. Listerella. Microbacterium.

CHAPTER   PAGE

Kurthia. Cellulomonas. Flavobacterium. Achromobacter. Actinobacillus. Bacteroides. Fusobacterium. Bacterium.

XXV. EUBACTERIALES: THE BACILLACEAE 383
Bacillus. *B. anthracis.* Anthrax. *B. subtilis. B. cereus. B. my-
coides. B. vulgatus.* Ropy bread. *B. megatherium. B. terminalis.*
Clostridium. Classification of Anaerobes. *Cl. butyricum.* Anaerobic
Nitrogen Fixation. Commercial Solvents. Anaerobic Cellulose De-
composition. Putrefactive Anaerobes. Gas Gangrene. Blackleg.
Tetanus. *Cl. tetani.* Botulism.

XXVI. THE ACTINOMYCETALES 397
Mycobacteriaceae. Mycobacterium. The Tubercle Bacilli. Tuberculosis. Diagnosis of Tuberculosis. Microscopic Examination of
the Sputum. Cultivation. Animal Inoculation. Tuberculin Reaction. Johne's Disease of Cattle. Leprosy. Saprophytic Acidfast
Bacilli. Acidfast Bacteria in the Soil. Corynebacterium. Corynebacteria a Key Group. Diphtheria. Diagnosis of Diphtheria.
Diphtheria Antitoxin. Preventive Vaccination. Other Corynebacteria. Proactinomyces. *Proactinomyces bovis. Proactinomyces
madurae. Proactinomyces asteroides.* Actinomycetaceae. Soil Actinomycetes. Activities of Soil Actinomycetes. Leptotrichia. Erysipelothrix.

XXVII. THE MOLDS 416
Biochemical Characters. Molds in the Soil. Molds in Foodstuffs.
Industrial Uses of Molds. Fungous Diseases. Ringworms. Other
Mycoses. Aspergillosis. Sporotrichosis. Blastomycosis. Coccidioi-
dal Granuloma. Methods for Studying Molds. Identifying Molds.
Species of Molds. Mucor and Rhizopus. Mucor. Rhizopus. As-
pergillus and Penicillium. Aspergillus. Penicillium.

XXVIII. YEASTS AND YEAST-LIKE FUNGI 429
Yeast-like Fungi. *Geotrichum lactis. Monilia albicans.* Classification of Yeasts. Yeasts with Endogenous Spores. Industrial Yeasts.
Yeasts with Exogenous Spores. Yeasts without Spores. Methods
for Studying Yeasts. Activities of Yeasts.

XXIX. THE PATHOGENIC PROTOZOA 435
Geographic Distribution. Modes of Transmission. Recurrent
Character of Protozoan Diseases. Immunity in Protozoan Diseases.
Methods for Studying Protozoa. Types of Pathogenic Protozoa.
Parasitic Amoebae. Amoebic Dysentery. *Entamoeba histolytica.*
Transmission of Amoebic Dysentery. The Trypanosomes. African
Sleeping Sickness. Morphology of the Trypanosomes. Life Cycles.
Leishmania Infection. Kala-azar. Sporozoa. Malaria. Life Cycle
of the Malarial Parasite. Schizogony. Sporogony. Cycle in the
Mosquito. Transmission of Malaria.

CHAPTER   PAGE

XXX. THE SPIROCHAETALES 447
    Spirochaetes and Spirilla. Spirochaetes and Protozoa. Structure
of the Spirochaetes. Life Cycles: Filterability. Cytophaga. Spirochaeta. Cristispira. Saprospira. Treponema. Syphilis. *Treponema
pallidum*. Diagnosis of Syphilis. The Wassermann Reaction. Yaws.
Mouth Spirochaetes. Vincent's Angina. Borrelia. The Relapsing
Fevers. Leptospira. Infectious Jaundice. Rat-bite Fever.

XXXI. THE RICKETTSIA AND VIRUS DISEASES 460
    Rickettsiae. Typhus Fever. Trench Fever. Rocky Mountain
Spotted Fever. Virus Diseases. Inclusion Bodies. Transmission of
Virus Diseases. Immunity in Virus Diseases. Mosaic Disease.
Smallpox. Chickenpox. Herpes. Rabies. The Pasteur Treatment.
Anterior Poliomyelitis. Encephalitis. Influenza. Viruses and
Tumors. Virus Diseases in Lower Animals. Interrelationships of
the Viruses. Yellow Fever. Control of Yellow Fever. Noguchi and
the Leptospira. Yellow Fever in Africa.

INDEX 481

An Introduction to

GENERAL MICROBIOLOGY

THE BIOLOGY OF BACTERIA

CHAPTER I

A BRIEF HISTORY OF BACTERIOLOGY

During the latter part of the seventeenth century there lived in Delft, Holland, a very curious man, Anthony van Leeuwenhoek. He was curious in two senses of the word, for he was very inquisitive, poking his nose into this and that, trying to find out how the most insignificant creatures are built; and because of this inquisitiveness, because he did not attend strictly to his business, he must have been a matter of curiosity to his neighbors, the stolid burghers of Delft. For, although he kept a dry-goods store, and was janitor of the city hall, a larger share of his time was devoted to the making of lenses, and with their aid observing all manner of things. His microscopes were simple bits of glass mounted in blocks of metal, and compared with modern instruments were crude indeed; but they were superior in their day, and yielded clear enough images at high enough magnifications to open up to his astonished eyes a whole new universe. Never satisfied, he continued making new microscopes, literally hundreds of them, all his life.

Early Microscopy. More remarkable than the inexhaustible patience with which he kept grinding his little lenses was the insatiable curiosity that made him bring them to bear upon every sort of object that his imagination might suggest. Grains of sand, bits of diamond, the leg of a fly, the sting of a bee, drops of water, the scum on teeth, the eye of a whale, all had to be examined minutely. Many people since have spent happy hours similarly occupied, for the microscope reveals a new world full of charm and interest. But to van Leeuwenhoek was given the added thrill of a pioneer exploring this new world for the first time.

And the things that he discovered were of fundamental, epoch-making importance to science. He saw for the first time the cor-

1

puscles in blood, and their circulation in capillaries; the spermatozoa; the microscopic structures of animal tissues, such as the Haversian canals of bone, the dentinal tubules of the teeth, the striations of muscle fibers, the structure of nerves, of the crystalline lens and retina of the eye; and most important of all, he discovered that host of living organisms, too minute to be seen at all with the naked eye, which we now call microbes.

He was a "self-made" man, relatively uncultured and unlettered, a little jealous of the secrets he had uncovered, a little suspicious of those who came to see his microscopes and the wonders they revealed. If it had not been for a happy affiliation with the newly created Royal Society of England it is quite possible that van Leeuwenhoek's discoveries would have been lost to posterity. In 1674 the anatomist, de Graaf, who had peered through his lenses, persuaded him to communicate some of his discoveries to the Royal Society. The first communication was followed by "hundreds of others over a period of fifty years. They were talkative letters full of salty remarks about his ignorant neighbors, of exposures of charlatans and of skilled explodings of superstitions, of chatter about personal health — but sandwiched between paragraphs and pages of this homely stuff, in almost every letter, those Lords and Gentlemen of the Royal Society had the honor of reading immortal and gloriously accurate descriptions of the discoveries made by the magic eye of that janitor and shopkeeper. What discoveries!" *

In 1676 he announced the discovery of minute "animalcules" in rain, snow, and well water, and in watery infusions of pepper and ginger (the latter he had examined in the hope that he might discover what made them taste hot!). This announcement created intense interest, and two English microscopists, Grew and Hooke, were commissioned to repeat his observations. It was not until a year later that they were able to obtain a microscope with sufficient magnification to reveal van Leeuwenhoek's animalcules. And so the world of little creatures was made known to man!

These microbes that van Leeuwenhoek discovered (and that the gentlemen of the Royal Society so eagerly observed) were of many kinds, and naturally not at first clearly distinguished. But from the recorded communications it is clear that he saw both microscopic plants and animals. Of the latter, some were clearly the one-celled

* DE KRUIF, *Microbe Hunters.*

Protozoa, others were the multicellular rotifers. He observed the globular yeast cells in fermenting liquids and the protozoan parasite, Giardia, in his own stools.

Discovery of Bacteria. In 1683 he communicated to the Royal Society some observations, accompanied by a drawing, on microbes which he had found in white matter that had collected on his teeth. From his descriptions and the drawing it is quite certain that he had seen microörganisms belonging to that group whose members are the smallest and least differentiated of all visible living things — the bacteria. If he could have seen what a furore those bacteria were to create in the scientific world two hundred years later! For like many another pioneer, van Leeuwenhoek was far ahead of his time, and two long centuries were to elapse before the seeds which he had planted were to bear fruit in the researches of Pasteur. During this period the microbes remained for the most part objects of idle curiosity. Their tremendous importance in human affairs was not at all realized. With improvements in the microscope these little creatures were seen more clearly and their differentiation and classification were begun, the publications of Müller (1786) and Ehrenberg (1838) being most important. The latter separated the bacteria from the more complex microörganisms and introduced the names "bacterium" and "spirillum" which are in use today.

Before microbiology could be established as a science with a true understanding of its importance and relationships, two generally accepted but erroneous hypotheses had to be disproved. These were the theory of spontaneous generation, and the chemical theory of fermentation.

Spontaneous Generation. It is a curious fact that at a time when people believed religiously in a special creation of each kind of animal, they accepted equally the idea that new organisms were continually being generated from lifeless material. The origin of frogs and mice from mud, of bees and flies from putrid meat, was not seriously questioned by the ancients. As an observant and inquiring type of mind developed, the error with regard to these grosser organisms was easily detected. Redi (1626–1694) learned the true source of maggots in meat by the simple experiment of placing screens over the vessels in which the meat was kept. But with the microscopic organisms discovered by van Leeuwenhoek it was not so easy to determine their origin. Although the shrewd lens grinder of Delft was not fooled,

and definitely expressed the idea that, like larger organisms, his animalcules arose from preëxisting organisms of the same kind, this idea
was not generally accepted and the theory of spontaneous generation
of microbes was dominant until well into the nineteenth century.

This theory was upheld in the eighteenth century by the English
priest, Needham, who claimed that microbes developed in bottles of
meat broth heated to boiling and tightly stoppered. Since the heat
should have been sufficient to kill any organisms already present,
and the stoppers sufficient to prevent any new ones from entering,
Needham believed that he had experimentally proved the occurrence
of spontaneous generation. He postulated a "vegetative force"
whose action was responsible for the organization of the ingredients
of the meat broth into microbes. But in Italy, Spallanzani, also a
priest, showed that neither the heat nor the sealing in Needham's
experiments was sufficient. By placing the meat broth in hermeti-
cally sealed flasks and heating them for an hour or two, he found that
they remained, as we would say today, sterile, i.e., without any growth
of microörganisms. It was objected that the prolonged heating
destroyed the hypothetical "vegetative force," but this argument was
easily answered by simply cracking one of the sterile flasks of broth,
when at once (germs having been admitted in the air) a growth of
microbes developed.

This simple experiment of Spallanzani's was to prove of the utmost
practical importance, for it demonstrated a procedure by which foodstuffs might be kept from spoiling. It was used for this purpose by
Appert in 1810, and is the basis for our modern canning methods.

But with the growth of chemistry, a new viewpoint developed.
Not vegetative force, but oxygen, was the mysterious element necessary for spontaneous generation. A free access to the atmospheric
oxygen was, of course, excluded in Spallanzani's experiments. This
argument was partially answered by Schultze (1836) who heated
decomposable liquids in flasks to which air was admitted through
strong acid or alkaline solutions, and by Schwann (1837) who passed
air through intensely heated pipes. Here it might be argued that the
chemical or heat treatment had somehow altered the air, but no such
criticism could be applied to the experiments of Schroeder and Dusch
(1854) who excluded microbes from the air by simply filtering it
through cotton wool.

This last was an important discovery, for it provided a very simple technique by which extraneous microbes can be kept out of cultures of germs being studied in the laboratory. This procedure has been in use in microbiological experiments ever since, and its importance will be realized by the student later.

But there were some failures in the experiments of Schultze, Schwann, Schroeder and Dusch (due, as will be seen later, for the most part to insufficient heat); their results were not unequivocal, and the belief in spontaneous generation was far from being completely dispelled.

Fermentation and Putrefaction. Now in all of these experiments, one fact stands out. If the microbes appear, the meat broth, or other substances used, decomposes or putrefies. If no putrefaction occurs, no microbes are seen. The two things are somehow related. A similar relationship had been observed between yeasts and the alcoholic fermentation of sugar. In France, Cagniard-Latour, and in Germany, Theodor Schwann (who, two years later, was to announce the famous Cell Theory) had both observed (1836) the yeast cells discovered by Leeuwenhoek, had seen them multiply by budding, had found them always associated with alcoholic fermentation, and had expressed the belief that they were the cause of that reaction.

But the chemists had become interested in this business of putrefaction and fermentation. Gay-Lussac had expressed an opinion that the oxygen of the air was important in initiating such changes, an opinion that had much to do with the theory of spontaneous generation, as indicated above. The great organic chemist, Liebig, in 1840, brought forward a purely chemical theory of fermentation, in which microbes had no place. Substances which ferment or putrefy, he said, are all composed of large molecules, loosely held together, unstable. Let one of them start to fall apart, it will disturb the balance of the others, the whole thing will upset like a row of bricks, and the molecules will break up into simpler compounds. This would explain why adding a bit of fermenting solution to fresh sugar solution, a bit of rotten meat to fresh meat, would initiate or hasten the fermentation or putrefaction. It was an attractive theory, it seemed to fit the facts, but took no account of those microbes or yeasts that always appeared.

Putrefaction and Disease. Now Liebig applied his theory not only to putrefaction, but also to disease, which he believed to be a similar chemical process. He said, "When putrefying muscle or pus is put on a fresh wound, it occasions disease and death. It is obvious that these substances communicate their own state of putrefaction to the sound blood from which they were produced, exactly in the same manner as gluten in a state of decay or putrefaction causes a similar transformation in a solution of sugar." This was important because there had already been some suggestions that perhaps microbes had something to do with disease. The idea had been expressed by the ancients, but first clearly formulated by the Viennese physician, Plenciz (1762). Observations of the contagiousness of certain diseases, the ability to produce disease with minute quantities of infectious material, the apparently unlimited increase of this material in the diseased body, the incubation period before disease developed after exposure, and finally the specific differences in the symptoms of disease (to be explained by the occurrence of specific microbes for each disease) — all of these led to the view that such diseases were caused by an invisible living agent, a "contagium vivum."

This, then, was the stage set for Pasteur, the master mind who was to found modern microbiology: — Microbes (yeasts or bacteria) always appeared in fermenting or putrefying materials. Their relationship to these reactions was not clear, but it seemed that the fermentation or putrefaction was a spontaneous chemical reaction and that the microbes were either a product of the reaction, or an unimportant by-phenomenon. Disease and putrefaction were looked upon as similar things, and there was a hint that microbes were related to disease also.

Pasteur. In 1822, in the village Dole, in France, there was born Louis Pasteur, son of a tanner and ex-sergeant major in the army of Napoleon. Educated at the École Normale at Paris, he became fascinated by chemistry, and his earliest scientific work had to do with the structure of tartaric acid. *The Journal of Infectious Diseases*, an important American publication dealing with medical bacteriology, bears on its cover a picture of two crystals of tartaric acid, mirror images of each other, commemorating Pasteur's first researches. It is important to remember that Pasteur was, first of all, a chemist. His training, his viewpoint, as a chemist, influenced profoundly his researches in microbiology, influenced indeed the whole subsequent development of the science. He, and the microbiologists who followed him, were much more interested in what microbes *do* than in what they *are*. It is related that when a certain microscopist explained to Pasteur that an organism which he had described as a spherical form was in reality a rod form, Pasteur replied, "If you only knew how little difference that makes to me!"

In 1854 he was made Professor and Dean of the Faculté des Sciences at Lille, and there he was called upon to make some investigations of difficulties in the manufacture of alcohol from beet sugar, an important industry in that city. The readiness with which Pasteur acceded to this request was characteristic of the man and of the science which he founded. He was at all times passionately interested in making science of service to man, in the relief of suffering or the increase of well-being. And microbiology has developed, since his time, almost exclusively as an *applied* science. A large proportion of the basic facts have been uncovered incidentally during the course of researches upon particular economic or medical problems; a strange and risky sort of development.

Microbes the Cause of Fermentation. The observations which Pasteur made while puttering around the beet-sugar vats in Lille were to prove the beginnings of modern microbiology. Briefly, he discovered that the distillers' troubles were due to the replacement of the normal alcoholic fermentation by another type of fermentation in which the sugar was changed to the acid of sour milk, lactic acid. In the vats undergoing alcoholic fermentation he found the round, budding yeast cells; but in the vats undergoing lactic fermentation, these were replaced by a smaller rod-shaped organism. By transferring the yeasts to a sugar solution, he could make them grow, and by continually transferring them he could continue their cultivation in an indefinite series; and always the sugar turned to alcohol. In the same way he could grow the little rods in a continuous series of cultures in sugar solution, and always the sugar turned to lactic acid. There were different kinds of microbes associated with, specific for, each kind of fermentation! To his mind that meant but one thing: — *Microbes are the cause, not the result, of fermentation.*

But to prove it was another thing. Liebig said that fermentation was purely a spontaneous chemical reaction, that the microbes had nothing to do with it. When Pasteur transferred his yeasts to new sugar solution, he necessarily transferred some sugar undergoing alcoholic fermentation, which would transmit its reaction to the other unstable sugar molecules, and they also would turn to alcohol. When

he transferred the little rods, he carried over some sugar undergoing
lactic fermentation, which would similarly transfer its particular kind
of instability to the sugar. The round, budding yeast cells, and the
little rod-shaped lactic acid organisms might be specific by-products
of the two sorts of chemical reaction. Before he could prove the
causal relation of the microörganisms to fermentation, Pasteur had
to prove that they did not arise in the fermenting liquor, that they
came from the outside, that they grew from preëxisting germs of the
same kind. The old spectre of spontaneous generation had to be
laid low once and for all.

Disproof of Spontaneous Generation. But this spectre was not
to be laid low in a day. All of Spallanzani's old experiments were
repeated with all sorts of putrescible materials. Firmly believing
that the invisible microbes were in the air, elaborate experiments were
conducted to prove this. Air was filtered through cotton and asbestos
and bits of these dropped into flasks of sterilized culture medium to
show the abundance of microbes they had picked up. Sealed and
sterilized flasks of yeast infusion (a medium he found favorable for
the growth of bacteria) were carried to cellars, to the city streets, to
the country, to the tops of mountains, and there cracked open, allowing air to enter. These experiments showed that the flasks were more
likely to spoil and develop a growth of microbes when exposed to
the dusty air of the city than to the pure air of the country or the
mountains.

Other important experiments were performed. Liebig's contention that alcoholic fermentation was initiated by the albumen in his
yeast cultures was answered by growing yeast in a solution of pure
chemicals in which ammonium tartrate replaced the protein as a
source of nitrogen. Another type of fermentation was discovered
in which the sugar is converted to butyric acid (the acid of rancid
butter) and this was found to be due to a new microbe, a moving
fish-shaped body which not only could live without air, but was
immobilized by contact with that medium.

The final disproof of the theory of spontaneous generation was
obtained by a simple experiment which, according to de Kruif,
was suggested to Pasteur by his old teacher, the chemist Balard.
Flasks were prepared, whose necks were drawn out in narrow tubes,
first dipping down and then up to form a U-shaped trap for the
microbes of the air. The flasks were filled with solutions of organic

matter capable of undergoing putrefaction. They were heated to boiling to sterilize them, the steam passing through the bent tube killing any microbes within its walls. They were then left to stand *without sealing*. The outer air was given free access, but the air currents were insufficient to carry the germs of life around the U-turn and up the long tube to the interior of the flasks. Here was a crucial experiment towards which no criticism could be directed. The air was given free access, unimpeded or unaltered by chemicals, heat, or filters. And yet the flasks remained sterile.

These flasks were demonstrated by Pasteur at a public lecture given before "tout Paris" at the Sorbonne on April 7, 1864, after some of them had remained clear and unspoiled for four years. This lecture was closed with the following words:

"And, therefore, gentlemen, I could point to that liquid and say to you, I have taken my drop of water from the immensity of creation, and I have taken it full of the elements appropriated to the development of inferior beings. And I wait, I watch, I question it, begging it to recommence for me the spectacle of the first creation. But it is dumb, dumb since these experiments were begun several years ago; it is dumb because I have kept it from the only thing that man cannot produce, from the germs that float in the air, from Life, for Life is a germ and a germ is Life. Never will the doctrine of spontaneous generation recover from the mortal blow of this simple experiment."

And it never has! The possibility of spontaneous generation has never been disproved, but the probability of its occurrence commonly and under ordinary circumstances has been made very remote indeed. In one thing Pasteur was wrong. We now know that microbes do not change sugar to alcohol, or lactic or butyric acid, directly, as an essentially vital process, but by the secretion of substances called enzymes, complex chemical bodies in the twilight zone between the living and the lifeless, having the power to initiate extensive chemical reactions in other substances. We have, since Pasteur's time, come to recognize the existence of another order of minute beings, the filterable viruses, much smaller and simpler in organization than the microbes, too small indeed to be seen by the aid of the microscope, and yet presenting the essential attributes of living organisms. These ultra-microbes do not exist free; they are always parasitic in higher organisms, and there has been suggested the possibility that they have their origin in the latter through some process of disintegra-

tion and reorganization. There is a hint in the air that even the
protein molecules, the building stones of living protoplasm, may grow
like a living organism. In short, we are beginning to find the division
between living and lifeless matter "no longer a line but a broad black
smudge." And it is possible, though by no means proved or even
generally believed, it is still possible that from this border-line material at times and under certain circumstances, new organized living
beings may be generated. But as far as spontaneous generation in
the old sense of the word is concerned —

"No," said Pasteur, "there is now no circumstance known in
which it can be affirmed that microscopic beings came into the world
without germs, without parents similar to themselves. Those who
affirm it have been duped by illusions, by ill-conducted experiments,
spoilt by errors that they either did not perceive or did not know how
to avoid."

It has been hinted that Pasteur was not always willing to give
credit to those who had preceded him, that his ideas and experiments
were not always strictly original with him. It is one thing to discover a truth, another to get it established as an accepted fact.
Whatever criticism may be directed towards Pasteur as regards the
originality of his ideas, nothing can be said to belittle his ability to
put them across. His genius for quick and accurate thinking, for
keen argument, and for obtaining publicity, was not less important
to the development of microbiology than his ingenious experiments.
He "sold" the science to the public.

It is not recorded how the distillers of Lille succeeded with their
vats that soured instead of forming alcohol, but in the next decade
Pasteur was intensely active in a series of practical researches. He
studied what he called "diseases" of wine — undesirable fermentations leading to ropiness or bitterness or other changes — and showed
that these were due to extraneous microörganisms and could be prevented by gently heating the wine, a process which we apply to milk
today and call "pasteurization." He looked into vinegar making,
and showed that this process was due to a microbe that changed
alcohol to acetic acid, and how it might be controlled and made
certain. He investigated, by request, a disease of silkworms, pébrine,
which was ruining the silk industry in the south of France, and showed
that it was caused by a microbic parasite and could be prevented by
selecting eggs from disease-free moths. During the war of 1870,

from patriotic motives, he studied intensively the making of beer in France.

About all of this work he talked and wrote incessantly, and what he had to say became a matter of widespread interest. The little "animalcules" of Leeuwenhoek which had been objects of curiosity for all these years were suddenly brought into immediate, practical, dollars-and-cents relationship with mankind. At this point, micro-biology, which had been moving forward like an ox-cart, was suddenly accelerated to express-train speed. The remaining years of the century were crammed full with important events and discoveries.

Microbes a Cause of Disease. Liebig had said that putrefaction and disease were essentially similar phenomena, Plenciz had said that contagious diseases were caused by living germs, Pasteur had proved that putrefaction was caused by germs, he had talked about "diseases" of wine and beer, he had actually demonstrated a microbic disease of silkworms. In Glasgow, a surgeon, Lister, his imagination fired by the writings of Pasteur, began a warfare on the germs of wound suppuration. He dipped his knives in carbolic acid, he washed his hands and the patient's skin with carbolic acid, he soaked his dressings and sprayed the air with the same solution, until you could smell his hospital a block away. But his wounds healed "by first intention." For the first time in history, surgeons could proceed with an operation calm in the assurance that the wound would not immediately break open with the formation of pus. This "anti-septic" surgery was shortly to be replaced by "aseptic" surgery, in which steam sterilizers, soap and water, and less irritating antiseptics take the place of carbolic acid. Finally a number of people had been describing microörganisms which they had found in diseased blood, or tissue, or pus.

In short, it was fairly evident that microbes were probably the cause of disease as well as fermentation, but a great technical diffi-culty had to be overcome before any real progress could be made in investigating this relationship, or indeed in any of the various appli-cations of microbiology.

Pasteur had learned how to cultivate microörganisms in artificial media, broths made from meat or yeasts or other ingredients. He had learned how to sterilize these media by prolonged boiling, or by the use of steam under pressure to get a higher temperature. He had learned of the widespread distribution of germs in the air, par-

ticularly the dusty air of cities, and how to keep these out of his
cultures by using the cotton wool filters introduced by Schroeder and
Dusch.   He believed that each kind of fermentation has its own
specific microbe and by analogy it was reasoned that each disease
must have its own specific microbe.

Need for Pure Cultures.   The early searchers for disease germs
had no difficulty in finding microbes.   Their difficulty was in finding
too many.   Leeuwenhoek had learned long ago that animalcules
were abundant in the healthy mouth and intestine.   To find amongst
them the stranger that might be a cause of disease was like searching
for a needle in a haystack.   Different people began reporting entirely
dissimilar organisms as the cause of the same disease.   Which of them
was the true cause?   When antiseptic surgery came into use, it was
found that there might be microörganisms on clean, healthy wounds
as well as on those which were breaking open and forming pus.
But the champions of the germ theory of disease said that these
were different microbes, that there were harmless germs and dangerous germs, and that the organisms they saw in slides made from the
clean wounds did not look like the ones they saw in the suppurating
wounds.

But were they different?   Are there good germs and bad germs,
and how do you tell them apart?   How many kinds of germs are
there, anyhow?   Are germs always the same, are their characters
as immutable as the leopard's spots, or do they change like the
flounder's?   The botanists were beginning to become interested in
the lowly and minute forms of plant life, and in Germany de Bary
had discovered a marvelous thing.   There was found a microscopic
Fungus producing little spots on the under side of barberry leaves,
and another one forming red rust spots on the blades of wheat.   But
de Bary proved that these two parasites were the same organism,
which has a complex life cycle and appears in different forms at
different stages on different plants.   This phenomenon was called
pleomorphism, and was found to be exhibited by a number of other
lower Fungi.

Pleomorphism.   There were not lacking those who claimed to have
discovered a similar pleomorphism, more vaguely defined and much
wider in its implications, in the still smaller microbes, the bacteria
associated with disease and putrefaction and fermentation.   Fore-
most of these was Naegeli.   "The same species," he said, "assumes

in the course of generations widely different morphologically and physiologically unlike forms, which may give rise, in the course of years or decades, at one time to a souring of milk, at another rancidity of sauerkraut, or ropiness in wines, now a putrefaction of albumen, again a decomposition of urea, or a red pigmentation of starchy food-stuffs, or may cause now diphtheria, now typhus, later recurrent fever, and again cholera or malaria." To him there was but one germ, which might be good, bad, or indifferent, according to its mood!

These were the vexing problems that faced the early workers in microbiology. They could not be solved until some means could be devised for separating different kinds of bacteria from each other, getting each off by itself to see what it could do, what sort of change it might undergo. You couldn't (at that time at least) pick up one of these extremely minute bodies, pull him away from his neighbors, and pop him into a bottle by himself. There was needed just some little trick of technique.

Koch. That little trick was provided by the genius of a young country doctor in Germany, Robert Koch. He had already done an important "Arbeit." He had *proved* that the minute rod forms which had been found some years before by Davaine in the blood of sheep dying from anthrax were actually the cause of that disease. By grow-ing them continuously through a number of generations in drops of sterile liquid from the eyeballs of cattle where he could *see* under the microscope that no other germs were present, and then drying the liquid on splinters of wood and poking these into little cuts in the tails of mice, he proved beyond question that the bacteria were the cause of the disease, for all of the mice died of anthrax. This was tremendously important, for it was the first clear proof that a disease of man and animals was caused by a germ. Important too were the discoveries made after he had learned the little trick — the discovery of the tubercle bacillus and the cholera vibrio. But none of these was so important to the advancement of microbiology as the little trick.

Discovery of Pure Culture Technique. Like many another im-portant discovery, it was stumbled upon quite by accident, and was one of those things so simple that you wonder why no one had thought of it before. Half a boiled potato had been left standing on the laboratory table. It developed on the surface a number of little spots differing in color and texture. Examined under the microscope, each of these spots was found to be composed of countless numbers of microbes, *all of the same kind*. As germs settled out of the air on to the moist surface of the potato, they stuck there and grew, giving rise continually to new cells of the same kind, and so forming a *colony*. But as the potato was solid and not too moist, they could not swim about much, or they could not diffuse through it as in a liquid culture, and so become mixed up with the offspring of other kinds of germs that had fallen on another part of the potato. The way to get microbes in *pure culture* was to grow them in colonies on a *solid* medium instead of in liquid broth.

Koch first tried separating different kinds of bacteria by streaking the material, say a drop of pus or sputum, on slices of potato. But many organisms will not grow readily on potato, and their separation was uncertain because the place where the individual germs lodge on the potato is left too much to chance, and two different kinds might be deposited side by side and form a mixed rather than a pure colony. What was needed was something that could be both a liquid, so that the individual microörganisms could be well separated by stirring, and a solid, so that they would be trapped, held fast, and prevented from mingling with other kinds. Such a substance was found in gelatine; it melts when warm, and sets in a solid gel when cool. The gelatine solution was made with a meat-broth base to furnish suitable nutrient for the organisms.

Let us suppose that we have a drop of water containing an unknown number of organisms of different kinds. We heat a tube of sterilized meat-broth gelatine until it melts, then put the drop of water in it and stir it up well so that the individual cells will be well separated. This must then be spread in a thin layer. Koch did this by pouring it on a sterilized plate of glass carefully leveled under a sterile bell jar. This was too cumbersome a method, and we now use little flat glass dishes with overlapping lids, called Petri plates. The gelatine sets, the cells are trapped, they multiply, and in a day or two we can see the individual colonies with the naked eye. We heat a wire to sterilize it; and when cool, touch it to a colony, then to some sterile broth in a test tube, replace the sterile cotton plug, and lo, we have a pure culture, composed of individuals all of the same kind, all the offspring of one single germ. It may be that there were so many bacteria in our drop of water that the resultant colonies will be very numerous, very small, and very close together, so that it is impossible to touch just one of them. Since we cannot easily foresee how many colonies will develop, we make a series of dilutions. After the drop of water is stirred up in the first tube of gelatine, a drop of this is transferred to a second tube, and a drop from the second tube to a third. Each tube is poured into a separate Petri dish. Of the three, one is almost sure to have the different colonies widely separated.

Agar. Gelatine, however, has certain disadvantages. It melts at body temperature, or on a warm day, and so must be kept in a cooled room. Now microbes are finicky about little things like temperature, and the disease producers will not always grow at temperatures below that of the body. Also, some kinds of microbes digest gelatine; they change it to simpler compounds which do not jell but dissolve in water, and so the gelatine is liquefied. Whether from too warm a temperature, or the digesting action of bacteria, liquefaction of the gelatine, of course, leads to all the colonies running together, and no pure culture can be obtained. This difficulty was overcome by a certain Frau Hesse, who substituted for the gelatine a substance called agar. Agar is a Japanese product extracted from certain seaweeds. It dissolves in boiling water, and sets at a temperature of 40° C., which is not hot enough to kill any bacteria. When set it will not liquefy again until heated to the boiling point. It is not digested by any ordinary bacteria. It would seem to have been created on purpose for microbiologists.

It is a very simple thing to melt a tube of agar, put a drop of liquid in it, pour it in a dish, and then a day later leisurely fish out each kind of germ by itself — just a little trick of technique. And yet it is quite possible that without it, our hospital wards would still be crowded with typhoid cases, that cholera might again be sweeping through Europe, that we would know nothing about inoculations to prevent diphtheria. And it is highly probable that we would not be sure yet whether microbes are one being with many moods and aspects, or an orderly array of distinct species like mammals, and birds, and flowers.

Koch's method for *isolating* (i.e., separating one kind of bacterium from all others) in pure culture by *plating*, as the process is now called, was made public in 1881, and in the decade that followed the majority of the important microbic causes of disease were discovered. Many of these discoveries were made by Koch's own pupils, Loeffler,

Gaffky, Pfeiffer, Kitasato, Welch, and others, who gathered from all parts of the world to study in his laboratory at Berlin, for he was no longer an unknown country doctor. But together with all of these discoveries whose validity is confirmed by years of experience since, there were brought forward large numbers of others, false discoveries which made things at first confusing. This was the boom period of microbiology. Everybody was hoping for the honor of finding for the first time the germ of this or that disease. Now Koch had become firmly convinced of the *specificity* of disease-producing microörganisms. Each kind of infectious disease, he said, was caused by one, and only one, particular kind of microbe. It was a problem, then, to pick, from the many claimants brought forward, the one true cause for each disease.

Koch's Postulates. To do this Koch formulated what have since been known as his *postulates*, the rules of the game for medical microbiologists. They are:

1. The organism in question must always be present in the lesions, that is, the areas of diseased tissue, in the disease in question. That means that you must always find the tuberculosis bacteria in the tubercles, the little white lumps that appear in the lungs or the glands of people suffering from tuberculosis; always find the typhoid germs in the ulcers that form in the intestines in typhoid fever, and so on.

2. The organism in question must be isolated in pure culture and grown in an artificial medium away from the animal body. The reason for the pure culture was explained above. Growth on artificial media is necessary to exclude the possibility that the disease might be caused by some other agent, a poison in the blood, for instance, that could be transferred directly from one animal to another.

3. When a pure culture of the organism in question is inoculated into one of the susceptible laboratory animals (mice, rabbits, guinea pigs, and sometimes monkeys) it must give rise in the animal to the same disease with the same characteristic changes in the tissues.

4. The same organism as was inoculated must be found in the lesions which develop in the experimentally inoculated animal.

These were the rules that Koch applied before he was ready to announce the proof that anthrax is caused by a bacterium, and the rules that have been applied to nearly all of the microbic causes of disease since. It has not been possible to adhere to them rigidly in all cases. Some of the germs that cause disease in man have either been quite harmless to lower animals or have produced disease without the specific earmarks of the disease in man. But with practically all of these, bacteriologists themselves have been the guinea pigs, by becoming accidentally (or even intentionally) inoculated with pure cultures of the microbes in the laboratory. The organisms, if such they are, which we call filterable viruses, cannot be cultivated in artificial media. They may be grown in cultures containing living cells, but mostly our knowledge of these infectious agents has been obtained by transmitting the disease from one animal to another by inoculating blood or other infectious material. But in general, the rigid enforcement of Koch's rules served to clarify the situation and put the medical side of microbiology on a firm scientific foundation.

Koch's postulates may be applied, with a little modification, to fermentation processes as well, for now that it was easy to obtain pure cultures, it was possible to prove what Pasteur had claimed, that there is a specific microörganism concerned with each type of fermentation. In Copenhagen a Captain Emil Christian Hansen took up the study of beer, which had been begun without much success by Pasteur. He found that there are different kinds of yeasts as well as different kinds of bacteria, and that if you want to get good beer you must have the right kind of yeast. By heating the beer wort to kill or inhibit undesirable yeasts, and then inoculating it with a pure culture of a desirable one for a starter, he converted a chance or haphazard process to one with certain results. This use of *pure culture starters* was soon applied to other fermentation industries, to the making of wine, and industrial alcohol, of butter, and more recently, of cheese, and stimulated a search for other types of useful fermentation which is far from ended even now. As Koch's works had founded a Medical Bacteriology, so did Hansen's found an Industrial Microbiology.

Many Applications. We cannot spare any more space to a detailed discussion of all the events that now followed in rapid sequence — how an American dentist in Berlin, Miller, studied the microorganisms of the mouth in relation to the decay of teeth, and founded a Dental Bacteriology; how the various microbes of disease in domestic animals were discovered and there developed a Veterinary Bacteriology; how Burrill, in Illinois, discovered the bacterial cause of fire blight in pears, and opened a field of investigation to be intensively cultivated by Erwin F. Smith, which was to become an important part of Plant Pathology; how the importance of microbes in milk and other dairy products came to be recognized, and a Dairy Bacteriology was founded; and finally how in Russia, Winogradsky, in Holland, Beijerinck, and in Germany, Hellriegel and Wilfarth, by their studies of microbes concerned with the transformations of nitrogen in the soil, began a Soil Microbiology.

You may see how microbiology developed in a few decades as an intensely practical applied science. The hobby of a few curious ones in the middle of the last century, it was being taught in medical schools and agricultural colleges at the beginning of this one. But its tremendous growth was due to its great importance to the welfare of mankind. The first courses were taught by departments of pathology, or dairying, or soil science, occasionally by a department of botany. People were interested only in what bacteria do. Only very recently has the pendulum begun to swing slowly in the other direction towards a purely scientific interest in what microbes really are, and their relationships to each other and to the rest of the living world.

Cohn. When Koch had worked out his proof of the bacterial causation of anthrax, he took the results of his researches first to Ferdinand Cohn, professor of botany at Breslau. Cohn had been studying bacteria for some time. He had more clearly separated them from the rest of the microbes than had Ehrenberg, separating the *budding* yeasts from the *dividing* bacteria. He had concluded that they were plants and not animals, and believed that they were closely related to certain other microscopic plants, the Blue-green Algae, which form scums on ponds. He had recognized the three main morphologic types of bacteria, the spherical "coccus" forms, the rod-shaped "bacillus" forms, and the corkscrew-shaped "spirillum" forms. He had discovered why Spallanzani and Pasteur had to heat their flasks such a long time to sterilize them; some kinds of bacteria form inside their cells little bodies which he called *spores*, that can stand the heat of boiling water longer than any other known living things. This botanist knew more about what microbes are than anyone else at that time, and it is quite probable that his advice had a great deal to do with Koch's successes.

Monomorphism. The little trick for getting pure cultures which Koch had discovered provided Cohn with a powerful tool for studying these bacteria more certainly and more intimately. He grew them in pure cultures, he watched them as they grew, he looked at them over and over again. And he came to the conclusion that so far as bacteria were concerned, all this talk of pleomorphism was wrong. Cocci always appeared as cocci, bacilli as bacilli, spirilla as spirilla. Their spots are like the leopard's, not the flounder's. Now this agreed perfectly with what Koch was finding about each disease having its one specific kind of germ. And so there was pronounced what has since been termed the Cohn-Koch dogma: *Each species of microbe is unchangeable in form and in properties, and cannot transform into another species.* We know now that this was going too far; that frequently bacteria may " mutate" or "dissociate" into types at times very dissimilar from the parent type, and that the form of the cells is not invariable, even in a single culture. But in general, the Cohn-Koch dogma agreed with the common sense and experience of skilled workers and was generally accepted. We are still confident that from the blood of a typhoid fever patient we shall cultivate a germ having all of the characters of the typhoid bacillus of Gaffky, and no others. And we are equally confident that a milk-souring organism will not suddenly begin attacking man and causing, say, malaria.

CHAPTER II

THE MICROSCOPE AND MICROSCOPY

Microbiology differs from ordinary biology in that it deals with organisms, living beings, too minute to be seen with the naked eye. Some of them, notably the bacteria, can be seen clearly only with the highest powered lenses of the compound microscope; and others, the filterable viruses, cannot be seen at all, even with the best instruments available. To understand microbiology, then, one must, to some degree, understand the microscope and how to use it.

Accommodation. Suppose you place this book on a table and view it from across the room. You may see the lines of type and how they are broken up into words but you cannot distinguish the individual letters. If you move towards the book, the type will appear larger and larger, you will be able to make out the characters of the letters more and more clearly. Pick up the book and bring it towards your eyes. The letters will appear still larger, you may begin to pick out little imperfections in the type or determine the grain of the paper. But as you bring the book nearer, you find a little feeling of tension in the eyes, and finally the letters become blurred; it is no longer possible to see clearly. Move the book away again, and you find a point of clearest vision, where the type is seen most clearly without any strain. This distance from the eyes will vary with different people. It will be farther if you are far-sighted, nearer if you are near-sighted, but for people of average or normal vision it will be about 25 cm.

Now bring the book close to your eyes again, to a point where the type appears blurred and the eyes begin to feel tense. Then bring between your eye and the book a low-powered convex lens, such as a reading glass. The type will again become beautifully clear, the individual letters much larger than at the point of best vision. At this close distance the lens of the eye cannot become convex enough to focus the image. The reading glass helps the lens of the eye to focus. Now, holding the lens in position, bring the book still closer

20

to the eye. Again the letters will become blurred; no position of the lens will clear them up. If you have another, more convex lens, bring it between the eye and the paper. Once more the letters will be seen clearly, larger still, and you may now begin to distinguish the fibers of the paper.

What the Microscope Does. Roughly speaking, this is what the microscope does. It helps the eye to focus upon objects close enough to it so that they may be seen in all their details, even though they are very minute. The first microscopes were simple convex lenses.

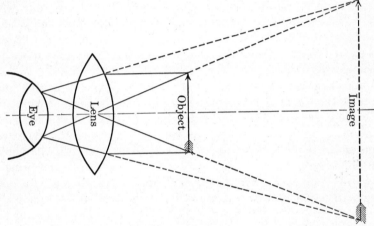

FIG. 1. Path of Light Rays in Formation of an Image by a Simple Magnifying Glass.

Actually, the magnification of a lens is due to its bending the light rays coming from the object so that, at the eye, the rays from the extremities of the object subtend a greater angle than would be the case if the object were viewed at the same distance without the lens. This may be understood from the diagram, Fig. 1. From each point on the object, a beam of divergent light rays is given off. Those rays which pass through the lens to the eye are bent, and the angle at which they strike the eye is changed, so that the image formed on the retina is interpreted by the brain as though it came from a point on the image. This is called a *virtual* image to distinguish it from a *real* image. It is an illusion, produced by bending the light rays so that the mind interprets the visual sensation as though an enlarged object were being viewed from a farther distance. A real image is formed when light rays are converged to a focus at a given plane. The virtual image formed by the use of a lens appears to be formed at the conventional distance of clearest vision, 25 cm.

Simple Microscopes. When using a simple lens as a magnifying glass, the greatest magnification is obtained when the object is placed a certain distance behind the lens, equivalent to the *focal length* of the lens. The focal length is defined, approximately, as the distance from the lens to a point at which a parallel beam of rays would be brought to a focus as a point of light. It is determined by the convexity of the lens; the greater the curvature, the shorter

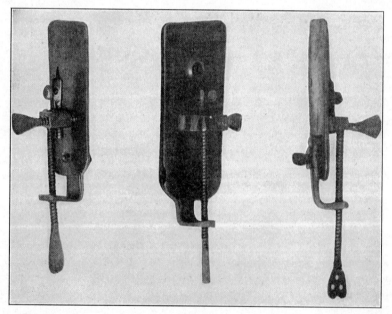

Fig. 2.   Van Leeuwenhoek's Microscopes.   (After Stein; "On the Trail of van Leeuwenhoek," *The Scientific Monthly*, Feb., 1931.)

the focal length. The focal length, in turn, determines the magnifying power of the lens; the shorter the focal length, the greater the magnification.

Van Leeuwenhoek's microscopes were simple lenses, either convex on both sides, or flat on one side and convex on the other. They were ground from the clearest rock crystal. Their mode of mounting is shown in Fig. 2. Two plates of metal had depressions ground in them, to hold the lens. A small hole was drilled through the depressions to allow light to pass through. The lens was then placed in position between the two plates, which were riveted together. The object to be examined was mounted on a pin, or, if liquid, placed in a minute tube which could be manipulated in front of the lens by screws, that served to center the object and bring it into focus. The lenses had to be very close to the eye. They varied in magnifying power from 40 to 270 times; the highest must have given images that were very dim and fuzzy. When you consider the limitations and defects of his microscopes you cannot help marvel at the accuracy of his observations.

Aberrations. A simple lens has certain inherent defects which limit the useful magnification that can be obtained with it. These are called *aberrations*. Spherical aberration is the inability to bring all of the rays from a point source to a focus at a single point, resulting in a blurred image. This difficulty is greater in lenses convex on both surfaces than in those that are flat on one side. Chromatic aberration is the inability to bring the rays of differing wave length or color to a focus at the same point, resulting in a color fringe about the image. It may be corrected by combining lenses, one convex and one concave, made of two different kinds of glass, crown and flint, having different powers of bending light rays.

Compound Microscopes. The difficulty due to these aberrations increases with the magnifying power of the lens, and with lenses of very short focal length they become so disturbing that the lens is almost useless. They may be diminished by using two lenses, spaced a certain distance apart, and high-powered hand lenses are always made as *doublets*, two lenses mounted in a tube. But to obtain clear images at still higher magnifications, it is necessary to use a still more complicated system of lenses, in which an initial *real* image formed by an *objective* lens is observed through an *eyepiece*, which forms a *virtual* image still more highly magnified. Such an instrument is called a *compound* microscope.

The origin of the compound microscope is somewhat obscure, but is generally attributed to a Dutchman named Zaccharias Jansen, about 1590. Certainly at the time of Leeuwenhoek's investigations this instrument was well known, but these early instruments must have been very imperfect, for Hooke could not see with his compound microscope the animalcules that Leeuwenhoek had discovered with his simple lenses. But with the discovery of the optical principles involved, the microscope steadily improved, great progress being made especially about the middle of the last century with the introduction of *immersion* lenses and the development of the *substage condenser*.

A compound microscope differs from a simple magnifier in using two series of lenses. The objective consists of a series of lenses, some convex, some concave, of different kinds of glass, to correct for the various aberrations. The type commonly used is called an *achromatic* objective, which indicates a certain degree of correction for color. The eyepiece usually used is known as the Huygens type, and is composed of two lenses spaced a certain distance apart, with a diaphragm, that is, a piece of metal with a hole in it, placed between them. The lens of the eyepiece nearest the eye is called the *eye lens*; that which is placed in the barrel of the microscope is the *field lens*.

What happens when you look through a compound microscope may be learned by studying the diagram in Fig. 3. The mirror beneath the stage of the microscope reflects parallel rays of light through a substage diaphragm, CD, into the lenses of the condenser. These lenses bring the rays to a sharp focus in the plane of the object, O_1, so that the object is brightly illuminated. From the various points of the object divergent pencils of rays are collected by the objective lens and bent to form convergent rays which cross in the barrel of the microscope, are collected by the field lens of the eyepiece, and brought to a focus in the plane of the eyepiece diaphragm, O_3, where a reversed real image of the object is formed. If you focus a microscope upon an object, remove the eye lens of the eyepiece, then drop a little disc of ground glass on the diaphragm, you will see this real image.

The eye now observes this image through the eye lens of the eyepiece, which is a simple magnifying glass. The real image is thus further magnified; the light rays are bent and strike the eye at such an angle that they seem to come from a point about 25 cm. away, where the virtual image, O_4, appears. The compound microscope thus differs from a simple microscope in that, instead of making it possible to bring the object close to the eye, an enlarged image

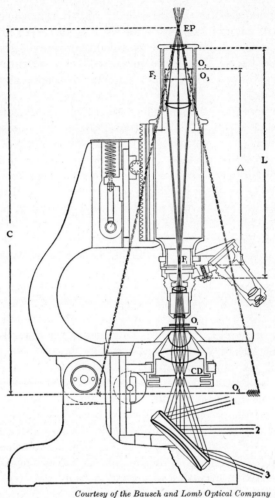

Courtesy of the Bausch and Lomb Optical Company

FIG. 3. Path of Light Rays through a Compound Microscope.

of the object is brought near to the eye. The eye lens makes it possible for the eye to focus upon the image at this close distance.

Magnification. You may see how the magnification obtained in this way can be much greater than with a simple microscope. The magnification of compound microscopes depends upon the initial magnification of the objective, and the degree to which the real image is enlarged by the eyepiece. Most microscopes used in microbiology have three objectives, of 16 mm., 4 mm., and 2 mm. focal length, giving initial magnifications of about 10, 40, and 90 times, respectively. The eyepiece most useful in microbiological work magnifies 10 times, giving a maximum possible magnification of 900 diameters, which is, as will be seen later, about the limit of useful magnification with such an instrument.

Resolving Power. It would appear, on first thought, that by a series of lenses one might continue this magnification indefinitely, that one might eventually see the smallest possible things, even the molecules themselves. But this is impossible because of the limitations imposed by another quality of lenses, their resolving power. This resolving power is defined as the ability to show, as separate and distinct, two points which are close together. The degree to which these two points may be brought together and still appear as separate is a measure of the resolving power. The resolving power of a lens is limited because it cannot focus the image of a point as a point; it is always a small disc. The smaller this disc, the more nearly it approximates a point, the greater is the resolving power. Now this resolving power is a measure of the size of an object that can be seen with the microscope, for if an object is smaller than the resolving power, the disc images from points about it will overlap its image, and it will be obscured.

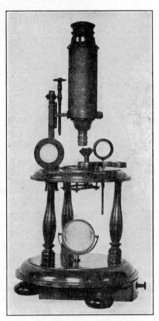

FIG. 4. A Compound Microscope of the Eighteenth Century. This microscope was presented by Linnæus to the French botanist, Bernard Jussieu, in 1738. It now rests in the Carnegie Museum in Pittsburgh.

The resolving power of a microscope is determined by two factors, the wave length of light, and a value for the lens known as its *numerical aperture.* This may be shown by an equation:

$$\text{Smallest structure visible} = \frac{\text{Wave length}}{\text{Numerical aperture}}.$$

The wave length is, for practical purposes, fixed. Calculations of resolving power are usually based upon the yellow light, that part of the spectrum which appears brightest to the eye. The numerical aperture of the lens is dependent upon the actual diameter of the objective in relation to its focal length, and upon the refractive index, or light-bending power, of whatever substance lies between the lens and the object being examined.

Useful Magnification. Now the *useful magnification* of a microscope is limited by the resolving power. If an object is too small to yield an image with a certain objective lens, there is no use in increasing the magnification by the eyepiece, which enlarges only that image. To increase the usefulness of the microscope, every effort must be directed towards increasing the resolving power rather than the degree of magnification.

The resolving power may be increased by using light of shorter wave length, or by increasing the numerical aperture. With direct observation we are of course limited to the visible range of the spectrum. Some attempts have been made to use ultraviolet light with quartz lenses and a photographic plate as the observer instead of the eye.

Courtesy of the Bausch and Lomb Optical Company

Fig. 5. A Modern Research Microscope.

As far as the lens itself is concerned, there are mechanical difficulties which limit any increase in the numerical aperture. But we may *increase the refractive index of the medium which comes between the object and the objective lens.* The numerical aperture can be no greater than the refractive index of this medium.

Oil Immersion. Of the three objectives found on an ordinary students' or physicians' microscope, two are designed for use with air between them and the object. They are known as dry objectives, the low-power lens of 16 mm. focus, and the medium-power, or "high dry" lens of 4 mm. focus. But the third one, the 2 mm. lens of highest magnification, is designed for use with cedar oil interposed between it and the object. It is called an *immersion* lens, because it is to be used dipped in a drop of oil placed on the object, or on a coverslip over the object. The cedar oil is frequently called immersion oil. This is used because it has a much higher refractive index than air, and so increases the resolving power of the high-power lens.

Use of Condenser. The equation for the resolving power given on page 27 is based upon the assumption that the object is illuminated by a beam of parallel rays from the plane surface of the mirror. If, however, it is lighted by strongly oblique rays, such as are provided by the beam of convergent rays from a substage condenser, then the size of the smallest visible object is reduced by one-half; the denominator of the fraction becomes:

$$2 \times \text{Numerical aperture.}$$

With an object illuminated by a properly focused substage condenser, and examined with an oil immersion lens, one obtains the greatest possible resolving power. For the usual students' microscope with a 2 mm. oil immersion lens having a numerical aperture of 1.25, this resolving power is 0.00022 millimeter, or 0.22 μ (μ, the symbol for a *micron*, is the unit of microscopic measurement, and equals .001 mm.). Very high-grade and expensive objectives are made with numerical apertures up to 1.60, whose resolving power is 0.16 μ. While these are very superior for some sorts of work, such as photomicrography, they do not yield any great wealth of information which cannot be obtained by the use of the ordinary students' oil immersion lens. The *useful magnification* of such lenses has been variously calculated as lying between about 900 diameters and 1500 diameters.

Limitations of Microscopes. It is important to keep in mind this limitation set upon visual observations of organisms through the microscope. The smallest visible microörganisms, the bacteria, range in size through an almost continuous series down to the very limits of resolution. We have every reason to believe that this range extends considerably lower, but we cannot see these ultra-microscopic organisms. With the very small organisms whose cells are visible, it is quite possible that they may possess important *intracellular structures* whose existence cannot be determined by visual observations.

The Electronic Microscope. The limitation of magnification imposed by the limited resolving power of the microscope has been very irksome to all users of the instrument. If we could only magnify a little more! Modern microscopes have about reached the limit which the laws of optics will permit. But at the moment another type of microscope is being developed, which uses, instead of light, a beam of electrons. This promises to greatly extend the possibilities of microscopy.

In the electronic microscope, the "light" source is a cathode, connected to a source of high voltage, in a vacuum. From it, electrons are discharged at high velocity toward the anode, which is perforated. These electrons may be deflected by a magnetic field, and a circular electromagnet may serve to cause them to converge, just as a lens causes light rays to converge. So, with high velocity electrons instead of light rays, and with electromagnets serving in place of condenser, objective, and eyepiece, compound electronic microscopes have been constructed which do not have the limitations of ordinary microscopes, and with which useful magnifications of 20,000 to 100,000 diameters have been obtained. The image is viewed on a fluorescent screen, or it may be registered on a photographic film. Such instruments are, however, still very much in the developmental stage, and have not yet been used in microbiology.

Dark Field Illumination. There is another optical principle which may be applied to the microscope to detect the presence of minute bodies, even though their size is smaller than the limits of resolution. From a ship at sea one may, at night, detect the flash from a lighthouse on the shore at such a distance that in broad daylight no trace of the lighthouse can be seen. We may, with a dark background, visually detect the *light* emitted from an object even though we cannot see the *object* itself. This is the basis for the *ultramicroscope*, which is used in detecting colloidal particles suspended in a liquid, and the method of examination by *dark field illumination* which is a valuable method for bacteriological work.

Dark field illumination is obtained by replacing the usual condenser of the microscope with a special dark field condenser. This differs in that it illuminates the object with a *hollow* cone of rays instead of a *solid* cone such as is furnished by the usual condenser. These are brought to a focus in the plane of the object on the stage of the microscope, and then diverge at such a wide angle that none

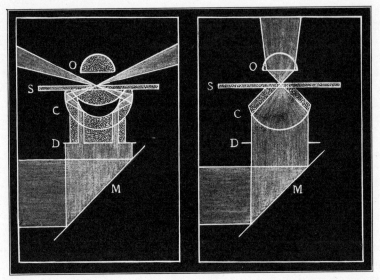

FIG. 6. Path of Light Rays through Dark Field (left) and Bright Field (right) Condensers.

M, mirror; D, diaphragm; C, condenser; S, slide;
O, objective lens of microscope.

of them strikes the objective lens of the microscope. If one looks through the microscope, so arranged, at a clean glass slide, nothing is seen — the field is perfectly dark. But if there is present some object having surfaces that reflect light, such as a bacterial cell, some of the light so reflected will reach the objective and form an image. One then sees the bacterium as an apparently self-luminous body sharply outlined against a dark background. Only the reflecting surfaces may be seen, either the outlines of the cells, or of the bodies within the cells. But with the very small bodies, below the limits of resolution, the image will appear merely as a point of light, regardless of their size. With such bodies, then, you may be made aware of their presence by vision, you may count them or observe their motion, but you cannot *see* them in the sense that you observe an image which is the counterpart of their form.

Observing Bacteria. There are two ways of examining micro-organisms through the microscope. One may observe the living unstained organisms in water, or the dead cells, stained with dyes, in balsam or cedar oil. Each method has certain advantages and disadvantages, and a true conception of the structure of an organism is best obtained by using both methods. The living cells of most organisms are, in color and refractility, so like the water in which they are immersed that they do not present sufficient *contrast* to be clearly visible. This lack of contrast is more noticeable with bright illumination than when the light is not so brilliant. To see the living cells, then, one must reduce the light, either by closing the diaphragm under the condenser or by throwing the condenser out of focus. One cannot use immersion oil directly on the wet cells; a coverglass has to be used, and water is necessarily part of the optical system. All of these factors tend to reduce the resolving power obtainable. Some of this difficulty may be overcome by the use of dark field illumination, where a maximum of contrast is obtained. But the more usual method for obtaining contrast is to stain the organisms with aniline dyes. To do this the cells must first be killed and *fixed*, i.e., their protoplasm is coagulated by heat or by chemicals. This causes considerable shrinkage, and with some organisms, distortion. But this disadvantage is offset by the fact that they may be examined in a medium of high refractive index with the full illumination of the condenser system. When examining unstained micro-organisms, since the highest resolving power cannot be attained, it is more convenient to use the 4 mm. dry objective. *Stained bacteria should always be examined with the 2 mm. oil immersion lens.*

Wet Preparations. The unstained cells are examined in a *wet preparation*. Put a drop of water containing the organisms on a slide, place a coverglass on this, and put the slide on the stage of the microscope. Arrange the lighting with the plane mirror, so that the field is uniformly illuminated. With a microscope provided with a condenser, the flat side of the mirror is to be used at all times. Looking through the eyepiece, reduce the light by closing partly the diaphragm below the condenser. The proper amount of light to be used can be learned only by experience. Now with the low-power (16 mm.) lens, focus upon the slide with the coarse adjustment. If dealing with very small organisms which cannot be seen readily with the low power, focus upon an air bubble or the edge of the coverglass. Now replace the 16 mm. objective with the medium power, or high dry lens. If the objectives are "parfocal," which is true of most modern microscopes, the organisms should now be in focus, or nearly so. If not, sight with one eye along the top of the slide, and rack down the objective until it nearly touches the coverglass. Again looking through the eyepiece, gradually move the lens *upward* with the fine adjustment until the organisms are in focus. Now readjust the light intensity until the clearest possible picture is obtained.

One may add to the liquid in which the organisms are suspended a drop of weak iodine solution (the Gram's iodine to be described later), which will stain the protoplasm a light yellowish brown, without producing any appreciable shrinkage or distortion. Such a procedure is particularly valuable in observing yeasts, molds, and some protozoa. The iodine, of course, kills the cells, but one may in a similar manner carry out a *vital staining* with a dye, neutral red, which will bring out certain granules or vacuoles in some living microorganisms.

Hanging Drops. In a wet preparation there are frequently currents in the liquid due to capillarity or to evaporation at the edge, which may give a false impression of motility when examining the cells. This difficulty is avoided by examining the microbes suspended in a *hanging drop*. For this you need a hollow-ground slide, which is a glass slide with a concave depression ground in the center. A drop of water containing the organisms to be examined is deposited in the center of a clean coverglass. Vaseline is

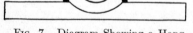

applied to the edge of the concavity in the slide. The slide is

Fig. 7. Diagram Showing a Hanging Drop Preparation as Seen in Cross Section.

inverted over the coverglass and applied to it so that the drop occupies the center of the depression. You press gently on the slide to cause the vaseline to adhere, and then quickly turn it over. Now you have the drop hanging from the under side of the coverglass, not touching the slide, and sealed from the air to prevent evaporation, as in Fig. 7. This preparation should be examined in the same manner as a wet preparation, focusing preferably on the edge of the drop, where most of the organisms will lie in the focal plane. It is the only safe procedure for determining motility in bacteria.

Stains. The use of *aniline dyes* for staining cells and their internal structures has been almost as important as the microscope in revealing to us the minute structure of living organisms. The use of stains in microscopy is generally attributed to Gerlach (1858), who used carmine as a stain for animal tissues, but the aniline dyes introduced several years later yielded more information. The aniline dyes are derived from coal tar, by chemical transformations of substances found in that by-product. To act as dyes, these substances must not only be deeply colored, but they must exist chemically as salts, which will dissociate in solution into positively and negatively charged ions. We divide the aniline dyes into two groups, which are designated *basic* and *acid* dyes, according to whether the coloring power is situated in the positive or negative ion. Thus methylene blue, a basic dye, is actually a salt formed by combining the organic blue pigment with hydrochloric acid, and might be represented thus:

$$\overset{+}{\text{Methylene blue}} \quad \overset{-}{\text{chloride.}}$$

And eosin, an acid dye, has its coloring power situated in the negative ion, and might be represented thus:

$$\overset{+}{\text{Sodium}} \quad \overset{-}{\text{eosinate.}}$$

The substances in cells which stain with these aniline dyes are almost exclusively proteins. These substances are *amphoteric*, which means that they may act as either an acid or a base, depending upon the reaction of the solution in which they are immersed. They will combine with bases if the solution in which they are placed is on the acid side of a certain point in the scale of acidity to alkalinity; with acids, if the solution is on the basic side of this point. This certain point on the scale at which the protein changes its reaction is the *isoelectric point*. Whether a protein will be colored by a given dye depends upon the isoelectric point of the protein and the reaction of the dye solution. Since the dye solutions used are usually neutral or nearly so, the staining is governed by the isoelectric point of the proteins. When the protein is stained by methylene blue, the reaction might be represented thus:

Methylene blue chloride + sodium proteinate → sodium chloride
+ methylene blue proteinate.

Similarly, if a protein is stained by eosin, the reaction might be represented thus:

Sodium eosinate + protein chloride → sodium chloride + protein eosinate.

Theories of Staining. This view of the mechanism of staining is based upon the assumption that the reaction is purely chemical. It is not universally accepted, because certain quantitative relationships between the intensity of staining and the concentration of the dye solution indicate that physical laws rather than chemical laws govern the reaction. According to the physical theory, the dyestuff does not actually combine with the protein, but is *adsorbed* by it, forming a thin film on the surfaces of the colloidal particles. It is fixed here by the mutual attraction of opposite electric charges. Thus if a certain substance is stained by methylene blue, its particles must carry a negative charge, since the coloring power of this stain resides in its positively charged ion. The charge on the particles of protein is positive on the acid side of its isoelectric point, negative on the basic side.

Whether we look upon staining as a purely chemical reaction or as an adsorption phenomenon makes no great difference in our interpretation of the results when we examine stained organisms under the microscope. *Stains are not specific chemical reagents.* A basic dye will color any structure in the cell which presents an acid character (or carries a negative charge). Substances which are not at all identical will be similarly stained. When one stains the larger microorganisms, or the cells of higher organisms, with both basic and acid dyes, the chromatin of the nucleus takes the basic dye, the cytoplasm usually takes the acid dye. Thus in double staining with methylene blue and eosin, the nucleus will usually be blue and the rest of the cell red. But this is no justification for assuming that everything in a cell which stains blue is chromatin.

With the larger and more complex of the microörganisms such as yeasts, molds, Algae, and Protozoa, stained preparations are not necessary for routine study. These are large enough and contain sufficient naturally colored or refractile material that they may be fairly easily seen in the living state. With such organisms, stains are used primarily to study the finer structure of the cells. The staining methods are rather complicated and too tedious to be used routinely. The student is referred to books on microscopic technique for information on the fixing and staining of such organisms.

Staining Bacteria. But with the bacteria stained slides are essential to a clear observation of their size, form, arrangement, and other characters by which they are recognized. Such stained preparations may be made very simply and quickly and are therefore used for routine observations. To prepare a slide of bacteria for staining, spread a drop of water, or pus, or sputum, or other material containing the organisms, in a very thin film on the surface of a clean microscope slide, and allow it to dry. When dealing with bacteria growing on the surface of agar, some of the solid or pasty growth is first mixed with a drop of water on the slide, and this drop is then spread out in a film. The film must be thin enough so that the individual organisms will be well separated, not piled up in more than one layer; and thick enough so that they may be easily found. This can be learned only by experience. After the film is quite dry, it is fixed by heating gently. The usual procedure is to pass the slide rather quickly, film side up, through the flame of a Bunsen burner, three times. It should be hot enough to feel just a bit uncomfortable when held against the back of the hand. If heated too much, the bacteria will be scorched, distorted in form, and altered in their staining reactions. The purpose of this heating is to kill the cells, coagulate their protein, and also to make them adhere to the glass. If not fixed, the film will promptly wash off when the slide is immersed in staining fluid. After heating, the slide is ready to be stained. A slide prepared as above is called, rather inelegantly, a smear preparation.

Bacteria do not reveal much internal structure. There are, in some kinds of bacteria, certain bodies formed within the cell, and certain appendages to the cell, which are of importance. These are revealed by special staining methods which will be described in their proper place. But mostly we stain bacteria merely to reveal the form and arrangement of the cells, and for this purpose a simple staining procedure is sufficient. The protoplasm of bacteria takes the basic dyes. Those commonly used are methylene blue, crystal violet, basic fuchsin, and safranin. These dyes are usually prepared as a concentrated alcoholic solution which is then diluted to the proper strength with water, sometimes with the addition of a little phenol (carbolic acid), which seems to aid in the staining. Stained with the above dyes, the bacteria will appear blue, violet, rose red, or brick red, respectively. After staining, the dye solution is washed off with water, the film is dried, and is ready for examination with the oil immersion lens. If we were to use the acid dyes, eosin, acid fuchsin, aniline blue, congo red, or nigrosin, we would find that the bacteria are colored very faintly or not at all.

To examine a stained smear with the oil immersion lens, place a generous drop of cedar oil on the surface of the smear. No cover-glass is necessary. Place the slide on the stage of the microscope. See that the substage diaphragm is open. Focus on the slide with the low-power objective, adjusting the flat surface of the mirror so that the slide is illuminated. With the surface of the slide in focus, now focus the substage condenser, moving it up and down until the image of the light source can be seen through the microscope. You will see the window, or lamp, in the same plane as the slide. Now swing the oil immersion lens in line with the barrel of the microscope. Remove the eye from the eyepiece, and sighting along the top of the slide, rack the lens down until it almost touches the slide. Again looking through the eyepiece, move the lens slowly upward with the fine adjustment until the bacteria are in focus. These adjustments will require some thought at first. With a little experience, they will become almost automatic.

Gram's Stain. In 1884 a Danish physician named Gram discovered accidentally a staining process which not only clearly reveals the bacteria under the microscope but helps to distinguish different kinds. This staining process is the one to be preferred for routine examinations, because it is just as good as a simple stain for making the cells visible, and in addition, by its differential character, brings us one step further toward identification.

There have been many modifications of the original Gram technique, which give a sharper differentiation. Some of them are too complicated for routine use. All of them require four solutions: — a *basic dye* of the pararosaniline group, of which crystal violet is most commonly used; a *mordant*, iodine being the best; a *decolorizing agent*, alcohol or acetone; and a *counterstain*, i.e., a dye of a different color from the first one used. Hucker's modification requires the following reagents:

I.   STAIN
                         Solution A
          Crystal violet   4 grams
          Ethyl alcohol   20 cc.

                         Solution B
          Ammonium oxalate   0.8 gram
          Water   80.0 cc.
          Mix solutions *A* and *B*

II.   MORDANT
          Iodine   1 gram
          Potassium iodide   2 grams
          Water   200 cc.

III.   DECOLORIZING AGENT
          Ethyl alcohol   95 per cent

IV.   COUNTERSTAIN
          Safranin (saturated solution in alcohol)   10 cc.
          Water   100 cc.

According to their reactions when stained by this method, all bacteria may be divided into two classes which are called *Gram positive* and *Gram negative*. Let us suppose that we have, side by side on a slide, two kinds of bacteria, one Gram positive and the other Gram negative. We flood the slide with the crystal violet stain solution for one minute. Both kinds will be colored violet, for all bacteria behave much alike with a simple basic stain. Next we wash off the excess of the violet stain with water, and flood the slide with the iodine solution for one minute. This iodine forms a compound with the crystal violet which is of a deep blue-black color. After this treatment, both kinds of bacteria will still be of the same color, now a blue-black. Again we wash with water, and now we apply the alcohol. This is the important part of the process, for *alcohol will dissolve the violet-iodine compound out of the Gram negative bacteria* much more quickly than from the Gram positive organisms. If the alcohol has been used just the right length of time (about 30 seconds for a smear of normal density), the Gram positive bacteria will still be colored a shade varying from violet to blue-black, while the Gram negative cells will be colorless. Being colorless they cannot be easily seen, but they may now be stained with a basic dye of a different color. The red safranin counterstain is applied for ten seconds. Now we are ready to examine the slide. The Gram positive bacteria will appear violet or blue-black, the Gram negative ones will be red.

Significance of Gram's Stain. The Gram stain is something more than an aid in identifying microörganisms. It indicates a deep-seated fundamental difference in the constitution of the protoplasm of the two groups of bacteria. While there are a few exceptions in both groups, in a general way, Gram positive bacteria react to many agents in a manner just the reverse of the Gram negative ones. Gram positive bacteria are not so readily digested by the protein-splitting enzymes, pepsin and trypsin, as the Gram negative bacteria, and similarly do not so readily undergo self-digestion, or autolysis, after death. The Gram positive organisms seem mechanically more resistant than the Gram negative ones; they are not so easily disrupted by the sudden expansion of dissolved gases in their interior. Probably because of this resistance to dissolving or disrupting tendencies, Gram positive bacteria do not give rise to antibodies in the animal body as readily as do Gram negative organisms. Gram positive bacteria are more resistant to the inhibiting effect of a high osmotic pressure in the culture medium, such as is obtained by adding salt. On the other hand, they are much more susceptible to the injurious action of basic dyes, such as crystal violet, and of substances which lower the surface tension of the medium, such as soaps.

Theory of Gram's Stain. Because of these differences between the groups, bacteriologists have become more and more interested in the mechanism of the staining reaction. A number of ingenious experiments have been performed and various theories proposed. The most plausible explanation offered is that of Stearn and Stearn, who showed that the proteins of the Gram positive bacteria exhibit an isoelectric point further on the acid side of neutrality than the proteins of the Gram negative bacteria. With both kinds of bacteria, the isoelectric point is on the acid side of neutrality, and both will therefore be stained with the basic dyes. But the Gram positive species hold these dyes more tenaciously. According to this theory the action of iodine is that of an oxidizing agent whose effect is to shift the isoelectric point of the proteins further to the acid side and therefore increase the tenacity of the staining. After treatment with iodine, therefore, alcohol cannot wash out the violet so easily from the Gram positive bacteria.

Negative Staining. While it is true that acid dyes will not stain the cells of bacteria, certain of them may be used to good advantage for making the cells of microörganisms visible under the microscope. Nigrosin is one of the acid dyes. If one stirs up some bacteria in a drop of nigrosin solution (1% in water), and then spreads the drop of stain on the slide in a thin film and dries it, the bacteria may be seen as colorless bodies surrounded by a stained background. The dye does not penetrate the cells, but it dries to form a solid layer of pigment around them. This is called *negative staining*, and is very useful for certain types of work since it presents a dimly lighted field with the bacteria as bright spots. This is less fatiguing to the eye than when examining the bacteria as dark spots in a bright background. A better procedure is to use another acid dye, Congo red (2% aqueous solution). When the film is dry, the slide is immersed for a moment in a solution of hydrochloric acid (1%) in alcohol. This changes the film of Congo red to a dark blue color. The slide is then dried and examined with the oil immersion lens.

CHAPTER III

A SURVEY OF MICROBIC LIFE: THE PROTOZOA

In the preceding pages we have spoken rather indiscriminately of microörganisms, microbes, and germs. We have mentioned yeasts, bacteria, and Protozoa as particular sorts of microbes. We must now define these terms more clearly and inquire into those characters which distinguish the different sorts of microörganisms from each other. We may define as microbes, or microörganisms, all of those living things which are too small to be easily distinguished by the naked eye, and which therefore require some sort of microscope for their study. Some of the organisms we shall study, for instance the molds, may be easily seen with the naked eye, but the microscope is necessary to reveal their distinguishing characters. As microbes, we shall include widely diverse organisms, some animals, some plants; some one-celled, some many-celled. They differ greatly in structure and in modes of living, but all have this in common, that they are much smaller in size and simpler in organization than the animals and plants which we are accustomed to seeing with our unaided eyes.

Amoeba. In biology courses, the amoeba is usually presented as a type of the simplest forms of life. As will be seen later, there are many microörganisms which are much smaller in size, and much simpler in structure than an amoeba. But it will serve as a convenient starting point for a discussion and comparison of the various types of microbes.

The amoeba is a *one-celled animal*. The individual animal consists of a single continuous mass of protoplasm. When at rest it may be round in form, but the living cell is usually in constant motion. This motion is accomplished by a sort of flowing of the protoplasm in various directions; portions of the cell project from the rest as finger-like processes called *pseudopodia*. These stretch out, and then the rest of the protoplasm flows into them. The cell is thus constantly changing its form. This indicates that there is no

40

cell membrane, such as is possessed by most other cells, which serves to maintain a constant cell form. Cells of higher organisms which move and change form like the amoeba are called *amoeboid* cells.

Structure of Amoeba. The amoeba cell does not present a very complex structure. There is an outer layer of protoplasm, glassy and structureless in appearance, called the *ectoplasm,* and an inner portion, granular and more differentiated, the *endoplasm.* Within

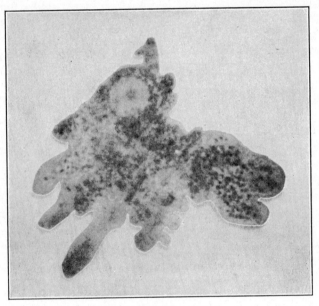

Fig. 8. *Amoeba proteus.*
Photomicrograph of the living cell.

the latter is a *nucleus,* similar in structure and functions to the nuclei of higher organisms. There is also a *contractile vacuole,* a sort of bubble within the protoplasm, filled with liquid, which slowly enlarges and, moving to the surface of the cell, bursts and discharges its contents. Its function is mainly to preserve the water-balance in the cell. It bails out excess water which has passed into the cell. In this water there are probably some waste products dissolved. Its function, therefore, is similar to that of the urinary apparatus of higher animals.

Nutrition. An amoeba feeds upon other microörganisms, especially smaller protozoa or bacteria. When one of these is encountered by the animal in its wanderings, one or more pseudopodia wrap themselves around it; they flow together and take the object into the interior of the cell. Here it is contained in a droplet of water, forming another vacuole, into which digestive enzymes are secreted. These dissolve the foreign cell, the products of digestion are absorbed into the protoplasm, and become a part of the amoeba. Thus the nutrition of the amoeba is much like that of a higher animal, save that mouth and stomach are created when the need arises! Such a mode of nutrition, in which solid organic matter created or synthesized by other organisms is taken into the body and there digested and assimilated, is essentially characteristic of animals, and is called *holozoic* nutrition.

Some amoebae are *parasitic* on higher forms of animal life. There is one which lives normally in the human mouth, another which is found frequently in the intestines of man, and a third which also lives in the intestines but invades the tissues and produces a disease, amoebic dysentery. But most kinds of amoebae are *free-living* forms, found in stagnant water.

Reproduction. The reproduction of an amoeba is very simple. When the animal has reached a sufficient size, the nucleus divides into two parts. The nuclear division is *mitotic*, i.e., the chromatin in the nucleus first becomes arranged in chromosomes, which then divide and separate. Following this, the whole cell tears itself apart into two halves, each with a nucleus. This type of reproduction, a simple division of the cell into two new cells, is called *binary fission*.

After a number of generations have been produced by binary fission, another process may intervene. The cell comes to rest, assumes a rounded form, and develops a cell wall. This resting form is known as a *cyst*. In the encysted state the animal may remain dormant for considerable periods of time, and is able to withstand extremes of temperature or drought which would be injurious to the organism in its active state. With free-living amoebae, encystment occurs rarely. With parasitic amoebae, cysts are produced commonly. The biological significance of encystment is not fully understood.

Amoeba an Animal. In its essential characters an amoeba is like any other animal. It moves about seeking food which it takes into its interior, and there digests and assimilates it. It excretes waste products. It grows and reproduces its kind. But there are vast differences between an amoeba and one of the higher animals. In an amoeba all of the life processes are reduced to the simplest terms, and they are carried on by a single cell, which is relatively undifferentiated. Any part of the cell (outside the nucleus) may take part in locomotion, in engulfing and digesting food, in excretion. No specialized organs are present to carry on particular functions. And in reproduction, the whole individual takes part. There are no special bodies, like the germ cells of higher animals, set aside to carry on the race, the rest of the individual necessarily dying at a certain age. When the amoeba divides, all of it lives on in the two individuals so formed. It is potentially immortal! Moreover, this reproduction is asexual. The amoeba does not need to seek a mate to reproduce. Its offspring derive their inheritance from but one individual.

Protozoa.   The amoeba is but one kind of one-celled animal, a member of a great group of organisms which are very diverse in many characters, but which are all alike in being like animals (especially as regards their nutrition) and in consisting of but a single cell. These unicellular animals comprise a subdivision, or *phylum*, of the animal kingdom called *Protozoa*.

Classes of Protozoa.   The amoeba is a representative of a certain *class* of Protozoa, the members of which do not have a definite cell wall or pellicle, and which can therefore change their form and move by pseudopodia. There are several other classes of Protozoa. They are distinguished from each other by the particular sort of organs of locomotion which they possess. Here is a list of them:

Phylum PROTOZOA

Class 1.   The *Mastigophora*, which move by one or a few long whip-like processes, called *flagella*.

Class 2.   The *Sarcodina*, which move by means of *pseudopodia*.

Class 3.   The *Sporozoa*, which have no special cell organs for locomotion.

Class 4.   The *Ciliata*, which move by means of many short bristle-like processes, the *cilia*.

Class 5.   The *Suctoria*, which have cilia in the early stages of development, but later lose them and develop *tentacles* for capturing prey.

Mastigophora.   The *Mastigophora* include a great many different kinds of Protozoa of widely varying structure and modes of living, which, however, all possess the same locomotory organs, the flagella. These are long hair-like processes of the protoplasm, very fine, actively vibrating or lashing about. They arise from the front, or anterior, end of the cell in most cases, and serve to pull the organism forward. They vary in number, the number being a constant character of the species.

The cells possess an outer membrane, or pellicle, which serves to preserve a constant form. The organisms are frequently elongated, pear-shaped, fish-like, or cigar-shaped in form, tending to assume a stream-line body which is in keeping with their very active movements.

Structure of Flagellates. In most of the flagellated Protozoa, the cell structure is a little more complex than in the amoeba. There is usually a single nucleus. There is also found a body at the base of the flagellum which has been looked upon as a sort of secondary nucleus governing locomotion. It is called the *blepharoplast*. There are contractile vacuoles present in the free-living forms, serving to govern the water-balance of the cell, and probably also to excrete waste products. In the free-living forms there is usually an opening at the anterior end, near the base of the flagella, from which a canal leads to a vacuole or reservoir within the protoplasm. This apparatus is now looked upon as serving an excretory function. In some species solid food particles may be taken into the cell through an area of naked protoplasm near the base of the flagellum, or through a funnel-shaped opening distinct from the excretory one mentioned above. Microörganisms may be actually grasped by the flagella and brought into the food opening. Such a mode of nutrition, like that of the amoeba, is holozoic.

Chlorophyll. But in a number of different kinds of Mastigophora there is another mode of nutrition. Such forms contain within their protoplasm a number of small rounded bodies which are bright green in color. This color is due to the pigment *chlorophyll*, and the bodies which contain this pigment are *chloroplasts*. Now this chlorophyll is the same substance that colors the leaves of plants, and is essential in the nutrition of plants. By its aid the plant may build up its protoplasm directly from simple inorganic compounds through the energy of sunlight, energy which is absorbed and somehow utilized by the chlorophyll. Organisms possessing chlorophyll may absorb their nitrogen from the water or soil in the form of nitrates or ammonium salts, and these salts, combined with carbon obtained in the form of carbon dioxide from the water or atmosphere, together with some potassium and magnesium, sulphur and phosphorous (also absorbed as simple salts), are built up into protoplasm. This sort of nutrition is essentially characteristic of plants, and is called *holophytic* nutrition.

Subclasses of Flagellates. The species of Mastigophora which possess chloroplasts and have therefore a holophytic mode of nutrition are placed in a special subclass, the *Phytomastigina.*   The remaining forms, without chlorophyll, comprise a second subclass, the *Zoömastigina.*

The Phytomastigina possess all of the structures which are present in the cells of the Zoömastigina, and in addition the special mechanisms for their plant-like nutrition, the chloroplasts, and another body, the *stigma.* This is a small reddish-brown spot near the anterior portion of the cell, which is sensitive to light. The green flagellated Protozoa move toward the light, a reaction which is of great value to an organism that depends upon sunlight for its nutrition.

Nutrition of Flagellates. In addition to these two modes of nutrition, the holozoic and holophytic, two other types of feeding may be exhibited by certain species.

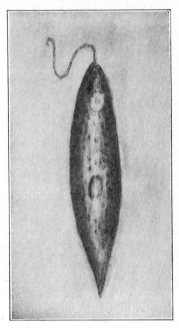

FIG. 9. *Euglena viridis*, a Free-living Green Flagellate.

Many do not apparently capture prey, and being devoid of chlorophyll, are dependent for their nutrition upon organic matter dissolved in the water — products set free in the decomposition of dead plant and animal matter. These substances, already at least partially digested, are absorbed directly through the cell membranes. Such a mode of nutrition is termed *saprozoic.* Finally, quite a number of species of Zoömastigina are *parasitic* in animals, living in the intestines or in the blood stream. Such forms also absorb organic matter in solution directly through the membrane, substances digested or perhaps synthesized by their host. Some of these parasitic forms injure their host; they produce disease.

Flagellated Protozoa are widely distributed in nature, the majority being free-living aquatic forms found both in the sea and in fresh water. One large group, the *Dinoflagellates*, forms an important part of the microscopic life of the sea. These are peculiar forms with two flagella, one of which is wrapped around the cell in a groove, or girdle, while the other extends free. They are forms with chloroplasts which, while predominantly brown in color, yet contain chlorophyll; they are therefore holophytic in their nutrition, and because of their abundance are important "producing" organisms in the sea. Both green and colorless flagellates are abundant in fresh water, particularly in ponds and stagnant pools. Many forms occur in soil.

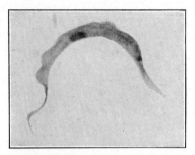

Fig. 10. *Trypanosoma lewisi*, a Blood-inhabiting Parasitic Flagellate.

Parasitic types occur in a wide variety of animals from the lowest to the highest. The blood-inhabiting *Trypanosomes* are the most important.

Reproduction. In the Mastigophora the usual mode of reproduction is by binary fission, and in most species this is the only method known. It is noteworthy that in most forms in which the cell is elongated, the division occurs in the plane of the long axis; it is *longitudinal*. In many forms, after a period of growth and cell division, the cells go into a resting stage, become encysted. The cysts develop a rather thick protecting wall, and become rounded in form. The cell within the cyst divides, forming sometimes only two, but frequently many, daughter cells.

Colonies. With most species, after cell division the two individual cells become completely separated, swimming apart. But in some kinds, the cells remain held together by a common mucilaginous secretion, forming *colonies*. Such colonies may be free-swimming masses of cells, or they may become attached to a stone or a submerged plant, sometimes by rather complicated branched stalks secreted by the cells. These masses of cells are looked upon as simple aggregates of individuals rather than as a single multicellular individual, because the cells are all alike; there is no apparent *differentiation* into tissues or aggregates of living cells having different functions.

Differentiation. But in some of the colonial green flagellates there is some degree of differentiation. *Volvox* is such an organism usually included with the flagellated Protozoa. Some of the cells in the colony, instead of dividing into merely two cells, undergo a multiple division, giving rise to a larger number of small cells. Other cells in the colony become greatly enlarged. The small cells, actively motile, swim to the large cells, and fuse with them. They are male, or sperm cells, and the large cell is a female reproductive cell, or ovum. After this fertilization, the large cell develops into a new colony. Here, then, we have sexual reproduction, and a differentiation in the colony into vegetative and reproductive cells.

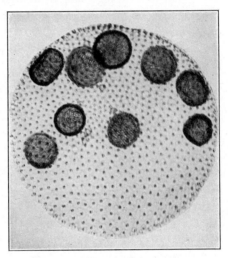

FIG. 11. *Volvox*, a Colonial Green Flagellate.

Flagellates a Common Ancestor. From the above discussions it will be apparent to the student that the flagellated Protozoa present transitions between plants and animals on the one hand and between unicellular and multicellular organisms on the other. *The flagellates are considered to be primitive forms from which probably all higher forms of both plant and animal life have originated.* And the transitions which they present are so closely graded that it is impossible to decide where to divide plant from animal, the one-celled from the many-celled.

Plant or Animal? One might arbitrarily decide that those forms with green color and holophytic nutrition are plants. He could support this viewpoint with other evidence. The wall formed about the cysts of the green flagellates is composed of cellulose, a carbohydrate substance characteristic of plants, while the cyst wall in the other forms is chitin, a glucosamine characteristic of higher animals. The forms with chlorophyll store up food in the form of a substance chemically very much like the starch stored in higher plants. One might further argue that the occurrence of free-swimming flagellated cells is not essentially an animal characteristic, since it occurs in reproductive cells in the plant kingdom as high as the ferns. But the green flagellates possess so many features in common with the colorless forms that to separate them into two different kingdoms of the organic world would be too obviously artificial.

Unicellular or Multicellular? Similarly, it is difficult to draw any sharp line between the unicellular and the multicellular organisms. There are almost infinite gradations between the single-celled, free-swimming forms, the undifferentiated aggregates (or colonies) and the multicellular plants and animals — from the one-celled green flagellate, through the Green Algae, to the lowest multicellular plants; and from the colorless flagellates to the sponges, the lowest forms of multicellular animals. Here it is impossible in many cases to decide which is the individual — the cell or the aggregate of cells.

We shall find these difficulties recurring in our discussion of other groups of microörganisms. They may serve to emphasize the fact that microbiology is in some respects different from the biology of larger organisms. Distinctions which seem to be of fundamental importance with the higher organisms melt away when we consider the lowly and the minute. Many of the flagellates, as well as some other groups of microörganisms, are claimed both by Botany and Zoölogy.

Sarcodina. We have already considered the essential characters of the Sarcodina in our discussion of the amoeba — the lack of a pellicle or cell membrane, and the amoeboid locomotion by means of pseudopodia. This class also contains a great variety of different kinds of Protozoa, which differ mainly in the character of their pseudopodia, and in the presence or absence of a shell or protective covering secreted by the animal.

Pseudopodia. Pseudopodia may be broad and blunt lobes, or fine and filamentous. The latter may be branched, and branches from different pseudopodia may run together forming a constantly moving network of protoplasm. In some Sarcodina the pseudopodium is semi-permanent, containing a central rigid body, the axial filament, over which the protoplasm flows. Such pseudopodia are named *axopodia*, and are characteristic of a subclass of the Sarcodina called *Actinopoda*. The remaining species, with temporary pseudo-podia, form the second subclass, the *Rhizopoda*.

Tests. Shells, or *tests*, are formed by a number of different kinds of Sarcodina. In the simplest forms these are composed of chitin secreted by the organism, but they may be impregnated with silica or lime salts, or may be built up of bits of sand, spicules from sponges,

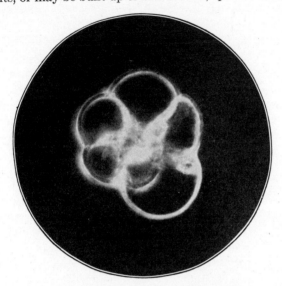

Fig. 12. Chambered Shell of a Foraminiferan.
Photomicrograph by dark field illumination.

diatom shells, or other hard foreign matter cemented to the test. The test may have one or more openings through which pseudopodia project for locomotion or the capture of prey.

Foraminifera. Prominent among the shell-forming Rhizopoda are the *Foraminifera*, sea forms which live mostly in the mud at the bottom. They form rather complicated shells of varied forms, with many chambers. The shells are usually calcareous, and accumulate in places at the bottom of the sea, forming the *globigerina ooze*. These forms were very abundant in past ages, as is shown by deposits of fossil shells.

The Foraminifera present a somewhat more complicated life cycle than the amoebae, exhibiting *alternating sexual and non-sexual generations*. The organism begins life as a small, naked cell, moving

by its pseudopodia. It secretes a shell, at first a single chamber,
with an opening at one end. As it grows, new chambers are added,
each a little larger than the preceding. The nucleus divides repeatedly, so that the many chambers become filled with a multi-

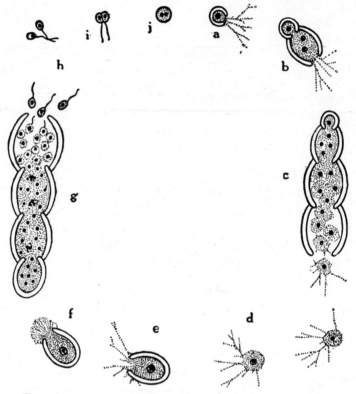

FIG. 13.   Diagram Showing the Development of Foraminifera.

a–c, non-sexual phase; *d*, uninucleate amoeboid cells emerging from the shell, *c;*
g, flagellate gametes emerging from shell; *h–j*, conjugation. (After Kudo,
Handbook of Protozoölogy, C. C. Thomas, Springfield, Ill.)

nucleated mass of protoplasm. From the final chamber of the shell,
this protoplasm now *buds* off a number of small cells, each with
a single nucleus. These develop each a flagellum, and swim
away, looking much like a small flagellate. They are sexual cells,
and fuse two by two. The cell formed by such fusion now also secretes a shell, grows, adds to its shell, and becomes multinucleated.

But at the mouth of the shell this organism buds off larger naked cells, with pseudopodia instead of flagella, which proceed to develop a new shell without any fusion process and so complete the cycle.

Slime Molds. Many zoölogists also include with the Rhizopoda a group of organisms whose position in the organic world is not known with certainty. These present two very distinct phases of growth: — a vegetative phase, in which the organisms present many of the characters of the amoebae, and a reproductive phase which, superficially at least, presents many of the characters of a mold or Fungus. They are called *Mycetozoa* (fungus-animals) if classified with the Protozoa, or *Myxomycetes* (slime-fungi) if classified with the Fungi.

Their life cycle begins with a spore, or resting cell, which, lodging upon a substance fitted for its growth, germinates. This is accomplished by rupturing the spore wall, the protoplasm flowing out. The cell thus freed looks and moves like a little amoeba, but also develops for a time a flagellum at one end. It grows, and divides, feeding upon bacteria. But later a number of these little cells flow together, fuse, to make a large multinucleated mass of protoplasm, the *plasmodium*.

The plasmodium now moves as a whole like an amoeba, flowing over the ground or creeping into the crevices of rotting logs, picking up all sorts of decaying organic matter which it digests in vacuoles within the mass of protoplasm. Indigestible fragments accumulate within the protoplasm, but are eventually extruded.

After a time the plasmodium comes to rest, and enters the reproductive phase. Little knobs or lobules appear on its surface. These are formed by a protrusion of part of the protoplasm, which secretes a wall of protecting material. The protrusions continue to elevate, and differentiate into an upper expanded portion, the *sporangium* (spore-vessel) and a narrow supporting *stalk*. In the sporangium the protoplasm segregates into as many individual cells as there were nuclei originally. Each uninucleate cell develops a rather thick protecting membrane and becomes a spore. When ripe, the sporangium bursts and liberates the spores, which are carried by the wind to a new locality to begin the cycle over again.

The similarity of the vegetative phase to the amoebae is obvious. The multiplication by spores formed in a sporangium is quite foreign to the Protozoa, and very similar to the mode of multiplication found in certain molds, for instance, *Mucor* (see Fig. 28). On the other hand, the formation of threads of protoplasm (mycelium), so characteristic of the molds, is lacking.

Sporozoa. These are all strictly parasitic forms, not growing as free-living organisms. They will be considered in a later chapter, but for comparison with the other classes, their main features will be briefly related here.

The specialized parasitic mode of life has led to a simplification of structure but to a complexity of life cycle. Food is absorbed by simple absorption through the cell wall. Therefore there is no mouth, no digestive vacuole. Although in some forms certain stages of the life cycle show amoeboid movement, special organs of locomotion are completely lacking.

Life Cycles of Sporozoa. Two modes of multiplication occur alternately to complete the life cycle. In the first, a single cell undergoes segmentation into a number of new individuals. This process, called *schizogony*, serves for rapid multiplication in the body of the host animal, and the cells concerned in this mode of growth are called *trophozoites*. The second mode of multiplication results from the fusion of certain sex cells, or *gametes*, which have become differentiated from the trophozoites. From their fusion and later division there arises a new form of cell, the *sporozoite*. This phase of the cycle is called *sporogony*.

In some species of Sporozoa the parasite lives in two different hosts which are necessary to complete the life cycle. In malaria, for example, schizogony occurs in the blood of man, sporogony in the body of the mosquito. The sporozoites produced in the mosquito escape in the saliva and are introduced into the blood when the mosquito bites a man. There they transform into trophozoites. In other species of Sporozoa, however, the whole cycle is completed in one host. Here the sporozoites are discharged from the body, encased in a protecting membrane, to form a spore. They are capable of remaining dormant until swallowed by another individual of the host species, when they transform into trophozoites.

Ciliata. The highest development of one-celled organisms, at least from the standpoint of complexity of structure, is presented by the *Ciliata*. Here the cell becomes differentiated into a number of parts, which in diversity of structure and function are analogous to the organs of higher animals and sometimes referred to as *organelles*.

Paramecium. *Paramecium* is the best known of the ciliates, a form familiar to all students of biology. The individual is a single cell which, while elastic and capable of bending or squeezing through narrow openings, is yet maintained in a constant form by a cell membrane or pellicle. This pellicle may be removed by treatment with alcohol, and is found to be made up of a mosaic of hexagonal plates, from each of which a *cilium* arises. These cilia, given off from all parts of the surface, are the organs of locomotion. They differ from flagella in being shorter (relative to the size of the cell) and in propelling the organism by a backward lashing movement instead of a rotary screw-like movement.

Structure. The cell of Paramecium is elongated, "stream-line" in form. Running diagonally across one side is a groove, the *oral groove*, leading to a short funnel, the *gullet*. The oral groove is also covered with cilia which serve to sweep a current of water (bearing food) to the mouth of the gullet. The pressure of this current is sufficient to force small droplets of water, containing bacteria or minute Protozoa, into the interior of the cell where they form food vacuoles. These vacuoles are carried away into the cell, new ones form in turn, and so there is produced a continuous succession of

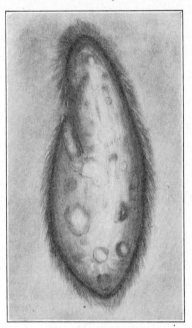

Fig. 14. *Paramecium sp.,* a Ciliate Protozoön.

vacuoles which follow a definite path, first backwards, then forwards to the anterior end and finally backwards again. As the vacuoles make this journey, digestive enzymes are secreted into them, digestible material is dissolved and absorbed into the protoplasm, and the remaining material is ejected from the cell when the vacuole reaches a certain spot near the posterior extremity of the cell, called the *anal opening.* Paramecium has something approaching a digestive tract.

An excretory system is represented by two *contractile vacuoles,* one at either end. These differ from the contractile vacuoles of amoeba in being constant in position and in having *radiating canals* which serve to collect water from a wide zone of protoplasm. They enlarge, burst through the cell wall and discharge, then fill again, rhythmically and alternately, i.e., when one is emptying the other is filling.

In addition to organs of locomotion, digestion and assimilation, and excretion, Paramecium possesses organs of defense which are called *trichocysts*. These are bodies, very numerous, found in the protoplasm just beneath the pellicle and opening through it by minute pores. They secrete a substance which, when the animal is disturbed, is discharged into the surrounding water. Here it immediately coagulates in the form of long sticky threads. These adhere to and entangle the locomotor organs of other microörganisms which may attack.

Paramecium moves forward by a backward lashing of the cilia, but the diagonal oral groove disturbs the symmetry of their effect and results in a spiral movement. If the cell moves into a zone where conditions of light, aeration, or chemical reaction are unfavorable, it stops, the cilia reverse their motion and the cell moves backwards. Then it stops and moves forward again in a new direction. These reflexes result from sensations derived from the water current in the oral groove. They indicate a rather high development as regards those mechanisms of coördination which in higher animals is the function of the nervous system.

Reproduction. Within the cell of Paramecium there are two nuclei, the larger *macronucleus* and the smaller *micronucleus*. The macronucleus is said to govern the metabolism of the cell, and the micronucleus, apparently, bears the hereditary characters. Paramecium multiplies by binary fission. In the ciliates the plane of division is *transverse*, i.e., in a plane at right angles to the long axis of the cell, as contrasted with the longitudinal fission characteristic of the flagellates. When Paramecium divides, both nuclei divide. The division of the macronucleus is *amitotic;* it merely elongates and becomes constricted in the middle. The division of the micronucleus, as with the nuclei of all other protozoa, is by *mitosis*. Following the division of the nuclei, a cleavage plane appears, and the two cells separate.

After a number of generations by cell division, Paramecium undergoes *conjugation*. This is a rather specialized sexual process, involving the union of two cells by a narrow tubular process. The micronuclei of the two cells each divide twice. Three of the four nuclei thus formed disappear. The remaining one divides again, forming one large and one small nucleus. The small nucleus of each cell passes through the tubular bridge over into the opposite cell where it fuses with the large nucleus. Following this the two cells, mutually fertilized, separate. The macronucleus of each cell, which has taken no part in this process, now disappears. The micronucleus undergoes a series of divisions, part of the resultant nuclei developing into new macronuclei, the remainder into micronuclei. A series of cell divisions now leaves one macronucleus and one micronucleus in each cell.

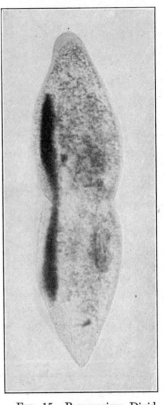

This process is quite evidently of the same general character as sexual reproduction in higher organisms. A maturation of the nucleus leads to a *haploid* state (each nucleus containing half the normal number of chromosomes) and is followed by fertilization with a return to the *diploid state* (with the normal number of chromosomes). It occurs, however, only at rather long intervals, and is not essential to the organism, for cultures of Paramecium have been grown through hundreds of generations without any signs of conjugation.

FIG. 15. Paramecium Dividing. The micronucleus has divided; the macronucleus, greatly elongated, is dividing.

This brief description of Paramecium may serve to indicate the complexity of the Ciliata, both in structure and in functions, and to emphasize the fact that the unicellular state does not necessarily involve simplicity. Compared with the amoeba, Paramecium is a highly developed organism, and there are some multicellular animals which are less complex.

The Ciliata comprise a great variety of forms which differ largely in modifications of the cilia, and in variations in their distribution. In some, rather stout *cirri* are formed by a fusion of the cilia. Such forms show a differentiation into dorsal and ventral aspects,

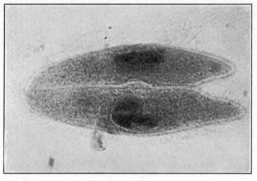

FIG. 16.   Paramecium; Conjugation.

and are adapted for creeping over a surface rather than swimming through water. In others, as *Vorticella*, the cilia are reduced to a ring about the anterior end. These forms are usually attached to some object by a contractile stalk, remaining for long periods of time in one place, though they may break loose and swim away. Mostly the ciliates are holozoic in nutrition. A few are parasitic in the alimentary tracts of higher animals. Some exhibit green coloring matter, but this is due to a growth within the cell of minute green *Algae*. These forms are said to live together in *symbiosis,* i.e., to the mutual benefit of both.

Suctoria. The *Suctoria* comprise a still more highly specialized group of Protozoa, which exist in two growth phases. The young cells are ciliated, and swim free in the water. Later they become attached to some solid object, lose their cilia, and develop *tentacles*. These are long tubular processes ending in a knob. Ciliates, swimming by, adhere to these knobs, and their contents are sucked through the tentacle into the interior of their captor. Reproduction is mainly by *budding;* small parts of the cell become pinched off, develop cilia, and swim away.

This, then, is the picture of the Protozoa: — a group of widely diversified forms having very little in common save the predominance of the one-celled state, and of animal over plant characters in habits and nutrition, but shading off into the plant kingdom on the one hand and into the multicellular animals on the other. Mostly they are free-living, in fresh water or salt; a few forms are found in soil; but one whole class and many representatives of the other classes are parasitic in higher animals. Mostly they are animal-like, or holozoic, in their nutrition, taking solid organic matter into the body and there digesting it; but all of the parasitic forms and some of the free-living forms absorb organic matter in solution through the cell wall, while the green flagellates are predominantly plant-like in nutrition. All are nucleate, and for the most part nuclear division

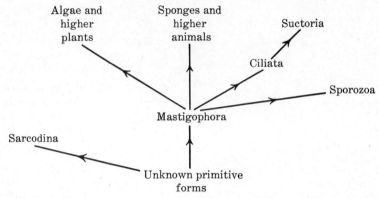

FIG. 17.   Diagram Showing Relations of the Protozoa.

is by mitosis. They vary in reproduction and life cycles from the simple cell division and resting cysts of the Amoeba to the complex alternating sexual and non-sexual generations of the Sporozoa. They vary in complexity of structure from the simple undifferentiated Amoeba to the highly differentiated Paramecium with its organelles.

Some of the Mastigophora present amoeboid forms in some stages of their growth, and similarly some Sarcodina may at times produce flagellated forms. These two classes are considered to be more primitive than the other classes of Protozoa, to be closely related to each other, and to have been derived from some common, unknown, primitive ancestral type. The Ciliata and Sporozoa have probably evolved from the Mastigophora. While our knowledge of the origin and evolution of these primitive forms is undoubtedly rather speculative, it is none the less interesting. The relations of the Protozoa may be indicated as in Fig. 17.

CHAPTER IV

A SURVEY OF MICROBIC LIFE: THE ALGAE

We have seen how some of the flagellated Protozoa are plant-like in the possession of green coloring matter which is contained within chloroplasts. These green flagellates are also claimed by the botanists, who place them in a subdivision of the plant kingdom called *Algae*. There are a great many other microscopic plant forms which belong in the same group, so that a survey of microbic life would be quite incomplete without their consideration. At first glance they do not seem to be of as great practical importance as the other groups of microbes — Protozoa, Fungi, and bacteria — for they cause neither disease nor spoilage. But they are important as *producing* organisms in the water, both fresh and salt. They are as important in producing fish as are corn and oats in producing meat. And some day, no doubt, man will control their growth, just as he now controls the growth of terrestrial plant life. The Algae are of immediate practical importance only as a source of trouble in city water supplies, where their presence may give rise to disagreeable odors and flavors.

Thallophytes. The Algae form one of two subdivisions of a subkingdom of the plant kingdom called *Thallophytes*. Thallophytes are plants which do not show a characteristic differentiation into root, stem, and leaf, but which consist of a relatively undifferentiated mass of tissue, the *thallus*. A thallus may vary from a single free cell to a very large and complicated mass of tissue which approaches the differentiation seen in the higher plants. The Thallophytes include, in addition to the Algae, the *Fungi*. These differ from the Algae in lacking chlorophyll, in being incapable of photosynthesis; and therefore they are dependent upon other organisms for their nutrition.

Classes of Algae. The one-celled green flagellates with chloroplasts are placed by botanists in a certain class of Algae called Green Algae, or *Chlorophyceae*. There are five of these classes:

58

I. The Cyanophyceae, or Blue-green Algae
II. The Rhodophyceae, or Red Algae
III. The Phaeophyceae, or Brown Algae
IV. The Chrysophyceae, or Yellow Algae
V. The Chlorophyceae, or Green Algae

The green color of the Chlorophyceae is due to the occurrence of chlorophyll as the main pigment. In the other classes other kinds of pigments occur in sufficient amount to greatly modify or mask the green of the chlorophyll. The Algae are undoubtedly the oldest of the plants with chlorophyll, and it seems probable that in this primitive group nature experimented with a number of different pigment substances. While grossly the divisions are characterized by different colors, they are actually distinguished mainly by peculiarities of cell structure and their modes of reproduction.

The Red and Brown Algae can hardly be considered microbes; some of the Brown Algae form plants over a hundred feet long! They are almost exclusively marine plants which have evolved from the Green Algae. They differ from them in their pigments, in their larger size, and especially in more complicated modes of sexual reproduction. Our sole interest in these groups lies in the fact that some of them, certain Red Algae, secrete a gum which, under the name of agar, has been of such great importance in the development of microbiology.

Green Algae. Some of the simpler types of green flagellates exhibit two growth phases. In one, the flagellate phase, they are free-swimming forms, dispersed through the water. In the other (known as the *palmella* phase) they settle down on some solid substrate, lose their flagella, become rounded, and surround themselves with a gelatinous secretion. This process is somewhat similar to the encystment of Protozoa, but differs in this, that the cells are still actively growing and dividing and may thus give rise to a colony of non-motile cells surrounded by a common jelly-like sheath. At times, some of these cells break loose from the colony, develop flagella, and swim away. To the algologist, the colony is the normal growth form; the flagellated cells are reproductive bodies whose function is to spread the range of the species. It is in this way that the Green Algae have originated from the flagellated Protozoa — by settling down, losing their flagella, and assuming an entirely plant-like mode of life.

Within the class of Chlorophyceae are included a wide variety of forms, varying from simple free cells reproducing by cell division only, up to complex forms very similar to higher plants, with a root-like "holdfast" supporting a much branched filamentous structure, and with reproduction both by non-sexual spores and by rather complicated sexual processes. Whether unicellular or multicellular, the cells of the Green Algae are much alike, i.e., excepting the special sexual cells of the higher forms, there is not much differentiation.

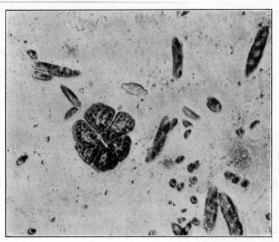

FIG. 18.   Unicellular Green Algae.

They contain distinct nuclei which divide by mitosis. In some forms the cells are multinucleate. These are species which grow out in threads or filaments, in which the cell continues to grow, and its nucleus to divide, without forming cross-walls. Such a continuous mass of protoplasm with many nuclei is called a *coenocyte*. The cells of the Green Algae all contain chloroplasts. These may be single or numerous. The Green Algae are characterized by the variety of forms which may be exhibited by these chloroplasts — from simple globular bodies to the elaborate spiral bands of Spirogyra. Embedded within the chloroplasts are small bodies (*pyrenoids*) composed of a central granule of protein nature, surrounded by starch. They are supposed to be centers of starch synthesis.

The class of Green Algae is separated into divisions according to the character of the reproductive cells, whether these have flagella or not, and if flagellated, according to the number and relative sizes of the flagella. In each of these divisions (excepting one), there occur both unicellular forms and filamentous forms.

FIG. 19. Portion of a Filament of Spirogyra.

Chrysophyceae. This class differs from the Chlorophyceae in the occurrence of a yellow pigment, xanthophyll, in the chloroplasts, in sufficient quantity to mask the green color of the chlorophyll, so that a mass of the cells appears yellow or yellowish brown instead of green. They also differ in that they do not store starch, like the Green Algae and all of the higher green plants; instead food is stored in the form of an oil.

In this division of the Algae, most of the species are unicellular forms. Some, like the Dinoflagellates mentioned in the preceding chapter, are so animal-like that they are claimed by the protozoölogists as well as by the botanists. One group of Chrysophyceae, the diatoms, are so peculiar and striking that they are more important and more interesting than the others.

Diatoms. The *Diatoms* (Bacillarieae) are unicellular algae particularly characterized by the secretion of siliceous shells. They are found both in fresh water and in the sea, being particularly abundant in the colder parts of the ocean, where they are the most important of the producing organisms, furnishing, directly or indirectly, the food for the abundant fish life. The silica of their shells is very resistant to disintegrating agencies, and upon the death of the cell, falls to the bottom of the sea. Great deposits of these shells have been produced in past geologic ages, forming beds known as "diatomaceous earth." This diatomaceous earth is used for a variety of purposes: — under the name "tripoli" it is used as a polishing powder; it forms an ingredient of some tooth pastes; it is mixed with nitroglycerine to make dynamite; and pressed into hollow cylinders or "bougies," it forms the basis of some of the fine porous filters used by bacteriologists to filter the cells of bacteria out of liquids in which they have grown.

Shells of Diatoms. The shells of Diatoms are in two parts, or *valves*, one of which fits over the other like the lid of a pasteboard box. The joint between these two valves is closed by two overlapping bands which form the *girdle*. The shells are quite varied in form, but two general types may be recognized. In the *centric* Diatoms the shell is symmetric about a central point; they may be round like a pill-box, or triangular. Most of the marine forms are centric Diatoms. The *pennate* Diatoms are elongated, needle-like, cigar-shaped, boat-shaped, etc., and are more abundant in fresh water. In all of the Diatoms the shell is marked with ridges and grooves and pits to form a beautifully symmetrical, sculptured body. They have been a favorite object of collectors, and based upon the characters of the shells, some 12,000 species are known. In some of the Diatoms the markings are very fine and regular, and thus serve admirably for testing the resolving power, flatness of field, and other qualities of microscope objectives. *Pleurosigma* is such a "test diatom."

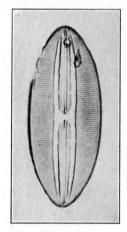

Fig. 20. Shell of a Diatom.

The Diatoms may float free in the water or may be attached to rocks, seaweeds, etc. Such attached forms are frequently supported on stalks of gelatinous material secreted by the cells. These stalks may be branched, forming rather elaborate-appearing colonies, with the Diatoms in clusters at the tips of the branches. The free-floating forms are usually single, but they may remain attached to each other at alternate corners in a zigzag arrangement.

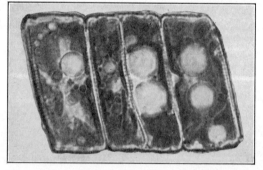

Fig. 21. Diatoms. The overlapping of the shells may be seen at the edge. The central cell is dividing. The large round bodies are globules of oil.

Within the shell is the cell proper, or protoplast. It contains a central nucleus which divides by mitosis. There are one or more *chromatophores* ("pigment-bearers") which, unlike the chloroplasts of the Green Algae, are yellow to brown in color.

Blue-green Algae. The *Cyanophyceae* or *Blue-green Algae* form a group isolated from the other forms, and of unknown relationships. As will be seen later, they show some affinities with the bacteria. They are the simplest, most primitive forms of green plant life. Essentially unicellular forms, the cells are usually bound together by a common gelatinous capsule to form colonies, or are connected to form filaments, frequently enclosed within a sheath. They are mainly fresh-water forms, but a few are found in brackish water, and many are semi-terrestrial, growing upon damp rocks or trees, and among mosses. They have become adapted to a wide range of habitats. Some forms are found growing in hot springs at temperatures which would, a priori, seem incompatible with life.

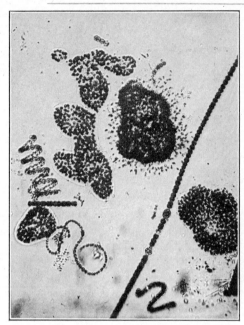

Fig. 22. Various Blue-green Algae, from Water Bloom.

While essentially photosynthetic in their nutrition, it is known that they may lead a partially saprophytic life. Many species grow upon the higher aquatic plants, and it is possible that they are tending toward parasitism. A few forms are known to live as parasites in the mouths and intestines of animals.

In fresh-water lakes, Blue-green Algae may grow attached to rocks or plants, or may float free in the water. Such floating forms comprise the bulk of the vegetable *plankton*, or floating population of the water, as do the Diatoms in the sea. The amount of floating Blue-green Algae in the water is subject to pronounced variations.

At times it increases enormously in a short time, making the water turbid, and forming a green scum on the surface. When this occurs the lake is said to be "blooming," and the scum is referred to as "water bloom." This growth quickly dies down, and decaying, gives rise to a disagreeable odor and to a peculiar flavor of the water.

Structure. The Blue-green Algae differ from the Green Algae in

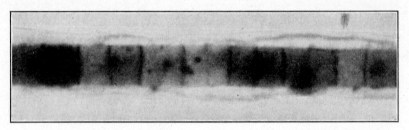

Fig. 23. A Filamentous Blue-green Alga, *Lyngbya*. Portion of a filament stained with iron haematoxyline to show the "incipient" nuclei.

their color. In addition to chlorophyll they contain a blue pigment, *phycocyanin*. These colors are not contained within a chromatophore, but are diffused through the protoplast. While a bluish-green is the predominant color, some species are yellow, olive, or brown, due to the production of other pigments. The cells of the Blue-green Algae are much simpler in organization than those of the Green Algae. *There is no distinct nucleus.* There is a rather vaguely differentiated central portion, staining more deeply than the rest of the cell, called the *central body*. It has been looked upon as a sort of nucleus, and recent microchemical investigations have shown that it contains granules of thymonucleic acid, an essential ingredient of the chromatin of the cells of higher organisms. It is therefore probably functionally analogous to a nucleus, but not so highly organized as a true nucleus. It has been called an *incipient* nucleus.

Within the cells are also found various reserve materials. One of these, *volutin*, appears in the form of granules or droplets which stain very deeply with the basic aniline dyes. This substance is also found in the cells of some Protozoa, Green Algae, and Diatoms, and, as will be seen later, it is a prominent feature of the cells of Fungi, especially the yeasts, and of some bacteria. Its exact nature has but recently been determined; it is very probably composed of free nucleic acid, different, however, from the nucleic acid of the chromatin of the nuclei. It is important because it has frequently been mistaken for nuclear material. The Blue-green Algae store carbohydrate in the form of glycogen, as do Fungi and animals; not as starch, which is characteristic of all other green plants. They also frequently contain oil globules.

Reproduction. In the Cyanophyceae, reproduction is almost exclusively by simple cell fission. Since this is also true of the bacteria, and since there are other resemblances between bacteria and Blue-green Algae, the German botanist, Cohn, proposed to include both of these primitive groups in a separate subdivision of the plant kingdom, the *Schizophytes*, or "fission plants." But it has since been found that the similarity between the bacteria and the Blue-green Algae is more apparent than real, and that bacteria are more closely related to certain Fungi.

In some of the filamentous species, a portion of a filament, composed of several or a number of cells, may be broken off to multiply the species. Such a body is a *hormogone*. In many species, certain cells may become enlarged, filled with reserve food, and develop a thick cell wall. These *resting spores* serve to maintain life in a dormant state when conditions are unfavorable for growth. In some species reproduction may occur by means of minute bodies, *gonidia*, formed within a cell by a multiple division of the protoplast. Sexual reproduction is unknown. In some species which occur in filaments, or chains of cells, certain cells become thick-walled, lose their color, and are almost devoid of contents. Their function is unknown. They are called *heterocysts*.

The Blue-green Algae vary with regard to the nature of their cell groupings. Two main orders are recognized. In the *Coccogoneae*, the cells are grouped together in more or less irregular clusters. In the *Hormogoneae*, they are grouped in chains or closely fitted together to form long filaments. In the former, the cells are mostly round or oval in form; in the latter the cells vary from round or oval to cylindrical or disc-shaped. Some of the filamentous forms are spirally twisted.

Relationships of the Algae. The Cyanophyceae are the most primitive of the plants with chlorophyll. The absence of a distinct nucleus, the absence of chloroplasts, and the very simple modes of reproduction all indicate this. They have no near relatives, save possibly the bacteria. It is believed by some authorities, however, that the Rhodophyceae have been derived from the Blue-green Algae. There have been found some primitive unicellular Red Algae which are considered to be transition forms.

Neither the Cyanophyceae nor the Rhodophyceae contain any species with motile, flagellated cells. In the remaining classes there are found such flagellated species, or species which develop flagellated cells at some stage in their life-cycles. This is considered evidence that they have had their origin from ancestral types which were similar to existing species of flagellated Protozoa. The Chlorophyceae are supposed to have developed from a flagellate with green chloroplasts, the Chrysophyceae from one with yellowish chloroplasts. The Brown Algae are believed by some authorities to be a higher development of the Chrysophyceae, by others to have arisen independently. The mosses and higher plants very obviously developed from the Green Algae.

These relationships are indicated in the diagram, Fig. 24.

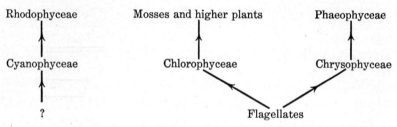

FIG. 24.   Relationships of the Algae.

CHAPTER V

A SURVEY OF MICROBIC LIFE: THE FUNGI

Every fisherman who has kept bait minnows in a live box is familiar with a "water mold" which frequently grows upon fish after they have been handled or injured. This mold, *Saprolegnia*, appears upon the surface of the fish as a thick whitish scum. It is representative of a group of Fungi, some parasitic and others saprophytic, which are aquatic in habits.

Mycelium. If one examines with a hand lens the white scum or feltwork that appears upon the minnow, it is found to be made up of interlacing filaments or threads, which, at the outer surface of the growth, end in slightly swollen or club-shaped tips. These filaments or threads are collectively known as *mycelium*, individually as *hyphae*. They look very much like the filaments of some of the Green Algae, save that they are colorless, lacking chlorophyll. Examined in stained preparations under the microscope, they are found to contain a continuous mass of protoplasm with many minute nuclei. This protoplasm is not cut up into cells by cross-walls; it is *coenocytic*, as in the filaments of the Green Alga, *Vaucheria*.

Fig. 25. A Sporangium of Saprolegnia, Filled with Zoospores.

Reproduction of Saprolegnia. If the tips of the hyphae are examined under the microscope, it is found that in some of them the swollen extremity is separated from the rest of the filament by a cross-wall. The cell thus cut off develops into a reproductive body. Its protoplasm divides into a number of small rounded cells which contain one nucleus each. An opening appears in the cell wall at the tip, and the rounded cells, which have now become pear-shaped and have developed a pair of flagella, emerge and swim away to seek a new place suitable for growth. These motile reproductive cells are called *zoöspores,* and the body from which they were liberated is a *zoösporangium.* They are *asexual* spores, produced simply by the separation of a portion of the coenocytic mycelium into its component nuclei with surrounding protoplasm.

Sexual Reproduction. Saprolegnia also reproduces by *sexual* spores. These result from the fusion of two sexually differentiated cells, an *oögonium* and *antheridium.* They are formed from the tips of side branches of a hypha, being separated by cross-walls. The oögonium becomes swollen, globular, while the antheridium remains filamentous. They are usually formed from neighboring branches of the same hypha. Several antheridia are formed in the neighborhood of a single oögonium.

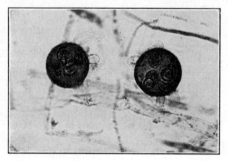

In the oögonium the multinucleate protoplast undergoes division to form several smaller cells, each with one nucleus. Many of the nuclei disappear. Fertilization occurs through a fusion

FIG. 26. Fertilized Oögonia of Saprolegnia. Each oögonium contains several oöspores; several tubular antheridia have fused with each oögonium.

of one or more antheridia with the oögonium. The nuclei of the antheridia fuse with the nuclei of the cells in the oögonium, one male nucleus passing to each cell. The fertilized cell so formed becomes an oöspore.

Classes of Fungi. The water molds are types representative of one class of Fungi, the *Phycomycetes,* or "algal Fungi," so called because of their close resemblance to the Green Algae. There are three other classes. Together they comprise the true Fungi, or *Eumycetes:*

I. The Phycomycetes
II. The Ascomycetes
III. The Basidiomycetes
IV. The Fungi imperfecti

In addition to these four classes, many botanists recognize two other classes of organisms which certainly are not very closely related to the Eumycetes, but which show some fungus-like characters.

V. The Myxomycetes
VI. The Schizomycetes

Slime Molds Again. The *Myxomycetes,* or slime molds, have already been described in the chapter on Protozoa under the name Mycetozoa — organisms which are protozoan in character during the vegetative phase of their existence, but which reproduce by spores on stalks like a mold. The *Schizomycetes,* or fission-fungi, are the bacteria, which will be discussed in the next chapter. For the present, then, we will consider only the true Fungi.

Fungi may be unicellular or multicellular. In all of the multicellular forms, single cells in the form of spores occur in some stages of the life cycle. And many of the forms which are predominantly unicellular may form at least rudimentary multicellular types at times. A typical multicellular Fungus is a mold or a mushroom; a typical unicellular Fungus is a yeast.

Structure of Mycelium. In the multicellular Fungi the cells are always arranged in the form of filaments of mycelium. At times solid masses of cells may appear without any thread-like structure, but these are always the result of a twisting together of mycelium into a compact mass. This mycelium is characteristically non-septate, or coenocytic, in the Phycomycetes, and cut up by cross-walls or septa into separate cells in the other classes of Fungi.

The cells of Fungi contain one or more nuclei. In some cases the cells may be multinucleate in some stage of development, and uninucleate in others. The nuclei of the Fungi are very minute and can be studied only with difficulty. The cytoplasm may be quite homogeneous in young, actively growing hyphae, but soon shows vacuoles and numerous granules of various reserve foodstuffs. Carbohydrate is stored in the form of glycogen. Fat droplets are often present. Volutin, which occurs in the Algae, is very prominent in

the cells of Fungi, especially the yeasts. The cell wall is composed
of chitin, not of cellulose as in Algae.

The mycelium of Fungi may be differentiated into two parts.
There is a vegetative portion which burrows into the substance upon

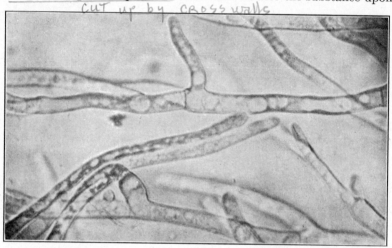

FIG. 27. Mycelium. This is *septate* (not coenocytic) mycelium.

which the Fungus is growing — plant or animal matter, living or
dead. There is also a reproductive portion, generally extending into
the air, which forms the spores that serve to multiply the species.
These are called submerged and aerial mycelium, respectively.

Spores. The spores of Fungi may be produced sexually or asexually; in most forms both methods occur, as in Saprolegnia. The
mode of spore formation is quite characteristic of the different classes
of Fungi, but the production of sexual spores occurs in a manner
more constant and characteristic than the production of the non-
sexual spores, and is the main basis for the classification of the Fungi.
Asexual spores may develop by two quite different mechanisms,
endogenous and *exogenous* spore formation. The production of the
zoöspores in Saprolegnia is an example of endogenous spore formation.
A cell becomes cut off from the rest of the mycelium, and develops
into a *sporangium.* Within it, the protoplast is divided into a number
of small cells. This is brought about by the appearance of vacuoles,
which, growing and coalescing, separate the protoplasm into smaller
units. When mature, the spores are liberated by a rupture or dissolu-

tion of the sporangium or by the appearance of an opening in its wall. The spores are flagellated in the water molds, but are distributed by the wind in the terrestrial forms. In the latter case they are called *sporangiospores.* The endogenous production of non-sexual spores is characteristic of the Phycomycetes, although in some species within this class exogenous spore formation also occurs. But sporangia are not found in the other classes of Fungi.

Exogenous Spores. Asexual spores are produced exogenously by single cells being constricted from the tips of filaments, usually those projecting into the air. This may occur in two ways. The more usual method is as follows: — a cell is constricted off, and immediately the filament cuts off another cell which pushes the first one ahead of it, and so on. These cells do not become completely separated at once; material may flow

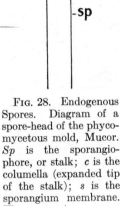

FIG. 28. Endogenous Spores. Diagram of a spore-head of the phycomycetous mold, Mucor. *Sp* is the sporangiophore, or stalk; *c* is the columella (expanded tip of the stalk); *s* is the sporangium membrane. The sporangiospores are the dark bodies within this membrane.

through the cells for a time, and so the outermost cell, which is the oldest, is frequently also the largest. The less frequent method consists in separating a cell at the tip, which then buds out a second cell, and so on; sometimes such a cell may give rise to two buds at once, in which case the chain of cells becomes branched. Here, obviously, the outermost cells are the youngest and smallest.

Conidia. Exogenous asexual spores are called *conidia.* When

FIG. 29. Exogenous Spores. Diagram showing different modes of forming conidia.

mature they become separated from the hypha which formed them, and are distributed by the wind or by insects. Conidia are not always formed on the tips of hyphae; they may be produced by lateral budding. Sometimes they occur singly, or in clusters, rather than in chains. In some Fungi each conidium is composed of two cells; in a few species it may be divided into several cells. Conidia are the characteristic asexual spores of the Ascomycetes and the Fungi imperfecti, but also occur in some of the Phycomycetes and Basidiomycetes.

Chlamydospores. In addition to conidia, and sporangiospores or zoöspores, still a third type of asexual spore occurs in Fungi. This is a cell especially set aside to maintain life in a dormant state during unfavorable conditions. Its protoplasm is filled with reserve food, its wall is tremendously thickened. Such a cell is known as a chlamydospore (ensheathed spore). Chlamydospores are usually cells occurring in the course of the mycelium, although they may arise at the tips of hyphae. They are functionally similar to the resting spores of the Blue-green Algae or the cysts of Protozoa. They occur in all classes of Fungi.

Sexual Spores. The sexual spores vary characteristically with the different classes of Fungi. The oöspores of Saprolegnia are characteristic of one large subclass of Phycomycetes, called *Oömycetes.* They result from the fusion of morphologically differentiated elements, a large female cell and a small male cell. The process is therefore *heterogamous.* Both cells are produced on a single plant or thallus, and the process is therefore *homothallous.* But in the bread molds, which are also Phycomycetes, the sexual spores result from a somewhat different process. Hyphae from two different plants unite to form them. This *heterothallous* conjugation implies that some plants are of one sex and some of the other; but the two sexes cannot be distinguished by any outward characters, even under the microscope. The conjugating cells appear exactly alike. The spore formation is said to be *isogamous,* and the sexes are designated *plus* and *minus* rather than male and female. The resulting spore is a *zygospore,* and such molds form a second subdivision of the Phycomycetes, viz., the *Zygomycetes.*

Phycomycetes. We may now define the Phycomycetes more precisely. They are Fungi characterized by coenocytic mycelium and endogenous asexual spores. Two main divisions may be recognized —

the aquatic Oömycetes, with motile asexual zoöspores, and sexual oöspores which are heterogamous and homothallous; and the terrestrial Zygomycetes with non-motile asexual sporangiospores, and mostly isogamous heterothallous sexual spores, the zygospores.

Ascomycetes. In the Ascomycetes, the sexual spores are produced within a cell which, when mature, is called an *ascus.* These spores are ascospores. In some of the more primitive forms of Ascomycetes the ascospores may be indefinite in number, but in all of the higher forms the number of ascospores within an ascus is invariably eight. The general characters of the

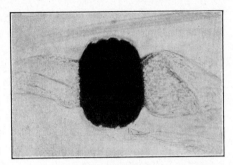

Fig. 30. A Zygospore of the Mold, *Rhizopus nigricans.*

Ascomycetes may vary widely, but the occurrence of eight sexual spores within a sac or membrane is a very constant character.

The production of ascospores may be heterothallous or homothallous, usually the latter. In the simplest forms they result simply from the fusion of two cells, whose nuclei unite, followed by three divisions to yield the characteristic eight spores. The cells which fuse may be alike, but in most cases are differentiated into a larger oögonium, and a smaller antheridium. In the higher Ascomycetes, however, the process is more complex. After fusion of the two cells, the resultant cell does not at once give rise to spores. Instead it forms a new meshwork of mycelium. Some of this mycelium grows into a protecting membrane or tissue, the *perithecium*, within which the asci are formed. These are produced from other filaments arising from the fertilized cell, the *ascogenous hyphae.* The next to the last cell of these hyphae is binucleate. Its two nuclei fuse, the resultant nucleus divides three times, forming the eight ascospores. Thus two nuclear fusions are concerned in the production of these spores.

In addition to the characteristic ascospores within asci, the Ascomycetes are characterized by septate mycelium and non-sexual multiplication by conidia.

Basidiomycetes. In the *Basidiomycetes* the formation of sexual spores is heterothallous and isogamous. Hyphae that have arisen from two separate spores, coming together, unite, i.e., the cells at their tips fuse. But the nuclei of these two cells do not fuse at once. From the fusion-cell there arises an extensive mycelium, which is characteristically *binucleate*, each of the two nuclei dividing inde-

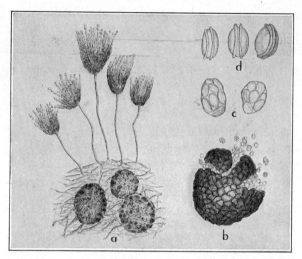

FIG. 31. Ascospores. *a*, sketch of the mold, *Aspergillus glaucus*, showing (above) the asexual conidia borne on stalks, and (below) the globular perithecia which contain the sexual spores; *b*, a perithecium crushed with asci emerging; *c*, asci — each ascus contains several ascopores; *d*, ascospores, greatly enlarged.

pendently at every cell division. This mycelium eventually gives rise to the sexual spores. The tips of the filaments become expanded to form club- or pear-shaped bodies, the *basidia*. In the basidium the two nuclei fuse, the fusion nucleus divides twice, forming four nuclei. Four little stalks or *sterigmata* now arise from the end of the basidium. Each nucleus with some surrounding cytoplasm passes through one of these sterigmata to form a *basidiospore* at its tip. When mature the basidiospores are forcibly discharged into the air, to be distributed by the wind.

The Basidiomycetes comprise the large fleshy Fungi, the mushrooms and puffballs, and bracket Fungi. In these forms the basidiospore is the only reproductive body. The mushroom, or puffball, or bracket is the reproductive portion of the plant, which bears the basidia; there is also an extensive vegetative mycelium. The *smuts* and *rusts* are important Fungi parasitic upon plants, which are included in the Basidiomycetes. But in these forms, other types of spores are interpolated into the life cycles. Rust parasites exhibit a very complex life cycle, involving two species of host plants, with as many as five different kinds of spores at as many different stages of their cycle.

The occurrence of both non-sexual and sexual modes of reproduction, and of homothallism and heterothallism, in the Fungi, makes their life cycles somewhat complicated. Tracing the occurrence of nuclear fusions (resulting in the diploid or 2x phase with regard to number of chromosomes) and of reduction divisions (leading to haploid or x phase) throughout the cycle, provides an intricate and interesting problem which is engaging the attention of a number of biologists. A solution of this problem promises to throw light upon the mechanism of heredity and evolution in the Fungi. On account of the minute size of the nuclei, however, the problem is a difficult one.

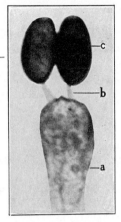

Fig. 32. Basidiospores. *a*, basidium; *b*, sterigma; *c*, basidiospore. Only two of the four basidiospores are shown. Photomicrograph from a section of *Coprinus.*

Fungi Imperfecti. With many species of Fungi the sexual spores are produced sparingly or only under certain conditions, the multiplication and spread of the species being due mainly to the non-sexual spores. If such Fungi are observed in an environment which does not favor the production of sexual spores, their true relationship cannot be determined with certainty. With heterothallous species no sexual spores will appear unless both plus and minus strains are present. A large number of Fungi are known whose sexual spores have not been discovered. If these exhibit coenocytic mycelium and sporangia, they may of course be definitely referred to the Phycomycetes. But if they reproduce by conidia alone, they cannot be placed in one of the three true classes of Fungi, but are instead referred to an artificial class, the *Fungi imperfecti.* This class is given a rank equal to the other three, but is admittedly an arrangement for convenience only. Most of the organisms placed in this class are probably not truly imperfect, i.e., entirely lacking in sexual reproduction, but are only imperfectly known; their sexual

spores have not yet been discovered. From time to time, such sexual
spores are found, and then such species are referred to their proper
class. Usually these species are found to be Ascomycetes. Some
Fungi formerly classed with the imperfect Fungi have later been
referred to the Phycomycetes or Basidiomycetes when more completely known, but undoubtedly the great majority of the Fungi
imperfecti are really Ascomycetes which either have lost the power
of forming ascospores, or whose ascospores have not been discovered.
The Fungi imperfecti comprise an important group to the micro-
biologist, for many of the molds of industrial or medical importance
are placed in this class.

Oidia. In addition to the varied modes of reproduction described
above, many filamentous Fungi exhibit another mode of multiplica-

tion. Septate hyphae may undergo
fragmentation, the individual cells
separating at the cross-walls. This
is especially prone to occur in the
vegetative mycelium immersed in
a liquid. The cells set free in this
manner float away. In many cases
they continue to grow, and dividing,
produce more cells of the same

Fig. 33.   Diagram Showing the
Formation of *Oidia* by Fragmentation of Mycelium.

type. These cells are usually cylindrical or oval in form, but in some
Fungi may become globular. They are called *oidia*, and differ from
conidia in being produced from the vegetative mycelium and in
continuing to grow and multiply after having been set free. Unlike
spores, they are not equipped with thick walls and reserve food
enabling them to remain dormant and to resist injury. They are
not reproductive bodies, but growth forms. Similar one-celled
growth forms may be produced from mycelium by budding. The
cells of the filaments bulge here and there, the bulgings enlarge and
constrict at the base, cutting off the bud, which floats away. The
cells so budded off may also continue to grow, producing new globular cells by budding.

Such one-celled growth forms, produced either by fragmentation
of the mycelium or by budding, are not peculiar to any class of
Fungi. They may be formed by some species of all of the classes.
The degree to which a Fungus may thus transform itself into a
unicellular growth form varies greatly with different species, and

varies with the environment in a single species. Some of the molds belonging to the Phycomycetes may be largely unicellular when grown submerged in liquids where aeration is imperfect, but will be entirely filamentous when grown on the surface where an abundance of oxygen is available. Conversely, molds of the genus Monilia (Fungi imperfecti) are entirely unicellular when well aerated, and develop mycelium only under partially anaerobic conditions. Some of the Fungi causing disease in man and animals are unicellular in the body tissues and filamentous when grown on artificial culture media in the laboratory.

Yeasts. *Yeasts* are Fungi which are permanently unicellular, which are not known to produce mycelium. The term is a common name having no taxonomic value. Some yeasts produce ascospores, and therefore belong to the Ascomycetes. One small group forms basidiospores and belongs to the Basidiomycetes. A very large number of species produce no spores, and must be referred to the Fungi imperfecti. While some of the primitive Phycomycetes form no mycelium, they are not called yeasts.

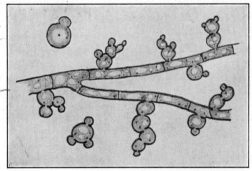

FIG. 34.   Diagram Showing the Origin of Yeast Cells from Mycelium, in *Monilia albicans.*

Yeasts usually reproduce by budding, but in some species multiplication occurs by transverse fission. Ascospores may be produced by the fusion of two cells which send out small tubular processes toward each other. These unite, and the nucleus of one cell passes over into the other. The fusion nucleus divides, giving rise usually to four, but in some species to eight, daughter nuclei. Each of these now becomes surrounded by condensed cytoplasm and develops a spore wall. In some species of yeasts, fusion tubes are formed, but these fail to unite. Instead, each cell proceeds to form spores by itself. In other yeasts, no trace of sex can be demonstrated. Spores are formed simply by the repeated division of the nucleus without relation to any other cell. Such spores, though non-sexual, are still looked upon as ascospores, because they are formed within a cell which may be considered an ascus, because they are fairly constant (usually four) in number, and because we may trace an evolution from the truly sexual forms as indicated above. Basidiospores are formed by some yeasts much as in a mushroom. A small stalk, or sterigma, is formed on the surface of the yeast cell. Upon this stalk a kidney-shaped spore is formed which is forcibly discharged when mature. Several (probably four) such spores may be formed in succession on a single sterigma. No trace of sexuality has been demonstrated in the process.

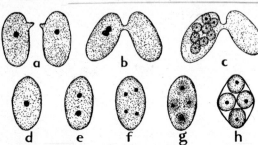

Yeasts may be looked upon as Fungi which have undergone a sort of retrograde evolution. They have become specialized for very rapid growth in certain environments, but have become simplified in struc-

FIG. 35. Spore Formation in Yeasts. *a-c*, by isogamous conjugation (as in *Zygosaccharomyces*); *d-h*, by parthenogenesis (as in *Saccharomyces*).

ture, losing the power to form mycelium, and either completely lacking in spore production, or tending to produce sexual spores asexually.

Yeasts cells are not very large, about 4–5 μ in diameter on the average. Being minute unicellular organisms, there has been some interest in the structure of their cells. They are, as far as is known, uninucleate. The nuclei are very small, but definite, structures. As far as can be determined, the nuclear division is amitotic. The cytoplasm contains granules and vacuoles. These are reserve materials — glycogen, fat, and volutin. In most yeasts there is generally one rather large vacuole in each cell. Within this vacuole a small granule may be seen at times. The granule moves rapidly about in the vacuole, it exhibits Brownian movement, and has been termed the "dancing body." This Brownian movement indicates that the vacuoles contain a fluid of not very high viscosity. When "vitally" stained with neutral red, the fluid of the vacuole is pinkish in color, the dancing body takes on a deeper shade. Sometimes the dancing body suddenly disappears, and then after a time reappears; it goes into solution, and then solidifies again. The material forming the granule is supposed to be volutin, and the vacuole contains the same material in solution. While similar vacuoles and granules may be found in the cells of filamentous fungi, they form a very prominent feature of the yeast cell.

Nutrition of Fungi. We have seen in the preceding chapters that the Protozoa are mostly animal-like, or *holozoic*, in their nutrition, taking other organisms into the interior of the cell and digesting them there; however, some are *saprozoic*, absorbing organic matter in so-

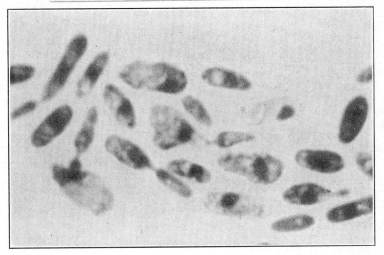

FIG. 36.   Yeast Cells Stained with Iron Haematoxylin to Show Nuclei.

lution directly through the cell membrane, and many are parasitic, especially in higher animals. The Algae are almost completely plant-like, or *holophytic* in their nutrition, absorbing inorganic matter in solution through the cell membrane, and building it into organic matter by photosynthesis, i.e., with the energy of sunlight absorbed by the green chlorophyll; but some Algae may be forced to grow as *saprophytes* artificially in the laboratory, and undoubtedly many are at least partially saprophytic in growth in nature, especially some Diatoms and Blue-green Algae. Fungi are wholly *saprophytic* or *parasitic* in their nutrition; i.e., they live entirely upon plant and animal matter, either as agents of decay or as causes of disease.

While some of the Fungi, such as Saprolegnia, are aquatic organisms like the Algae, from which they had their origin, the Fungi became terrestrial in habit early in their evolution, and most species are terrestrial forms. They are abundant and widespread in soil and leaf mold, on rotting logs, wherever there is dead plant or animal matter. Fungi are the most important causes of disease in green plants; there is hardly a plant species that does not have a dozen or more species of Fungi capable of infecting it. And, while they do not parasitize animals to the same extent as they do plants, there is nevertheless a formidable list of Fungi which grow in or upon all sorts of animals, either as simple parasites or as agents of disease. As causes of spoilage of foods, or of leather or cloth or other organic commodities, and as causes of disease in cultivated plants and animals, Fungi are of tremendous importance to man.

Many of the substances which serve as foodstuffs for Fungi (proteins, fats, starch, cellulose, etc.) are solids, or at least not soluble in water. Before they may be absorbed by the vegetative mycelium, they must be dissolved. This the Fungus accomplishes by secreting digestive ferments or enzymes into its surroundings. What the protozoan accomplishes with its digestive vacuole, or the higher animal with its intestinal tract, the Fungus carries out with its entire body surface! Enzymes are poured out, they dissolve the foodstuff, which is then absorbed through the cell wall, and built up into protoplasm or burned to yield energy. These enzymes are often quite potent, and secreted in quantities much greater than the needs of the organism. They are the agents of destruction which spoil foods and other goods, but in a few cases man has learned to use them for his own ends, to carry out useful chemical reactions, such as the production of sugar from starch, or of gallic acid from tannic acid.

Relationships of the Fungi. It was formerly believed that the Fungi arose from the Algae. The water mold bears very close similarities to the Green Alga, Vaucheria, both in the coenocytic character of its mycelium and in the mode of formation of its sexual spores. It was thought to have arisen from Green Algae through a loss of chlorophyll and the adoption of a saprophytic mode of nutrition. Similarly some of the Ascomycetes show similarities to certain of the Red Algae, and were thought to have arisen independently from that group.

Later, however, there were discovered a number of very primitive unicellular Fungi that show strong resemblances to the Protozoa. They are placed in the Phycomycetes (a subclass called Archimycetes) which are undoubtedly the most primitive of the classes of true Fungi. The Phycomycetes are now believed to have developed independently from the Protozoa, probably from a primitive flagellate. Also there have been discovered some primitive Ascomycetes which indicate a transition from the Phycomycetes, and they are now looked upon as a further evolution of the Phycomycetes. The origin of the Basidiomycetes is still rather obscure, but most authorities consider them to have evolved from the Ascomycetes. The descent of the Fungi appears therefore to have been fairly direct, as may be indicated by the following diagram:

Protozoa → Phycomycetes → Ascomycetes → Basidiomycetes

CHAPTER VI

A SURVEY OF MICROBIC LIFE: THE BACTERIA

We must assume that all life has had its origin in some very simple, very primitive form, undoubtedly unicellular. As we trace the course of evolution backwards, from the complex to the simple, we see how the various lines run together; the main branches all seem to come together in the Protozoa. But as we trace these lines of evolution to their origin, we find that it becomes increasingly more difficult to keep the main stems separate. We finally have difficulty in separating plants from animals! The difficulty lies not in a lack of relationships, but in a superabundance. The primitive forms are so much alike that each group shows some resemblances to several diverse forms. This difficulty reaches an extreme in the bacteria — the smallest, and so far as visible structure is concerned, the simplest of living things which can be seen.

Some of the organisms which we include under the bacteria show strong resemblances to certain of the Blue-green Algae, others to the Fungi, others to the Myxomycetes, and still others to the Protozoa. We may look upon them either as a very primitive but fairly homogeneous group from which higher types of micro-organisms have arisen, or as a heterogeneous group of unrelated forms which have been derived from higher forms by a retrograde evolution — by degradation. There is some evidence to support both views.

What Are Bacteria? It is somewhat difficult to define the bacteria. They have been defined as one-celled Fungi reproducing by simple fission only; this is probably the most widely accepted definition of the group. But they are not strictly unicellular. In several subdivisions, there occur filamentous types composed of a number of cells closely united. They are Fungi only in the broad sense that they are Thallophytes without chlorophyll. But even in this broad sense we must note an exception in the case of the red sulphur bacteria and the green sulphur bacteria, both of which possess pig-

82

ments that enable them to utilize the energy of sunlight in a sort of photosynthesis. The Fungi proper (Eumycetes) form a very homogeneous group to which only one subdivision of the bacteria (Actinomycetales) shows any strong resemblance. Finally, we are beginning to doubt that bacteria reproduce only by simple binary fission. A whole series of other types of reproductive processes have recently been described for them.

Size. The bacteria may, in general, be distinguished from the microörganisms we have described so far by their much smaller size. The largest of the bacteria are of about the size of the smallest of the yeasts, Blue-green Algae, and Protozoa. The majority of bacterial cells will not exceed one micron in diameter. They are also apparently much simpler in structure than the other microörganisms. While some species show intracellular granules or vacuoles, so far as is known these are all simple reserve foodstuffs, not differentiated portions of the cell itself. And in the great majority of species of bacteria, the cell appears to be perfectly homogeneous, a simple mass of protoplasm completely undifferentiated.

Structure. It may be that in organisms so small there is actually as complex a structure as in the larger types of microörganisms, but that the individual parts of the cell are themselves too small to be resolved by the microscope. While this may be true to an extent, there are physical reasons for believing that cells so small in size must be less differentiated in structure. *No one has as yet satisfactorily demonstrated the existence of nuclei in bacteria.* Many authorities have recorded the observation of nuclei in one or another species of bacterium, but none of these observations is beyond criticism. We cannot, in the present state of our knowledge, deny that bacteria possess discrete nuclei, but neither can we affirm it. This rather indefinite negative character is perhaps the only one which we may apply to the bacteria as a whole. Rather than attempting to define bacteria, it might be better to describe the different kinds of organisms which we group together under this name.

Orders of Bacteria. As was indicated in the preceding chapter, bacteria are usually placed with the Fungi, as a class, the *Schizomycetes.* Some botanists group them with the Blue-green Algae in a separate subdivision of the plant kingdom, the *Schizophytes*, or fission plants. But since it has become evident that only some of the bacteria show relationships to the Blue-green Algae, this arrangement has fallen into disuse. The class, *Schizomycetes*, is subdivided into seven orders, as follows:

     I. The Chlamydobacteriales, or ensheathed bacteria
    II. The Caulobacteriales, or stalked bacteria
  III. The Thiobacteriales, or sulphur bacteria
  IV. The Myxobacteriales, or slime bacteria
    V. The Actinomycetales, or ray Fungi
  VI. The Eubacteriales, or true bacteria
 VII. The Spirochaetales

Iron Bacteria. Where springs gush forth whose waters bear in solution compounds of iron in the reduced or ferrous form (as when they drain bogs or peat lands), one finds on the ground over which this water flows a reddish yellow deposit, generally of a loose or flocculent character and feeling somewhat greasy when rubbed between the fingers. If one examines some of this deposit under the microscope, it will be found to consist largely of amorphous masses of ferric hydroxide, but scattered through this material there are numerous long straight filaments of a tubular character, and twisted flat bands. These straight or twisted filaments are products of the growth of two species of iron bacteria — the former of *Leptothrix ochracea*, the latter of *Gallionella ferruginea*. They are found almost universally where deposits of iron are being formed in this manner. *Leptothrix ochracea* is a representative of the ensheathed bacteria, or Chlamydobacteriales; *Gallionella ferruginea* of the stalked bacteria, or Caulobacteriales.

Leptothrix. The presence of *Leptothrix ochracea* in the iron-bearing water is indicated mainly by the deposits of its empty sheaths. These are long straight tubes. Only an occasional one contains the living bacteria. The latter are small, cylindrical bodies, about 1 μ in diameter and of varying length, arranged end to end to form filaments. About these filaments the tubular sheath is deposited. This sheath is composed entirely of a deposit of ferric hydroxide in colloidal form. Apply strong hydrochloric acid, and it is completely dissolved. The sheath gradually increases in thickness with the continued life of the bacteria within it, reaching a diameter of 2–3 μ. As it becomes thicker, it interferes more and more with the diffusion of water to the living cells within. When this occurs, the chain, or filament, of bacterial cells slips out of the tubular sheath. The naked cells now acquire a new sheath. The old, abandoned sheath may remain

intact for a considerable period of time. Part of the deposits of bog
iron ore is made up of such sheaths of *Leptothrix ochracea*, and they
may be recognized in ground sections of the oldest fossil-bearing rocks
of which we have knowledge.

The mode of reproduction of *L. ochracea*
is unknown. In the closely related species,
L. crassa, multiplication is accomplished by a
separation of cells at the ends of the filaments,
which acquire flagella and swim away to start
growth in a new situation. These motile cells
are called "swarmers."

Nutrition of Iron Bacteria. It is quite evident that the presence of iron compounds in
the water is a vital factor for the growth of
these microörganisms. Winogradsky cultivated *Leptothrix ochracea*, and found that this
organism would grow only in the presence of
ferrous compounds. He concluded that the
organism obtains the energy necessary for its
growth by the oxidation of ferrous to ferric

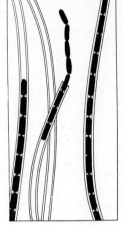

Fig. 37. *Leptothrix
ochracea.*

compounds. Here is a type of nutrition which we have not encountered so far in our survey of microbic life — organisms without
chlorophyll, yet living entirely upon inorganic compounds, and obtaining their energy not from the sun, nor by the oxidation of organic
matter formed by other organisms, but by the oxidation of an inorganic substance, iron. Such organisms are quite independent of
all other organisms, and are called *autotrophic*, or self-nourishing
organisms. We shall meet other examples of this type of nutrition
among the bacteria.

Winogradsky's theory regarding the nutrition of the iron bacteria has been widely accepted, and since the empty sheaths of
Leptothrix and the twisted bands of Gallionella are abundant in
deposits of bog iron ore, it has been generally believed that such
deposits are due to the activity of the iron bacteria. The more
recent investigations of Halvorson and Starkey indicate, however,
that such is not the case. They point out that the ferrous iron
compounds dissolved in water will spontaneously change to the ferric
form on exposure to air whether bacteria are present or not, and the
iron bacteria do not themselves alter the degree of this reaction. The

oxidation of the ferrous compounds is dependent upon the oxidation-reduction potential of the water and upon its hydrogen ion concentration, factors which may be markedly influenced by the growth of other kinds of bacteria, living upon organic matter.

While the bacteria do not themselves cause the oxidation of the ferrous to ferric iron, they do somehow or other cause this reaction to occur upon their surfaces, do somehow or other obtain and utilize the energy which is liberated by the reaction. The deposition of the ferric hydroxide is a vital part of their nutrition.

Chlamydobacteriales. *Leptothrix ochracea* is but one of a number of species of ensheathed bacteria. Not all of them are iron bacteria. In some the sheath is apparently composed entirely of an iron compound completely soluble in hydrochloric acid. But with most of the species the sheath is organic in nature, probably a polysaccharide; it may be entirely organic, or may have iron deposited upon it. The ensheathed bacteria are aquatic forms, found in lakes and streams and springs everywhere. They are all filamentous, i.e., composed of a chain or cells within the sheath, and in most species they grow attached at one end to some firm object under the water. We shall consider two further species which are rather common, *Crenothrix polyspora* and *Sphaerotilus dichotomus*.

FIG. 38. *Crenothrix polyspora.*

Crenothrix. *Crenothrix polyspora* is an ensheathed filamentous water bacterium. The filaments, unlike those of *Leptothrix ochracea* (which float free), are attached at one end to a stone or other solid base. The filaments increase in thickness from the attached base to the free tip. They are enclosed within a sheath which is not composed entirely of ferric hydroxide, as in the case of *Leptothrix ochracea*, but consists of an organic matrix of unknown composition upon which iron oxide may be deposited; it does not completely disappear when treated with strong hydrochloric acid. Within this sheath the cells of the bacteria appear as cylindrical bodies arranged in a chain or filament. These increase in thickness toward the tip of the filament, and the sheath also expands toward the tip, forming a funnel-shaped tube which is open at the extremity. Within this funnel-shaped tube the cells divide not only transversely, but by longitudinal fission as well, giving rise to a thick cluster of smaller rounded cells which break off at the mouth of the tube and float away to start a new filament. These cells formed at the mouths of the tubes by division in three planes may be looked upon as special reproductive cells, and are called *gonidia*.

Crenothrix polyspora is of some practical importance in that at times it develops to an enormous extent in public water reservoirs, giving a very disagreeable odor and flavor to the water upon decomposition. It grows also within water pipes, and may completely plug them.

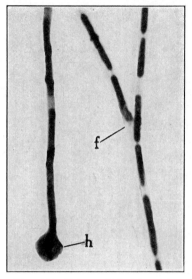

Sphaerotilus. While the sheaths of Crenothrix are not composed of iron, this organism lives in iron-containing waters, and ferric hydroxide is deposited within or upon the sheath. It is undoubtedly an iron bacterium. But in the case of *Sphaerotilus dichotomus* we have to deal with an ensheathed bacterium belonging to the Chlamydobacteriales, which is, however, not an iron bacterium. Iron is not deposited on its sheath, and it does not grow by preference in iron-bearing waters.

Fig. 39. *Sphaerotilus dichotomus.* *h*, holdfast; *f*, "false" branching.

Sphaerotilus dichotomus is an attached filamentous bacterium. The base of the filament is cemented to a stone or plant or other submerged surface by a disc of mucilaginous material. The cylindrical cells are arranged end-to-end in a single row, within a tubular sheath of organic matter secreted by them. The sheaths branch in a characteristic manner, but the cells within do not, i.e., the first cell within a branch is completely separated from the one in the main stem. This so-called "false" branching is very characteristic of Sphaerotilus. The organism multiplies by a liberation of the end cells of a filament, which emerge from the open tip of the sheath, develop a tuft of flagella at one end, and swim away to seek a new habitat. *Cladothrix dichotoma* is a common synonym for *Sphaerotilus dichotomus.*

Caulobacteriales. The stalked bacteria are also found growing attached to submerged surfaces in fresh-water habitats. They differ from the Chlamydobacteriales in occurring as single cells, not as filaments or chains of cells. They differ from other orders of bacteria in the fact that these cells grow attached to shorter or longer stalks, the base of the stalk being attached to the submerged surface by a

FIG. 40. *Gallionella ferruginea.*

little plate or disc, the holdfast. In one family, the Gallionellaceae, the stalks are composed of ferric hydroxide; like the sheaths of *Leptothrix ochracea*, they are completely dissolved by hydrochloric acid. In the other three families, the stalks are of organic matter. In some species they are broad and lobe-like, but in most cases they are fine, hair-like. The stalks are often branched. A little bacterial cell sits at the tip of each branch.

This order of bacteria has only recently been described. Only a few species are known, and they have not been adequately studied because so far they have not been grown in artificial cultures. We shall consider but one species, the iron bacterium *Gallionella ferruginea.*

Gallionella. The flat, twisted bands which indicate the presence of *Gallionella ferruginea* are, like the tubular sheaths of *Leptothrix ochracea*, inert masses of ferric hydroxide completely soluble in hydrochloric acid. The bacterium itself is a very minute cell shaped like a bean or kidney. The colloidal ferric hydroxide is deposited only on the concave side of the cell. As this cell continues to grow it deposits more and more of the iron which extends from the cell as a flat band or ribbon. This ribbon becomes twisted about its own axis. The bacterium multiplies by simple cell division. After fission has occurred, each of the daughter cells continues to spin its twisted band of iron hydroxide, and the two cells may move about each other for a time, forming a double spiral band. But soon they separate, the bands diverging to form eventually a rather complicated branching structure with a little kidney-shaped cell at the end of each branch. The cells may be separated easily from these branches. No reproduction other than simple cell division is known.

Sulphur Bacteria. Springs occur in many localities whose waters bear hydrogen sulphide (H_2S) in solution. Upon the bottoms of brooks which drain such springs one usually finds an extensive white coating made up of fine interlacing filaments. If these filaments be teased out in a drop of water and examined under the microscope, they are found to be living organisms of a peculiar character. They look somewhat like bleached-out filaments of Blue-green Algae, such as Oscillatoria, and this similarity is heightened by their peculiar creeping motions. Slowly, but perceptibly, the threads glide upon one another, or their free extremities wave back and forth, motions of precisely the same sort as are exhibited by Oscillatoria.

The cells which compose these filaments are filled with minute, refractile globules. These may be removed by appropriate solvents, and are found to be composed of elemental sulphur. The filamentous organisms live, therefore, in water bearing hydrogen sulphide, and they store sulphur within their protoplasm. It is evident that sulphur plays an important rôle in their metabolism. The opaque white appearance is due to these droplets of stored sulphur.

While these filamentous sulphur bacteria occur abundantly only in the drainage of sulphur springs, they are actually widespread in nature. If one places some mud from the bottom of a pond or ditch in a glass jar, partially filled with water, and adds a tiny bit of sodium sulphide every few days, he will soon obtain a heavy growth of these white sulphur bacteria, upon the bottom mud if the vessel is shallow, but only at the top of the liquid if it is deep, for these organisms must have air for their growth.

Nutrition of Sulphur Bacteria. The rôle which sulphur plays in the nutrition of the white sulphur bacteria was also discovered by Winogradsky. Like the iron bacteria, they are autotrophic, and obtain the energy necessary for their growth by oxidizing inorganic matter, in this case H_2S. The chemical reaction which provides this energy is:

$$2H_2S + O_2 = 2H_2O + 2S,$$

the S being stored in the cells. This stored sulphur, however, eventually disappears, being itself oxidized to yield more energy:

$$2S + 3O_2 + 2H_2O = 2H_2SO_4,$$

the sulphuric acid so formed combining with lime or other substances in the water to form sulphates.

The filamentous white sulphur bacteria which have just been described belong to the genus called *Beggiatoa*, the common species being *Beggiatoa alba*. There are several other species, varying mainly in size. There is another kind of filamentous white sulphur bacteria, the genus *Thiothrix*, which differs from Beggiatoa in forming a sheath about the filaments, and in becoming attached at one end by a hold-fast to some solid object in the water. There are also some unicellular, or non-filamentous, white sulphur bacteria, the genus *Thiophysa*. In all of these forms the cells are mostly larger than those of other

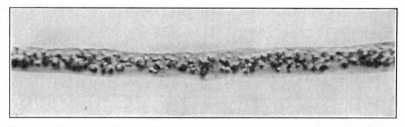

FIG. 41. *Beggiatoa alba.* Portion of a filament containing globules of sulphur.

types of bacteria, but this large size is due mainly to the masses of sulphur stored within the protoplasm.

Purple and Green Sulphur Bacteria. Included in the order of Thiobacteriales is another group of sulphur bacteria. Like the white sulphur bacteria they are abundant in waters bearing hydrogen sulphide, but may be found in mud or waters everywhere. They are different from the white sulphur bacteria in bearing pigments. There are two sorts, the red or purple sulphur bacteria, and the green sulphur bacteria. The conditions necessary for their growth are quite different from those required by the white sulphur bacteria. They must have *light*, and an *absence of oxygen*. One may obtain a crude culture of the colored sulphur bacteria in much the same way as with the white sulphur bacteria, by placing some mud in a vessel of water to which sodium sulphide has been added. But the bottles must be filled to the top and tightly stoppered to exclude air, and they must be placed by a window or an electric light.

Nutrition. The peculiar nutrition of the red and green sulphur bacteria has been cleared up by the researches of van Niel, who first succeeded in growing them in pure cultures.   The white sulphur bacteria obtain the energy necessary to synthesize their protoplasm by burning H_2S.   The colored sulphur bacteria obtain their energy from sunlight; they are photosynthetic like a green plant.   The pigments, *bacteriopurpurin* and *bacterioviridin,* serve like chlorophyll to absorb this energy from the light.

A green plant synthesizes its protoplasm from inorganic compounds.   The first step in this synthesis is the production of formaldehyde from carbon dioxide and water:

$$CO_2 + 2H_2O = HCOH + H_2O + O_2.$$

The synthesis of the *green* sulphur bacteria takes place in a similar manner, save that hydrogen sulphide replaces the water:

$$CO_2 + 2H_2S = HCOH + H_2O + 2S.$$

In the case of the green sulphur bacteria, the residual sulphur is set free in the medium, and the reaction ends here in pure cultures. With the *red* sulphur bacteria, a similar reaction occurs, but the residual sulphur is stored in the cells as in the white sulphur bacteria. This sulphur is eventually used up, appearing in the medium as sulphates.   In the case of the red sulphur bacteria, then, the total reaction may be expressed by the equation:

$$2CO_2 + H_2S + 4H_2O = 2HCOH + 2H_2O + H_2SO_4.$$

Types of Red Sulphur Bacteria.   The red sulphur bacteria occur in a variety of morphologic forms, and it was formerly believed that these were different species; therefore a number of genera and species have been named.   But van Niel's studies show that in a single pure culture the cells vary widely in size and form, and that actually the morphologic types encountered may be reduced to three main types:

1. The *Chromatium* type.   The cells are typically rather large and ellipsoidal in form, sometimes somewhat bent or curved, sometimes quite elongated or cylindrical.   Sulphur granules are stored in the cells.

2. The *Thiocystis* type.   The cells are typically somewhat smaller and spherical in form.   Often they occur characteristically in pairs. The cells secrete mucus in older cultures, and become clustered in large aggregates.   Sulphur granules are stored in the cells.

3. The *Pseudomonas* type.   The cells are typically very small, slender rod forms, slightly curved.   In certain cultures the cells

become rounded, and gather together in clusters. No sulphur granules are stored in the cells.

All three of these types are motile by means of polar flagella. No true filamentous forms occur.

The *green* sulphur bacteria are typically very small spherical forms occurring in chains, but in certain cultures they produce striking "involution" forms: elliptical to rod-shaped cells, and especially twisted Spirillum types. They do not store sulphur granules.

Myxobacteriales. The slime bacteria comprise a peculiar and little known group of microörganisms. They are distinguished by the complicated form of their cell aggregates, or colonies. They are not commonly encountered in ordinary bacteriological work.

If one gathers the droppings of wild animals found on the ground in forests, and places these in a moist chamber in the incubator, there occurs a characteristic growth of various microörganisms. First the fecal masses become covered with a feltwork of mold mycelium. These molds may form and discharge their spores, but after some days the mycelium dies down, and then one may distinguish here and there little glistening colonies of bacteria. These are moist, mucoid in character, yellowish or pinkish in color, at first smooth and round, but eventually developing on their surfaces little knobs which project upward, which grow and expand, and finally develop into characteristically shaped *fruiting bodies*. These fruiting bodies may vary from simple knob-like expansions of the supporting stalk to elaborate branched or lobulated structures.

Microscopic examination of these colonies shows that they are made up of minute rod-shaped bacterial cells, embedded in slime. At first glance they resemble closely the cells of ordinary bacteria. They differ in possessing a peculiar type of motility. Without any demonstrable organs of locomotion, they show a characteristic slow creeping motion, similar to that exhibited by some Blue-green Algae. The cells are also flexible, instead of being rigid as is the case with most bacteria. Within the cells there have been found certain bodies which may be true nuclei.

Reproduction. The fruiting bodies result from a creeping motion of the cells upon each other. As the colony matures, the cells proceed to glide over each other (the mode of locomotion is unknown) and to gather in denser masses, forming the bulgings on the surface. As this "swarming" continues, the cells are forced further into the air, forming a stalk, and they accumulate at the apex of this stalk to form the expanded "cyst." Within this cyst the cells become

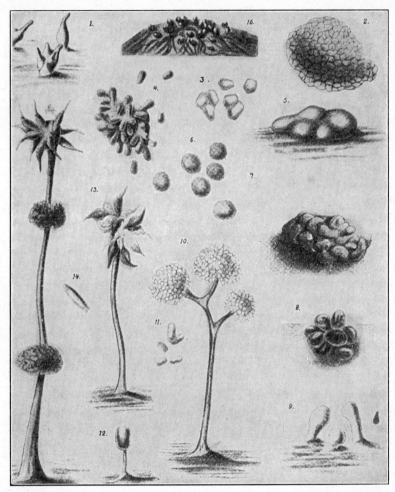

FIG. 42. Myxobacteria. Drawings of colonies of various species of Myxobacteria. (After Quehl, *Centralblatt für Bakteriologie*, 1906, vol. 16.)

rounded in most species, at least shortened in the others, to form the mature reproductive cells. These dry out, and are discharged into the air to be distributed by the wind.

The whole process is very similar to the reproduction in the

group of slime molds, the _Myxomycetes or Mycetozoa,_ which have
been mentioned in preceding chapters, and some authorities would
consider the Myxobacteria to be closely related to these. But the
minute rod-shaped cells of the Myxobacteria are so different from
the nucleated plasmodium characteristic of the Myxomycetes that
the resemblance must be looked upon as only superficial. They

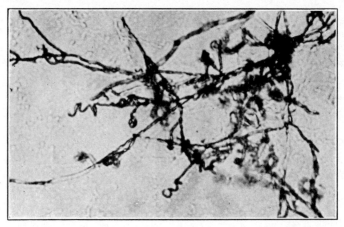

FIG. 43. An Actinomyces. Photomicrograph of a slide culture.
The dark filaments are in the air, the light ones are in agar. Note
the coiled filaments, which are producing conidia.

are rather to be considered true bacteria which have developed a
specialized method of distribution.

The slime bacteria may also be found in soil, and may be cultivated upon manure-infusion agar. Crude cultures can be obtained
by moistening filter paper in closed dishes with a watery suspension
of soil, and then placing sterilized rabbit droppings on the surface of
the paper. They have been found growing upon cultures of fungi in
the laboratory, and upon the exoskeletons of crabs. Now both of
these contain _chitin,_ and it was found possible to grow these bacteria
in pure cultures upon media containing chitin as the sole source of
carbon; the chitin was decomposed.

Actinomycetales. This order comprises microörganisms which
possess some of the characters of true bacteria, and some of the
characters of molds. The organisms contained in this order are
divided into two families: the _Actinomycetaceae,_ which are mold-like

in that they form long branched filaments of mycelium that grow up into the air and give rise to spores resembling the conidia of the higher fungi; and the *Mycobacteriaceae*, which are more nearly like the true bacteria. The latter may form branched mycelium, but they do not give rise to conidia on aerial filaments.

Actinomycetaceae. The Actinomycetaceae are abundant in soil where they carry on chemical transformations important in maintaining soil fertility. They grow in the soil, and in artificial cultures, as tangled masses of very fine mycelium. They reproduce entirely by conidia formed by a constriction of cells at the ends of filaments projecting into the air. These conidia, round or oval in form, are formed in long chains which in many species are spirally twisted.

Apparently, then, these Actinomycetes are just like molds in their essential characters, and indeed some authorities would classify them with the higher Fungi rather than with the bacteria. But they are different from the higher Fungi in one important particular; their mycelium is *extremely fine*, not greater than one micron in thickness. It is continuous, i.e., not cut up into cells by cross walls, and so far as we can observe, contains *no nuclei*. In dimensions and lack of internal structure, the mycelium of the Actinomycetaceae is similar to the true bacteria. But the relationship of these organisms to the true bacteria is supported better by the finding of many intergrading species, which are contained in the Mycobacteriaceae.

Mycobacteriaceae. This family contains species which are transitional in character between the mold-like Actinomycetaceae and the Eubacteriales. There are three genera, *Proactinomyces, Mycobacterium,* and *Corynebacterium.*

Proactinomyces. This genus contains microörganisms which, like the Actinomycetaceae, form branched filaments of mycelium. However, after growing for a time in this form, the mycelium undergoes a *fragmentation* into short rod-shaped elements which look much like true bacteria. These elements are formed in a manner very similar to the oidia of higher Fungi. After the mycelium has undergone fragmentation, the elements resulting are set free, and may continue to grow, multiplying by transverse fission just like the Eubacteriales. In some species fragmentation occurs early in the course of growth, and on continued cultivation the mycelial stage becomes shorter and shorter; eventually the ability to form mycelium may completely disappear. In other species, fragmentation occurs late and to a lesser degree. Thus one finds in this genus a series of species which show a gradation in characters between the mold-like Actinomycetaceae and the bacteria-like Corynebacteria and Mycobacteria.

Many of the species of the genus Proactinomyces are pathogenic, causing disease in man and animals. The commonest and best

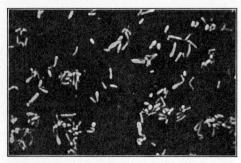

known of these is *Proactinomyces bovis*, an anaerobic species which causes a disease of cattle called "lumpy jaw."

Corynebacteria. The organism of diphtheria belongs to a group, the genus *Corynebacterium*, which is also included with the Actinomycetales. This group, the diphtheroid bacteria, comprises organisms which have a

FIG. 44. Corynebacteria. Photomicrograph of diphtheria bacilli as revealed by negative staining with Congo red.

purely unicellular growth form, not producing true filaments of mycelium, but nevertheless exhibiting some characters which relate them to the Actinomycetes proper. They are characterized by a tendency to irregularity in the form and staining reactions of the cells. Typically rod-shaped, their cells may be swollen at one end (club-shaped) or they may be branched, forming Y- or X-shaped cells. These branched forms are looked upon as an abortive attempt to form mycelium, branching being a characteristic of the Actinomycetes proper. The irregularity in staining is due to the presence of vacuoles, producing clear or unstained areas in the cell (barring), and the presence of deeply stained granules of volutin. The cells are typically arranged in nearly parallel bundles. This parallel arrangement, the occurrence of barring, of granules, and of irregular cells is also characteristic of the oidia of Proactinomyces, and therefore the Corynebacteria, although very like the true bacteria, or Eubacteria, are classified in the Actinomycetales.

Mycobacteria. The tubercle bacillus belongs to a genus, *Mycobacterium*, which presents many of the same morphologic characters as the Corynebacteria, and in addition the property of *acidfastness*.

By this is meant that the cells are not easily decolorized by strong acid solutions after they have been stained with basic aniline dyes. All other kinds of bacteria will be quickly decolorized with acids.

Acidfast bacteria may be distinguished from other kinds by the use of the *Ziehl-Neelsen* stain. Smears, prepared as described on page 35, are *stained* with a very powerful red dye, carbol fuchsin. This is composed of

Basic fuchsin	1 part
Alcohol	10 parts
Phenol, 5% solution in water	100 parts

The stain penetrates the acidfast bacteria very slowly. One must therefore either leave the slides in the stain overnight, or hasten the penetration by heating the stain to just below the boiling point. If heat is used, ten minutes is sufficient for the staining. After staining, the excess dye is washed off with running water, and then the slide is *decolorized* with acid alcohol (5% HCl in 95% alcohol). The time of decolorization will vary with the density of the film, and can be learned only by experience, but usually one minute is about right. The acid alcohol is now washed off with water, and a *counterstain*, methylene blue, is applied for a minute or two. The acidfast bacteria will retain the fuchsin dye, and appear red; other species of bacteria will appear blue. (See Frontispiece.)

In addition to the tubercle bacillus, several other species of bacteria, some pathogenic, others harmless, also possess this property. But they are all closely related, showing many other similarities in addition to their acidfastness. Their cells are often arranged in parallel bundles, are sometimes barred and often show deeply stained granules, and at times branched cells are found. They all grow in cultures with a buff, yellowish, or orange-colored growth, appearing waxy to the eye, and feel greasy to the touch.

Some members of the genus Proactinomyces are also acidfast. There are only a few rather rare species, which are, however, of great importance in establishing the bacterial relationships of the group. They grow as branched, tangled filaments of mycelium, which breaks up into fragments that look very much like tubercle bacilli. They produce disease in man and animals which in its course and symptoms, and the nature of the tissue changes produced, resembles very closely tuberculosis. They also grow in cultures with a buff, yellowish, or orange growth of a waxy character. These acidfast Proactinomycetes therefore form a direct transition between the purely bacteria-like acidfast bacteria and the mold-like non-acidfast Actinomycetaceae.

Eubacteriales. The true bacteria form the great majority of the known species, and nearly all of those which are of such great practical importance as causes of disease and fermentation or putrefaction. They are for the most part somewhat simpler in their organization and arrangement than the bacteria so far considered. They cannot, however, be defined by any one character. We place in this order all of the bacteria which do not fit in the other orders. While some of them grow characteristically in rows or chains of cells, they never form compact filaments like the white sulphur bacteria, nor a sheath like the Chlamydobacteria. None of them grow on stalks. While a few autotrophic species can oxidize sulphur or sulphur compounds, they do not store sulphur in their cells like the Thiobacteria, nor do they posses bacteriopurpurin or bacterioviridin. They grow in colonies, or masses of cells, which are often characteristic in form, but never produce the complex fruiting bodies of the Myxobacteria. They never form long branched filaments like the Actinomycetes. While some of them may occasionally produce branched cells, and some may at times exhibit intracellular granules, they do not exhibit these characters regularly, as group characteristics, like the Corynebacteria; nor are any of them acidfast, like the Mycobacteria.

Since the earliest days of bacteriology, the common bacteria have been divided into three main morphologic types — the spherical forms, or *Cocci;* the rod-shaped forms, or *Bacilli;* and the curved or twisted spiral forms, the *Spirilla.* For a long time such a simple classification sufficed, but as we came to learn more and more species of bacteria, it became necessary to divide them into a larger number of smaller groups for greater convenience.

Since the Eubacteriales are so important as causes of disease, and in industry and agriculture, their *physiological* characters, i.e., the nature of their toxins and enzymes, and the reactions which these produce, have been of the utmost importance and have been very intensively investigated. These reactions have been found to show well-defined correlations, and have come to serve more and more as the basis for classifying the simpler kinds of bacteria, which are very monotonous in their morphology. A brief description of the families contained in this order will serve to indicate what sorts of bacteria are included in the Eubacteriales.

I. The *Nitrobacteriaceae* are *autotrophic* species, mostly very minute rods, which can grow upon inorganic media, and obtain their energy by the oxidation of such substances as sulphur or ammonia or hydrogen.

All of the remaining Eubacteriales are *heterotrophic*, i.e., they require some form of organic matter, living or dead, which has been synthesized by some other organism.

II. The *Rhizobacteriaceae* are rod-shaped bacteria which can utilize an inorganic source of nitrogen (N_2, ammonia, or nitrate) but require an *organic source of carbon*, such as glucose, for their energy. Some of them, the bacteria which live in the roots of clovers and similar leguminous plants, can use atmospheric nitrogen. Others are simple saprophytes.

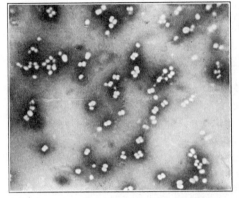

FIG. 45. Micrococci; negative staining with Congo red.

III. The *Pseudomonadaceae* are similar to the preceding in their nutrition, but differ in the fact that they move by means of terminal flagella. There are two tribes: the *Spirilleae* have curved cells, comma- or corkscrew-shaped; the *Pseudomonadeae* have straight cells, rod-shaped.

IV. The *Acetobacteriaceae* are the vinegar bacteria, rod-shaped, which can oxidize alcohol to acetic acid.

V. The *Azotobacteriaceae* are large oval or rod-shaped bacteria found in the soil, which can utilize atmospheric nitrogen.

All of the species contained in the remaining families require an *organic source of nitrogen* as well as an organic source of carbon for their nutrition.

VI. The *Micrococcaceae* are bacteria with spherical cells which may grow singly, or in clusters, or in cubical bundles, but never in chains. They are Gram positive.

VII. The *Neisseriaceae* are bacteria which usually grow as pairs of hemispherical cells. They are Gram negative.

VIII. The *Parvobacteriaceae* are very minute oval or rod-shaped Gram negative bacteria, all of which are parasitic. The organisms which cause plague and undulent fever and related diseases belong in this family.

IX. The *Streptobacteriaceae* are Gram positive bacteria which produce lactic acid abundantly from sugars. There are two tribes: the *Streptococceae* with spherical cells, and the *Lactobacilleae* with rod-shaped cells. The former tribe contains a number of species of great importance as causes of disease, the latter a number of industrial ferments.

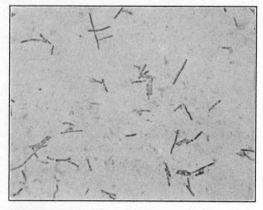

Fig. 46. Bacillaceae. *Bacillus terminalis;* photomicrograph of living, unstained cells.

X. The *Enterobacteriaceae* form a large and important group of Gram negative rod-shaped bacteria which occur in the intestines of man and the higher animals, either as normal parasites or as causes of disease (typhoid fever, dysentery, etc.).

XI. The *Bacteriaceae* form a miscellaneous division of Gram negative rod-shaped bacteria which do not fit in any of the preceding families. They are mostly saprophytic species, with varied but complex nutritional requirements.

XII. The *Bacillaceae* differ from all other bacteria in that they form *spores*, special highly resistant bodies contained within the cells and liberated upon their disintegration. They are all Gram positive and rod-shaped.

Spirochaetales. The last of the seven orders of bacteria contains certain very slender corkscrew-shaped microbes. Their systematic relationships are somewhat obscure. They present certain characters resembling true bacteria of the genus Spirillum, and also characters resembling those of certain Protozoa (the Trypanosomes).

The Spirochaetes resemble the Spirilla in possessing spirally twisted or corkscrew-shaped cells. Mostly the turns are more numerous and closer than in the Spirilla. The Spirochaetes are flexible. They move by a sinuous snake-like motion of the whole body, and while the ends of the cells may taper to a fine hair-like process, there are no true flagella. The Spirilla possess rigid cells, and move entirely by means of a tuft of flagella at one end of the cell. Nearly all of the

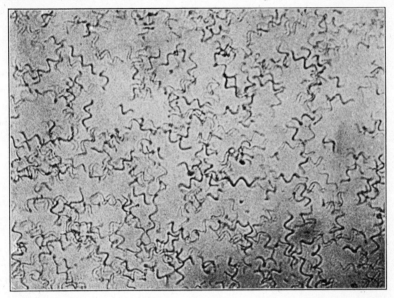

FIG. 47. Spirilleae. *Spirillum volutans;* photomicrograph of living, unstained cells.

Spirochaetes are strict parasites in the bodies of various animals, but a few are aquatic saprophytes. All of the Spirilla are aquatic saprophytes.

The relationship of the Spirochaetes to the Protozoa is exhibited mainly in their pathogenicity. Some of them are blood-inhabiting parasites, living free in the blood stream like the Trypanosomes. They produce diseases which, in their recurrent or relapsing character, resemble protozoan diseases more than bacterial diseases. Some of these diseases, like protozoan diseases, are transmitted from man to man by insects which serve as necessary intermediate hosts. Finally, disease caused by Spirochaetes may be cured or ameliorated by certain organic arsenic compounds which are also beneficial in Trypanosome infections, but have no influence upon purely bacterial diseases. One may see some similarity between the sinuous flexible cells of the Spirochaetes with their tapered extremities and the flexible fish-like

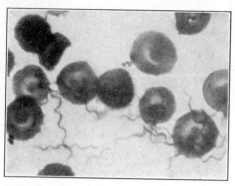

FIG. 48. Spirochaetales. *Borrelia novyi* in the blood of a rat.

bodies of the Trypanosomes with their single terminal flagellum, but the morphologic resemblance is not so great as the physiologic.

The Spirochaetes, while varying much in length, are mostly very small, especially very narrow. They do not stain so readily with the aniline dyes as do the bacteria, and for this reason they are not so easily observed under the microscope. The method of dark-field illumination is the most satisfactory procedure for the observation of Spirochaetes.

Relationships of the Bacteria. The ensheathed filamentous Chlamydobacteriales show strong resemblances to the filamentous Blue-green Algae, as do also the filamentous white sulphur bacteria. The peculiar creeping motions of Beggiatoa imitate exactly those of the alga Oscillatoria. The grouping of some of the spherical Eubacteriales in squares and cubes is repeated in the Cyanophyceae. On the basis of these similarities, together with the very simple cell structure and mode of reproduction common to both groups, it was formerly believed that the bacteria had been derived from the Blue-green Algae. Having adopted a saprophytic or parasitic mode of life, they lost their chlorophyll.

More recently, however, the bacteria have been thought to be related to the Fungi rather than to the Algae. Some of the Actinomycetales are so mold-like that certain authorities would include them with the fungi rather than with the bacteria. The Actinomycetales show clear relationships with a number of true bacteria.

The Eubacteriales may be rather sharply divided into two groups upon the basis of Gram's stain. As was indicated in Chapter II, this is a character which signifies a deep-seated and fundamental differ-

ence in the bacteria.   It will be shown in a later chapter that the
Gram positive Eubacteriales are related to the Actinomycetales, and
are quite distinct from the Gram negative Eubacteriales in their
systematic relationships.   The relationships of this latter group are
entirely obscure.

The stalks of the Caulobacteriales occur also in very diverse
species of Algae and Protozoa, and do not show relationships.

The peculiar creeping motions of the cells of the Myxobacteriales
are looked upon as an alga-like character, but otherwise there is
nothing to indicate their origin.   The similarity of their colonies to
those of the Myxomycetes is entirely superficial.

As has been indicated, the Spirochaetales show definite relationship to the Protozoa.

The various similarities of the bacteria to other groups of microbes
may be summarized in the following table:

Chlamydobacteriales ⟶ Cyanophyceae
Thiobacteriales ⟶ Cyanophyceae
Caulobacteriales ⟶ Unknown
Myxobacteriales ⟶ Unknown
Actinomycetales ⟶ Fungi
Eubacteriales
    Gram positive species ⟶ Fungi
    Gram negative species ⟶ Unknown
Spirochaetales ⟶ Protozoa

Thus the microörganisms which we call bacteria show strong similarities to three different other groups of microbes, the Blue-green
Algae, the Fungi, and Protozoa.   It is possible, and at the present
seems most probable, that they are not a homogeneous group, but are
descendants of widely different stocks.   Having become saprophytic
or parasitic, they have become simplified in structure, degraded in
their evolution, and have thus come to be similar to each other.

The Origin of Life.   Another theory is that bacteria represent the
earliest and most simple forms of life, which have come down to us
through the ages relatively unchanged, descendants of the first living
creatures.   Their minute size and structureless cells, especially the
absence of a nucleus, at once suggest such a possibility.

Geologists believe that life began upon the earth about a billion
years ago, when the earth had cooled sufficiently for water to condense
upon its surface.   It is believed that at this time the earth was still
quite warm; that because of clouds and volcanic dust in the atmos-

phere, light intensity was very low. The first living organisms must have been autotrophic, capable of living upon inorganic matter, since there was as yet no organic matter available. It is interesting that there are found today in the bacteria organisms which can fulfill these requirements — growth at high temperatures in the dark, and derivation of their energy from the oxidation of ammonia or sulphur or other inorganic substances.

Perhaps the first microbe was such a thermophilic, autotrophic bacterium. From this beginning evolution must have taken place in a number of directions. Bacteria, as will be seen later, are more highly varied in their chemical activities than any other group of organisms. It would seem that, in them, nature had tried every possible experiment in nutrition. The red and green sulphur bacteria may represent such an experiment in the direction of photosynthesis, to be later followed by the chlorophyll-bearing Cyanophyceae. When life had continued long enough for organic matter to accumulate, another experiment led to the development of enzymes to digest this material, so that saprophytic bacteria appeared, to be followed later by parasitic species capable of growing upon higher forms of life.

CHAPTER VII

A SURVEY OF MICROBIC LIFE: THE ULTRAMICROBES

The chief characteristic which serves to distinguish microörganisms from higher forms of life is the minute size of the individuals. This minute size involves to a considerable degree a simplification of structure, a lack of differentiation, a more generalized distribution of function through the protoplasm. In most cases the microörganisms are unicellular; the organization of the individual is bound up within the limits of a single cell wall. But here one is confronted with the difficulty of determining in many cases just what is to be considered the individual — the cell or the aggregate of cells.

What Is an Individual? In a culture of bacteria in broth — free cells floating in a liquid, not in any way connected with each other, all apparently alike in structure — there is at first glance no question of individuation involved. The bacterial cell is the individual and the culture is a population. And yet, as will be shown in a later chapter, such a population shows, as regards the nature of its growth and the cyclic changes of its component cells, some of the characteristics of a multicellular individual. When such bacteria are grown upon solid media, agar or potato, for instance, the cells are perforce held together in a compact mass or colony. The colonies of bacteria and yeasts and unicellular Algae, when grown on solid media, present a form and structure which are characteristic for the species. There may be a slight degree of morphologic variation in the cells as regards their position in the colony — a primitive differentiation. And yet we still look upon such a colony as a population, the cells as individuals. With the filamentous Algae, both green and blue-green, and with some of the colonial Protozoa, the cells are so closely united that here we are prone to look upon the filament or the colony as the individual. And yet in such forms, save for perhaps a slight gradation from base to tip, there is no cell differentiation which characterizes the higher multicellular organisms. In the Fungi we have met with a rather high degree of organization into multicellular individuals, with a differentiation into vegetative and reproductive portions. And yet, even here, we have seen how easily the organism may transform itself from a differentiated multicellular individual to a population of free cells — from a mold to a yeast.

Jordan aptly compares a colony of bacteria to a grove of trees. A grove of oak trees seen as a mass from a distance presents a characteristic appearance by which it may be readily distinguished from a grove of pine trees, for example. Here there is no question as to which is the individual, and the analogy is perfect. But some populations of higher organisms, as colonies of ants or bees, present a degree of organization and differentiation which we associate with individuation, and there have been biologists who would consider, in the case of the social insects, the colony, rather than the single ant or bee, to be the individual. Perhaps in the present state of our knowledge, this problem of individuation is a little too metaphysical to be profitably discussed. Certainly with a great majority of the microörganisms it is customary to look upon the single cell as the individual.

Size of Microörganisms. The various one-celled microörganisms show an extreme range in size. The organisms illustrated to scale in figures 49 and 50 exhibit this range. Note that Fig. 49 is drawn to a scale of magnification one-tenth as great as is Fig. 50. The smallest organism shown, *Micrococcus progrediens*, is 0.15 μ in diameter, just within the limits of resolution of the best microscopes. Its volume is 0.0018 cubic micron. The largest organism, the unicellular protozoön *Spirostomum ambiguum*, measures 125 μ × 1600 μ, and has a volume of 13,100,000 cubic microns. One of the Spirostomum cells would contain nearly 7,300,000,000 of the Micrococcus cells! The difference between a mouse and an elephant is not nearly so great.

The little Micrococcus is a mere spot, an infinitesimal round mass of protoplasm, without any visible differentiation, and probably with very little, if any, actual differentiation. The Spirostomum is a highly organized creature with a sort of alimentary tract and excretory system. Between these two extremes is every gradation in size and complexity of structure, and it is very clear that there is a correlation between these two properties — the larger the cell, the more we can see within it. It might be argued that the increase of complexity of the cells with size is only apparent; that as the cells decrease in size, their internal structures, being smaller than the

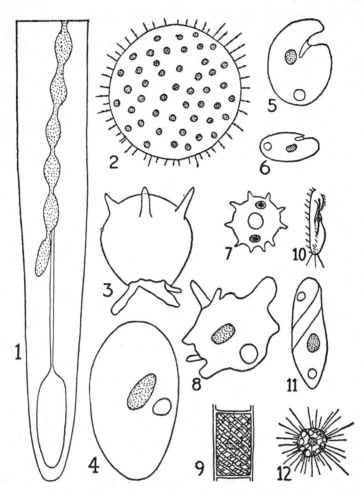

FIG. 49. Relative Sizes of Some Microörganisms. 1, *Spirostomum ambiguum* (posterior half only); 2, *Actinosphaerium eichhorni* (pseudopodia amputated); 3, *Difflugia corona;* 4, *Frontonia leucas;* 5, *Colpoda cucullus;* 6, *Colpidium colpoda;* 7, *Arcella dentata;* 8, *Amoeba proteus;* 9, *Spirogyra bellis;* 10, *Stylonychia pustulata;* 11, *Paramecium caudatum;* 12, *Actinophrys sol.* (After Adolph, *The Regulation of Size in Unicellular Organisms,* C. C. Thomas, Springfield, Ill.)

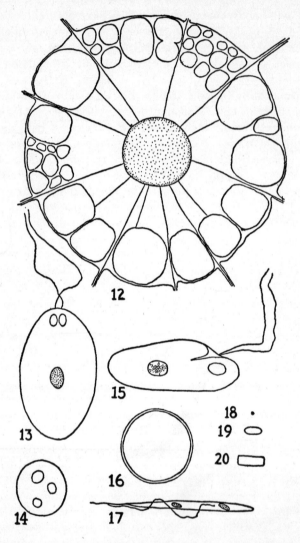

Fig. 50. Relative Sizes of Some Microörganisms. These are drawn to a scale ten times greater in magnification than the preceding figure.   12, *Actinophrys sol* (pseudopodia amputated); 13, *Polytoma uvella;* 14, *Saccharomyces cerevisiae;* 15, *Chilomonas paramecium;* 16, *Pleurococcus vulgaris;* 17, *Trypanosoma lewisi;* 18, *Micrococcus progrediens;* 19, *Escherichia coli;* 20, *Bacillus ramosus.* (After Adolph, *The Regulation of Size in Unicellular Organisms*, C. C. Thomas, Springfield, Ill.)

cell itself, will one by one reach the limits of resolution of the microscope, and disappear. The Micrococcus may have as much in the way of internal structure as the Spirostomum, but we cannot see it. However, certain theoretical considerations are opposed to such a hypothesis.

How Small May Organisms Be? For there must be a lower limit to the size of organisms. This limit is set by the size of the molecules of which the protoplasm is composed. Protoplasm is built up mainly of proteins; these are the essential compounds. They exist in large molecules. Errera has calculated that an organism as small as *Micrococcus progrediens* would contain somewhere in the neighborhood of 10,000 to 30,000 protein molecules. One might concede a slight amount of differentiation in an organism of this size, but what of still smaller ones? A reduction to one-tenth the diameter of the Micrococcus would allow only 10 to 30 molecules. The limit of 0.15 μ, set as the diameter of the smallest organism we can see, is determined by the resolving power of our microscopes, as indicated in Chapter II. But we have some evidence that there are still smaller microörganisms which we cannot see — the filterable viruses.

Filters. By filterable viruses we mean agents (presumably living) which are capable of causing infectious diseases, but which will pass through filters of such a character that they will not permit the passage of ordinary visible bacteria. These filters have been used by bacteriologists for many years to separate bacteria from their toxins, or to sterilize serums or other substances which cannot be heated. There are several kinds, the most important being the Berkefeld, Chamberland, and Seitz filters. Berkefeld filters are made from "Kieselguhr," a naturally occurring earth composed of the fossil shells of Diatoms. Chamberland filters are made of unglazed porcelain, i.e., clay which is baked but not glazed over so as to make it impermeable. Seitz filters are made of asbestos compressed into discs. These filters are made in various grades of porosity, but with all of them there are grades which long experience has taught us are practically impermeable to bacteria under the usual conditions of filtration. The degree of porosity is usually measured by the air pressure necessary to cause bubbles to form on the surface of the filter when it is immersed in water. In using these filters the bacteria are removed from the liquid in which they are contained by forcing this liquid through the filter by moderate air pressure or by suction.

How Filters Work. The filters have two actions. They may remove material from the solution by *adsorption*, for the capillary pores of the filter present an extensive surface. Thus they will remove dyes or proteins from solutions which are forced through them. But their pores are also very fine, and they therefore present a *sieve action*, tending mechanically to remove solid particles in suspension. It is not quite certain to which of these two factors the removal of bacteria from fluids is due, since we do not know precisely the diameters of the pores in the filters. Calculations by Mudd, based upon the pressure necessary to force air through, indicate that the mean diameter of the pores of Berkefeld and Chamberland filters which are "tight" to bacteria is in the neighborhood of 3 to 4 microns. Perhaps both factors are involved.

Filterable Viruses. There are a great many diseases of man and of lower animals, some in plants also, which are clearly of an infectious nature, being contagious and experimentally transmissible, in which no visible microörganisms have been found. They resemble bacterial diseases in their febrile reaction, their limited course, and in the immunity which is left after recovery. And yet no bacteria may be seen in the diseased tissues, no growth occurs when these are cultured. In many cases it has been possible to transmit these diseases to lower animals with blood, or tissue extracts, which have been passed through the finer grades of Berkefeld or Chamberland filters, which are known to hold back visible bacteria. We state that such diseases are caused by filterable viruses. The diseases will be discussed in a later chapter; for the moment we wish to consider the nature of these invisible viruses.

Infantile paralysis, or anterior poliomyelitis, is one of these virus diseases. If one removes a portion of the spinal cord from a person who has died of this disease, and inoculates it into a monkey, the latter will develop the same disease. It will become paralyzed, and one may demonstrate in its spinal cord the same sort of tissue changes as could be observed in the spinal cord used for inoculation. If one first grinds the spinal cord with sand and physiological salt solution, filters this solution through a Berkefeld candle and injects the filtrate into a monkey, the same result is obtained. Therefore the agent which causes the disease must be very minute, at least of the order of magnitude of the very smallest of the bacteria, perhaps much smaller. One may inoculate a second monkey with spinal cord of the first, a third with spinal cord of the second, and still produce the same disease. One may continue this through a hundred thousand monkeys — the spinal cord of the last one will contain just as much infectious material as the first. This can be explained only by assuming that the agent which causes the disease has the property of perpetuating itself, that it grows. Growth is, so far as we know, solely an attribute of living things. Therefore we feel justified in assuming that infantile paralysis is caused by an ultramicroscopic filter-passing living organism.

The same experiment, with appropriate modifications, may be performed with all of the other diseases which we at present classify as "virus" diseases, both of animals and plants. Closely similar to the virus diseases of higher organisms is a condition which occurs in cultures of bacteria, called *bacteriophagy.*

The Bacteriophage. This phenomenon was discovered independently by Twort and d'Herelle. If one prepares a suspension of feces from a convalescent case of dysentery, passes the fluid through a Berkefeld filter, and adds some of this filtrate to a broth culture of dysentery bacilli, there occurs a characteristic phenomenon. The turbid culture gradually becomes clear, and if observed under the microscope, this clearing is seen to be due to a dissolution of the bacterial cells. They gradually swell and finally rather suddenly disappear. If, now, one filters such a culture through a Berkefeld candle and adds a drop or two of the filtrate to another culture of dysentery bacilli, the same thing occurs, and this may be done again and again. Like the virus of infantile paralysis, this agent which causes the dysentery bacilli to dissolve perpetuates itself, multiplies indefinitely in the cultures of dysentery bacilli. D'Herelle believes that this agent, the *bacteriophage,* is an ultramicroscopic filterable organism parasitic upon bacteria.

Bacteriophages have been found which are active upon many other species of bacteria. They may be found in many places, but are abundant in sewage. There is a multiplicity of "species" of bacteriophages which act specifically upon different species of bacteria.

The Bacteriophage Is Particulate. If one inoculates an agar plate rather heavily with dysentery bacilli, and seeds this plate with a culture filtrate containing bacteriophage properly diluted, there will be observed a development of cleared areas or "plaques" within the coating of dysentery bacilli on the agar. By making a series of such plates inoculated with a series of dilutions of the bacteriophage, one may demonstrate that the number of these plaques is proportional to the dilution of the filtrate. Therefore, the bacteriophage is *particu-*

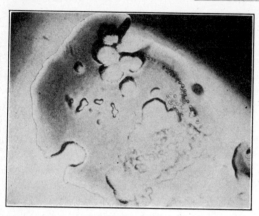

Fig. 51.   A "Moth-eaten" Colony, Showing the Action of the Bacteriophage.

late, i.e., it is made up of particles suspended in the liquid, not of a substance in solution.

Although the bacteriophage may be maintained *alive* for some time after it has been separated from the bacteria, it will not *grow* except in the presence of bacteria which are susceptible to its dissolving action.

Cultivation of Viruses. Like the bacteriophage, the viruses which cause disease in higher plants and animals will not grow except in the presence of living cells which are susceptible to infection with them. Nearly all we know about these ultramicrobes has been learned by experimentally transmitting them through series of susceptible hosts. Very recently, however, it has been found possible to grow the viruses outside of the animal body in *tissue cultures,* i.e., artificial cultures of living animal tissues, and later in a sort of mass tissue culture obtained by hashing chick embryos in a physiological saline solution. In such ways one may obtain considerable quantities of virus material to work with. But even in these artificial cultures, living animal cells are present, and it is impossible to learn very much about the characters and functions of the virus, since the picture is obscured by the activities of the animal cells.

No Free-living Ultramicrobes. This is a very important character of the ultramicrobes — that they apparently cannot exist save in association with living cells. We have pointed out in the preceding chapter how we may look upon the minute autotrophic bacteria as the most primitive organisms we know — primitive not only in their morphology, but in their nutrition.   But the viruses and the 'phage are all highly specialized parasites, incapable of existence except within certain kinds of cells.   We know of their existence only through their actions, the production of disease or the dissolution of the host cells.

We know that the harmless, saprophytic bacteria also produce characteristic changes in their environment, fermentations and putre-factions and other chemical reactions, by which their presence is made manifest.   Many attempts have been made to isolate ultrami-croscopic filter-passing organisms from soil and water, from ferment-ing and putrefying organic matter, and although minute bacteria have been obtained from time to time by such methods, they have all been within the range of visibility of the microscope, and no true free-living ultramicrobes have ever been discovered.

Nature of Viruses.   Concerning the nature of the bacteriophage there are several opposing theories, and these may be considered equally applicable to the filterable viruses as well.   In the present state of our knowledge they must be considered merely working hypotheses upon which further experimental study may be based.

The Enzyme Theory.   One group of bacteriologists looks upon the 'phage as a sort of self-perpetuating enzyme generated by and from the bacteria.   Something happens to some dysentery organisms which causes them to form a sort of ferment which not only dissolves their cells but, in the process, causes these cells to liberate more ferment which will act upon still other cells, and so on.   Similarly one might postulate that in infantile paralysis, something happens to the cells in the spinal cord which causes them to liberate an agent (enzyme?) that not only injures themselves, but also, acting upon other cells, causes them to produce more of this same agent.   Pro-ponents of this viewpoint emphasize the fact that *growth* of the 'phage or virus *cannot take place except in the presence of the cells which are injured.*   This, they claim, is best explained by assum-ing that the injured cells themselves produce the injurious agent.

The enzyme theory has received rather strong support in the re-cent discovery, by Stanley and by Wyckoff and others, that some of the viruses can apparently be obtained in pure form.   By ultracentrif-ugation (whirling in a special centrifugal machine at very high speed), by chemical precipitations and by crystallization, there has been obtained a substance which appears to be a pure chemical, that has all of the properties of the virus.   This substance has been obtained

mainly from plants affected with a virus disease (mosaic disease) but
has also been obtained from the tissues of animals affected with virus
diseases. The material so obtained seems to be composed entirely of
a nucleoprotein, occurring as molecules of enormous size. The various viruses obtained have been given molecular weights of from
20,000,000 to 300,000,000. It has been questioned that these are
true molecules; it has been suggested that they are rather aggregates
of molecules, particles. The behavior of these molecules or particles
in the ultracentrifuge, and when observed by polarized light, indicates that they are needle-like in form. It has further been suggested
that the apparent crystalline structure does not mean that the substance is chemically homogeneous; it merely means that the particles
arrange themselves in a regular and characteristic manner as bacteria
often do in a colony, or other kinds of cells in aggregates.

The enzyme theory is not readily acceptable because it is so
difficult to conceive of a self-perpetuating homogeneous substance.
Growth as we know it is solely an attribute of *living* things, and life
appears to be too complex a process to be carried on by a single chemical compound.

The Life Cycle Theory. A second group looks upon the viruses as
living organisms which are not an independent category of beings,
but are submicroscopic filterable stages in the life cycles of known
bacteria. This viewpoint is supported by the finding, at times,
of visible bacteria in the lesions of some of the virus diseases, both
by microscopic examination and by cultures. Opponents of this
theory claim that such bacteria are merely "secondary" invaders,
opportunists which have crept into tissues already injured by the
virus. Several workers have claimed to have transformed visible
bacteria into ultramicroscopic viruses, and conversely, by various
methods of cultivation or animal inoculation, but their data are not
convincing. Possibly true bacteria may sometimes pass through bacterial filters under properly controlled conditions of filtration, but it is
very doubtful that these filterable forms of bacteria have anything to
do with the filterable viruses. The virus diseases, as a class, present
certain specific characters which serve to distinguish them from the
bacterial diseases. Rivers criticizes this theory as follows: "Since
even the existence of bacterial life cycles is doubtful, it seems unwar-
rantable to offer presumptive filterable forms of them as the explanation of another unsolved problem, the nature of the viruses." It

might be mentioned, in connection with this theory, that even the bacteriophage itself has been considered (by Hadley) to be a minute filterable phase in the life cycles of the organisms upon which it acts.

Retrograde Evolution. Another theory, proposed by Green, would seek the origin of the viruses in the bacteria, not as part of the life-cycles of existing bacteria, but as part of a process of evolution which has been going on for a long time. He points out that all of the viruses are essential intracellular parasites, and that in the case of parasites in general there is a tendency for the organism to discard structures unnecessary to a parasite for its nutrition, retaining in general only the reproductive functions. According to this theory the viruses may be bacterial parasites which have become entirely dependent upon the protoplasm of their host for their metabolic activities, retaining only enough of their own structure for multiplication. Gortner has developed this theory further; he suggests that the viruses are "naked nuclei" of parasites which have lost the synthetic functions necessary for the production of cytoplasm, and retained only the ability to build up new chromatin and to divide. It had been previously suggested that the viruses might be "naked genes."

The Ultramicrobe Theory. Most workers with the viruses have come to look upon them as an independent group of very minute, strictly parasitic organisms. In addition to growth, they show certain attributes of living things — their susceptibility to heat and ultraviolet light and other injurious agents, and especially their capability of variation and adaptation. They may be increased or decreased in disease-producing power, or the kind of disease which they produce may be modified, by passage through different species of animals.

Opposed to this theory is the very minute size of the virus particles. We cannot, of course, measure them in the same way that we do visible organisms, but their size may be estimated by various physical means, such as filtration through collodion membranes of graded porosities. The results of such measurements by various workers are somewhat conflicting. The viruses vary considerably in size. The largest appear to be about $0.03\,\mu$ in diameter, while the smallest are around $0.008\,\mu$, not much larger than a single molecule of haemoglobin. These are dimensions which will allow only a very small number of molecules to each "cell."

A Frontier of Science.   The true nature of the viruses is still an unsolved mystery.   Whether they are self-perpetuating enzymes composed of a single chemical substance, or minute simple aggregates of compounds, they evidently represent life in its most elemental form, and it seems probable that from an investigation of the ultramicrobes we may eventually obtain a clue to the nature of life itself.

CHAPTER VIII

THE FINER STRUCTURE OF BACTERIAL CELLS

Cells. Living matter exists in units of protoplasm which are called cells. Cells vary widely in size and form and internal structure throughout the living world, but in all of the higher cells we may differentiate three parts — an outer limiting portion or *membrane*, a *cytoplasm* or cell body proper, and a *nucleus*. The cell membrane may be merely a condensation of the protoplasm at the outer part of the cell, or it may have added a secretion of chitin or cellulose or other material to give it rigidity. The cytoplasm is looked upon as the vegetative part of the cell which absorbs and metabolizes food, which carries on the specialized functions of the cell. The nucleus has been considered a sort of governing body, the "dynamic center" of the cell, but in recent years it has been looked upon more as a special "carrier" of hereditary characters. In higher organisms a cell cannot exist without a nucleus.

To these structures may be added various others which are characteristic of particular sorts of cells but which are not common to all. These may be structures necessary for the particular functions of the cell, as flagella or contractile fibrils, secretory vacuoles, pigment-bearing bodies or chromatophores, etc. In unicellular forms we may find various sorts of these accessory structures adapted for the particular mode of nutrition or activity of the species. We may also find within cells various sorts of reserve foodstuffs which may be stored in the cytoplasm or nucleus, and various types of excretory matter in the process of elimination. In certain cells structures have been found, the nature and function of which are unknown. But all of these bodies are specializations, not common to all cells. The *essential* parts of a cell are membrane, cytoplasm, and nucleus.

We have seen in the preceding chapter how there is a definite lower limit to the size of the cells. Protoplasm is a semi-fluid colloidal mixture or aggregate of proteins. It certainly cannot be subdivided into units smaller than a protein molecule, and we cannot, at present, conceive of protoplasm composed of a single protein. How small may an organism be and still retain the characteristic organization of cells? And what is the structure, the character of the organization, of units smaller than this? Does protoplasm exist in units which are not, typically, cells such as we see them in larger organisms? These are questions to be kept in mind in a consideration of the minute structure of bacteria, questions of fundamental biological importance which various workers have tried to answer.

In a consideration of these questions one must keep constantly in mind the limitations of the microscope. This has not always been done by the various investigators who have published work on the subject. If an individual *Micrococcus progrediens* has a diameter of 0.15 μ, at the very limits of resolution, it is obviously useless to try to see anything inside the organism. This is, of course, an extreme case, but even with larger bacteria the question of resolving power becomes of paramount importance in a consideration of their internal structure. Faced by questions of such great scientific importance, one is tempted to strain the magnifying power of his microscope to the limit, to try to see what cannot be seen. And it is therefore not surprising that with regard to the finer structure of bacteria there exists a great deal of contradictory and polemical literature.

Cells of Bacteria. If one examines the unstained living cells of bacteria, these appear for the most part as simple undifferentiated, homogeneous masses of protoplasm of definite form. Stained by the ordinary methods, nothing further is seen. In some cases there may be seen granules or vacuoles or refractive bodies within the cell, or certain attachments on the outside, but these are special cases, not common to all bacteria. There is then, definitely, a protoplasm with some sort of a limiting membrane. Whether there is a nucleus or not is a debated question. Some years ago Zettnow claimed to have observed a differentiation of the protoplasm of bacteria into an inner *endoplasm* and a narrow denser outer zone, the *ectoplasm*. Whether such a differentiation can be seen is doubtful, but there are reasons for believing that it exists, and such a division serves as a convenient starting point for a discussion of the finer structure of the bacterial cell. We shall, therefore, discuss first the ectoplasmic portion of the cell — the cell wall and structures attached to it, viz., capsules and flagella; and then the endoplasmic portion, the cytoplasm and its contents, various granules, the spores, and finally the nucleus problem.

Cell Membrane. When bacteria, suspended in water, are examined by dark field illumination, the cells are outlined by a luminous line, the interior is dark and invisible. This picture is due to reflection of light from the surface of the cell, and serves to emphasize the sharp division between the protoplasm and the external medium. By ordinary illumination, however, whether stained or unstained, one cannot see for certain whether there is a definite cell wall or not. When stained very lightly with basic aniline dyes, particularly with old cultures where the inner protoplasm does not stain so deeply, one may see a darker line at the border of the cell.

Physical chemistry teaches us that since the protoplasm is different in composition from the fluid in which it is immersed, a *surface* must exist between the two, that there must necessarily be a concentration of materials at this surface. In this sense then we may assume the existence of a *cell membrane*, though it may consist of nothing but a denser layer of protoplasm. But whether, in addition, there is a definite *cell wall*, composed of a special protecting material like cellulose or chitin, is still uncertain.

Cell Wall. While certain authorities have claimed to have differentially stained an outer zone or "ectoplasm" (Gutstein) or to have shown that the Gram-positiveness of certain bacteria is due to a specially differentiated outer layer or "cortex" (Churchman), these results have not been generally confirmed or accepted, and we may state that the existence of a true cell wall has not been directly demonstrated. Its existence, however, may in certain cases be assumed from indirect evidence.

Perhaps the best evidence for the existence of a cell wall is the *rigidity* of the cell, and the maintenance of a *constant cell form* other than spherical. With practically all bacteria, the cells, although somewhat elastic, are rigid. The protoplasm does not flow, the cell does not change form, as in an amoeba. If the cell in its motions meets an obstruction, it acts like a solid body; it may bend somewhat, but immediately springs back to its original form. According to laws of physical chemistry, a naked mass of protoplasm suspended in water should assume a spherical form, due to the surface tension acting upon it. But with the majority of bacteria the cells are elongated, straight or curved rods. This may best be explained by assuming that the cells are made rigid by a deposit of some solid material at their exterior. In a discussion of the form of bacteria as influenced by the surface tension of the medium, Frobisher states that the cells of bacteria behave as though they were contained within rigid tubes which are open at the ends.

Plasmolysis. If one immerses the cells of higher plants, with their rigid walls of cellulose, in a fluid of osmotic pressure higher than the protoplasm, water is extracted from the cell, and the protoplasm shrinks away from the cell wall, leaving a space between. This phenomenon, *plasmolysis*, reveals clearly the existence of a cell wall. The occurrence of plasmolysis has been clearly demonstrated in the

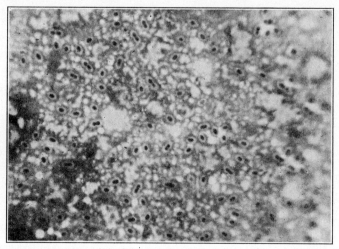

Fig. 52. Pneumococci, Stained to Show Capsules.
Smear of peritoneal fluid from a mouse.

case of some bacteria, particularly large forms like *Spirillum volutans*, but not with most bacteria. We know definitely, then, that some species of bacteria possess a rigid cell wall, and can safely assume its existence in others.

But we know nothing of the nature of this cell wall. Cellulose is definitely absent. Chitin has been claimed to be present, but its general occurrence is not proved. It is thought that waxes are deposited in the cell walls of the acidfast bacteria.

Capsules. Several species of bacteria, under certain circumstances, develop an enclosing envelope or sheath of gummy material which is called a capsule. Many species of bacteria not ordinarily considered as capsule-forming organisms have been observed to exhibit capsules under particular conditions, so that we have come to look upon capsule formation as a potential character of all bacteria, which, however, is regularly developed only in certain species.

Capsule-forming organisms may be separated into two classes, those which form capsules regularly *only in the animal body* or in artificial media containing blood serum, and those which form their capsules regularly in media containing high concentrations of sugar.

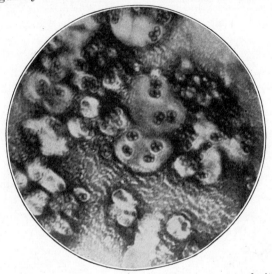

FIG. 53. A Zoögloea. *Azotobacter chroöcoccum*, negatively stained with Congo red, to show the capsular material surrounding the cells.

The former are important pathogens, the latter are saprophytes troublesome in sugar refineries.

In both cases the capsules appear to be of the same nature, a layer of gelatinous or gummy material surrounding the cells. In both cases the capsular material appears to be chemically homogeneous, a *polysaccharide gum* formed from sugars. These gums on hydrolysis yield simple sugars, and they are given specific names according to the nature of the sugar yielded, as galactan (yielding galactose) or dextran (yielding dextrose), etc. Since similar gums may be obtained from cultures of bacteria which do not form distinct capsules, it is assumed that such material is present on the exterior of the cells of most, if not all, bacteria, but that it becomes sufficiently voluminous to be visible only in certain species or in certain environments.

Mucinous sheaths of gum are a very characteristic feature of nearly all of the Algae, and in some of the unicellular forms these present the same general appearance as the capsules of bacteria. The slimy envelopes of the algal cells are also polysaccharides of the same general character as those of the bacteria.

Capsules may surround each cell in a culture, or if the cells are arranged characteristically in pairs or chains the capsule may surround all of the cells in a group. In some cases the capsules of many cells may become confluent, and considerable masses may become surrounded by a common sheath of gum. Such a mass of bacterial cells cemented together is called a *zoögloea,* and such zoögloeae are especially characteristic of certain organisms growing in sugar solutions. In Azotobacter the individual cells may have a capsule, and pairs of encapsulated cells may be enclosed in a second envelope, and this may continue for some generations, forming capsules within capsules. Such a condition is also exhibited by the Blue-green Alga, Gloeocapsa.

Capsule Stains. The capsules of pathogenic bacteria are not easily observed. They are generally absent in artificial cultures except when first isolated from the animal body on media containing blood or blood serum. They are best observed in slides prepared directly from body fluids of the infected animal, and cannot be clearly seen except when special staining methods are used. Two such methods in common use are Welch's stain and Hiss's stain.

Welch's Method

1. Dry the film but do not heat.
2. Flood the slide with glacial acetic acid for a minute.
3. Pour off the excess acid and flood the slide repeatedly with the crystal violet solution used in Gram's stain (see p. 37). Finally allow the violet to stand on the slide for a minute.
4. Wash off the violet with 2% sodium chloride solution.

Hiss's Method

1. Dry the film and fix by flaming.
2. Flood the slide with the carbol fuchsin solution used in staining tubercle bacilli (see p. 97). Allow the stain to act for several minutes.
3. Wash the slide with 20% copper sulphate solution.

Note that in both the above methods the slide is not to be washed with water, which would dissolve out the capsular material. After the final washing the capsules may be seen more clearly, in both cases, if the slides are not dried. Allow a little of the salt solution, or copper sulphate, to remain on the slide, place a coverslip over this, immersion oil on the coverslip, and examine with the immersion lens. The capsules will appear as faintly but definitely stained haloes surrounding the deeply stained cells.

Capsules and Virulence. Those disease-producing bacteria which regularly form capsules are among the most virulent. They are the organisms of lobar pneumonia (pneumococcus and Friedländer's pneumobacillus), of anthrax, and of gas gangrene (the bacillus of Welch). The plague bacillus may also form capsules at times. In all of these cases the infections may develop very suddenly and produce a fatal illness in a very brief space of time. This fact, together with the observation that the capsules develop only in the animal body, has led to the theory that capsules serve these bacteria as a mechanism by which they are protected from the defensive factors (antibodies, phagocytes) of the infected animal. Thus they are of prime importance in the virulence of the bacteria. This theory has been well supported by the recent discovery that it is possible to separate, from strains of capsule-forming bacteria, variants which produce no capsules, no gum. Such variants have been invariably found to lack virulence, or disease-producing power.

The gums or polysaccharides forming the capsules of bacteria differ chemically with the different species that form them. But more than that, they differ with subspecies or *types*, of a single species. Thus with the pneumococcus there are known to exist a number of types which differ from each other only in their reactions toward antibodies. The immunologic specificity of these types is due to chemical differences in the polysaccharides which form their capsules.

It was formerly believed that the capsules represent a gelatinization of the outer layers of the protoplasm, or ectoplasm, and are therefore actually part of the cell. In the light of newer knowledge, the demonstration that they are apparently purely carbohydrate in composition, this seems unlikely. They are rather a material synthesized by the organism but deposited upon its exterior.

Sheaths. In connection with capsules, the student should be reminded that certain of the higher bacteria form *sheaths* which are somewhat analogous.   In the case of some of the iron bacteria, these are apparently composed entirely of ferric hydroxide.   But with such organisms as Sphaerotilus and the filamentous sulphur bac-

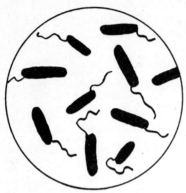

FIG. 54.   Monotrichous Flagella.

teria, the sheaths are of organic matter, probably also polysaccharides, though of firmer consistency than capsules.

Flagella.   *Flagella* are the organs of motility of bacteria.   The filamentous sulphur bacteria and the Myxobacteria exhibit gliding motions, the mechanism for which is unknown.   But the motility of the true bacteria is due entirely to their flagella.   Not all bacteria are motile.   Practically none of the Coccaceae exhibit motility.   The rod-shaped bacteria are about evenly divided between motile and non-motile species.   All of the Spirillaceae are motile.

Staining Flagella.   With some of the larger aquatic Spirilla the flagella may be readily seen by examination of slides stained by the ordinary methods, or even on the living cells. But with most bacteria the flagella are quite invisible by ordinary methods of examination. The reason for this is their extreme fineness. Their diameter in fixed films probably falls below the limits of resolution.   Flagella have been observed by

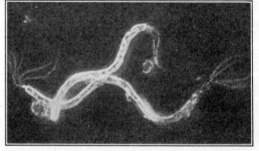

FIG. 55.   Lophotrichous Flagella.   *Spirillum volutans*, photomicrograph by dark field illumination.

dark field illumination in certain cases, and by the use of negative staining methods, but here there is some question whether individual flagella, or tufts of entangled flagella, have been seen.   Flagella may be made visible by several different staining methods, all of which involve the use of a *mordant* or preliminary chemical treatment.

These mordants are all highly complex colloidal solutions of tannates, and probably serve to make the flagella visible by becoming deposited upon their surfaces, increasing both the diameter and the intensity of their staining.

The success of flagella staining depends largely upon the colloidal state of the mordant, and this apparently can be disturbed by many

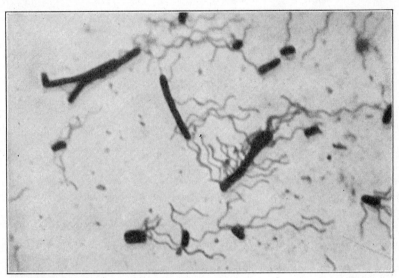

FIG. 56.   Peritrichous Flagella.   Typhoid bacilli stained with Loeffler's
flagella stain.

factors. A good mordant carefully preserved will yield consistent results for some time, but of several batches of mordant prepared by apparently identical methods, some may work and others not. The flagella of bacteria are extraordinarily brittle, breaking off easily with slight handling. Slides for flagella staining must be specially prepared with very little manipulation. Flagella may be easily demonstrated only with very young actively growing cultures, preferably on solid media, which, however, must be unusually moist. All of these factors make the staining of flagella too laborious and uncertain a procedure for routine use in examining cultures.

Types of Flagellation. Examination of many species of bacteria stained to show their flagella indicates that the flagellation is a specific character of remarkable constancy. Bacteria may be divided into four classes as regards their flagella: — the *atrichous* non-motile bacteria, without flagella; the *monotrichous* bacteria, with a single polar flagellum; the *lophotrichous* bacteria, with a tuft of flagella at one extremity; and the *peritrichous* bacteria, with flagella distributed over the surface of the cell. The motile rod forms of bacteria exhibit peritrichous flagellation in some species, monotrichous in others. The Spirilla are all lophotrichous. The single flagellum of the monotrichous organisms is not given off at the very extremity of the cell, but from one side of the end portion.

Motion of Flagella. By means of dark-field illumination the flagella have been observed in action in living organisms. In peritrichous forms the flagella project backwards, but stand away from the axis of the cell at an angle of about 45°. They move the organism forward, not by a backward and forward lashing movement, like the cilia of Infusoria, but by a rotary movement of the spirally twisted filaments — their action is like that of a propeller, not like that of an oar. Although very fine, the flagella may attain a considerable length, several times that of the cell which gives them origin.

Cytoplasm. There is but little that can be said about the cytoplasm of bacteria. With some of the larger species the cells may be crushed between a slide and coverslip, and the protoplasm may be seen to flow out as a semi-liquid substance. Under the microscope it appears as a perfectly homogeneous material. Older theories ascribing a granular or foamy structure to the protoplasm are now known to be erroneous, the apparent structure being due to non-living matter in the form of granules or vacuoles included within the cell.

Many chemical analyses of various species of bacteria have been made. These indicate that the cells consist largely of water (about 85%) and that they are richer in proteins and poorer in carbohydrates than many higher organisms. But the chemical analyses have been found to vary enormously with the nature of the medium in which the organisms have been grown, and one must either conclude that the composition of protoplasm may vary widely with different environments, or that the analyses have included much inert material, either food in the process of metabolism, or storage products. The latter seems more likely. It is noteworthy that various nucleic acids and nucleoproteins have been obtained from bacteria.

As was mentioned previously, the cells of bacteria stain better with the basic aniline dyes than with the acid dyes, the Gram positive species showing a stronger affinity for basic dyes than the Gram negative ones. With many higher forms it is found that the cytoplasm is differentiated from the nucleus by its affinity for acid dyes. The intense basophilic character of bacteria may be considered a special characteristic of their cytoplasm.

Reserve Materials. While in general the protoplasm of bacteria appears perfectly homogeneous, there are many exceptions. In a number of cases the cells may be seen to contain granules and vacuoles of varying degrees of refractility. Study of these by microchemical methods and observation at various stages of growth have revealed that for the most part they are reserve food materials of various sorts which are stored within the cells. They tend to accumulate as growth slows up or ceases, and to disappear again when the cells become active. We have noted that the various Thiobacteriales tend to become filled up with globules of sulphur, which may be looked upon as such a reserve material.

Mostly these reserve materials fall into three classes — fats, carbohydrates, and nitrogenous materials. Fat appears in the cells of many species of bacteria, as highly refractile bodies. It may be identified by staining with osmic acid (black) or Sudan III (red). Carbohydrates appear usually as glycogen (as in the Fungi), though some bacteria form a substance very similar to starch, called *granulose*. Glycogen and granulose are found frequently in the cells of the spore-forming bacteria, especially the anaerobic species. Fat also occurs most frequently in the large spore-forming organisms. When such materials are present in abundance they give the cytoplasm a granular or vacuolated appearance.

Very little is known about albuminous or other nitrogenous reserve material, save for a particular substance which appears frequently in the cells of various microörganisms, *volutin.*

Volutin. This substance has been briefly mentioned before. It occurs in the cells of all the lower Algae and Fungi, the yeasts, and many of the bacteria. It has been recorded in some Protozoa, but here it may be material which has been ingested in the cells of bacteria and Algae, not formed by the Protozoa themselves. It has been claimed that the basophilic granules of certain white blood cells are the same material, but this is doubtful. It would seem that volutin is a substance peculiar to the cells of the lower forms of plant life.

Volutin occurs most regularly and abundantly in the diphtheria bacillus and related species, the Corynebacteria. It is also common in the Actinomycetes, the spore-forming bacteria, the Lactobacilli, and Azotobacter. All of the above are Gram positive organisms. It may appear abundantly in some strains of Coccaceae, particularly the Gram negative cocci of the throat. It is abundant in *Spirillum volutans* (from which the term "volutin" was derived), which is Gram negative. But while occasional Gram negative organisms may show granules of volutin within their cells, this substance is on the whole much more characteristic of the Gram positive bacteria.

Volutin is composed of free nucleic acid, and serves as a reserve substance. Its chemical nature was suspected a number of years ago by Meyer, who stated that it is either free nucleic acid or a nucleoprotein different from the nucleoprotein which forms the chromatin of nuclei. This statement was based upon observations of its staining reactions with basic dyes, and upon chemical analyses of cells rich in volutin. The true nature was more recently determined by Schumacher, who succeeded in obtaining the material in pure form by chemical extraction, identifying it by chemical reactions, and then re-identifying the material within the cells by microchemical reactions. It is highly probable that it occurs in the cells as free nucleic acid, and that it is the substance which the biochemists refer to as "plant" or "yeast" nucleic acid, a substance different from the thymonucleic acid which occurs in the nucleoprotein that forms the chromatin of nuclei. It is considered a reserve material because it accumulates during the later stages of growth in cultures and disappears again when growth becomes rapid. Phosphorus is, of course, necessary for its development, and it may fail to appear in cultures poor in phosphates. In molds, yeasts, and spore-forming bacteria, volutin appears abundantly in those cells which are to form spores, but disappears in the maturation of the spores.

Staining of Volutin. Volutin appears in the unstained cells as granules or vacuoles, somewhat more refractile than the cytoplasm, but not as refractile as fat droplets or spores. In molds and yeasts, it may occur in droplets of some size. Here it is probably in solution. Occasionally it appears in vacuoles in bacteria, but more usually as dense granules. These granules stain deeply with the basic aniline dyes, more deeply than the cytoplasm. If diphtheria bacilli are stained lightly with methylene blue, the granules appear a deep blue, the rest of the cell a paler blue. When an old "ripened" solution of methylene blue is used, the granules often take on a purple or even red tint. The same may be observed with haematoxylin and with toluidin blue. For this reason the granules are frequently called *metachromatic* granules, because they stain a color different from that of the dye used to stain them. This phenomenon has not been satisfactorily explained. When heavily stained with basic dyes the granules resist decolorization longer than the cytoplasm. This serves as a basis for a number of differential stains. Thus one may stain heavily with methylene blue, decolorize with a weak acid solution, and counterstain with a red dye. The granules will appear blue on a red ground. Using Gram's stain, and decolorizing longer with alcohol, the granules will appear Gram positive on a Gram negative ground. One of the most common stains depends upon the decolorizing action of vesuvin or Bismarck brown. If diphtheria bacilli are stained with methylene blue and counterstained with Bismarck brown, the latter

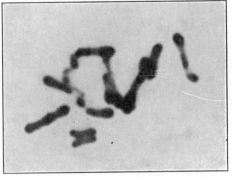

Fig. 57. Volutin Granules. Diphtheria bacilli stained with methylene blue.

dye will remove the blue from the cytoplasm but not from the granules; at the same time the cytoplasm is stained, so that the granules appear as blue-black bodies on a yellowish brown ground.

Volutin may be stained *vitally* with dilute methylene blue or with neutral red. The latter method serves to differentiate volutin granules from nuclei. If yeast cells are suspended in a dilute solution of neutral red, the volutin granules take on a deep pink color, but the nucleus is unstained. Volutin granules may be differentiated from nuclei also by their solubility in hot water. If slides are immersed in water heated to near the boiling point, volutin is dissolved out of the cells and disappears, whereas the nucleoproteins of the nuclei are coagulated or fixed by this procedure.

Spores. Rod-shaped bacteria of the family Bacillaceae form *endospores*. These are essentially condensations of the protoplasm within the cells, which are liberated by a dissolution of the cells

which formed them.   They are extraordinarily resistant to all sorts
of injurious agents, and may remain dormant for long periods of
time.   Only one spore is formed by each cell, and upon germination
each spore gives rise to but one cell.   They are, therefore, not reproductive in function but are essentially *resting forms.*

Spores appear in cultures after the growth has begun to slow
up in rate.   The principal factor determining spore formation appears
to be a partial exhaustion of the nutrients in the medium.   The
first evidence of spore formation is the appearance of darker, or
denser, portions in the cell, generally at one pole.   These areas become
larger and more sharply differentiated from
the cytoplasm.   When mature, the spore appears as a round, oval, or cylindrical body
within the cell, and is very refractile.   It will
appear much darker or much lighter than the
cytoplasm, depending upon the level of focus
of the microscope.   The size, form, and position of the spore within the cell are characters
fairly constant for the species.   The spores
may be terminal, subterminal, or central in
position; they may be large and bulge the
cell, or small, not changing the contour.   These characters determine
the six types of spore-bearing cells illustrated in Fig. 58.

Fig. 58.   Showing
Various Types of Spore-
bearing Bacteria.   The
appearance of the cell
depends upon the rela-
tive size of the spore,
and its position within
the cell.

Spore Formation.   The process of spore formation may be followed
in stained preparations.   The first evidences of beginning spores are
manifested by a deeper staining of the cell at one or both poles.   While
it is true that each cell forms but one spore, in many cases spore
formation begins simultaneously at both ends of a cell.   A cell division
precedes the maturation of each spore, so that ultimately there are
two cells with one spore each.   The more deeply stained portion at the
poles of the cell frequently become a discrete deeply stained body,
the *sporogenous granule.*   These granules may be differentiated from
volutin granules (which may also be present) by their failure to
stain with neutral red and their insolubility in hot water.   They are
not always sharply differentiated from the cytoplasm.   The transition to the next step is not very clear.   The granules enlarge, become
refractile, become sharply separated from the cytoplasm by the development of a *spore wall,* and no longer stain with the aniline dyes.
The mature spore appears as a refractile unstained area in the cell.

With free spores, the spore wall is seen to stain deeply, but the interior remains uncolored by ordinary staining methods.

Staining of Spores. The failure of the mature spores to stain is attributed to the relative impermeability of the spore wall. The interior of the spore may be colored by the use of penetrating dyes allowed to act for a long time, or hastened in their penetration by the use of heat. Such a dye is carbol fuchsin. If slides of spore-bearing bacteria are flooded with carbol fuchsin and kept steaming for ten minutes, both spores and vegetative cells will be deeply stained. If, now, the

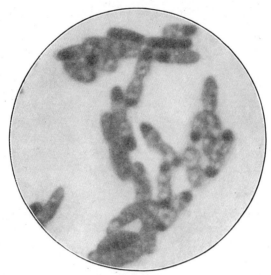

FIG. 59. Sporogenous Granules. *Bacillus megatherium;* photomicrograph of a smear from a culture which was just beginning to form spores.

slide is washed quickly with alcohol, it will be possible to decolorize the vegetative cells and leave the spores still stained. This also is attributed to the lesser permeability of the spore wall; the alcohol can easily penetrate the vegetative cells, but requires a longer time to penetrate the spores. If, now, the alcohol is followed by a counterstain, say methylene blue, we have a double staining; spores will be red, vegetative cells blue.

Properties of Spores. Nowhere else in the living world can we find organisms so tenacious of life as the endospores of bacteria. They are known to remain viable in cultures for thirty or forty years, and probably will remain alive for much longer periods. Practically all of them will withstand the temperature of boiling water for short periods, some will remain alive after treatment with steam under pressure at a temperature of 120° C. They will withstand the action of disinfectants that kill the vegetative cells almost instantly. This extreme resistance to aging, drying, heat, and chemicals, is attributed in part to their thick and relatively impermeable cell wall, but more particularly to the character of their protoplasm. It has been found that, while the total water content of spores is about the same as that of the vegetative cells, the proportion of *bound* water is greater. This may affect the coagulability of the proteins by heat, and thus confer greater heat resistance to the spores.

The extreme resistance and longevity of spores has given rise to some interesting ideas. It has been claimed that living bacteria have been recovered from oil, coal, or rocks buried in the earth for thousands of years. It has been suggested, however, that these are recent bacteria that have been carried into the rocks by water seeping through fine crevices. It has been calculated that bacterial spores are small enough and light enough in weight to be propelled through space by a beam of light, and the transmission of life from distant planets to the earth by this means has been suggested as a possibility.

Germination of Spores. When spores are transferred to an environment favorable for growth, they germinate and give rise to vegetative cells. This is brought about by an imbibition of water; the protoplasm of the spore swells. It may burst the spore wall, which is then cast off as an empty hull, or the spore wall may stretch and become thin. Both processes may be seen to occur in a single pure culture. For a short period the emergent vegetative cell shows a deeply stained granule, but before the first cell division this has disappeared.

Nuclei of Bacteria. We may define a nucleus as *a body present in all of the cells of higher organisms which are living and capable of further division, which is morphologically distinct from the cytoplasm, which is composed mainly of nucleoprotein* (the chromatin), *and which alone bears the hereditary characters* of the organism. Nuclei in this sense have been demonstrated in all groups of microörganisms save the bacteria and the Blue-green Algae. The latter possess, as was described previously, a central body which is looked upon as a primitive nucleus, not sharply differentiated from the cytoplasm, but showing a tendency in that direction. The recent demonstration by microchemical reactions that this central body contains nucleo-protein of the same sort as that forming the chromatin of the nucleus of higher organisms confirms the opinion that this central body is truly a nucleus. With the bacteria, however, we find that the presence of a nucleus is far from certain. The literature on this subject is voluminous and conflicting. One finds in current literature a tendency to take for granted the presence of a nucleus, mainly because it is difficult to conceive of a cell without a nucleus. All our ideas of biology are based upon a conception of protoplasm divided into cells which are differentiated into nucleus and cytoplasm. But we have seen how such a conception cannot hold with organisms which are very minute. Somewhere on the scale down we must come to a point where the organism is too small to allow differentiation. Is this point reached in the bacteria?

Theories about Nuclei. We may divide theories regarding the nuclei of bacteria into four groups: I. The bacteria possess no nucleus or its equivalent. II. The entire cell is nucleus, cytoplasm being lacking, or reduced to an invisible layer. III. There is present a true, discrete nucleus. IV. The equivalent of a nucleus is present in the form of material finely diffused through the cytoplasm, not morphologically distinct from it.

No Nucleus. The first of these theories was proposed many years ago and supported by Haeckel, who assumed that primitive forms of life do not have the cell structure of higher forms, and that the development of a nucleus was a later development in evolution. Haeckel called such imperfect cells, without nuclei, "cytodes." Not much can be said for or against this theory. It satisfies the facts as we know them, but does not satisfy the mind. It makes it necessary to assume in primitive forms some sort of mechanism for hereditary transmission different from that which we have come to recognize in all higher forms of life.

All Nucleus. The second theory is based largely upon the uniform basophilic staining of the protoplasm of bacterial cells. The whole cell reacts toward aniline dyes like the chromatin of the nuclei of higher organisms. This theory is no more satisfactory than the first; a nucleus without cytoplasm is as inconceivable as cytoplasm without a nucleus.

True Nucleus. The third theory has been supported by a host of investigators who have been eager to discover the nuclei of the smallest of organisms. There has been a tendency on the part of bacteriologists to assume that nuclei must be present in the cells of bacteria simply because of the number of authors who have claimed to have found them. But when one examines these claims, he finds that such a wide variety of structures have been described as nuclei that certainly not all of them can be accepted. Each author has found some flaw in the claims of those who have preceded him. In short, these claims are largely mutually exclusive — if Meyer's nucleus is the true one, then certainly Nakanishi's is not, and so on. As a matter of fact, none of the claims for the existence of true discrete nuclei will stand critical examination. They may be criticized on various grounds:

1. *The supposed nucleus is obviously volutin or has not been properly differentiated from volutin.* This criticism will apply to nearly all of the earlier claims. Volutin reacts toward the usual nuclear stains, such as methylene blue or haematoxylin, in much the same manner as the chromatin of nuclei; it may or may not show the metachromatic effect. The behavior of both volutin and chromatin toward dyes is due to their nucleic acid content; but it has recently been shown that the nucleic acid of volutin is chemically different from that in chromatin. We have already pointed out how volutin may be differentiated from true nuclei. This criticism will at once throw out a large proportion of the claims.

2. *The supposed nucleus has been observed in organisms which are obviously not bacteria, or which are so little known and so poorly described that it is impossible to determine whether they are true bacteria or not.* Vejdowsky described nuclei in an organism parasitic in the intestines of the aquatic arthropod Gammarus. This organism has since been shown to be a protozoan parasite. But in many other cases the nuclei have been observed in supposed bacteria parasitic in the intestines of cockroaches, or frogs, or lizards, or other animals; they have not been cultivated; and there is no way of telling whether the various organisms were of one species or several, or indeed whether they were truly bacteria or not.

In this connection the student should be reminded of the opinion expressed in a previous chapter, that the organisms which we group together as bacteria are probably to some extent a heterogeneous mixture of unrelated forms. The finding of a nucleus in one will not warrant a generalization for the group. And to accept a statement that nuclei are present in bacteria, it is not asking too much to demand that this nucleus be regularly demonstrated in at least one species which, by study in pure culture, can be proved to be a true bacterium.

3. *The supposed nucleus is compressed protoplasm in cells filled with reserve materials.* Several of the larger spore-forming bacteria develop numerous vacuoles of fat or other reserve material which distend the cells. The protoplasm is concentrated in masses between the vacuoles, and in stained cells appears as deeply stained areas. These have been described as nuclei in several cases.

4. *The supposed nuclei cannot be found by subsequent observers.* Meyer described minute bodies demonstrated in the cells of various bacteria by a special staining method, which he considered to be nuclei. None of the above criticisms will apply to his observation, but subsequent investigators fail to confirm his findings, notably Zettnow and Guilliermond. The author himself has failed to demonstrate any such bodies by Meyer's technique, save in spore-forming bacteria in the process of spore production, and has concluded that these are the sporogenous granules previously referred to.

If, so far, true discrete nuclei have not been shown to exist in bacteria, there still remains the possibility that such are present, but are too small to be seen. Some of the larger bacteria are, however, as large as some of the smaller yeasts, in which true nuclei may readily be demonstrated. It would seem that, if minute size is the only factor, nuclei should be visible in the largest of the bacteria.

Diffuse Nucleus. The last of the four theories, that nuclear material is diffused through the cell, seems the most plausible and is probably more generally accepted than the others. This theory, proposed by Zettnow, has been supported and elaborated upon by a number of subsequent workers. According to this hypothesis, bacteria possess the *chemical* equivalent of a nucleus in the form of nucleoprotein, or chromatin, which is not *morphologically* distinguished from the cytoplasm as a definite body, but is scattered through the cell in solution, or more probably as finely divided granules. At times, in certain cells, this material may become separated, or "unmixed" from the cytoplasm, either as irregular amorphous masses or as discrete bodies, but such a condition is only temporary, and unusual.

The theory of the diffuse nucleus has recently received considerable support from several workers, particularly Pietschmann, through microchemical studies by means of the *Feulgen reaction*. Briefly it has been found that *thymonucleic acid* is an essential constituent of chromatin. By the Feulgen reaction it has been possible to demonstrate specifically this substance in the nuclei of all higher organisms where the test has been used. Here, then, is a reagent which is in no sense a general nuclear stain, but a specific microchemical indicator for an essential ingredient of the nuclear material. Those parts of the cell which contain thymonucleic acid turn pink when treated by this method, and if properly controlled, no other ingredient reacts.

The Feulgen test has been found to give a positive reaction with central bodies, or "primitive" nuclei, of the Blue-green Algae. When the Feulgen reaction is applied to bacterial cells, they stain

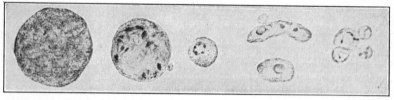

Fig. 60. Involution forms of *Bacillus mycoides* from a culture containing magnesium sulphate, stained by Feulgen's method, showing the "unmixing" of the material containing thymonucleic acid. This is the only approach to a true nucleus which has been demonstrated in bacteria. (After Pietschmann and Rippel, *Arch. f. Mikrobiologie*, 1932, vol. 3.)

diffusely a pale pink color. This is the normal condition. The whole protoplasm gives the reaction, but faintly. In cells which have formed spores, a small, more deeply stained body may be found, sometimes within the spore, sometimes outside. In certain *abnormal* cells appearing in cultures to which various substances (such as magnesium sulphate or lithium chloride) have been added, irregular masses of pink material appear in the unstained protoplasm. Pietschmann refers to this as an "unmixing" of the chromatin from the protoplasm, and states that such cells are incapable of further development; such an "unmixing" never occurs in normal cultures.

It would appear, then, that we have good grounds for believing that bacteria possess chromatin in a diffuse form, but do not have a discrete nucleus. In spore-forming organisms this chromatin may concentrate, and form, in part at least, the sporogenous granule.

The granules which appear in germinating spores may also consist of this material in concentrated form, which immediately becomes diffuse again upon complete germination. This alone is the extent to which we are justified in assuming that bacteria possess nuclei.

An Important Problem. The nucleus question is one of the most important biological problems of the bacteria. If it be granted that the bacteria do not possess a differentiated, morphologic nucleus, we must admit that the cells are different, simpler in organization than those of all other known organisms. Here is protoplasm a step lower in evolution than that of the rest of the living world, a step closer, it may be, to that intangible line which separates the living from the inanimate world.

In the somatic cells of higher organisms, the chromatin of the nucleus becomes arranged in chromosomes which are equationally divided at cell division so that each daughter cell receives precisely half of the chromatin and exactly the same sort of hereditary material. These hereditary characters are arranged in a linear manner in the chromosomes, being deposited in the *genes*. How are hereditary characters transmitted in bacteria? The smallest known chromosomes are of the same order of magnitude as the bacterial cell. We cannot see any change in the staining reactions or distribution of the diffused chromatin material in the cells of bacteria which are dividing. Are the hereditary characters of bacteria resident in the chromatin diffused through the cell? If so, how are they distributed at cell division? These are questions which have an important bearing upon the vexed problem of microbic variation. Throughout the recent literature upon life cycles in bacteria, one finds the tacit assumption that bacteria possess nuclei of the same sort as larger organisms, which go through the same sort of changes in conjugation and cell division. A little thought will show how unwarranted is such an assumption. Even if it be granted that bacteria have true nuclei, these would be so minute as to make the possibility of a chromosomal apparatus highly improbable.

CHAPTER IX

THE GROWTH AND REPRODUCTION OF BACTERIA

Cell Division. Bacteria multiply normally and usually by binary fission, a simple division of the cell into two parts. This process may be observed directly by imbedding some cells in nutrient agar mounted on a coverslip placed over the depression of a hollow-ground slide. The cells are seen to increase in size to a certain point and then divide. Division may occur in two ways. First, a *cross-wall* may appear in the middle of the cell, and this may split into two layers, thus separating the two daughter cells. Or the cell may simply *constrict* in the middle, the side walls coming together and pinching the cell into two parts. Both methods may be seen to occur in a single pure culture and all transitions between these two modes of cell division may be observed. When the rate of growth is high, constriction is more common; when multiplication is slower, cross-walls are prominent.

With all those bacteria which present an elongated cell form, the rods and spirals, cell division occurs in a plane at right angles to the long axis of the cell, i.e., transversely rather than longitudinally. The spherical bacteria may elongate, becoming oval in form, but more usually this is not the case. The two daughter cells are then at first hemispherical in form, and this form is often maintained for some time after division.

Cell Groupings. When cell division has been completed, the two cells may immediately separate, or they may remain temporarily attached to each other. The latter gives rise to characteristic arrangements of the cell. In the case of the spherical bacteria, several possibilities present themselves, because cell division may occur in more than one plane. If the cells remain attached after one cell division, but separate before the next, they will be seen grouped in pairs (diplococci). If they remain attached through a series of consecutive cell divisions, they will be arranged in chains (Streptococci) if these divisions all occur in the same plane, in flat plates if

138

they occur in only two planes, and in cubical bundles (Sarcinae) if they occur in all three planes. With the rod-shaped bacteria, only two of these groupings are possible, in pairs or chains. The spiral bacteria almost invariably separate immediately after division.

Plasmodesmids. If one observes a motile chain of rod-shaped bacteria, it is seen that the individual cells are firmly attached to each other. The cells themselves are rigid. The chain may bend

Fig. 61. Plasmodesmids.

and undulate, the cells behaving much like a train of railroad cars coupled together. And yet, ordinarily, nothing can be seen between the cells, serving to attach them. Moreover, the whole chain moves as a unit, there is a coördination of activity throughout the chain, all of the cells are working to move the chain in the same direction. In carefully stained preparations of some of the larger bacteria which occur in chains, such as *Bacillus megatherium* or *Sphaerotilus dichotomus*, one may see extremely fine filaments of basic-staining material running from the extremity of one cell to that of the next. These are *plasmodesmids*, or protoplasmic bridges, which not only serve to hold the cells together, but also bring about a continuity of the protoplasm through the whole chain of cells. The plasmodesmids, where they may be seen, are extremely fine, just within the limits of visibility. Since, in smaller organisms, the chains of cells behave in the same way, we must assume that they also have plasmodesmids, which are, however, too fine to be seen.

Post-fission Movements. In the case of the rod forms, final separation of the two cells is accomplished by *post-fission movements*. These are of three types. In one, the two cells push against each other, becoming bent in the middle, so that the attached ends tend to become separated; the plasmodesmid is made tense and finally snaps. The cells may then rather suddenly straighten. Such *snapping* movements are characteristic of the aerobic spore-formers. These usually grow in chains. The separation of cells by snapping may occur in any part of the chain, causing the chain to break. The two chains now continue to grow in the new direction. The result is a characteristic arrangement of the cells in loops, or festoons of chains, seen at the edge of colonies of such organisms as the anthrax bacillus. A second type of post-fission movement is that character-istic of the Corynebacteria. One cell moves through an arc of a circle, the center of which is the point of attachment of the two cells, the moving cell forming the radius. The moving cell does not bend. The motion may sometimes be rather sudden, and is designated a *whipping* motion. Such post-fission movements are also seen when the filaments of Actinomycetes fragment into oidia, and the same thing is observed in the mold, *Geotrichum lactis*. Here the motions tend to produce a characteristic zig-zag arrangement of the elements. With the diphtheria bacilli these post-fission movements are more complete and tend to bring the cells together in rows or bundles of cells which are parallel with each other, the so-called palisade arrangement. With the non-spore-forming rods of the type represented by the typhoid and colon bacilli, the third type of movement is found. The cells become completely separated, and one of the two glides partially past the other. This *slipping* movement also tends to produce a somewhat parallel arrangement of the cells which may be seen at the edge of a growing colony.

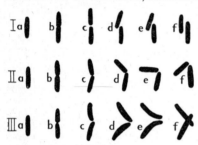

FIG. 62. Post-fission Movements. I, "slipping" movements of the colon-typhoid group; II, "whipping" movements of the diphtheroid group; III, "snapping" movements of the spore-formers.

Rate of Growth. It seems to be a general rule that the smaller the organism, the greater is its reproductive rate. Mice and guinea pigs are notoriously more prolific than horses and elephants. Protozoa may divide, grow and divide again in a few hours, and with bacteria, this period, the *generation time*, is reduced to minutes. The average generation time of rapidly growing bacteria during the period of maxi-mum growth rate is about 20 minutes. The author has observed an individual cell of *Bacillus megatherium* to more than double in size and divide within a space of 9 minutes. Some one statistically minded has calculated that if such a rate of growth were maintained, a single bacterium could fill the oceans with its progeny within a few days. But actually this maximum growth rate is maintained for but a short time.

When one transplants bacteria to a fresh culture medium, they usually do not begin to grow at once, but after a shorter or longer resting period they begin to multiply. The rate at which cell division occurs gradually accelerates, multiplication proceeds more and more rapidly until a maximum growth rate is attained. But shortly after this the growth rate begins to slow up, and becomes slower and slower until growth ceases. The number of bacteria may remain constant for a time, but sooner or later they begin to die, and for a time the number of living cells decreases with great rapidity. However, usually some of the organisms are very tenacious of life and will remain alive, capable of inoculating a new culture, even after weeks or months.

The Growth Curve. These facts may be demonstrated by counting the bacteria at regular time intervals, and plotting a curve of the numbers of organisms counted, against the time intervals. If, instead of the actual numbers, one plots the logarithms of the numbers, the resulting curve will show the *rate* of growth rather than the mere numerical increase; the steepness of the curve will indicate the proportional increase or decrease at any instant. Such a growth curve shows an initial *lag phase* during which little or no growth occurs; a period of *accelerating growth* during which the cells multiply at an ever increasing rate, until a *mid-point*, or period of maximum growth, is attained; and a phase of *negative acceleration*, with a steadily decreasing growth rate until growth ceases. There may be a short resting period when the population of bacteria just holds its own, but usually the curve immediately turns over into the phase of *accelerating death;* in most cases, after reaching a maximum death rate, the cells cease to die so rapidly, and one may recognize a phase of *negative acceleration* in death.

The Law of Growth. Such growth curves may be compared with similar curves indicating the rate of growth of other populations, or of individual organisms. Whether we are dealing with individual organisms, such as a plant or animal; or parts of organisms, such as a regenerating tadpole's tail; or populations of organisms in a limited environment, as people in a country, or fruit flies in a bottle, the same sort of curve is obtained. This curve expresses a general *law of growth*, formulated by Pearl, which states that at any moment the rate of growth is determined by the proportion between the number of individuals (or cells) which are growing, and the amount of foodstuff available in the limited environment. At first the amount of food is in excess of the needs of the organisms, and they grow more and more rapidly. But, increasing in logarithmic proportion, they soon reach a point where the food available to each unit (cell or organism) is insufficient to maintain this rate, and so growth decreases again. It seems also to be a general law that things which cannot grow must die, and there follows the negative part of the growth curve. With bacteria, in some cases, the accumulation of acids or other injurious products of growth also serves to slow up the growth and cause the death of the organisms, but these special cases do not invalidate the general law.

Morphological Changes during Growth. If, at regular intervals, one examines under the microscope samples of the bacteria from a growing culture, these are seen to undergo regular changes in size and form, in internal structure and staining reactions, corresponding with the various phases of the growth curve. During the initial period of dormancy the cells show but little change, but with the beginning of growth they alter markedly. In most cases the cells increase greatly in size; the Corynebacteria are an exception, the cells becoming smaller during active growth. In those species which possess volutin granules or other sorts of reserve material in the cells, those bodies disappear. The bacteria stain more deeply with the basic dyes; Gram negative species show a tendency to retain the Gram's stain. Increased size, homogeneity of the protoplasm, and intense basophilic staining characterize the young, actively growing cells of bacteria.

But as soon as growth slows up, the cells begin to change again in the reverse direction, and if one examines a culture in which growth has almost ceased, he will find that in general the cells are smaller (larger in the case of the Corynebacteria), and less deeply stained. In many species granules of volutin, globules of fat, or other reserve materials will appear to make the protoplasm appear less homogeneous. With the spore-forming bacteria, the development of spores begins as soon as the growth rate decreases, and proceeds steadily until after growth has ceased. It is in this phase that the bacteria exhibit the morphology usually ascribed to them. With most species they will present this appearance in agar cultures 24 to 48 hours old, the standard source of material for morphologic study in the identification of bacterial species.

Involution Forms.   As the process continues into the death phase the cells change still further.   They stain more and more faintly with the basic dyes, some appear as mere shadows; but now they begin to show an affinity for acid dyes, and may be stained deeply with Congo red, which will not color the young growing cells at all. However, this period is characterized particularly by variation in the *form* of the cells.   All sorts of unusual or bizarre forms may appear. In cultures of normally rod-shaped organisms may be found long filaments, or large and small spherical cells.   Some show little bud-like processes sprouting from the sides, others are definitely branched. These irregular forms which appear in old cultures have been known (and have been a source of trouble) to bacteriologists since the very beginning of the science.   They are usually interpreted as evidences of injury, of beginning disintegration in the dying culture, and are called *involution forms*.   But, as will shortly be seen, such an interpretation is by no means generally accepted.

These changes in the appearance of the cells are also accompanied by variations in their physiologic properties.   During the period of accelerating growth the bacteria are much more susceptible to various injurious agents, heat, cold, or antiseptics, than are the resting cells. This change in susceptibility reaches an extreme, of course, in the case of the spore-formers, whose spores formed in the resting period are vastly more resistant than the young growing cells.

Apparently the aging of a culture, i.e., the partial exhaustion of the nutrients with resultant cessation of growth, affects the cells in two sorts of ways.   Some of the cells are injured and die, while others go into a dormant or resting state, in which they are more resistant than the growing cells.   In the spore-forming bacteria this dormant resistant form is a special body, the spore.   But spores may be looked upon as merely a high development of a general phenomenon, for even with bacteria which do not form spores we know that the mature cells are more resistant than the growing cells.   These cells also, then, may be looked upon as resting forms. The lag phase is probably best explained by assuming that these resting cells must be first transformed into growing types before growth may proceed; actually we may see such a morphologic transformation occur.   If an actively growing culture is transplanted, there is no lag in the new culture.

Cytomorphosis.   If we examine the tissues of an animal at various stages in its life, we also find striking changes in the cells. In the embryo the cells are smaller, the nucleus relatively larger and deeply stained. They are all much alike. In the mature animal the cells become differentiated into several sorts performing different functions, and this differentiation depends largely upon an increase in the cytoplasm, which has deposited within it the various structures (fibrils, granules, vacuoles, etc.) which are characteristic of this function. The nucleus is relatively smaller, and in general not so deeply

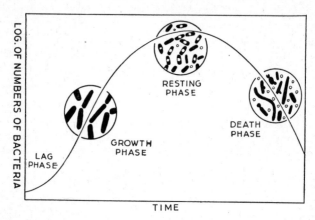

Fig. 63. Cytomorphosis and the Growth Curve. The curve shows the variations in *rate* of growth. The drawings illustrate cell changes observed in a spore-forming bacillus with changes in the rate of growth. The *embryonic* types occur in the growth phase; they are large and stain solidly. The *mature* types are found in the resting phase; they are smaller, and many are forming spores. The *senescent* forms occurring in the death phase are irregular in form, and many free spores appear.

stained. In the aged animal, the cells show various degenerative changes. The cytoplasm may become filled with fat droplets or other materials, the nucleus is still smaller, and the staining reactions are altered. These progressive changes in the cells of an animal have been designated by Minot as a *cytomorphosis*.

Now there is a striking parallelism between the progressive cell changes in a culture of bacteria and in a multicellular animal. We have seen how the growth curves are similar. In both we find three types of cells, characteristic of the periods of growth, of maturity (or cessation of growth), and of beginning death, respectively. It has been found that the cells of an embryonic, rapidly growing animal are much more susceptible to injurious agents than those of an adult. It is quite evident that similar laws govern the development of both the multicellular organism and the population of free unicellular individuals. To some extent a culture of bacteria, even though the cells are unattached and suspended in a liquid, behaves like an individual, and we may look upon the progressive cell changes as the same sort of phenomenon as the cytomorphosis occurring in an animal.

Pleomorphism. In the introductory chapter we noted that the early years of bacteriology were marked by a controversy between two schools of thought regarding the growth and reproduction of bacteria. One school, the *pleomorphists*, maintained that bacterial forms are very unstable; that they go through complex life cycles, and that the various "species" of bacteria are merely different forms of one, or at the most a very few; that perhaps bacteria are not an autonomous group at all, but merely phases in the life history of higher organisms, the Fungi. Opposed to this view was the teaching of the *monomorphists*, Cohn and Koch, that bacteria exist as a series of constant and immutable species with only one mode of reproduction, simple binary fission; that they are constant in their morphologic types, and that any departure from the normal type is to be looked upon as an abnormal or "involution" form. As was related before, the Cohn-Koch dogma became the accepted teaching. It was so frequently shown that apparent variations in cultures were due to accidental contaminations that bacteriologists came to look upon any departure from the expected as a sign of contamination and to discard at once such cultures.

But within the last two decades there has appeared a new school of pleomorphists who have struggled against the firmly entrenched Cohn-Koch dogma until they have finally succeeded in overthrowing it. The leaders of this new movement have been Löhnis, Mellon, Hort, Almquist, and Enderlein, but a number of other workers have contributed to it. While the majority of bacteriologists have probably not accepted completely the various findings and theories brought forward by these men, they have now been convinced that the teachings of Cohn and Koch were too rigid and that the truth probably lies somewhere between the extremes of pleomorphism and monomorphism.

Life Cycles of Bacteria. This controversy has centered largely in the question of the nature of the so-called involution forms. These unusual forms appear mostly in old cultures which are known to be in the death phase. Their production may be stimulated by adding to the culture medium various substances such as magnesium sulphate or lithium chloride or minute quantities of phenol or potassium bichromate, all substances known to have an injurious action when used in larger amounts. The view that they are injured or abnormal cells thus at first glance seems to be very logical. But we know that in such cultures not all of the cells die, that in fact some of them become transformed into a new form, the spores. The pleomorphists maintain that these unusual forms are cells which are viable, which have undertaken some new form of growth or reproduction different from simple fission, and that they represent stages in a rather complex *life cycle*. Since many of these forms seem to resemble reproductive bodies found in the life cycles of some of the Fungi, it is supposed that bacteria are actually Fungi which go through the same sort of cycle. *Branching* and *budding* are looked upon as fungous characters. The terms *zygospore* and *ascospore* have been borrowed from mycology to designate certain structures found in bacteria.

Branching. The occurrence of branched Y- or X-shaped cells in cultures of diphtheria bacilli was at one time considered a character of sufficient importance to warrant separating them from the rest of bacteria as a higher form related to the molds. But in recent years such branched forms have been observed in a wide variety of organisms. Nearly all of the rod-shaped bacteria have been found to produce branched cells at times. Gardner has noted that such branched forms are frequently observed in the first stages of growth when an old culture is transferred to fresh medium, and believes that they are due to some local alteration in the cell membrane caused by an injurious agent in the former culture. Such cells, however, are viable. Y-shaped cells may be seen to grow out in three directions, with fission occurring in all three limbs, a condition which Gardner designates "three-point multiplication."

Budding. The division of bacterial cells does not always occur precisely in the middle. Often the division is quite unequal. If this occurs very near the end, the appearance resembles more closely the pinching off of a bud, as is seen in yeasts, than the fission which is characteristic of bacteria. However, in old cultures one also observes at times cells with a little globule projecting from the side. These have been considered to be buds by some authors, though they may be incipient branches, a beginning of "three-point" multiplication. When speaking of budding one thinks of a cell continually giving off a series of little sprouts, one after another. This has not been observed in bacteria.

Gonidia. These are described as minute bodies formed in some number within the bacterial cell, which are liberated from the mother cell, and which later develop into the typical bacterial form of the species. Such bodies have been described by a number of observers working with different species of bacteria. Many bacteria accumulate granules of reserve material of one sort or another and undoubtedly uncritical workers have observed and interpreted these (particularly the deeply staining volutin granules) as intracellular reproductive bodies.

The best evidence for the occurrence of gonidia has been brought forward by Thornton and Gangulee in the case of the bacteria which live symbiotically in the root nodules of leguminous plants. The root nodule organism (*Rhizobium leguminosarum*) has long been known to occur in two forms. If one crushes a nodule from a rootlet of, say, alfalfa, and stains the exuding sap, it is seen to contain large numbers of bacterial forms, rather large, some straight rods, some swollen or club-shaped, others distinctly branched. These frequently show irregularity in staining, deeply stained bands alternating with clear areas. These cells are not motile; no flagella may be demonstrated. When one transfers some of this material to artificial culture media, he obtains a growth of a very different form — much smaller, uniformly stained rod forms which are actively motile, with flagella, and showing no tendency to branching or other irregular forms. Thornton and Gangulee claimed that these small motile forms develop *within* the large rods characteristic of the root nodules. The protoplasm separates into several bands with clear spaces between. These become rounded and develop a single flagellum. The mother cell ruptures, and the minute coccoid forms swim away. They become elongated and develop further flagella. They also showed that these small motile forms occur free in the soil.

Here, then, is apparently a true life cycle, with two growth forms, one characteristic of the free life in the soil, the other characteristic of the parasitic life in the legumes. The more recent work of Lewis, however, throws some doubt upon the occurrence of gonidia in this species. He considers the banded forms to be merely cells containing a number of fat globules which have compressed the protoplasm and separated it into several portions.

Sexual Reproduction. The leaders of the newer pleomorphism have all maintained that in addition to vegetative multiplication by fission, bacteria reproduce sexually like higher organisms. No very tangible proof, however, has been brought forth. The appear-

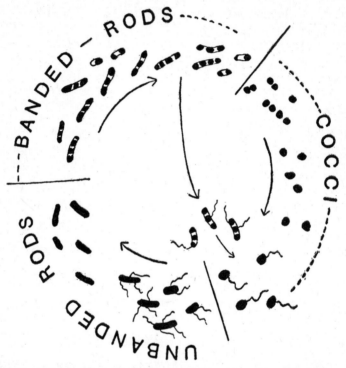

Fig. 64. Life Cycle of *Rhizobium leguminosarum*. (After Thornton, "Soil Bacteria," in *A System of Bacteriology*, vol. III, H. M. Stationery Office, London.)

ance of cells in contact, or cells which have apparently fused, may just as well be considered as evidence of division as of conjugation. Mellon describes as *zygospores* in the colon bacillus, cells with swollen portions in the middle, believing that these result from a fusion of two cells. The occurrence of two different cell types, particularly of large and small cells, has been considered evidence of sexual differentiation into male and female forms. But no one has convincingly recorded the actual observation of two cells fusing and then giving rise to a new reproductive body.

Mere fusion of cells is not necessarily evidence of sex. In many of the Fungi, the non-sexual spores may be seen to fuse during germination, or cells from different plants may unite, without this fusion resulting in a special reproductive cell, and without any evidence of nuclear fusion. Sexual reproduction implies a union of chromatin from two individuals. All of the pleomorphists have assumed that bacteria possess nuclei of the same sort as are found in higher organisms, but we have already seen how unwarranted and unsafe is such an assumption. The occurrence of permanent transmissible variations or "mutations" in bacteria has been brought forward as evidence of sexual reproduction, on the ground that such variations must necessarily result from new combinations of hereditary characters, that they are evidences of hybridization. But permanent variations are known to occur in higher organisms in which no sexual reproduction occurs; variation is *not* necessarily an evidence of sex. If the inheritance of characters in bacteria could be shown to follow the Mendelian formula, we should have proof of sexual reproduction. But this has not been done. We must consider the occurrence of sex in bacteria as unproved.

Symplasm. Löhnis believed that at times a whole group of bacteria may fuse, may melt together to form an amorphous faintly staining mass, which he called a *symplasm*. Within this mass there eventually appear very minute deeply stained bodies, the *regenerative granules*, which in time will grow into recognizable bacterial forms again. Such symplasms are found in old cultures and they probably represent masses of gum secreted by the bacteria, or more likely, masses of débris formed from dead and dissolved bacterial cells.

Filterable Forms. Buds, gonidia, and "regenerative granules" are so much smaller than the usual growth forms that it would seem probable that they might be separated from the "typical" bacterial cells by filtration, and all of the above authors have stressed the occurrence of positive cultures after filtration as evidence of the occurrence of minute filterable forms of bacteria as phases in their life cycles. Unfortunately we have no criteria of the porosity of filters other than their ability to hold back the cells of bacteria and yield sterile filtrates. The occurrence of a growth of the filtered organisms in the filtrate merely means that the particular filter used, under the particular conditions of filtration, was permeable to some of the cells of the organism tested. Whether these were the "typical" cells, or some smaller reproductive body, cannot be determined. If one obtains in the filtrate a growth different from that of the organism filtered, it may have been that a contamination has occurred, or that one has actually separated a variant, or a filterable phase in the life cycle. If this different or variant form can later be shown to return to the form of the original organism filtered, as has been claimed by Hadley, we shall have strong presumptive evidence of the existence of some minute filterable form produced by bacteria. But this observation has not been generally confirmed or established.

The contention that the filterable viruses are filterable stages in the life histories of visible bacteria is purely hypothetical, and because of characteristic differences between virus diseases and bacterial diseases does not seem probable.

In one respect, the new pleomorphists differ from those led by Naegeli at the beginnings of bacteriology. They have, for the most part, maintained the purity of their cultures, and one does not hear any more of the transmutation of species. In the case of a few closely related forms, like the Streptococci and the pneumococci, there may still be some question of the limits of normal variation overlapping, but the old idea that all bacteria are merely growth forms of a few species cannot be revived. Bacterial species may give rise to variants which are permanently different from the parent type, but considering the rapidity of growth and the number of generations which may be observed in a short space of time, bacterial species are remarkably stable.

CHAPTER X

HEREDITY AND VARIATION IN BACTERIA

In a world of living things two opposing tendencies lead to a fairly sharp separation of the component organisms into groups of like individuals, the species, and to a continuous progressive evolution of new species. These are the phenomena of heredity and variation. The offspring of mice are mice, of men are men, and yet no two mice or no two men are precisely alike.

Variation. Variations in living organisms are to be differentiated into two sorts, those which are transmissible to the offspring, and therefore more or less permanent; and those which are not thus transmissible, temporary *modifications*. Acquired characters, i.e., those impressed upon the organism by its environment after it has received its inheritance, *are not transmissible*.

Hybrids. In higher forms reproducing sexually, variations result from two processes, a segregation of hereditary characters in the reduction divisions during the maturations of the sexual cells, whereby the number of chromosomes is reduced to half the normal number (the haploid state), and a chance *combination* of these hereditary characters in the fusion of the two sex cells, when the number of chromosomes returns to the normal number (the diploid state). Such variations, however, do not exceed the normal limits of the species, at least within an observable number of generations. One may explain in this way why some men have blue eyes and light hair and others have brown eyes and dark hair, but one cannot thus explain why men are men and mice are mice.

Mutations. New species probably arise more frequently as the result of *mutations*, i.e., as the rather sudden appearance of new forms, whose new characters cannot be explained by their hereditary constitution. Such mutations are supposed to result from accidents to the heredity-bearing material, the chromosomes of the sex cells, such as a failure of equal division during the reduction division, whereby one cell gets more than half, the other less than half, of the

151

chromosomes; or a union of cells which have not undergone reduction, whereby the number of chromosomes is doubled.

In recent years it has been found possible to induce mutations by exposing organisms or their eggs or seeds to X-rays, or heat, or other injurious agents, and such mutations are found to be similar to some which occur spontaneously. It is believed that in these cases the injurious agent destroys, or modifies, certain *genes*, the elementary bearers of hereditary characters. In some cases the variations which result are reversible, i.e., after a few generations the variant will revert to the parent type; this is explained by assuming that genes may at times become unstable. Variations due to modifications of the genes are called *gene mutations*, and appear to be of great importance, especially in the lower forms.

In the above paragraphs the author has tried to state concisely (and rather dogmatically) the essential facts regarding heredity and variation as far as we know them. But there are many phenomena of heredity and variation which are not fully understood. Particularly with regard to the question of mutation and the origin of new species, there is much difference of opinion. Biologists are, in general, in agreement with regard to the occurrence of evolution, but disagree regarding the mechanism. If this be the state of affairs with regard to the higher organisms, where much of the mechanism of heredity and variation has already been laid bare, the student may readily surmise the confusion existing regarding variation in the lowly bacteria, where neither sex nor nuclei, chromosomes nor genes, are known.

Variations in Lower Organisms. In lower forms whose reproduction is entirely non-sexual, one must assume that the constancy of the species is maintained by perfectly equational cell division, each of the daughter cells receiving precisely the same amount of hereditary material. Variations may arise from a failure to maintain perfectly equational cell division, one of the cells receiving more, and the other less of the hereditary materials; or they may arise from loss or modifications of the genes.

Artificial Selection. The problem of variation in bacteria involves other difficulties peculiar to this group. Most of our knowledge of bacteria has been acquired from the study of their growth in artificial media. The conditions of their growth are kept as constant as possible. Continuous cultivation of an organism upon the same medium, at the same temperature, and with other conditions as nearly the same as possible may tend to keep the organism constant in its characters and to suppress any innate tendencies to variation. It may well be that bacteria in their natural habitat are much more variable than in the laboratory. On the other hand, we are able, with artificial cultures, to vary the environment, suddenly, within wide limits. After our first pure cultures have been obtained, we usually transfer, not single cells, but loopfuls, a mass inoculation. When such an inoculation is made, it is probable that not all of the inoculated cells will grow in the new environment. In fact, conditions may be favorable for only one or a few of the cells which happen to be variants adapted to the new environment. In short, under the conditions of artificial cultivation necessary for a study of bacteria, we may suppress a tendency to variation by keeping conditions constant, or we may exaggerate it by an *artificial selection* unconsciously performed when we transfer a mass inoculum from one medium to the other.

An example of this artificial selection may explain it more clearly. In cultures of spore-forming bacteria, not all of the cells form spores at the same time. Some spores will appear early, say within 18 hours, but several days or a week will elapse before a very large proportion of the cells will have developed into spores. If such a culture is transferred to a new medium after 24 hours' growth, those cells which have not yet formed spores will be in a position to grow sooner than the spores, since they need not germinate. They will become the predominant organisms of the new culture. Presumably the cells which had not yet formed spores in the old medium have less of a constitutional tendency to form spores than those which had already developed into spores, and in this new culture we might expect a smaller proportion of spores at the end of 24 hours. Such a change in the proportion of spores to vegetative cells may not be apparent in the first culture, but if we make subcultures every day, or better every 12 hours, for a number of days (it may take weeks), we shall find the proportion of spores formed in 24 hours to decrease gradually until finally the culture appears entirely asporogenous. Such cultures will, however, eventually form spores, though it may require some days. It is probably quite impossible in this way to make a spore-forming organism completely and permanently asporogenous. We may reverse the experiment by transferring the apparently asporogenous culture at intervals of weeks or months, when spores will gradually reappear again in larger and larger numbers. Here we are selecting those cells with the greatest longevity, namely, the spores. This reversal may be accelerated by taking one of the cultures a week or more old and heating it to 80° C. for a few minutes, when everything except the spores will be killed. The new subculture from this heated material should now show an abundance of spores.

Adaptations. Undoubtedly a great many of the variations in bacteria belong in this category. They are frequently spoken of as *adaptations*, and involve a large number of subcultures in different media or other environments. Thus bacteria may be accustomed to higher or lower temperatures, or to growth in cultures containing a small amount of antiseptics; they may be augmented in disease-producing power by animal passage, or reduced by cultivation on artificial media; and so on. Probably in all of these cases we are dealing with the same sort of phenomenon, involving, on the one hand, a *continous variation* of the cells in the culture, with regard to the character being observed, and, on the other, an artificial selection, by the conditions of the experiment, of some particular variant within this range. By a continous variation we mean that in the mass of the cells of the culture, all degrees of variation are exhibited. Thus, with the spore-formers, some cells may develop into spores at the first signs of a decrease of nutritive matter in the culture, while others will not undergo this change until the medium is nearly exhausted, and there exists every gradation in between.

But note that we cannot produce *permanent* new varieties or species in this way. The spore-forming organisms will probably never become completely and permanently asporogenous, no matter how rapidly we make our subcultures or how long we continue them. And no amount of aging or heating cultures of bacteria that do not form spores will make them sporogenous. There is some evidence that long-continued cultivation of disease-producing bacteria may make them completely and permanently harmless, but this involves another mechanism to be described later. But no amount of animal inoculation will confer virulence upon a species of organism which is non-pathogenic. All we may accomplish by this artificial selection is *temporarily to suppress or exaggerate characters already latent in the hereditary constitution of the organism.*

Temporary Modifications. Often bacteria in cultures will show the loss or acquisition of a character immediately upon transfer to some new medium or upon some alteration in the conditions of the environment. In some cases these may also be the result of artificial selection, but more frequently they are due to the immediate effect of the altered environmental factor upon all of the cells. Thus an organism may be able to produce a pigment if some certain element is available in the medium, or within a certain temperature range; it may grow without the pigment if the element is lacking or the temperature is higher or lower. Such temporary modifications are very common. If an organism is subcultured simultaneously on a variety of media, it will not be precisely the same on any two.

Mutation-like Variations. Undoubtedly the great majority of variations encountered in the study of bacteria belong to either of these two classes of change — temporary modifications due to factors in the environment, or the somewhat more stable but not completely permanent results of artificial selection. According to the old Cohn-Koch dogma, these would be the limits of variation possible in bacteria, for bacterial species were supposed to be immutable. But more recently we have come to recognize the occurrence of another category of variations in bacteria. They are mutation-like in that they may appear, sometimes rather suddenly, without any variation in their environment to explain the change. They are of such a degree as to require either a modification of our conception of the term "species" for bacteria, or an admission that they transcend the normal limits of the species. While not absolutely permanent, they show a greater stability than variations of the type we have so far considered. They have often been referred to as mutations, but until we know more about their real significance and the mechanism back of their development, it would be better not to apply this term to bacteria.

One of the earliest clear-cut observations of this sort of variation in bacteria was recorded independently by Neisser and Massini. An account of their studies may serve to illustrate the general features of this type of mutation-like change.

The colon bacillus ferments the sugar, lactose, with the production of an aldehyde. The pathogenic intestinal bacteria do not possess this property. In medical practice, these disease-producing bacteria (typhoid and dysentery organisms) are separated from the morphologically similar colon bacilli by this property. Plate cultures of feces are prepared on a special agar containing lactose and an indicator (basic fuchsin and sodium sulphite) to show the presence of aldehyde. On this medium the colon bacillus, fermenting the lactose, will turn the indicator red, and the whole colony will be stained red; while typhoid bacilli, unable to ferment lactose, will produce white or colorless colonies.

Neisser and Massini observed that sometimes on their plates they obtained colonies which were white at first, but later developed little elevated papillae that were red. Within the mass of cells which formed the colonies, and which did not ferment the lactose, *some cells acquired this property*, produced the small elevated red knobs.

Now when these red knobs or papillae were transferred to a new plate of lactose agar, they gave rise to pure red colonies; all of their offspring exhibited the power to ferment lactose. But when white portions were plated on lactose agar, they gave rise to white colonies which again produced red papillae. And these phenomena occurred over and over again, red papillae giving rise to pure red offspring, white colonies continually developing red papillae.

In all other respects this organism appeared to be a typical colon bacillus, and it was named *Bacterium coli mutabile*.

It was not long before similar phenomena were observed with other organisms grown upon media containing other carbohydrates that could be fermented, and then it was found that colonies might develop little elevated papillae which differed from the parent colony in some respect other than their power to ferment sugars, such as pigment production, or opacity, or consistency of the growth, etc. And always the same results — the little papillae breed true, the original type always keeps splitting off the new type in papillae.

Secondary Colonies. These elevated papillae which develop on the colonies are called *secondary colonies*. While they may sometimes appear in a few days, they are seen most frequently when the cultures are kept longer. If the agar plates may be kept for some weeks, and the colonies are spaced apart sufficiently so that they may grow extensively, large *giant colonies* may be obtained. These secondary colonies are especially prone to develop upon such giant colonies. In fact, the longer the growth is allowed to proceed, the greater is the chance of getting secondary colonies. This observation has led to the theory that such secondary colonies result from a sort of cannibalism. As the colony ages, most of the cells in the middle die and begin to disintegrate, but a few remain alive, and eventually begin to grow again upon the foodstuff liberated from the disintegrating bacteria. But microscopic study of the secondary colonies often shows that these are composed of morphologically peculiar cells, swollen spherical forms or club-shaped cells or other types differing from the normal cell type for the organism; in short, what we have been accustomed to call involution forms. And the pleomorphists have been quick to seize upon this fact, and to explain the secondary colonies as the result of some new reproductive process, probably sexual, which is occurring in the colony.

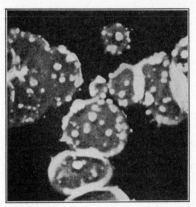

Sectors. Mutation-like changes may be manifested in growing colonies in another way. A colony, if allowed enough space, will grow extensively from the center outward, spreading over the surface of the agar. Growth is active only at the periphery; the cells in the center of the colony quickly pass into a resting state. Often such spreading

Fig. 65. Secondary Colonies. Colonies of anthrax bacilli, with secondary papillae. (After Haag, *Der Milzbrandbacillus, seine Kreislaufformen und Varietäten*, R. Oldenbourg, Munich.)

colonies will show a development of wedge-shaped areas, or *sectors*, which differ strikingly from the main mass of the colony. Such sectors are particularly striking in colonies of pigment-forming bacteria. One may thus frequently observe a white sector in a colony of orange Micrococci. But sectors may often be found which differ in other qualities, as opacity, or consistency of the growth. Sectors do not usually differ so markedly in morphology as do secondary colonies, but one may find asporogenous sectors, for instance, in colonies of spore-forming bacteria.

Sectors may appear early in the growth of the colony, in which case they extend nearly to the center, or they may develop late, in which case they are narrow and extend only a short distance into the colony. The older the colonies, the greater is the likelihood of sectors developing. Sectors are explained by assuming that something happens to one of the cells at the growing edge of the colony, which alters its hereditary characters, and it continues to reproduce cells of this new type. In general, sectors behave much like secondary colonies. The sector continues to breed true, at least for some gener-

ations, while the bulk of the colony will continually give rise to colonies that develop sectors.

Unstable Cultures. This continuous instability in cultures which are developing sectors, or secondary colonies, is a striking characteristic. From *B. coli mutabile*, one may readily obtain strains which constantly ferment lactose, but the non-fermenting part of the colony continuously gives rise to fermenting strains; it is impossible to obtain a pure non-fermenting strain. From the white sectors of an orange *Micrococcus*, one may readily

Fig. 66. Sectors. Dark sectors in a light-colored colony of an unidentified organism. (After Nirula, *Annals of Botany*, 1928, vol. 42.)

obtain a pure white strain, but the orange part of the colony will continue to give rise to orange colonies with white sectors; it is impossible to obtain a pure orange strain. The continuous instability of strains of bacteria which give rise to mutation-like variants has its counterpart in higher forms of life, in the "eversporting" races of snapdragons and evening primrose and fruit flies which have been studied by the geneticists.

In the above types of variation, aging of the colonies appears to be a factor of prime importance. This influence of aging may be illustrated in other cultures. If unstable strains of bacteria are grown in broth, and the broth cultures are allowed to stand for some weeks, plate cultures prepared from these broth cultures may show several *different types of colonies*, varying in color, or consistency, or transparency, or contour; whereas plate cultures made from the broth culture early in its growth would show colonies all of the same type. The variant colonies obtained by plating old cultures may in some cases breed true, i.e., exhibit at least some degree of permanency; in other cases they may revert to the original type.

Spontaneous and Induced Variations. Mutation-like variations, then, may arise *spontaneously* in cultures under various conditions, but aging, i.e., maintaining the culture continuously in the same medium, appears to be the most important factor.   But many experiments have been reported in which the variation was *induced* by some factor intentionally introduced into the culture, or the conditions of cultivation, by the observer.   A wide variety of such factors has been recorded, as growth above or below the optimum temperature, or optimum hydrogen ion concentration, or optimum osmotic pressure, of the organism; or the addition of minute quantities of injurious substances, antiseptics like phenol, or of various salts, such as lithium chloride.   Variations have been claimed to have been induced by passage through laboratory animals.   But the most potent factors in this regard appear to be the action of specific *immune serums*, and the action of the *bacteriophage*.

One is immediately struck by the fact that all of these agents are unfavorable, that they tend to limit the growth of the organisms, or to injure them.   This may be compared with the conditions of spontaneous variation, namely, aging in the culture, which we know also involves death and disintegration of the cells, an inhibition of growth, and injury.

Microbic Dissociation.   A list of the various characters of bacteria which have been recorded as undergoing variations would involve a catalogue of all the specific properties of bacteria, morphologic, biochemical, and pathogenic.   We shall limit this description to a particular type of variation in a series of correlated characters, which has come to be known as *microbic dissociation.*

The colonies of typhoid and colon and dysentery bacilli, of Micrococci and Streptococci, and, indeed, of a large proportion of cultivable bacteria, are normally quite round, their edges and surfaces perfectly *smooth*, usually rather moist and glistening.   The colonies of most spore-forming bacteria, and of the acidfast bacteria (tubercle bacilli and related species) are generally somewhat irregular in form, their edges curled or toothed, their surfaces often wrinkled, and frequently dull and dry; their colonies are normally *rough.*

Smooth and Rough Variants.   Now it has been possible to obtain from cultures of bacteria with normally smooth, or S, colonies, variants that produce rough, or R, colonies.   These may arise spontaneously as secondary colonies, or sectors, or they may be induced by various factors, particularly growth in immune serums, or the action of the bacteriophage. The action of the bacteriophage is particularly striking. If one adds bacteriophage to a broth culture of normal, S type, dysentery bacilli, the culture will clear and the bacteria will apparently disappear. But not all of the cells are destroyed, the culture is not sterilized, for after subculturing it is found that growth will still occur. But this growth occurs in the form of rough, or R, colonies. We must assume that some of the cells in the culture were

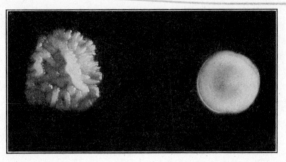

FIG. 67.   Rough and Smooth Colonies.   The rough colony at the left is *Neisseria catarrhalis;* the smooth colony at the right is *N. flava;* but these two "species," which occur together in the throat, may be smooth and rough variants of the same organism.

resistant to the action of the bacteriophage, and that these were variant cells of the R type.

The change in the gross appearance of the colonies in these variants is an outward manifestation of a rather profound change in the characters of the bacteria. In many cases the morphology of the cells is altered. R forms of some species of spherical bacteria tend to become elongated, rod-shaped; in many cases species which do not form chains in the S form tend to grow in this manner in the R form. In the case of bacteria of the colon-typhoid group there has been noted a change in the character of the post-fission movements; in the R variants of these species the normal "slipping" movements are found to have changed to the "snapping" movements characteristic of the spore-forming bacteria. It is probable that these movements determine the colony form. When grown in liquid media, the S forms usually grow diffusely through the liquid, making it turbid, while the R forms tend to grow as a scum upon the surface or as a sediment at the bottom of the tube.

The characters mentioned in the preceding paragraph tend to

váry together in a constant manner, and are probably all manifestations of a single change in the structure of the microbe. Other characters may also change in the variation from S to R types, but these
are not constant throughout the various species of bacteria which
have been studied. In some species which are motile in the S form,
motility is absent in the R form. If the S type is pigmented, the
R type may fail to form pigment. The R types may fail to exhibit
fermentative properties shown by the S types. Most important of all,
if the S type is *virulent,* or capable of producing disease, the R type
usually lacks this property.

The change from S to R is not always immediately complete;
transition forms are often encountered. From a single strain of the
S type there may be obtained several variants, all rough, but varying
among themselves in certain characters. More recently there has
been observed another type of mutation-like variation in colony form,
the mucoid or M type. These variants form smooth colonies which
are moist, elevated, watery-looking. In general they show the characters of the S type, intensified.

The S-R dissociation behaves much like the variations in fermentation and pigment production which we have considered with
B. coli mutabile and the orange Micrococci. The R types tend to be
stable, while the S type, once it has begun to throw R variants, tends
to be continuously unstable. While the R variants tend to remain
stable, they have been observed to revert to the S form frequently
enough to indicate that the process is by no means irreversible.
Bacteria which are known normally in the rough form (spore-formers
and acidfast bacteria) have been known to give rise to S variants.

Theories. Several theories have been proposed to explain the
mutation-like variations of bacteria. It has been suggested that
strains which give rise to variants are not pure species, but hybrids;
that the variants represent stages in a complex life cycle; and that
they are true mutants such as occur in higher organisms.

Sex. The assumption that mutation-like variation is an evidence
of sexual reproduction must be considered unwarranted. We have
seen in the preceding chapter that the occurrence of sexual reproduction in bacteria has not been demonstrated. The occurrence of variants has been brought forward as evidence of sexual reproduction.
But various workers have shown that in no case can the observed
variations be made to fit the Mendelian formula. From an unstable

strain of a bacterial species, it is possible to obtain only one race stable with regard to the varying character; thus with the *B. coli mutabile* we may obtain strains which constantly ferment lactose, but none which constantly fail to show this character. If the variation were due to hybridization, it should be possible to "breed out" both of the parent strains.

Variations similar to those described for bacteria have been observed in cultures of molds and yeasts and Algae. Such organisms grown on agar also show secondary colonies and sectors; and in yeasts, at least, one may find S and R forms. Now such organisms, when they reproduce sexually, form readily recognizable sexual spores. These variations have been found to occur in strains where sexual reproduction was entirely absent, where sexual spores could not be found. They have been observed in cultures of a fungus which was started from a single spore known to be in the haploid state. Here there could be but one sex in the culture; therefore no sexual reproduction could take place, yet variations occurred.

Cyclostages. The theory that the variants of bacteria represent more or less fixed stages in a rather complex life cycle has been expressed or implied in nearly all of the writings of the various pleomorphists named in the preceding chapter, but it has been most clearly formulated by Enderlein, who has described a very elaborate (but purely hypothetical) sort of cyclic development in bacteria. All species of bacteria, he states, tend to grow through a series of forms progressing from the simple to the complex, with several types of vegetative multiplication alternating with sexual reproduction. But this *cyclogeny* requires a series of different environments for its completion, and when we grow bacteria continuously on an artificial medium in the laboratory, the organisms tend to become *fixed* in one particular form or *cyclostage* which is adapted to this medium. This theory has been strongly supported by Hadley, who has maintained that the S and R forms of bacteria are such cyclostages. Very recently he has claimed to have demonstrated a third cyclostage, the G form. These result from a dissociation of the S forms, or more frequently, a further dissociation of the R forms. They may be separated from the parent culture by filtration, and are not at first visible in the subcultures. But on continued cultivation they form very tiny dewdrop colonies in which the cells are found as minute spherical forms. These slowly develop in size through several subcultures, reverting to the normal S form. According to Hadley's conception, then, the cyclogeny of the organisms he studied might be represented by the formula,

$$S \longrightarrow R \longrightarrow G \longrightarrow S.$$

The S forms are vegetative growth forms; the function of the R forms is reproduction. The G forms arise (mainly from the R forms) as minute, filterable gonidia, and their function is the dissemination of the species.

True Mutations. The present tendency among workers on variations in bacteria is to look upon these changes as true mutations, due either to accidents in cell division, or to the actions of external agents upon the genes. It has been pointed out by several writers, most clearly by Reed, that the change from S to R forms, and similar transformations, could be readily explained by a loss of genes resulting from unequal cell division. Facts brought out in recent studies, however, indicate that modifications of the genes through the action of injurious agents may be a more plausible explanation.

Recent studies emphasize that while an organism may vary with regard to several characters simultaneously, these are not linked characters; each character varies independently. Thus from a normally smooth red bacterium, one may get rough red, smooth white, and rough white variants. This indicates that the observed variations are due to modifications of individual genes. Further it has been found that the observed variations are seldom completely irreversible. While there are regularly obtained variants which are relatively very stable, if studied long enough these are usually found to give rise eventually to new variants which have reverted to the original type. This indicates that the observed variations are not due to a complete loss of genes, but to a modification or suppression.

Genes in Bacteria. Before entering into a discussion of variation in bacteria the author wishes again to emphasize the complete lack of knowledge of the minute structure of these microörganisms, and of the mechanisms involved in their cell divisions and the transmission of hereditary characters. We are prone to assume that these mechanisms are the same as in the higher forms, but we have seen why, because of their minute size, such assumptions are unwarranted and may lead us astray. Pietschmann has made a calculation which is of interest from this standpoint. If we assume that a small bacterium has a nucleus of from 0.1 to 0.25 micron in diameter (values given by Enderlein for the nuclei of bacteria), and if we further assume that a single gene may consist of but a single protein molecule, there would be space enough for only 20 to 50 genes linearly arranged in such an organism.

Bacteria have been observed to vary independently with regard to a number of different characters, as colony texture, pigmentation, flagellation, virulence, fermentative powers, etc. Moreover, each of these variations may occur in different degrees; thus from a red organism one may get mutants which are various shades of pink, down to colorless strains. Such quantitative differences in variation are explained by geneticists on the basis that the given character is determined not by a single gene, but by multiple genes. One must assume then that bacteria contain a large number of genes. If these genes are protein molecules, the question arises whether there is space enough for them in a single bacterial cell. Perhaps there is. But what about the ultramicrobes, the filterable viruses, some of which clearly show mutation-like variations? These are themselves either single protein molecules or at the most simple aggregations of a few molecules. Can they have genes?

These statements have been presented to emphasize the fact that with the smallest and simplest forms of life some of the laws and theories of general biology either do not apply or require modification.

CHAPTER XI

THE METABOLISM OF BACTERIA

In our survey of microbic life we have already noted certain important differences in the mode of nutrition of the various groups of microörganisms. The essential differences are to be found in the sources of energy utilized by each. Some, as the various Algae, and the green and purple sulphur bacteria, obtain their energy directly from the sun, and need only inorganic matter for building material. Others, as the true iron bacteria and the white sulphur bacteria, may obtain their energy by the oxidation (or burning) of certain inorganic compounds. They may also utilize a purely inorganic diet — certain salts, carbon dioxide, and water — for building material. These two groups of organisms can live quite independently of all other living organisms. As far as their nutrition is concerned they are self-sufficient, or *autotrophic*. Their nutrition is designated *photosynthetic* in those cases where the energy of sunlight is used, *chemosynthetic* when the oxidation of inorganic matter supplies the energy.*

The remaining microörganisms all require organic matter for at least part of their food. They must obtain their energy by the combustion of organic matter which has been synthesized by other organisms. They are not self-sufficient, but dependent upon others; therefore their nutrition is *heterotrophic*. The Protozoa are mainly animal-like, or *holozoic*, in their nutrition, capturing living prey which they take into their interior to be digested and absorbed, but some are *saprozoic*, absorbing through the cell wall organic matter dissolved in the water, and a number of species are *parasitic* on higher animals or plants. The heterotrophic bacteria, the yeasts, the molds, and higher Fungi, are either *saprophytic*, digesting and absorbing dead organic matter, or *parasitic*.

Builders and Destroyers. A number of microbes are adapted to more than one mode of nutrition. We have seen that some of the

* The term *autotrophic* is sometimes used in a limited sense for bacteria which oxidize inorganic compounds. The term *prototrophic* is used in the same sense.

Protozoa may be either photosynthetic or animal-like; that some of the Green Algae may be grown in the dark if they are furnished sugar, i.e., they may become saprophytic. And some of the bacteria may be either autotrophic or heterotrophic, according to their environment. But on the whole, living organisms of all sorts may be rather sharply divided into two great classes, the producers and the consumers, the builders and destroyers, the autotrophs and heterotrophs.

Green plants absorb from the soil nitrates and sulphates and phosphates and water, and from the air, carbon dioxide. With the energy obtained from sunshine these are built up into fats, proteins, and carbohydrates. Some of this material is again broken down in the plant, burned, and given off as carbon dioxide and water, for plants respire like animals. But mostly it is stored up as plant substance or as reserve material. The plant may live its span of time and die, returning all this material to the soil, or it may be killed by some fungous or bacterial parasite, or it may be eaten by an animal. In the latter case the fats, proteins, and carbohydrates are partially broken down in the digestive tract of the animal, to be absorbed and either burnt for energy, or synthesized into animal protoplasm, or into organic reserve materials. Part of this matter is returned to the air as carbon dioxide, part is returned to the soil in the animal excretions, urine and feces. The animal may be killed by some parasitic microörganism, or may be devoured by some other animal, or may live its normal time. But eventually, all the organic matter produced by the green plants, excepting that carbon which has been returned to the air in respiration, is returned to the soil in the form of dead plant matter, dead animal matter, or animal excretions.

The Work of Bacteria. Here the main work of the bacteria and Fungi begins. All of this organic matter in the soil provides food for an immeasurable host of heterotrophic microörganisms, which begin to tear it down, step by step, first changing the solid fats, proteins, and carbohydrates to soluble, absorbable substances, which are then still further decomposed and oxidized, until it has all been again converted to carbon dioxide and water, nitrates, sulphates, and phosphates. Some of the final stages in this process, particularly the formation of nitrates from ammonia, are brought about by autotrophic soil organisms, but the great majority of the bacteria are heterotrophic.

These considerations indicate the major rôle of the bacteria in

the living world. It is their function to keep the elements necessary
for life in circulation. They are the great destroyers. If it were not
for their activities the available constituents of living matter would
long ago have been used and stored as unavailable organic matter in
the dead bodies of plants and animals. The great natural habitat of
bacteria is the soil. For, while a similar circulation of the elements
undoubtedly occurs in the waters of the earth, it is slow and often
incomplete owing to lack of oxygen. Organic matter tends to accumulate in a bog or lake, to be stored up as peat, and eventually coal.
What occurs in the fathomless depths of the oceans is unknown.
But while microbic activities in aquatic habitats have been very imperfectly studied, it would seem that they must be considerably less
than in the soil.

Bacteriology and Biochemistry. On first thought one might think
that bacteria, being minute and simple organisms, must be simpler
in their metabolism than larger and more complex organisms.
Whether this is true or not we cannot say, since our knowledge
of the chemical changes produced by all sorts of organisms is still
very incomplete. But it is obvious that bacteria are extraordinarily
varied in their nutrition. A single species may carry on many different sorts of chemical changes, and the bacteria as a class are known
to produce practically all of the reactions known to biochemistry.
Microörganisms are especially favorable subjects for biochemical
studies, since one may inoculate them into a medium of known chemical composition in a closed vessel, and determine the products of
their activity with a facility not approached in the study of higher
plants and animals. As a consequence, a voluminous literature on
the biochemistry of the microörganisms has already appeared, and
the subject becomes daily more complex. To understand properly
this phase of bacteriology one must have considerable knowledge
of chemistry, and particularly of the newer physical chemistry. We
can do no more here than point out some of the major phases of the
subject.

The Nature of Protoplasm. We have, in the past, looked upon
protoplasm as a specific sort of chemical substance, of which living
matter is composed, containing as essential elements carbon, oxygen,
hydrogen, nitrogen, phosphorus, sulphur, and certain of the metals.
Modern biochemistry, particularly colloidal chemistry, has made
such a conception no longer tenable. Protoplasm is, rather, a mix-

ture, a "colloid complex," of various organic substances, largely proteins, which provides a special sort of mechanism for carrying on complicated chemical reactions. It is never at rest, never in equilibrium, and it is this *dynamic* quality of constant chemical or physico-chemical change which is looked upon as the essential character of living matter.

Metabolism. Living organisms require food for two purposes. They must take in raw material to be used in the *synthesis* of new protoplasm, in part to replace that which has been broken down in the normal "wear and tear" of the living machine, in part to provide for growth of the individual and multiplication of the race. And they must provide the *energy* necessary for the various life processes. It is difficult to separate these two processes and to study them separately, for the same substance absorbed by the organism may be used in part for building material and in part for fuel. These two processes together comprise the *metabolism* of the organism. The synthetic processes are collectively known as *assimilation*. The breaking-down processes are collectively known as *dissimilation*. Those processes which yield energy for the organism are *respiration*.

Energy Requirements. Just why the cells of bacteria require energy is not clearly known. Some of them, it is true, are motile, and a few are phosphorescent, and the production of motion and of light of course require energy. But the amount used is very small compared with the total amount liberated by the chemical activities of the organisms. In some cases considerable heat is liberated during the growth of bacteria. But there is no evidence that this is of benefit to the organism; in fact, if the heat is not dissipated it may reach a sufficient degree to kill the organisms, as in the heating of heaps of manure or hay. A certain amount of energy is required by the chemical syntheses going on within the cell, in the building up of new protoplasm. This much is certain — that a source of energy must be continuously available, that energy must be continuously transformed within the protoplasm, or the organism will die. Probably a large portion of this energy is utilized in maintaining that dynamic state, that lack of chemical or physical equilibrium, which we have noted before as the essential quality of living matter. A large portion of the metabolic studies of bacteria has to deal with the methods by which they obtain and utilize this energy.

Autotrophic Metabolism. We have already briefly considered the metabolism of the photosynthetic bacteria, the green and purple sulphur bacteria, which, in the absence of air and the presence of light, synthesize organic matter from carbon dioxide and hydrogen sulphide.

A variety of *chemosynthetic* autotrophic bacteria are known. These obtain their carbon from carbon dioxide in the air, or from carbonates in solution, and their energy by the oxidation of various inorganic substances — ammonia, nitrites, sulphur, sulphides, ferrous compounds, hydrogen, and carbon monoxide. Some of them are *obligatory* autotrophs, i.e., they cannot grow except by the oxidation of the particular inorganic compound for which they are adapted, but many are *facultative* autotrophs, which may live as heterotrophic bacteria on organic matter as well as by oxidizing inorganic matter. Mostly they are abundant only in limited habitats where their particular source of energy is abundant, as in iron or sulphur springs, bog lands, etc., although they may be widespread in nature.

Some of the autotrophic bacteria — the iron, and some of the sulphur bacteria — are relatively large and complex organisms. We have already considered their morphologic characters in a discussion of the Chlamydobacteriales and of the Thiobacteriales. The remaining autotrophs are smaller and simpler in structure, and are included in a family, the Nitrobacteriaceae, of the order Eubacteriales. Their particular characters will be discussed in a later chapter.

Chemistry of Autotrophic Metabolism. Although the actual mechanisms by which these organisms carry on their life processes are quite unknown, and are probably very complex, superficially at least, the chemistry of the autotrophs is relatively simple as compared with that of the heterotrophic bacteria. The elements necessary for the synthesis of protoplasm are absorbed as simple salts in solution — ammonia, sulphates, phosphates, carbon dioxide, some potassium, perhaps a little iron and magnesium are needed. The substance which is to yield energy, and oxygen, are also absorbed in solution. In the case of those organisms which utilize elemental sulphur, some mechanism must be available to bring this substance into solution, but what that mechanism is, is unknown.

Autotrophic Respiration. It is in their respiration that the chemo· synthetic autotrophs differ so markedly from other organisms. A heterotrophic organism will absorb some organic compound, sugar, for instance, and oxygen. Within the cell the sugar is burned, and the products of combustion are usually carbon dioxide and water, which are thrown off. But a nitrifying organism will take in ammonia and oxygen, and give off nitrite; or a sulphur bacterium will take in sulphur and oxygen and give off sulphates; a hydrogen oxidizing organism will give off only water, and so on.

Since with all of these chemosynthetic bacteria, energy results from an oxidation, it would appear that access to air is an essential requirement for growth. In several cases, however, growth can occur under anaerobic conditions if nitrates are present in the medium. There is a sulphur bacterium, for instance, a *Thiobacillus denitrificans*, which, in the presence of nitrates, will oxidize sulphur to sulphate. Here the oxidation of the sulphur is accomplished with oxygen obtained by reduction of the nitrate. This process, by which an organism obtains its energy under anaerobic conditions through the simultaneous reduction of one compound and oxidation of another, is sometimes called *intermolecular respiration*, and is a type of metabolism characteristic of several types of anaerobic bacteria, both heterotrophic and autotrophic.

Heterotrophic Metabolism. The remaining bacteria vary so widely in their nutritive requirements that no general statement may be made. Some may be grown in solutions of purely inorganic compounds — ammonia, sulphates, phosphates, etc. — if only a bit of some simple organic matter like glucose or glycerol is added to provide energy. A single species, *Pseudomonas putida*, has been found able to utilize each of seventy-seven different organic compounds as the sole source of energy. On the other hand, some of the parasitic species will grow only in the presence of unaltered blood or tissue, the most complex sort of a medium. Between these two extremes, there occurs every gradation in food requirements. The only feature common to all is the fact that they live by breaking down organic matter to simpler compounds. This they accomplish through the agency of certain substances known as *enzymes*. A study of the metabolism of the heterotrophic bacteria is largely a study of enzyme actions.

Enzymes. After the famous Liebig-Pasteur controversy, in which Pasteur proved that alcoholic fermentation is due solely to the presence and activities of yeasts, it was believed that this chemical reaction is strictly a *vital* process, somehow or other bound up with the life of the yeast cell, since all attempts to produce the reaction with killed cells, or with fluids in which they had grown, failed. This idea was overthrown by the classical experiment of Buchner, who showed that if yeast cells are ground with very fine sand or diatomaceous earth, and then subjected to high pressure by means of a hydraulic press, there can be expressed a cell-free fluid, the "cell sap," which, when added to a sugar solution, forms alcohol and carbon dioxide. Later it was shown that yeast cells might be killed by certain chemicals, acetone for instance, without destroying their ability to cause alcoholic fermentation. Alcoholic fermentation is, therefore, not an essentially vital process, but is brought about by some agent contained within the yeast cells, and separated from them with difficulty.

The chemical reaction involved in alcoholic fermentation may be roughly expressed as follows:

$$C_6H_{12}O_6 = 2C_2H_5OH + 2CO_2.$$

Actually, it is much more complex than this, occurring in several steps. But there are no products of the reaction which cannot be accounted for in the original sugar molecule. It is obvious, then, that the substance in the yeast juice which causes this reaction does not itself enter into the reaction, or at least does not appear in the final products of the reaction. The reaction is one which might occur spontaneously, though infinitely slowly, without the addition of any other compound to the sugar. The substance in the yeast cell merely accelerates this reaction. Such a substance, which accelerates a chemical reaction without itself appearing in the products of the reaction, is known to chemists as a *catalyst*. An example of such a catalyst is spongy platinum, which will cause hydrogen to unite with oxygen spontaneously and form water, though the platinum does not appear in the equation at all. *An enzyme is an organic catalyst secreted by a living cell.*

Since the discovery of the enzyme which causes alcoholic fermentation, a number of other enzymes have been obtained free from their cells, while a wide variety of chemical reactions caused by microorganisms can be explained only on the basis of enzyme action. Enzymes are very complex, unstable compounds. They decompose slowly on standing, and are easily inactivated by moderate heating. They are very evidently composed of large molecules which will not dialyze through semipermeable membranes. With regard to these properties the enzymes resemble proteins. A few of the enzymes have been obtained in apparently pure form. Some of these appear to be definitely proteins; others, while containing large amounts of nitrogen, do not give the chemical reactions of proteins. The chemical nature of most of the enzymes is still unknown. Some enzymes may be chemically split into two portions. One portion, a colloidal protein, is without enzyme activity, and is called the *carrier;* the other portion, non-protein in character, is the active part of the enzyme molecule, and is called the *prosthetic group.*

Theories of Enzyme Action. Several theories have been proposed to explain the action of enzymes. One theory supposes that their action is mainly *adsorption.* The reagents are concentrated by adsorption on the surfaces of the colloidal enzyme, and it is this concentration which accelerates the reaction. Another theory supposes that the enzyme actually enters into the equations that represent the reaction, but is not bound to any of the products of the reaction. Such a chemical reaction is known as an *induced reaction.* Several such reactions are known to inorganic chemistry.

The use of nitric oxide in the manufacture of sulphuric acid is an induced reaction. Its part in this process may be indicated in the following equations:

$$NO + O = NO_2,$$
$$NO_2 + SO_2 = SO_3 + NO.$$

Here the nitric oxide serves to transfer oxygen to the sulphur dioxide, but reappears again as nitrous oxide, to continue the reaction. In this case the nitric oxide serves as an oxygen *carrier.* But it is also a catalyst, in that it serves to accelerate a reaction which tends to occur spontaneously. It is becoming more and more probable that many of the enzyme reactions, occurring during the growth of microorganisms, are such induced reactions in which the enzyme serves as a carrier for one of the elements in the reaction, particularly hydrogen.

Specificity of Enzymes. Several different relationships must be kept in mind in considering the specificity of enzymes. Each kind of cell, or in the case of bacteria, each species of organism, will in general produce enzymes specific for that cell or species. We have seen in the chapter on microbic variation that this quality is not perfectly constant. Species may lose or acquire the property to produce certain chemical reactions. But in general, a given organism will tend to produce certain chemical changes with sufficient constancy to make this a reliable means of identifying species. Thus, colon bacilli will regularly produce acid and gas from the sugar, lactose, whereas the closely related typhoid bacilli will not. Even where two organisms attack the same substance, the end products of the reaction may be different. Thus from the sugar, glucose, a yeast will produce alcohol and carbon dioxide, a Streptococcus will produce lactic acid, and the mold, *Aspergillus niger*, will produce oxalic acid. This means that there may be a number of different enzymes for a single substance, each producing a different sort of chemical reaction.

Finally, each enzyme is itself rather highly specific for one particular substance. The enzyme of yeasts which produces alcoholic fermentation will act upon several closely related six-carbon sugars, but not upon other carbohydrates. An enzyme which will split the disaccharide sugar, sucrose, will not act upon the very closely related disaccharide, maltose, and so on.

Batteries of Enzymes. A single microbic species will produce a number of different enzymes acting upon different substances. Sometimes these will produce a series of reactions occurring in sequence, in which one enzyme acts upon the end products produced by another. The mold, *Mucor racemosus*, secretes an enzyme which splits starch to yield maltose. It forms another enzyme which converts maltose to glucose, and still a third which changes glucose to alcohol and CO_2. Thus the living cell may apparently produce a single chemical reaction, which is actually a series of reactions caused by different enzymes acting in sequence. Even in those cases where apparently a single enzyme and a single reaction are involved, careful study has shown that the process is much more complex. The alcoholic fermentation involves a whole series of equations, with several different catalytic agents. Since, in nature, in the soil or water or other habitat, a great variety of microbic species are always present working together, it will be seen that in general the decomposition of organic matter is a tremendously complicated process involving an almost infinite series of chemical reactions.

Nomenclature of Enzymes. Enzymes are frequently divided into three great classes according to the three main types of organic compounds acted upon; the *proteolytic* enzymes are those that break down proteins, the *lipolytic* enzymes split the fats and fat-like substances, while the *amylolytic* or *saccharolytic* enzymes attack carbohydrates. In the older literature enzymes were named without much regard to rules. Pepsin and trypsin are proteolytic enzymes of the stomach and pancreatic juice; rennin is an enzyme that curdles milk; amylopsin and steapsin are starch-splitting and fat-splitting enzymes respectively. Modern practice tends toward a uniform nomenclature, in which the name of the enzyme is derived from the name of the substance acted upon, with the ending *-ase*. Thus *gelatinase* acts upon gelatine, *maltase* acts upon maltose, etc. This leads to confusion where two different enzymes are known to act upon the same substance. Sometimes enzymes are named for the kind of chemical reaction which they produce, as *oxidase* and *reductase*. *Diastase* is a modern term for starch-splitting enzymes. *Zymase* was the name originally used to designate the alcohol-producing enzyme of yeasts; it is now frequently used as a general term for all those enzymes which cause fermentations of sugars. *Catalase* is an enzyme which breaks up hydrogen peroxide.

Exoenzymes and Endoenzymes. We have seen that the zymase of yeast is produced within the cells and is separated from the cells only with great difficulty. Such enzymes are also found in most other organisms. They are called *endoenzymes.* They act only within the cells, upon substances absorbed through the cell membrane. They perform two main functions in the cell. First, they *synthesize* — from the raw materials taken in — protoplasm, reserve foods, pigments, new enzymes, toxins, and the various other specific constituents of the organism. Secondly, the endoenzymes *liberate energy* by one or another type of chemical reaction, fermentation or oxidation of the absorbed organic matter, the products of the reaction being again passed through the cell membrane into the surrounding medium. All of the activities of the endoenzymes may be referred to one of these two categories.

But many microörganisms also produce another sort of enzyme which is liberated or secreted by the cells into the surrounding medium. These are the *exoenzymes.* If one cultivates in broth a gelatine-liquefying organism, then filters the broth culture through a Berkefeld filter, and adds the cell-free filtrate to some gelatine, the latter is liquefied or digested. Obviously the bacteria have shed off into the broth something which produces a chemical change in the gelatine.

Many of the organic substances utilized as food by bacteria and Fungi are either solid materials or complex colloidal substances which cannot diffuse through the cell membrane. They cannot be utilized as food until they are broken down to simpler substances which will form a true solution that will so diffuse. The exoenzymes are the agents which carry on this process. They act upon the proteins, fats, and the more complex carbohydrates, starch, cellulose, and gums.

The exoenzymes break up the complex carbohydrates, proteins, and fats by the chemical process called hydrolysis; they are therefore sometimes called *hydrolases*. The endoenzymes, particularly those concerned in respiration, are sometimes called *desmolases*.

Constitutive and Adaptive Enzymes. Enzymes may be subdivided in another way. Some enzymes are formed constantly by a microbic species, regardless of the composition of the medium in which it is grown. Thus one may grow a gelatine-liquefying species in peptone solution, containing no gelatine, then filter the liquid and find that it contains the enzyme gelatinase; it will dissolve gelatine. In this case the gelatinase is a *constitutive* enzyme, formed constantly whether its substrate, gelatine, is present or not. But in other cases the enzyme is formed only when its substrate is present in the medium in which the bacteria are growing. Such enzymes may be detected by the difference in rate of fermentation when cultures are transferred to a solution of the substrate from a medium containing the substrate, and from a medium not containing it. Thus an organism which was grown in a medium containing glucose fermented glucose immediately when put into a glucose solution, but did not ferment galactose until after some time. The same organism grown in a medium containing galactose was found to ferment both galactose and glucose immediately. In this instance, the enzyme for glucose was a constitutive enzyme, but the enzyme for galactose was an *adaptive* enzyme, formed only when the specific substrate is present in the medium in which the cells are growing.

Carbohydrate Metabolism. Most of the carbohydrate material which is decomposed in nature by the activities of microörganisms is in the form of *polysaccharides* — the starches, cellulose, and the hemicelluloses or gums. These are complex substances composed of large molecules, produced by a condensation or polymerization of an unknown number of sugar molecules. On hydrolysis, starch and cellulose yield the *hexose*, or six-carbon sugar, glucose. The gums in some cases yield six-carbon sugars, in others five-carbon sugars, or pentoses.

Hydrolysis of Polysaccharides. The first step in the decomposition of these substances by various organisms is a hydrolytic cleavage through the agency of secreted exoenzymes. This is probably always a rather complicated process involving a series of intermediary products, but the end product in the case of starch and cellulose is probably always a *disaccharide*, a sugar formed by the condensation of two molecules of six-carbon sugar. The equation for the hydrolysis of starch is:

$$2(C_6H_{10}O_5)_n + nH_2O = nC_{12}H_{22}O_{11}.$$
$$\text{starch} \qquad\qquad\qquad \text{maltose}$$

Here the disaccharide is *maltose*, or malt sugar. This reaction is brought about by the enzyme diastase. Diastase is formed by many molds, and by a number of species of bacteria, but not by yeasts.

The equation for the decomposition of starch will also suffice for that of cellulose, for both of these substances have the same empirical formulas, the difference being in the configuration of the molecules. In the digestion of cellulose, the disaccharide which forms the end product is called *cellobiose*. The decomposition of cellulose is also brought about by a hydrolytic enzyme, *cellulase*. It is formed by many of the higher Fungi, by Actinomycetes, and by some bacteria. Many of the bacteria which decompose cellulose are anaerobic bacteria which will not grow in the presence of air. We find thus that under conditions of good aeration the decomposition of cellulose is largely the work of molds and Actinomycetes, while bacteria predominate in this activity when aeration is insufficient for the higher Fungi.

The decomposition of the hemicelluloses is not so well understood because they are more varied in composition, because they have not been so thoroughly investigated, and because many of the organisms which attack these polysaccharides also possess enzymes that rapidly decompose the simple sugars resulting from their hydrolysis, so that intermediary stages are not easily determined. It is very probable, however, that in all cases the first stages use a hydrolysis to yield simple sugars, eventually hexoses or pentoses. The term *cytase* is applied to an enzyme which will decompose hemicelluloses. Cytase, also, is secreted by certain molds, Actinomycetes, and true bacteria.

Hydrolysis of Disaccharides. The principal, and best known, products of these complex carbohydrates, then, are the disaccharides, maltose and cellobiose. Two other disaccharides are important in the carbohydrate metabolism of bacteria, viz., cane sugar, or *sucrose*, and milk sugar, or *lactose*. Like maltose and cellobiose, these are formed by the condensation of two hexoses, or six-carbon sugars, and have the same general formulas as maltose.

The next step in carbohydrate decomposition is a hydrolytic cleavage of these disaccharides to yield monosaccharides, or hexoses. This proceeds according to the general formula:

$$C_{12}H_{22}O_{11} + H_2O = 2C_6H_{12}O_6.$$

This reaction with maltose yields two molecules of glucose; the enzyme is *maltase*. The splitting of cellobiose by *cellobiase* also yields two molecules of glucose. Sucrose is broken down by *sucrase* (also called *invertin*, or *invertase*) to yield one molecule of glucose and one molecule of fructose, two monosaccharides having the same general formula, but being structurally different. Similarly, lactose is converted by *lactase* into one molecule of glucose and one molecule of galactose.

The polysaccharides are all either solids or non-diffusible colloidal substances. The first steps in their decomposition must therefore be brought about by extracellular enzymes. But the disaccharides may diffuse into the cell, and as far as is known, the enzymes which convert the disaccharides to monosaccharides are all endoenzymes. Disaccharides may be split by a wide variety of microörganisms, including molds, yeasts, and bacteria of many sorts.

So far the chemical reactions involved in the breaking down of carbohydrates by microörganisms have all been simple hydrolyses. But the further utilization of the monosaccharides by microbes involves more complicated chemical reactions, mainly oxidations and reductions, which result in the liberation of energy. A further discussion of the fermentation of sugars will therefore be postponed until we have considered some features of the respiration of bacteria.

Respiration of Bacteria. We have had occasion to refer repeatedly in the preceding pages to *anaerobic* bacteria, which grow in the absence of oxygen. The first of these, an organism forming butyric acid from sugar, was discovered by Pasteur, who was greatly impressed by this hitherto unknown phenomenon, life without air. Since then a great variety of other anaerobic microbes have become known.

Some bacteria are *strictly* anaerobic, incapable of growth even when minute traces of oxygen are present. Others are strictly aerobic, unable to multiply if access to the air is cut off. But a large proportion of microbes are *facultatively* anaerobic, capable of growing in either condition, while a few species are *microaerophilic*, incapable of growing when fully exposed to the air, and also when oxygen is completely removed.

The discovery of anaerobic bacteria was, in Pasteur's time, an amazing thing, for it was believed that life could not continue without free access to the air. Plants and animals alike were smothered if their air supply was cut off. It was known that this air was necessary for *respiration*, and that respiration is a process of oxidation, or combustion of organic materials like sugar, to provide the energy necessary for the plant or animal. With the discovery of life without air, Pasteur at once became concerned with the mechanism by which these microbes could get energy, and thus maintain their life processes.

Intermolecular Respiration. We have already noted one such mechanism in the case of the anaerobic autotroph, *Thiobacillus denitrificans*, which carries on simultaneously an oxidation of sulphur and a reduction of nitrates. Nitrates may also be reduced by a variety of heterotrophic bacteria; in fact, the reduction of nitrates in broth cultures has long been noted as one of the characters useful in identifying bacteria. But other compounds may also be reduced during the growth of bacteria in cultures. It was long ago noted that the growth of bacteria in tubes of milk containing litmus led to a disappearance of the blue or red color of the litmus and a reappearance of the normal white color of the milk, due to a reduction of the litmus to a colorless base. More recently the dye, methylene blue, has been used as a more sensitive indicator of such reduction processes. If one shakes such a culture in which litmus or methylene blue has been decolorized, the color of the dye returns, due to the aeration of the liquid, i.e., to oxidation of the reduced pigment. It is now obvious that a great many, probably all, microörganisms capable of growing either as strict or facultative anaerobes, will bring about such reductions, and that if a reducible substance is available in the medium together with foodstuffs, they may obtain energy by this *intermolecular* respiration, by a simultaneous oxidation of one compound and reduction of another.

Intramolecular Respiration. But at the same time Pasteur's mind was occupied with the problem of fermentation. He had proved that yeasts converted sugar to alcohol; at the very beginning of his studies he had discovered a bacterium which produced lactic acid from sugar; and now here was another, an anaerobic bacterium which formed butyric acid. None of these products was apparently of any benefit to the microbes. In fact, if they accumulate in sufficient quantity in the cultures, they are injurious. What part, then, do these reactions play in the life process of the organism?

When the sugar, glucose, is fermented by the milk-souring microbe, *Streptococcus lactis*, all of the sugar molecule is converted to lactic acid. The reaction may be expressed empirically as:

$$C_6H_{12}O_6 = 2C_3H_6O_3.$$

Actually it is more complex than this, involving a whole chain of reactions. But the end product can all be accounted for in the initial material; in particular, no oxygen has been added, nor hydrogen subtracted. If now, the lactic acid is burned, it will not yield as much energy as would be obtained if the glucose from which it has been derived is burned. From an electrochemical standpoint, the conversion of the glucose to lactic acid is an oxidation, and energy has been liberated. Pasteur showed that the same thing is true when yeasts convert sugar to carbon dioxide and alcohol — although no oxygen is added, the alcohol will not yield as much energy as the sugar from which it was derived; therefore an oxidation has occurred and energy has been liberated. This, said Pasteur, is the function of fermentation; this is the way that bacteria can live without air. He called the process *intramolecular respiration*, since it is a method for obtaining energy entirely by a rearrangement of the atoms in the molecule which is fermented.

Three Kinds of Respiration. To recapitulate, we find in microbes three kinds of respiration, viz., direct oxidation, intermolecular respiration, and intramolecular respiration. Direct oxidation requires for the organism access to the air; it can occur only under aerobic conditions. The oxidation of the substance used for energy may be complete or incomplete. Thus some bacteria may burn glucose completely to carbon dioxide and water; but the mold, *Aspergillus niger*, oxidizes glucose to oxalic acid. The conversion of alcohol to acetic acid is another example of incomplete direct oxidation. Intermolecular and intramolecular respirations can both occur under anaerobic conditions. These methods for obtaining energy are not nearly so efficient as direct oxidation. When glucose is oxidized to carbon dioxide and water, 674 calories are liberated, as compared with 22.5 calories when the same amount of glucose is fermented to lactic acid. To grow to an equal degree, therefore, the anaerobic organism getting its energy by fermentation must convert a much larger amount of sugar than does the aerobic organism living by direct oxidation.

It should be noted that a single organism may employ all three processes under different conditions. Thus the colon bacillus, grown in a solution of simple salts with glucose as the sole organic ingredient, will at first rapidly ferment the glucose to lactic acid and other products, utilizing very little atmospheric oxygen; its energy is supplied largely by intramolecular respiration. Later the lactic acid will disappear, and oxygen consumption increases, indicating that combustion of the organic acid is supplying the energy. It may be grown in a solution containing salts of lactic acid as the sole organic ingredient, but only when given free access to the air, unless a reducible substance, nitrate, is added to the medium. In the latter case it will grow anaerobically, and energy is furnished by intermolecular respiration.

Oxidation and Reduction. We usually think of oxidation and reduction as the addition of oxygen, or its removal from compounds. The same result, however, may be obtained by transfers of hydrogen. Removal of hydrogen, or dehydrogenation, has the effect of oxidizing an organic compound; while the addition of hydrogen, or hydrogenation, reduces it. A theory of respiration proposed by Wieland has been very fruitful of thought and investigation regarding the chemical processes which occur in cells. This theory has been elaborated and particularly applied to microbic fermentations by Kluyver and his associates.

According to this theory, respiration involves first an *activation* or mobilization of certain hydrogen atoms in the substance to be oxidized, which is called the hydrogen *donator*, and a transfer of the activated hydrogen to another substance called the *acceptor*. Activation of the hydrogen atom involves a loosening of the bond by which it is united to the donator molecule. In ordinary respiration, represented by the combustion of, say, sugar to CO_2 and water, oxygen is the acceptor. With intermolecular respiration, the reducible substance, nitrate or methylene blue or other material, serves as the acceptor, while with intramolecular respiration, one portion of the molecule serves as the donator while another part serves as the acceptor.

Kluyver and his associates have shown that with all of the known fermentations investigated, such combined oxidations and reductions occur, sometimes intermolecular and sometimes intramolecular. The enzymes catalyze these reactions in part by activating the hydrogen atoms, in part by serving as carriers for the transfer of hydrogen from donator to acceptor. To serve in the latter capacity, the substance must be soluble in both the reduced and the oxidized form, readily reducible, and capable of spontaneous oxidation. It is interesting that such a substance has been found in various cells in the form of an organic sulphur compound called *glutathione.*

Induced Reactions in Fermentation. It has been found that glutathione may serve as a carrier for hydrogen in test tube experiments involving simultaneous oxidation-reductions. Let DH represent the hydrogen donator, and D its product of oxidation; let G represent glutathione in the oxidized form, and GH the reduced form; and let A represent the hydrogen acceptor, and AH its reduced form. Then the function of glutathione may be expressed by the equations:

$$DH + G = D + GH,$$
$$GH + A = AH + G.$$

It will be seen that these equations represent an induced reaction similar to that described on page 172. The glutathione serves in a capacity similar to that of the nitric oxide in the production of sulphuric acid. It enters into the reactions, but is not used up in the process. It merely serves as a carrier of hydrogen to catalyze the oxidation of the donator by reducing the acceptor. Now glutathione is a very definite chemical compound which apparently may serve as an enzyme. This discovery begins to lift the curtain of mystery surrounding the nature of enzymes and their actions.

Fermentation. The term fermentation has been used in several different senses, which has led to some confusion. Orginally used specifically to indicate the reaction by which alcohol is formed from sugar, it was used by Pasteur to designate all those reactions by which microörganisms obtain energy through intramolecular respiration. *Fermentation,* he said, *is life without air.* It is in this sense that the word has been most widely and properly used. But some authors have used the term to designate all enzyme reactions. Others have used the term to designate all of the processes concerned in the decomposition of carbohydrates, while still others employ the word to indicate all of the processes within the cell which yield energy, including aerobic respiration, or direct oxidation.

Fermentation of Monosaccharides. Let us return now to a further consideration of the carbohydrate metabolism of bacteria. We left our organisms with a supply of monosaccharides derived from the hydrolysis of polysaccharides and disaccharides. The subsequent reactions serve to yield energy to the cell. They must necessarily occur within the cells, and needless to say, these reactions are brought about by intracellular, or endoenzymes.

It is obvious that how the organism will utilize sugars depends largely upon the degree to which it also utilizes atmospheric oxygen. Sugar may be completely oxidized to carbon dioxide and water; or partially oxidized to gluconic, citric, or oxalic acid, utilizing atmospheric oxygen; or may be fermented to alcohol or various acids with or without gas production, without any need for atmospheric oxygen. A given organism may utilize two of these methods simultaneously, or may vary the reaction with the conditions of growth and age of the culture. Some of the sugar may also be used for synthetic processes rather than respiration. It would seem that not sufficient attention has been paid to the condition of the organisms in these fermentation studies, i.e., as to whether they are growing or resting. Thus when yeasts are actively growing in well aerated cultures, much of the sugar used is directly oxidized and the amount of sugar utilized is proportional to the rate of growth. The amount of sugar fermented to alcohol remains constant, whether the cells are growing or resting. After the sugar is all gone the yeasts may continue to grow by oxidizing the alcohol, but at a slower rate.

Direct oxidations, using atmospheric oxygen, appear to be more characteristic of the molds than the bacteria, though this phase of carbohydrate metabolism has not been so extensively studied as the fermentations proper. The production of gluconic, citric, and oxalic acids has been studied especially with species of Aspergillus and Penicillium.

Types of Fermentation. The true fermentations vary with the species of organism, and many different products may be obtained from the same sugar by the use of different kinds of microbes.

Kluyver and Donker have classified the fermentative microörganisms into eight groups, as follows:

I. The true yeasts, whose products are *ethyl alcohol* and *carbon dioxide*.

II. The lactic acid bacteria, members of the genera Lactobacillus and Streptococcus. They produce *lactic acid*, either alone or with *acetic acid* and carbon dioxide.

III. The propionic acid bacteria, members of the genus Propionibacterium, which yield *propionic acid*, lactic acid, acetic acid, and carbon dioxide.

IV. The colon-typhoid group, including such organisms as *Escherichia coli*, *Aerobacter aerogenes*, and *Eberthella typhi*, which yield lactic acid, ethyl alcohol, *formic acid*, sometimes *2-3-butylene glycol*. If gas is formed, both carbon dioxide and *hydrogen* are present.

V. The Proteus group. The same fermentation products occur as in the preceding group, but in addition the organisms are better equipped for the decomposition of proteins.

VI. Aerobic spore-forming bacteria (genus Bacillus). The products are acetic acid, ethyl alcohol, 2-3-butylene glycol, or *acetone*, carbon dioxide, and hydrogen.

VII. The non-proteolytic anaerobic spore-formers, of which *Clostridium butyricum* is an example. The products are *butyric acid*, acetic acid, *butyl alcohol*, *isopropyl alcohol*, acetone, carbon dioxide, and hydrogen.

VIII. The proteolytic butyric acid bacteria, of which *Clostridium botulinum* is an example. They form the same products as in Group VII, but in addition decompose proteins.

It is noteworthy that the organisms included in each of the above groups show marked morphologic similarities as well as related biochemical activities, i.e., morphology is well correlated with physiology.

Alcoholic Fermentation. The alcoholic fermentation by yeasts has been extensively studied. It was known long ago that the simple equation we have previously considered did not adequately express the reaction, since not all of the sugar can be accounted for as alcohol and carbon dioxide; various other products, especially glycerine, are formed. Buchner's discovery of zymase made it possible to study the fermentation separately from the other chemical activities of the yeast. Working with this zymase, Harden and Young found that it could be separated into two fractions, the enzyme proper and a *co-enzyme*. If one places yeast juice in a semipermeable sack and allows it to dialyze against water, these two fractions may be separated. The liquid within the sack will not cause fermentation, neither will that outside, but if the two are mixed a complete fermentation is again obtained. The enzyme is easily destroyed by heat, but the co-enzyme is stable.

Then Harden and Young found that phosphates are necessary for the reaction, and studying this further, they showed that the first step in alcoholic fermentation is a combination of the sugar with phosphate to form a phosphoric ester of the sugar. This ester is then split to yield glycerine and phosphates. The further discovery by Neuberg that pyruvic acid is a regular intermediary product gave a clue which led to further very fruitful studies.

Other Fermentations. These various facts and theories have been combined with Wieland's theory of respiration by Kluyver and Donker to yield a comprehensive picture of the fermentation process. They have shown that all of the fermentations proceed much the same in the preliminary phases, the various bacterial fermentations differing from alcoholic fermentation by yeasts mainly in the later stages. In every case a whole series of equations is required.

Fermentation in Nature. In the list of products of various fermentations on page 183, it is shown that a number of organic compounds, alcohols, acids, and other substances are formed. These are also capable of yielding energy and may be further utilized by microorganisms. In some cases the organism which produced the fermentation may itself utilize the products under aerobic conditions. Thus yeasts may slowly consume the alcohol, the colon bacillus may utilize lactic acid, and *Aspergillus niger* may oxidize the oxalic acid which it has produced from sugar. But, free in nature, where a mixture of microbes is present, these products of fermentation will usually be quickly taken hold of by some other organism especially adapted to use them in its nutrition. Thus alcohol will be converted to acetic acid by the vinegar bacteria. This acetic acid may be utilized by various molds, or by the nematode worms known as "vinegar eels." Similarly, other alcohols and acids may be utilized by various microbes. These final reactions are all direct oxidations, and the end products are eventually carbon dioxide and water.

The Carbon Cycle. The starch and cellulose and gums with which we started this discussion of carbohydrate metabolism were produced by green plants, as a result of photosynthesis, from carbon dioxide and water. The process required energy, which was furnished by the sunlight. We have seen how these substances have been decomposed, step by step, through the activities of a variety of

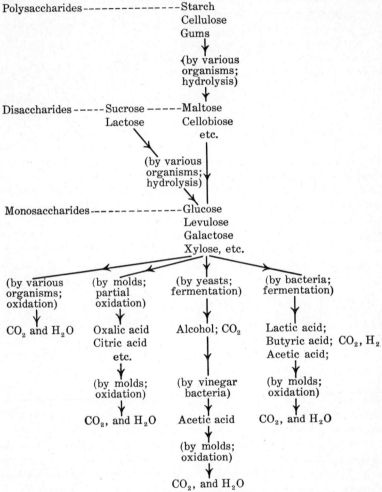

Fig. 68. Diagram of the Decomposition of Carbohydrates by Microörganisms.

organisms, by an exceedingly intricate series of reactions, to yield, finally, carbon dioxide and water, again available for green plants to build up into starch and cellulose and gums. In this process the energy stored up by the green plant has been gradually liberated. This cyclic transformation of carbon has been designated the *carbon cycle*. It is one of a series of cyclic transformations occurring in nature, each involving a particular element of protoplasm, in which the synthetic activities of the green plants are followed by destructive activities of heterotrophic bacteria.

Other Sources of Energy. In emphasizing the relationships of carbohydrate metabolism to the energy requirements of the microbes, it is not intended to convey the impression that *all* of the energy needed by microbes is derived from the carbohydrates. Bacteria may be grown in media containing proteins and their derivatives as the sole source of energy, and can utilize fats and other organic compounds. Also it should be kept in mind that not all of the carbohydrate is utilized to produce energy. Undoubtedly a certain amount is taken up for synthetic processes; this is necessarily the case when bacteria are grown in cultures where a carbohydrate is the only source of carbon present. Finally, in presenting these reactions of the carbohydrates as the "carbon cycle," it should be borne in mind that carbon is also found in proteins and fats and other organic substances. Here also it is finally converted to carbon dioxide, but the processes have not been so thoroughly studied.

Protein Metabolism. The nitrogenous material used by bacteria is presented to them in nature mainly in the form of proteins, of both plant and animal origin, though a considerable amount is present in the excreta of animals in less complex forms, especially as urea.

Proteins are very complex substances whose exact structural formulas are unknown. They are formed by a condensation of amino acids. The latter compounds are formed from organic acids by the substitution of the $-NH_2$ group for one or more of the hydrogen atoms. The occurrence of both the $-COOH$ and the $-NH_2$ radicles makes it possible for them to act both as acids or as bases, and this very important characteristic is also exhibited by the proteins. A number of these amino acids are known. Since they may be grouped in all sorts of possible combinations in the proteins, the number of possible proteins is inconceivably large. A very large number of different kinds have been differentiated chemically, but immunological studies indicate the existence of a great many more. Some of the commoner proteins are the caseinogen of milk, the albumen of egg white, the albumen and globulin of the blood, gluten and gliadin from wheat, and gelatine, derived from the collagen of white fibrous tissues of animals. The proteins all exist as very large molecules. They form colloidal solutions which will not diffuse through a semipermeable membrane. Therefore their decomposition must be initiated by extracellular enzymes. Theoretically, if one supplied a purified protein as the sole food to a culture of bacteria, the bacteria could not grow, since they could absorb no material with which to start growth and to secrete enzymes. Experiments indicate that this is actually so. A minute amount of products of protein decomposition must be supplied before growth can get started.

Products of Protein Decomposition. The decomposition of proteins by microörganisms yields a great variety of products, and the process has been only imperfectly investigated. Important products are ammonia, organic acids, phenol, cresol, skatol, indol, carbon dioxide, hydrogen sulphide, and mercaptans. Some of these products are quite malodorous. The term *putrefaction* was formerly used to designate the decomposition of proteins under anaerobic conditions, where the production of such odorous substances is more noticeable.

Hydrolysis to Amino Acids. The first stages of protein digestion are like those of complex carbohydrates. They are first broken down to their component elements, or "building stones," the amino acids. As with the carbohydrates, this does not occur in one step, but there are intermediate products. These intermediate products are also very complex substances which cannot as yet be given a definite structural formula. They are known as albumoses, proteoses, peptones, and polypeptides. They may be differentiated by various reactions, but cannot be completely described. It is only after the proteins have been broken down to amino acids that we are able to approach a full understanding of the chemistry involved. As with the carbohydrates, this preliminary splitting of the protein to its component building stones is brought about by hydrolysis.

Deaminization. The amino acids may be broken up or further decomposed in several ways. The most common and most important is the process called *deaminization*, in which the $-NH_2$ radicle is split off as ammonia, or NH_3. Probably it is in the form of ammonia that most bacteria take in the nitrogen necessary for the synthesis of their protoplasm. Certainly many species of heterotrophic bacteria may be grown with ammonium salts as the only source of nitrogen. It is in the form of ammonia that the heterotrophic bacteria return nitrogen from proteins to the soil.

Decarboxylation. Another method for decomposing the amino acids consists in decarboxylation, i.e., a splitting off of CO_2 from the $-COOH$ radicle. There is left another sort of organic compound, with the $-NH_2$ radicle, called an *amine*. Some of the amines are poisonous substances known as *ptomaines*. It was formerly thought that food poisonings were due to ptomaines present in food decomposed by putrefactive bacteria, but we now know that these so-called ptomaine poisonings are really infections with pathogenic intestinal bacteria.

It is stated that deaminization is characteristic of the decomposition of proteins under aerobic conditions, while decarboxylation is the main reaction in anaerobic putrefaction.

Putrefactive Bacteria. Putrefaction of proteins may be brought about by a variety of bacteria. Important aerobic forms are *Proteus vulgaris* and *Pseudomonas aeruginosa*. A number of aerobic spore-forming bacteria of the genus *Bacillus* are active; in the soil *B. mycoides* is a particularly important putrefier. There are also a number of anaerobic putrefactive bacteria, of which *Clostridum putrificum* is a type. Putrefactive bacteria show some specificity with regard to the proteins they may decompose. An organism which may digest egg-white may be unable to attack blood albumen, and so on. But in general these reactions are not so specific or useful in identifying bacteria as are the fermentations of various sugars.

Urea. The nitrogen set free in the animal body as a result of "wear and tear" of the tissues is excreted in the urine as urea, which is hydrolyzed by some species of bacteria to form ammonium carbonate. This reaction probably occurs in two steps:

$$(NH_2)_2CO + 2H_2O = H_2CO_3 + 2NH_3$$

The first reaction, a simple hydrolysis, yields no energy. The ammonia and carbonic acid now combine:

$$H_2CO_3 + 2NH_3 = (NH_4)_2CO_3.$$

This reaction does yield energy. Urea bacteria may utilize urea as the sole source of energy.

Ammonification. Only certain species of microbes may completely decompose proteins so that the nitrogen is liberated as ammonia.

With many organisms, when grown in pure culture, the process is incomplete. But in nature, we find that there are always enough different kinds of organisms present to complete the decomposition quickly. One species will attack the products of decomposition produced by another, and so carry the process forward. And eventually the nitrogen, oxygen, carbon, and hydrogen of the proteins appear as ammonia, carbon dioxide, and water.

This process, by which the nitrogen of proteins and urea is converted to ammonia, is called *ammonification*. A number of different species of microörganisms are capable of active ammonification in pure culture. The most active is an aerobic spore-former, *Bacillus mycoides*, but other members of the genus are also vigorous ammonifiers, as well as certain non-spore-forming bacteria, as *Proteus vulgaris*. Molds and Actinomycetes are also ammonifying organisms.

Nitrification. When proteins are decomposed by bacteria in pure culture in the test tube, the process stops with the formation of ammonia; but when this process occurs with the mixed flora of soil, nitrates are formed, ammonia being but a transitory intermediate product. If a solution of an ammonium salt is allowed to trickle through soil, it appears in the effluent water as nitrates. The famous experiment of Schloesing and Müntz proved that this conversion of ammonia to nitrates is due to the action of microbes. If the soil is sterilized by heat, or by antiseptics, the process stops, and ammonia will pass through unchanged.

The actual bacteria responsible for this change were not known for some time because they will not grow upon ordinary culture media. They were finally discovered by Winogradsky, who grew them in an inorganic medium composed of ammonium sulphate, potassium phosphate, and magnesium carbonate. His researches showed that the nitrifying bacteria are strictly autotrophic organisms, obtaining their energy by the oxidation of ammonia to nitrates, and synthesizing their protoplasm entirely from the inorganic compounds mentioned above. The medium must be alkaline in reaction.

The nitrifying bacteria, in pure culture, are inhibited by certain organic substances present in ordinary culture media. They could not be isolated in pure culture by plating until a semisolid inorganic medium was devised. Such a medium was obtained by the use of silica gel. When isolated in pure culture, it was discovered that there are two sorts of nitrifying bacteria, and that the oxidation of ammonia proceeds in two stages. One group converts ammonia to nitrites ($-NO_2$); the other group converts the nitrites so formed to nitrates ($-NO_3$). All of these organisms are very minute forms ranging from rod-shaped through oval or elliptical forms to spherical. The *nitrite* formers, which oxidize ammonia, belong to the genera *Nitrosomonas* and *Nitrosococcus;* the *nitrate* formers, which oxidize nitrites, belong to the genus *Nitrobacter*. They are all strictly aerobic.

The Nitrogen Cycle. The nitrates formed by the nitrifying bacteria may be utilized by green plants in the syntheses of, first, amino acids, and finally proteins. This nitrogen is returned to the soil, as we have seen before, as plant protein, as animal protein, or as urea. Through the action of putrefactive bacteria and the urea bacteria in the soil, the nitrogen appears as ammonia. Through the action of the autotrophic nitrifying bacteria this ammonia is changed to nitrates. This completes the major cycle of nitrogen in nature. There is, however, a minor cycle involving two other sorts of chemical reaction, in which only bacteria are concerned.

Denitrification. We have previously noted that under anaerobic or semianaerobic conditions, certain organisms may obtain their energy by intermolecular respiration, by the simultaneous oxidation of one substance and the reduction of another; and we have noted that nitrates may serve as the substance to be reduced, the hydrogen acceptor. A great variety of heterotrophic bacteria, grown in organic liquid media with nitrates, will reduce the latter. Usually this process is merely a reduction to nitrites, sometimes to ammonia.

A reduction of nitrates to nitrites or ammonia in the soil is of no great importance as regards fertility, since when conditions again favor oxidation rather than reduction, the nitrifying bacteria will convert these substances to nitrates. But certain species of bacteria also occur in soil which will reduce nitrates completely, liberating free atmospheric nitrogen. Now, free nitrogen cannot be assimilated by green plants. The transfer of nitrogen from the soil to the atmosphere constitutes a distinct loss of fertility. The conditions favoring denitrification are an abundance of organic matter to be oxidized and a lack of oxygen with which to carry on this oxidation. Such conditions are realized in a heavily manured soil with high moisture content, the occurrence of water in the soil preventing sufficient aeration.

The reduction of nitrates to free nitrogen is called *denitrification*. A number of different bacteria are responsible for this transformation. They are mostly heterotrophic sporeless Gram negative rod forms, of which *Bacterium denitrificans* is a type. Others are the autotrophic

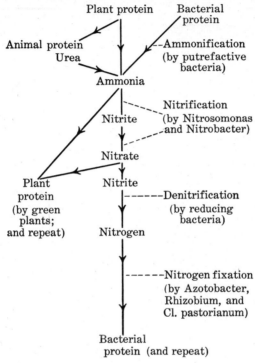

FIG. 69. Diagram of the Nitrogen Cycle.

facultative anaerobic sulphur bacteria, of which *Thiobacillus denitrificans* is a type.

Since conditions favoring denitrification must occur from time to time in all soils, it is reasonable to suppose that the available nitrogen would long ago have all been converted to atmospheric nitrogen, and life would become impossible, if this loss is not compensated for by some mechanism whereby atmospheric nitrogen may be fixed and returned to the soil.

Nitrogen Fixation. If, under certain conditions, a plot of ground is maintained free of plant life for a time, it can be shown that the nitrogen content of the soil has increased. When leguminous crops are grown, it often occurs that there is no loss of nitrogen in the soil, though a great deal of nitrogen is present in the crop harvested. These two phenomena are to be explained by the occurrence in the soil of two sorts of *nitrogen-fixing bacteria*. One group lives free in the soil, the other lives in *symbiosis* in the roots of leguminous plants.

Free-living Nitrogen Fixers. The free-living, or *non-symbiotic* nitrogen fixers are of two sorts, anaerobic and aerobic. The first to be discovered, by Winogradsky, is an anaerobic spore-forming rod. He named it *Clostridium pastorianum*, for Pasteur. It is an organism active in the butyric acid fermentation of sugars, closely related to *Clostridium butyricium*. Later, the aerobic nitrogen fixers were discovered by Beijerinck. They are large organisms of peculiar morphology, placed in the genus *Azotobacter*.

These nitrogen-fixing bacteria may be readily grown in artificial cultures. They are *heterotrophic* organisms, and require sugar to supply their energy. But they need no source of nitrogen save the atmosphere. If one prepares a solution containing potassium phosphate and a carbohydrate or other organic source of carbon for energy (mannitol is best), together with calcium carbonate to keep the solution neutral, and inoculates this with a little soil, there will occur an abundant growth of Azotobacter. This will not be a pure culture, because other bacteria will grow along with Azotobacter, and use the nitrogen it provides. But the nitrogen fixers will be relatively increased, and from such an enrichment culture, pure cultures may be readily obtained by plating.

Symbiotic Nitrogen Fixers. The *symbiotic nitrogen-*fixing bacteria were also first isolated by Beijerinck, though their presence in the root nodules of legumes was previously known, as was also the fact that leguminous plants can apparently take nitrogen from the air. The organism is known as *Bacterium radicicola*, or better as *Rhizobium leguminosarum*. It is capable of living free in the soil, but undergoes a more abundant development in the nodules of the legumes.

The actual proof that these symbiotic bacteria are responsible for the utilization of atmospheric nitrogen by the legumes may be demonstrated by an experiment first performed by Schloesing and Laurent. If one sterilizes some seeds of a legume, say clover, and plants these in two pots of washed and sterilized sand, watered with a nutrient solution containing all the mineral elements required by plants save nitrogen, and inoculates one of the pots with a culture of an appropriate strain of *Rhizobium*, the plants in the inoculated pot will show a normal development, while those in the uninoculated pot will be dwarfed and will shortly die. Chemical analysis of the inoculated plants will show a marked gain in nitrogen which is not found in the control.

It is not known just how these nitrogen-fixing bacteria bind the atmospheric nitrogen. In pure cultures the nitrogen appears as bacterial protein. On theoretical grounds there is some question whether the process requires energy or not. But practically, there is no doubt. The nitrogen-fixing bacteria require carbohydrate to be fermented or oxidized to yield energy, and the amount of nitrogen fixed is roughly proportional to the carbohydrate used. It should be noted that these organisms are not *necessarily* nitrogen fixers; they may utilize ammonia or organic sources of nitrogen, and when supplied sufficient nitrogen in this form they will not fix atmospheric nitrogen.

The fixation of atmospheric nitrogen balances the loss caused by denitrification, and so completes a minor nitrogen cycle, from the soil to the atmosphere and back again, in which only bacteria are concerned.

Fat Metabolism. It is well known that bacteria will attack fats, waxes, and certain hydrocarbons. This phase of bacteriological biochemistry has, however, hardly been touched. Such work as has been done has been concerned largely with practical aspects of the problem, such as preventing the spoilage of butter and lard and similar products. Here is a fertile field awaiting an investigator.

CHAPTER XII

ECOLOGY OF BACTERIA: ENVIRONMENTAL FACTORS

Ecology is the science which deals with the interrelationships of organisms and their environment. This is a very broad field. Almost any sort of biological research has for its ultimate aim a better understanding of the organism as a whole in relation to its environment. Ecologists hope to synthesize the results of all sorts of studies into a whole, a picture of the habitat and its inhabitants and their complex interactions. Very few bacteriologists have deliberately attempted to study extensively the ecology of bacteria, but a great many investigations undertaken for purely practical or economic reasons have contributed much information which can to some degree be put together, and so serve as an introduction to this phase of microbiology.

We shall first consider the effects of certain environmental factors upon bacteria and their growth. The early bacteriologists found that to grow bacteria in the laboratory they had to pay close attention to a number of factors or their microbes would fail to grow — a proper food supply, temperature, and the reaction were the most important. More recently, other factors, as the osmotic pressure, oxidation and reduction potential, and the influence of surfaces, have come to be recognized.

Nutrient Requirements of Bacteria. From what has already been stated concerning the metabolism of bacteria, the student may readily surmise that different species have different food requirements, and that there is no medium which will grow all of the bacteria. A medium suitable for Nitrosomonas would not support a growth of Micrococci. The media used by soil bacteriologists are quite useless to the medical bacteriologist. Media vary in composition from simple solutions of inorganic salts to complex preparations of blood and living animal tissues.

Knight has divided bacteria into four groups according to their food requirements. These are thought to represent four different stages in the evolution of bacteria from primitive autotrophic forms to complex parasitic species.

Stage 1. Carbon is assimilated as CO_2, and nitrogen from inorganic sources, especially ammonia. The energy required for this assimilation (reduction of CO_2 and the synthesis of protoplasm) is derived (*a*) by oxidations of simple inorganic compounds: chemosynthetic autotrophs; (*b*) by the use of radiant and chemical energy: photosynthetic autotrophs.

Stage 2. Energy and carbon compounds for assimilation are derived by utilization of carbon compounds already more reduced than CO_2 which is not assimilated; with the assimilation of nitrogen from simple sources (N_2, ammonia, nitrate) the organisms can carry out the synthesis of their protoplasm.

Stage 3. Energy and carbon compounds for assimilation are derived by utilization of carbon compounds more reduced than CO_2; nitrogen assimilation requires amino-acids, some as specific components for synthesis of protoplasm, in particular tryptophan; ammonia cannot be used as a source of nitrogen.

Stage 4. Energy and carbon compounds for assimilation are derived by utilization of carbon compounds more reduced than CO_2; nitrogen assimilation requires an array of amino-acids as specific components for synthesis of protoplasm. Accessory growth-promoting substances are also required, some organisms requiring probably more than one.

It will be seen that these stages increase progressively in the complexity of their food requirements, first as regards energy sources, and second as regards nitrogen for the synthesis of protoplasm. In the first stage we find the simple autotrophic forms which can grow entirely upon inorganic compounds, and obtain energy from sunlight or the oxidation of inorganic substances. The second stage comprises first some primitive types transitional between the autotrophic and heterotrophic species, such as Carboxydomonas (oxidizing carbon monoxide) and Methanomonas (oxidizing methane); second, the nitrogen-fixing bacteria; and third, a number of saprophytic heterotrophic species which require organic compounds as a source of energy (sugar or glycerol or similar substances) but which can utilize ammonia as the source of nitrogen. The third stage includes both saprophytic and parasitic species of heterotrophic bacteria, which require an organic source of nitrogen as well as an organic source of energy. The fourth stage would include mostly the pathogenic parasites, which are very choicy about their food, and require, in addition to the needs of the third group, substances like the vitamins which we call accessory growth-promoting substances.

Accessory Growth-promoting Substances. Many species of pathogenic bacteria can be grown only in very complex culture media, such as meat broth, or blood media. An analysis of the nutrient requirements of these bacteria indicated that in addition to sources of energy and building materials for protoplasm, there were required one or more additional substances. Often extremely minute amounts of blood or tissue extract will suffice to permit growth when added to a relatively simple organic culture medium; the amount needed is so small that the added substance can obviously serve neither as a source of energy nor as an essential material for synthesis. Such substances serve, then, as stimulants to growth, or as essential reagents in metabolism, like the vitamins required by animals and the auxins required by higher plants.

These substances have been investigated only recently, and our knowledge of them is still rather incomplete. A well-known example is found in the case of *Haemophilus influenzae*. For a long time this organism could be cultivated only in media containing fresh whole blood. Later it was found that extracts of potato or other vegetables would serve instead of blood. After many experiments, it was established that, in addition to the foodstuffs proper, the influenza bacillus requires two accessory substances which are designated the V-factor and the X-factor. The V-factor is destroyed by heating, and is formed by yeasts and by several species of bacteria, notably Staphylococci. The X-factor is heat stable, and is the haematin of the blood; it can be replaced by other iron compounds which have catalase activity.

Similar experiments with other species of bacteria indicate that many species which have previously been cultivated only on complex culture media of unknown composition may be grown on media of known composition (amino-acids, carbohydrates, and salts) with the addition of minute amounts of definite vitamin-like substances. Noteworthy examples are the Staphylococci and diphtheria bacilli.

Carbon Dioxide. The presence of carbon dioxide in the atmosphere is apparently essential for the growth of some species of bacteria, and an increase over the normal concentration of this gas definitely stimulates the growth of certain species, notably the gonococcus and *Brucella abortus*. The effect of the CO_2 is apparently independent of its influence upon the reaction of the medium or the degree of aeration, and its function in the metabolism of these bacteria is unknown.

Food Supply in Natural Habitats. Obviously, the kind of food supply available in a given habitat will to some extent determine the kinds of microbes that are found there. Thus, if carbohydrates are in excess, fermentative bacteria will predominate; if proteins are in excess, putrefactive species will get the upper hand. But many natural habitats provide such a wide variety of chemical compounds, both organic and inorganic, that representatives of nearly all physiological groups will be found in the flora.

It is important to remember that bacteria do not occur in nature in pure cultures, and that the chemical transformations which occur result from the action and interaction of a number of species. A sparrow falls, and shortly its body is converted into nitrates, phosphates, sulphates, carbon dioxide, and water. This transformation results from the teamwork of a multiplicity of species.

Not only the kind of food material, but also the quantity, or rather the concentration, is important in determining the growth of bacteria. Within certain limits, the number of bacteria which can be supported increases with the concentration of organic matter. But these limits vary with different species of bacteria. In lakes, for instance, which contain a relatively low content of organic matter, one may find bacteria growing which will not grow in ordinary laboratory culture media, though they will grow in these same media greatly diluted (0.1% peptone solution, for instance). There have been found heterotrophic bacteria which can grow in water carefully freed of organic matter; they grow on the slight amounts of volatile organic matter which the water absorbs from the air. Such bacteria are called *oligocarbophilic*.

Temperature. For the growth of bacteria there are three critical temperatures — a *minimum* below which no growth will occur, an *optimum* where growth occurs most rapidly (not always most abundantly), and a *maximum* above which no growth occurs. Between the minimum and optimum temperatures, the rate of growth is accelerated by each increase in temperature, and the relationship between the increase of temperature and increase of growth rate is linear; this has been interpreted as an operation of the van't Hoff law. With temperatures above the optimum, the rate of growth decreases rapidly.

Bacteria have been divided into three groups with regard to their optimum temperatures. *Psychrophilic* bacteria grow best at relatively low temperatures, their optimum being about 5°–10° C. Their minimum temperature has usually been set at 0° C., since it seemed inconceivable that organisms could absorb food at a temperature below freezing. Recently, however, in studies of frozen foods, bacteria have been found which actually grow (though slowly) at temperatures some degrees below freezing. *Mesophilic* bacteria are those that grow best at temperatures from 30°–37° C. This group comprises the majority of bacterial species. The lower temperature is near optimum for most saprophytic species, the higher one for species parasitic in the human body. *Thermophilic* bacteria are those whose optimum temperature is high, 55°–60° C. Such bacteria were first observed in hot springs, and in heating piles of hay or manure. More recently they have been found to be fairly widespread in nature, and are of considerable practical importance in pasteurizing milk, or in canning, since they will multiply at temperatures intended to kill bacteria.

The temperature range, i.e., the difference between the minimum and maximum temperatures, varies greatly with different species. Thus one organism with an optimum at 37° may show some growth at all temperatures between 5° and 45°, while another may fail to grow below 25° or above 40°. In general, saprophytic species show a wider range than do parasitic species.

Reaction. By the *reaction* of a medium, bacteriologists mean the degree of acidity or alkalinity. Formerly this was determined by titrating with normal acid or alkaline solutions. But this method did not measure the important character of the medium, namely the concentration of free hydrogen or hydroxyl ions in the solution; rather it measured the total amount of acid or base in the medium. Bacteriology made a great stride forward when Clark introduced the conception of hydrogen ion concentration as the factor which determines the reaction of the medium. The hydrogen ion concentration is determined not only by the amount of acid or base present, but also by the degree to which it dissociates or ionizes in the solution.

The hydrogen ion concentration of pure water, i.e., at neutrality, is 1×10^{-7} gram ions per liter. With higher concentrations, i.e., with acids, this negative exponent becomes lower, while with alkaline solutions it becomes higher. The hydrogen ion concentration is more conveniently expressed in terms of these exponents, which value is known as the pH of the solution. Thus the pH of pure water is 7. When the reaction becomes acid the value is lower than 7; when it becomes alkaline the value is higher than 7.

The pH of a solution may be measured electrometrically with great precision, but a more simple and convenient procedure is to use the *indicators* introduced by Clark and Lubs, which are sufficiently accurate for most purposes. These are dyes which change color when the reaction of their solution changes. Some of them change at neutrality, while others change at various points on the pH scale. By the use of a series of such indicators, the pH of any solution may be determined.

Most species of bacteria grow best in a medium which is neutral in reaction, and in making culture media we adjust the reaction so that after the final sterilization the reaction will be close to pH 7. Bacteria vary widely in their tolerance to changes in pH. Some delicate parasitic species may fail to grow in even small degrees of acidity or alkalinity, growing best in media very slightly alkaline, i.e., of the same pH as the blood. Thus the organism of pneumonia, the pneumococcus, may fail to grow below pH 7 or above pH 8.3, growing best at pH 7.8. For such organisms the initial pH of the culture media must be very carefully adjusted. Saprophytic species usually show a greater tolerance to changes in pH, and in general will show some growth between pH 5.0 and 9.0, while in some species the range is much greater. Bacteria have been found capable of growing in acidities as great as pH 1.0, and others in alkaline solutions as strong as pH 13.0.

Bacteria tend to change the pH of their environment, since the products of their metabolism are often acid or basic in character. We have noted in the preceding chapter that organisms which ferment carbohydrates usually form organic acids. Conversely, organisms which are putrefactive, i.e., decompose proteins, tend to produce basic substances. If deaminization occurs, there is produced a strong base, ammonia, and a weak acid; while if decarboxylation occurs, there results a basic amine. In order to live, the fermentative organisms must be to some degree tolerant of acid, putrefactive bacteria tolerant of alkali. The tolerance of the acid-producing fermentative bacteria is more striking. Such bacteria are sometimes designated as acidophilic, but more correctly as *aciduric*.

Thus there is a sort of antagonism between fermentation and

putrefaction. While there are some exceptions, organisms which are active in fermentation are usually sluggish in putrefaction, and conversely. In an environment containing sufficient carbohydrate, the more rapidly growing fermentative bacteria usually get the upper hand and produce acid, lowering the pH, which inhibits the growth of the putrefactive bacteria. This fact is important in the preservation of foodstuffs. Various foods are preserved by allowing them to undergo a natural fermentation, the lactic or acetic acid formed serving to preserve them from putrefaction. Thus, if milk sours it will not putrefy as long as the acid reaction is maintained. Sauerkraut and silage are preserved by a strong lactic acid fermentation; pickles and mayonnaise are preserved by the addition of acid.

It should be noted, however, that the organic acids may themselves serve as foodstuffs for certain kinds of microbes. Thus, if a bottle of sour milk is left exposed to the air, it will soon be covered by a growth of mold, *Geotrichum lactis*, which consumes the lactic acid, and causes the reaction to return to neutral, when putrefactive bacteria will be able to grow. The decomposition of the organic acids is, however, an oxidation, not a fermentation. It is usually brought about by molds rather than bacteria, and exposure to air is necessary. Fermented foodstuffs can therefore be preserved for a long time if they are completely sealed from the air.

Although fermentative bacteria are in general tolerant of acid, this tolerance is limited, and if sufficient fermentable carbohydrate is present, their growth is inhibited by the accumulation of acid. Usually the limit of tolerance is fairly constant for the species, and one of the important diagnostic characters for fermentative species is the *final pH* after growth has ceased, in media containing fermentable sugars.

Oxidation and Reduction. We have already noted that bacterial species vary with regard to their relationship to atmospheric oxygen. Anaerobic species cannot stand it, aerobic species cannot live without it, while facultative species can adapt themselves to its presence or absence. We have noted that this relationship depends upon the metabolic possibilities of the organism. Aerobic species obtain their energy by respiration, i.e., direct oxidation, anaerobic species by fermentation (intramolecular respiration) or by intermolecular respiration, while facultative organisms may utilize all three methods. It is obvious, therefore, that the aeration of a given environment will have an important effect in determining the kinds of bacteria that live there.

Oxidation is more than a mere matter of aeration, or combination with oxygen. Compounds may be oxidized by removing hydrogen from them, or reduced by adding hydrogen. Compounds may be oxidized without any transfer of either oxygen or hydrogen, as in the conversion of ferrous chloride to ferric chloride. The important feature about oxidations and reductions is the fact that electrons are transferred from the atoms which are being oxidized to some other atoms.

The influence of oxidation and reduction upon the growth of bacteria in an environment cannot be explained simply in terms of aeration. There are involved, in addition, the amount of oxidizable or reducible material, and the degree to which these are actually oxidized and reduced. This may be measured and given a value which is known as the *Eh* of the medium or environment. The Eh or *oxidation-reduction potential* measures the ratio of oxidized and reduced substances, much as the pH measures the ratio between hydrogen and hydroxyl ions. Like the pH, the Eh may be measured electrometrically. Pure hydrogen at atmospheric pressure in equilibrium with a normal solution of strong acid is arbitrarily given an Eh value of zero. Solutions which have oxidizing powers greater than this are given positive values, while solutions having greater reducing powers have negative values. The Eh of a solution may also be measured (more crudely) by the use of oxidation-reduction indicators, dyes which are of one color in their oxidized state, and a different color in their reduced state, and which change color at different points on the Eh scale. Methylene blue is such an indicator which has long been used by bacteriologists roughly to determine anaerobiosis. It is colorless in its reduced form.

Why Cannot Anaerobic Bacteria Grow in Air? The work on fermentation and respiration begun by Pasteur has explained how anaerobic bacteria can grow and obtain their energy without air. It has not, however, explained why they cannot grow in the presence of air. It was long supposed that they were merely inhibited by the injurious effect of oxygen, but it seemed remarkable that organisms could be so extraordinarily sensitive to a substance quite harmless to the great majority of living creatures. A development of the Wieland theory was the postulation that when oxygen serves as the hydrogen acceptor, organic peroxides are formed, which react with water to produce hydrogen peroxide. Actually the formation of hydrogen peroxide has been demonstrated with a number of species of bacteria when grown under aerobic conditions. Now, as is well known, hydrogen peroxide is a poison to bacteria; it has long been used as a disinfectant. But most cells are protected from its action in small concentrations by the secretion of an enzyme, catalase, which breaks down the peroxide to water and oxygen. It was found, however, that some of the strictly anaerobic bacteria lack the ability to form catalase. It is supposed that the inhibition of these organisms under aerobic conditions is due to the fact that they immediately form H_2O_2 on contact with the air, in concentrations sufficient to inhibit further growth.

This explanation, however, has not been generally accepted, and more recently it has been proposed that anaerobic bacteria will not grow in the presence of air because they can initiate growth only at a low, critical oxidation-reduction potential. It has been found that some anaerobic species could be cultivated in the presence of air if the medium contained reducing substances which would lower the Eh to this critical point.

It appears that bacterial species will be found to vary with regard to Eh as they do with regard to pH and temperature; that for each species there will be found an optimum value, and minimum and maximum values, beyond which growth cannot occur. This phase of the study of bacteria is, however, just developing, and so far we have but little information on the Eh ranges either of various species of bacteria or of the habitats where they occur. It is clear, however, that bacteria which we have designated as anaerobic will likely have a low range, aerobic species a high range, and facultative species a wide range.

Oxidation-Reduction in Natural Habitats. The degree of aeration of an environment is one of the most important factors in determining the kinds of microbes which will grow there, and the kinds of chemical transformation which they may bring about. If organic matter is freely exposed to the air, the bacteria which live by direct oxidation (the most efficient mode of respiration) will predominate, and the organic matter will be completely decomposed to mineral elements or compounds. This is what occurs when sewage is purified in a trickling filter. The sewage is allowed to flow slowly through a bed of rocks, so that the liquid is exposed to the air in a thin film, through which oxygen may rapidly diffuse. Through the action of oxidative bacteria, the organic matter is rapidly burned, so that the amount of organic matter in the effluent may be reduced 90% or more.

But if the physical nature of an environment does not permit of free aeration, the oxidative bacteria at the surface exposed to the air consume oxygen much more rapidly than it can diffuse through water, and conditions below this surface become anaerobic. Such a situation occurs when sewage is placed in a septic tank. Here there is no free oxygen save in the very surface layer of the liquid. Only anaerobic and facultative bacteria can grow. These will hydrolyze the complex organic compounds, and thus bring solid matter into solution. Fermentations and anaerobic putrefactions will occur, the more complex organic substances being converted to simpler ones. But the decomposition is necessarily incomplete; most of the organic matter is still organic matter, and cannot be completely mineralized until the effluent is exposed to the air, either by passing it through a trickling filter or by running it into the soil.

A well-tilled, well-drained, well-manured soil is a natural habitat comparable to a trickling sewage filter. Here we have organic matter forming a thin, extensive surface over the mineral particles that form the framework of the soil, freely exposed to the air which penetrates the spaces between the soil particles. Here organic matter added to the soil is quickly converted into substances available to green plants. The mud at the bottom of a lake, particularly a bog lake rich in organic matter, is comparable to the septic tank. Here oxygen cannot penetrate, and the bacteria can only partially decompose the organic matter, which tends to accumulate. Between these extremes we have all gradations of aeration in natural habitats for bacteria.

It must be kept in mind that whether a given habitat remains aerobic or becomes anaerobic depends not only upon the degree of aeration possible, but also upon the amount of organic matter present. If the amount is low, the consumption of oxygen by bacteria may be less than the rate of diffusion from the air, and conditions will remain aerobic; while if the amount of organic matter is higher, oxygen is consumed more rapidly than it can diffuse, and conditions become anaerobic. The fact that oxidative bacteria will consume oxygen in proportion to the amount of organic matter available to them is used in measuring the organic matter in water and sewage. The sample is thoroughly aerated, then bottled tightly and incubated for a rather long period. The remaining oxygen is then titrated, and the amount consumed by the bacteria is computed. This value, the biological oxygen demand (usually abbreviated to B.O.D.) serves as a measure of the organic matter in the sample.

In the mud at the bottoms of lakes or ponds there occur anaerobic bacteria which may obtain the energy necessary for growth by reducing sulphates in order to oxidize organic matter, i.e., by intermolecular respiration. The sulphates are reduced to sulphides, which eventually diffuse through the water to reach the surface layers exposed to the air. Here the sulphides are oxidized by autotrophic sulphur bacteria, converted to sulphates, which may diffuse to the bottom to repeat the process. Thus, through the circulation of sulphur in oxidized and reduced form, oxygen is carried to the bottom to aid in a slow decomposition of the organic matter there. A number of other substances which may be oxidized by aerobic bacteria when exposed to the air, and reduced by anaerobic bacteria where oxygen is lacking, may undergo similar cyclic transformations.

Surfaces. Bacteria are so small in size that when placed in watery solutions they behave like suspensoid colloids. The cells carry a negative electric charge. When placed between two electrodes they will move toward the anode. This is called *electrophoresis*. The charge, similar on all of the cells, tends to keep them separated and in suspension. If the charge is neutralized, they tend to come together, or *agglutinate*, and to settle out of suspension, forming a sediment.

Because of their electric charge, bacterial cells like other colloids tend to become attached to, or adsorbed onto, surfaces which carry an opposite charge. We have already noted in a previous chapter that this adsorption is a factor in removing bacteria from liquid suspensions by filtration. It is probably the major factor in the purification of water by filtration through sand. Here the pores between the sand particles are much too large for a purely mechanical sieve action to explain the removal of the bacteria. It is found that a sand filter, when first placed in operation, does not remove the bacteria; it must first be allowed to "ripen." This ripening process is found to consist in the development of a gelatinous coating of organic matter, derived from the water, upon the sand grains. It is this coating of colloidal organic matter that attracts and traps the bacteria from the water trickling through.

Soil is composed of inert mineral particles of different sizes and kinds, which, like the sand grains in a filter bed, become coated with a gelatinous film of organic matter. In and on this film there develops a population of microbes, which in a rich soil may reach enormous numbers. This film of organic matter serves as a support for the bacteria, provides nutrition, and holds moisture. The enormous surface presented by the large number of minute grains of soil minerals allows free aeration of the organic matter, and thus provides for rapid multiplication of the bacteria and rapid mineralization of the organic matter in the soil.

If one suspends microscope slides in the waters of lakes or ponds or even rapidly flowing streams, they become coated in a few days (sometimes in a few hours) with bacteria which may be readily stained and observed. The surfaces of rocks or submerged plants or the bottoms of boats are similarly coated with slimy material containing large numbers of bacteria. If a sample of lake water or sea water is collected in a bottle and allowed to stand, it is found that the numbers of bacteria increase in the stored water, sometimes very markedly. This will occur even if the bottle of water is suspended in the lake from which it was collected, so that the temperature and other conditions remain the same. It has been found that the increase of the bacteria in the stored water depends upon the surface of the storage vessel. When the glass surface is increased by adding pieces of glass tubing, the amount of increase of the bacteria is roughly proportional to the amount of surface introduced. It is probable that this increase of the bacteria in the stored water is due to an adsorption of organic matter upon the surface of the glass. There is enough *quantity* of organic matter in the natural lake or sea water to support a larger population of bacteria than occurs naturally, but it is too low in *concentration;* when concentrated upon the glass, the bacteria can multiply.

When bacteria suspended in water are shaken up with sand or powdered coke or brick dust, or other finely divided material, and this material is then allowed to settle to the bottom of the vessel, it is found that many of the bacteria have been removed from the liquid, carried down in the sediment. They have been adsorbed by the finely divided material. Enormous numbers of bacteria are found in the bottom muds of lakes or the sea, though the overlying water contains relatively few. The bacteria are carried to the bottom and held there by finely divided material, either organic or inorganic in nature, which has settled out of the water. The degree of adsorption varies with different sorts of adsorbing materials, and with different species of bacteria. The bottom muds of lakes adsorb species found in the mud to a greater degree than species found in the water.

All of these facts indicate that the occurrence and nature of solid surfaces in the environment are important factors in determining the numbers and kinds of bacteria that grow there. However, our knowledge of this aspect of microbic ecology is still rather meagre and inaccurate.

Moisture and Osmotic Pressure. Bacteria must, of course, have moisture for their growth, since they can live only by absorbing materials in solution. If the moisture in their environment is removed, they quickly die (if exposed to air), excepting the spore-forming species. Suspended in pure distilled water, most species also die rather rapidly, and conversely if suspended in strong solutions of salt or sugar or glycerine, many species are killed. These effects are attributed to the osmotic pressure of the liquid, too low in the case of water, too high in the case of the solutions. If the osmotic pressure of the medium is too low, water will pass into the cell, which may swell and burst (*plasmoptysis*), while if it is too high, water is abstracted from the cell, whose protoplasm then shrinks and may pull away from the cell wall (*plasmolysis*). In most species of bacteria, however, neither plasmolysis nor plasmoptysis may be observed under the microscope. And in many experiments designed to demonstrate the injurious effects of low and high osmotic pressures, there has been some question whether the results could not better be explained by a lack or excess of specific ions in the solution. Nevertheless, long experience in the preservation of foodstuffs — salted meats and fish, brine pickles, fruits in syrup, jellies, honey, etc. — indicates quite definitely that the growth of banal spoilage bacteria may be inhibited by high osmotic pressures.

Such materials with high osmotic pressures are not, however, sterile. There are bacteria and yeasts and molds which can grow in the brines of pickling vats or on the surfaces of salted meats and fish; there are yeasts that grow in honey; bacteria have been found growing in (and exploding) chocolate-coated candies, or even in crude sugar and damp salt.

If sea water is placed in culture media made with sea water and with tap water, more bacteria will grow in the former than the latter; there are in the sea bacteria which cannot grow at lower osmotic pressures. There are bacteria found in Great Salt Lake, the water of which is saturated with sodium chloride, which cannot grow in the concentration of salt found in sea water. Yeasts have been found in honey which fail to grow in media containing less than 15% sugar. The term *halophilic* has been applied to bacteria growing in brines and salt, *osmophilic* to yeasts growing in strong sugar solutions.

It is clear then that bacteria vary through a wide range with respect to their susceptibility to variations in osmotic pressure, and that with each species there could be found a minimum, optimum, and maximum.

Light. Light cannot penetrate to the more important habitats of bacteria — the soil, the bottoms of lakes and the sea, the intestines of animals. Most species of bacteria are injured by exposure to light of sufficient intensity. This injurious action will be discussed in a later chapter.

Habitats to which light can penetrate are the surfaces of plants, and the clear waters of lakes and streams. It is a curious fact that in both of these habitats, pigment-forming (chromogenic) bacteria form a large proportion of the natural flora. We have noted that the red and green sulphur bacteria are provided with pigments which, like chlorophyll, make use of the energy of sunlight in photosynthesis. Some species of red sulphur bacteria show a positive phototaxis, i.e., they move from the dark into the lighted portions of their environment. Most of the water bacteria, however, and probably all of the pigmented plant parasites, form pigments of the carotinoid type, the true function of which is not known. In a few species it has been found that pigment was formed when exposed to the light, but not when the bacteria were grown in the dark. It is possible that the pigments serve to protect the bacteria from the injurious effect of sunlight, but the whole matter needs investigation.

The Living Environment. So far we have considered physical and chemical factors of the environment. There remain to be mentioned, briefly, the relationships between bacteria and the living organisms of their environment. This is very complex, and we are as

yet in no position to do more than merely point out several possibilities.

Certain species of microbes live within the tissues or body cavities
of higher animals. These tissues or body cavities are the environment, and the study of parasitism and infection is a study of the
relationships between the microbe and this living environment. In
some cases the presence of the microbe is beneficial to the host, and
we speak of the relationship as *symbiosis*. Examples are the nitrogen-
fixing bacteria which occur in the roots of leguminous plants, and
cellulose-digesting bacteria which occur in the intestinal tracts of
herbivorous animals. The microbe may live within its host, doing
little or no damage, in which case it is called a *harmless parasite*, or
it may cause disease and death, in which case it is a *pathogenic parasite*.
The pathogenic parasite destroys its environment, therefore itself, and
is looked upon as an unsuccessful variant in the course of evolution.
Successful parasitic organisms establish relations with their host that
make it possible for them to live together in harmony, i.e., they become harmless parasites. There is some evidence that, within medical history, pathogenic microbes have evolved in this direction, tending
to produce milder diseases of longer duration; syphilis is an example.

With free-living microbes, the same possibilities occur. Two
species may live together, the association being to the advantage of
one, sometimes of both. Usually this relationship depends upon the
ability of one of the species to carry out a chemical reaction which is
favorable to the other, but which the latter cannot perform itself.
Thus an aerobic organism on the surface of a substrate may consume
oxygen so rapidly that an anaerobe can live beside it; or a starch-
splitting organism may provide sugar that can be consumed by another species. Good examples of this sort of relationship are found
where disaccharides are fermented by two species growing together,
though neither in pure culture can produce the fermentation. One
species may hydrolyze sucrose to the monosaccharides, but cannot
ferment the latter; while the second species can ferment glucose or
levulose, but cannot split the sucrose. Such a relationship has been
termed symbiosis, but is more properly called *synergism*.

Another example of a symbiosis-like relationship between bacterial
species may be seen when Staphylococci are grown with influenza
bacilli. It has been observed that in plate cultures of sputum made
on ordinary nutrient agar (on which *Haemophilus influenzae* does

not grow), colonies of the influenza bacilli may grow in the immediate neighborhood of Staphylococcus colonies. Here the Staphylococci synthesize the accessory growth-promoting substances essential for the influenza bacilli. The colonies of the latter are called *satellite* colonies.

Probably in the majority of cases where two species of bacteria are grown together on a medium containing nutrients suitable to growth, they will both grow to some degree, and their relationship is neither injurious nor beneficial. If, however, one of the species can grow much more rapidly than the other, the latter is crowded out and suppressed, merely because its mechanism for metabolism is less efficient. In this way delicate pathogenic bacteria are often lost when one attempts to grow them on artificial culture media in mixed cultures.

Sometimes bacterial species may secrete substances which are definitely injurious to other species, and so get the upper hand by poisoning their competitors. *Pseudomonas aeruginosa*, for instance, secretes a substance, *pyocyanase*, which is distinctly inhibitory to a number of other species of bacteria. Fermentative bacteria may produce acids which are injurious to putrefactive bacteria. Such incompatibilities are called *antibiosis*. Finally, it should be mentioned that protozoa may limit the growth of bacteria in many environments by actually preying upon them, devouring them.

Bacteria Are Versatile. Here are three statements which cannot be proved, which are probably not true without qualification, but which nevertheless approach so closely to the truth that they merit consideration. 1. *There are bacteria which can grow where any other kind of organism can grow.* 2. *There are bacteria which can grow where no other kinds of organism can grow.* 3. *There is no organic substance which cannot be attacked by bacteria.* If one includes the molds and yeasts with the bacteria, these statements approach more nearly to the truth.

Throughout the preceding discussion of the influence of environmental factors, the most important fact established is the wide range of conditions to which various bacterial species have become adapted. If the world were dipped in boiling water, though all other living things would be killed, there would be left bacteria ready to start growth when it had cooled off to about 80° C.; if frozen, there would still be bacteria capable of some slow growth. High degrees of acidity, alkalinity, salinity, or anaerobiosis are all factors which would suppress nearly all other living things but still leave bacteria capable of growing.

A bottle of distilled water in the laboratory, apparently containing nothing upon which anything could grow, develops a sediment of oligocarbophilic bacteria. Every chemist has sooner or later been astonished to find bacteria or molds growing in his reagent solutions, which apparently not only contain no nutrient material but often deadly poisons such as arsenic compounds. Apparently inert and indigestible substances like rubber and paraffin and coal are slowly decomposed in the soil.

Niches. If one inoculates some soil, neutral or alkaline in reaction, into an artificial culture medium containing a carbohydrate as a source of energy, phosphates and sulphates and other necessary salts, but with *no source of nitrogen*, there will occur a growth of bacteria, the dominant species being the nitrogen-fixing *Azotobacter chroöcoccum*. Or, if the medium used is composed of ammonium sulphate and calcium carbonate and potassium phosphate with minor quantities of other salts, but with no organic source of carbon, the autotrophic bacteria of the genus *Nitrosomonas* will grow, oxidizing the ammonia to nitrites. Or, in a medium containing nutrient salts but no source of carbon save cellulose, certain peculiar cellulose-decomposing bacteria will grow. If the medium contains no source of carbon, but is put under a bell jar with an open vessel containing gasoline, another peculiar group of microbes which can utilize hydrocarbons will grow. And so, by artificially creating a series of selective environments, one may isolate a whole series of bacterial species, each one of which appears to have a particular chemical function to perform in the soil. There seems to be almost no limit to the number of species which may be extracted from the soil in this manner; new ones are being discovered continuously. In some cases, if these experiments are repeated under anaerobic conditions, another series of species may be obtained which may perform the same functions when oxygen is lacking.

Thus it appears that each bacterial species has a particular part to play, a particular position to occupy in the living community in which it grows. Ecologists speak of this function of an organism, i.e., its special role in the economy of nature, as its *niche*, and it is clear that bacteria have niches just as well defined as higher organisms.

Parasitic and pathogenic bacteria have equally well-defined niches. Every plant or animal species that has been adequately studied has been found to suffer from bacterial infections. In many cases these bacteria are host specific, i.e., they will infect naturally only one species of plant or animal; in most cases their host specificity is limited; they will infect only a few species. This is to a large extent true also of the harmless parasites; the Streptococci which grow in the intestines of horses are different from those which grow in human intestines; those which grow in the human mouth are also different from the intestinal species.

One may readily understand that the niches occupied by the various saprophytic and autotrophic bacteria are very important to the economy of nature — these species keep the elements of life in circulation. But what of the pathogenic bacteria? Do they serve any useful function? If looked at objectively, it will be seen that they serve a very important function. Disease-producing bacteria, which kill their hosts, must be transmitted from individual to individual in order to survive. A rapid transfer is only possible if the host population is dense. It is found in nature that whenever an animal species becomes excessively abundant, an epidemic bacterial disease usually develops to reduce the population to normal numbers. Some species of wild animals undergo definite cyclic variations in the density of their populations. This is well established for the Northern hare, ruffed grouse, and the lemming. They increase gradually over a period of years until they become excessively abundant, then suddenly they are decimated, to repeat the process again. It has been suggested that the sudden reduction in numbers is due to a great epidemic, the survivors being individuals with some natural immunity. These generate a new population which eventually reaches sufficient density to permit the development of a new epidemic. Whether by such explosive epidemics, or by a more gradual process, the pathogenic microbes serve to prevent populations from becoming too dense for their environment to support.

A further discussion of the ecology of bacteria involves a consideration of the microbic populations of different natural habitats. It will be necessary first, however, to learn something about the methods of studying bacteria in such habitats. These methods depend almost entirely upon the cultivation of the bacteria in artificial media. We will therefore interpolate a chapter on the cultivation of bacteria.

CHAPTER XIII

THE CULTIVATION OF BACTERIA

When van Leeuwenhoek made his infusion of peppers and observed the animalcules that grew therein, he made use of a procedure which has been applied ever since in the study of microbes. The most minute organisms may be observed to best advantage in artificial cultures in the laboratory. Hay infusions and meat broths were most widely used for this purpose. However, little progress was made until a way could be found to separate the different kinds of microörganisms, and to grow each in a pure culture. For but little may be learned with certainty about the identity and activities of a microörganism until it has been cultivated in pure cultures. This is important enough to warrant repetition. *But little may be learned with certainty about the identity and activities of a microörganism until it has been cultivated in pure cultures.*

Plating. The procedure most commonly used for obtaining pure cultures from mixtures of microbes is the process of *plating* introduced by Koch. We have already considered the general principles of this operation in Chapter I. The diluted organisms are suspended in a liquefied jelly which is then allowed to set in a thin layer. Agar and gelatine are used for this purpose, but agar is much more useful than gelatine because the latter may be liquefied again by warming above 25° C., or by the enzymes of proteolytic bacteria.

Two general plating procedures are in use, the *pour plate* method and the *streak plate* method. The former is the procedure we have just considered. The bacteria are introduced into the agar while it is still melted. The agar solidifies at about 40° C. The bacteria may be safely brought into the agar when it has cooled to below 50° C. This gives a range of about 10° C. in which to work with the cultures. When the agar has set, the bacteria are entrapped and will develop into characteristic colonies. Those which are caught near the top of the agar will spread out to form *surface colonies*. Those that are held down in the agar will form *deep colonies*.

Streak Plates. Streak plates are made by first pouring the sterilized agar into a Petri dish and allowing it to solidify. Then the mixture of bacteria is spread over the surface by taking a loopful in a wire inoculating loop and streaking this back and forth across the agar plate. The majority of the bacteria will be deposited in the first few streaks, and as the process is continued, fewer and fewer organisms will be left on the agar, until finally well-separated single cells will be deposited, which will develop into pure cultures that may be readily transferred. With streak plates, of course, only surface colonies are obtained.

Success in obtaining pure cultures by the plating process depends on the degree to which the bacterial cells are separated from each other in or on the agar. It is obvious that if a drop of the bacterial suspension is vigorously stirred in a tube of melted agar, there is a better chance of the cells being so separated than if they are simply deposited by chance from a wire slipping over the surface of the agar. Therefore the pour plate method is more certain than the streak plate procedure. The latter is sufficient for merely determining the presence or absence of certain organisms which form characteristic colonies, and is widely used in routine bacteriological examinations, since it requires less time and material than pour plates. But for precise work, the pour plate is to be preferred.

With pour plates it is usually necessary to dilute the material containing the organisms, to insure a good separation of the resulting colonies. If the plates are too closely seeded, the colonies will be very small, and so close together that it is impossible to touch one with the inoculating wire without touching one of the others. The usual procedure is to make three dilutions, as follows: — a loopful of the material to be cultured is stirred into a tube of melted agar; two loopfuls of this agar are transferred to a second tube; and three loopfuls from the second are transferred to a third tube of agar. The content of each tube is poured into a separate sterile Petri dish. One of the three plates will almost certainly show a proper separation of the colonies. With streak plates a proper separation of the organisms is accomplished by spreading the material over a sufficient agar surface, though sometimes a preliminary dilution in a sterile solution may be desirable. Most beginners make the mistake of not utilizing enough of the agar surface. The wire loop or other spreader should be moved back and forth across the plate from one side to the other, making a series of lines *just as close together as possible;* if they overlap it does not matter. The main thing is to leave no agar surface untouched by the spreader. It is often advisable to streak a second or even a third plate without recharging the wire loop.

Quantitative Plating. Plating may be used also to measure or estimate the *number* of bacteria in a given substance. This operation is widely used for counting the number of bacteria in water, milk, or soil. The material is *quantitatively* diluted in a series of tubes containing a measured quantity of sterile water known as "water blanks." These water blanks usually contain 9 cc. or 99 cc. of water, and are used to prepare a series of dilutions in the order 1–10, 1–100, 1–1000, etc., or 1–100, 1–10,000, 1–1,000,000, etc. One cc. or one-tenth cc. quantities of these various dilutions are then distributed in sterile Petri plates with sterile pipettes. A tube of melted and properly cooled agar is then poured in each dish and thoroughly mixed with the diluted bacteria by moving the dish around on the surface of the table. Assuming that each colony develops from a single organism, the number per cc. in the original material may be computed by multiplying the number of colonies on the plate by the dilution.

The count should be determined from a plate in which the colonies are well distributed, and not too numerous or too few in number. Where the colonies are very numerous they are very small and therefore difficult to count accurately, and the number that develops is too small because, through competition, certain of the organisms are inhibited and do not develop visible colonies. Where the number of colonies is small, the error due to chance variation in the distribution becomes too great. It is generally agreed that the plate which gives a number of colonies nearest to 200 will yield the most accurate count. Where precision is necessary, it is desirable to make a number of replicate plates of the same dilution, at least five, and to average the results. The number of bacteria determined by plate counts always falls below the number determined by microscopic counts, because some of the colonies develop from clusters rather than from single cells, because some of the bacteria are dead, or because some of them will not grow on the medium used for plating.

Colonies. The colonies which develop upon agar or gelatine plates exhibit specific characters by which one may often identify the organism of which they are composed, or at least roughly surmise its nature. Surface colonies show these specific differences more distinctly than deep colonies. The differences are manifest in the size of the colony; in its shape, whether the edge be smooth or toothed or feathery, or extends over the surface as branched streamers; in the opacity or translucency to transmitted light; in the color; in the surface, whether it be glistening or dull, smooth or wrinkled, etc.; and in the texture when touched with a wire, whether the colony is mucoid or sticky, or buttery, or brittle, or firm and tenacious. An experienced bacteriologist may look over a plate and tell at a glance that one colony is a Micrococcus, another is a Gram negative rod, a third is an aerobic spore-former, and so on.

Dilution Methods. There are several other methods for obtaining pure cultures besides plating. One of the oldest methods is the process of *extinction dilution.* One dilutes the material containing the bacteria until a series of tubes of medium inoculated with samples of equal volume, say 1 cc. each, will show a growth in only some of the tubes. The idea is that, when so diluted, many of the 1 cc. portions will contain but one cell each. Whether this is so or not can be determined only by careful examination of the resulting cultures. This method is not very useful, and is resorted to only where plating is impossible for one reason or another. It provides a means for estimating the number of bacteria where one cannot use plating. By making a series of dilutions and inoculating a series of tubes with equal portions of each dilution, and by counting the number of tubes which do and do not show growth, the most probable number of bacteria in the original material may be calculated.

Single Cell Isolation. In certain types of work, such as experiments on variation, it is desirable to know for certainty that a given culture is derived from but one cell; it is not enough to know that all the cells are of the same species; we must be sure that they have arisen from a single individual. A culture obtained in this way is called a *pure line* culture. This involves picking out one cell under the microscope and separating it from its fellows. It would seem at first glance that this is impossible with things so minute as bacteria. But several ingenious procedures have been used for this purpose, the best depending upon the use of a *micromanipulator,* an instrument which makes it possible to control accurately the very short movements of very small instruments. The principle involved was worked out by Barber. A suspension of the bacteria in liquid is deposited in very minute drops upon the under side of a coverglass placed over a moist chamber. With the microscope, a drop is found containing but a single cell. With a sterile micropipette this drop with its contained cell is taken up and transferred to a tube of sterile medium. The process is tedious and nerve-racking, and is used only for special work.

Enrichment Cultures. Pure cultures may often be obtained more readily if one first grows the organism in an *enrichment culture*. We have seen an example of such a culture in the preceding chapter, in the case of the nitrogen-fixing Azotobacter; by inoculating soil into a nitrogen-free medium, the nitrogen-fixing bacteria are relatively increased over the other kinds of bacteria present, and may then be more easily isolated by plating. Enrichment cultures may be used with various kinds of bacteria, in each case using a *selective medium*, in which advantage is taken of some peculiarity of the organism desired.

Differential Media. The isolation of pure cultures is also frequently facilitated by the use of differential media, so constituted that they will give a color reaction with certain species of bacteria and so make the detection of their colonies more easy. One of the best examples is Endo's medium used for the isolation of typhoid bacilli from feces. The organism of typhoid fever forms colonies which are much like those of the colon bacillus, a normal intestinal organism. It is very difficult to pick the relatively few typhoid colonies from amongst the abundant colon bacillus colonies on ordinary nutrient agar. But the colon bacillus ferments lactose, with the production of aldehydes among other products, while the typhoid germ does not. Endo's agar has added to it some lactose, some basic fuchsin (a red aniline dye), and some sodium sulphite. The sodium sulphite decolorizes the basic fuchsin so that the agar is colorless. But in the presence of aldehydes, the red color returns. The colonies of colon bacilli, fermenting lactose, turn deep red, while the typhoid colonies are colorless. A number of such differential media are used.

Conditions Necessary for Cultivating Bacteria. The most important conditions which must be fulfilled in order to cultivate bacteria are a proper nutrient medium, a proper pH of the medium, the right degree of aeration, and a proper temperature.

The proper temperature is provided by placing the cultures in an incubator. Most modern incubators are heated by electricity, the temperature being controlled by a thermostat which operates a relay. Most laboratories maintain two incubators, one operated at body heat (37° C.), the other at 20° C. The latter requires both a heating element and a cooling element. It is used mainly for gelatine cultures, which will melt at higher temperatures.

The proper hydrogen ion concentration is obtained by titrating the medium. With nutrient broth made from meat, for instance, the solution as prepared is too acid for bacteria. A measured sample is removed, and using bromthymol blue as an indicator, normal alkali is added until the reaction of the sample is slightly alkaline. Then the calculated amount of normal alkali is added to the bulk of the medium. Since it will again become slightly acid on sterilizing, the acidity is slightly overcorrected with the alkali. Usually complex organic culture media naturally have a high buffer value, but with some of the simpler types of culture media it is helpful to add buffers (usually phosphates) to help maintain the pH near a constant level. Where large quantities of acid-forming bacteria are desired, powdered calcium carbonate may be added to the medium to neutralize the acid as it is formed.

Anaerobic Methods. The growth of aerobic organisms presents no difficulties. The cotton stoppers of test tube or flask cultures allow a free exchange of air. The cultivation of the anaerobic bacteria requires some procedure for removing the oxygen, and with strict anaerobes is often very difficult.

To obtain pure cultures of anaerobes, they may be separated in "shake agar" cultures. These are prepared just like pour plates, save that after the tubes of melted agar have been inoculated, the agar is rapidly solidified by placing the tubes in cold water. If the agar has been heated just before inoculating, the dissolved oxygen will have been driven off, and after solidifying, atmospheric oxygen will diffuse through the agar rather slowly, so that anaerobic conditions obtain at the bottom of the tube. These anaerobic conditions may be maintained for some time if the agar is sealed from the air by a mixture of sterile paraffin and vaseline poured in the top of the tube. Paraffin oil is sometimes used for this purpose, but it is quite useless, since oxygen will diffuse through it rapidly. Separate colonies will develop in the depths of the agar. They may be subcultured by sterilizing the outside of the tube with a chemical disinfectant, after which the tube is cut opposite a chosen colony that may then be transferred to a new medium which must also be free of oxygen.

A great variety of procedures have been advocated for obtaining anaerobic growth, but many of them are very unsatisfactory. After pure cultures are obtained, one may often secure a satisfactory growth in broth placed in long test tubes, with ground meat, brain, or other tissue in the bottom, and a paraffin-vaseline seal at the top. The tissue will rapidly absorb the oxygen dissolved in the medium.

The most successful anaerobic cultures are obtained by placing the tubes, or Petri plates, or other cultures in a McIntosh-Fildes jar. This is a stout glass jar with a cover that makes an air-tight joint. The air is exhausted as far as possible with a suction pump, and replaced with hydrogen gas. A wire within the jar, coated with platinum black, is heated by an electric current, which catalyzes a union of the hydrogen with what oxygen remains. There is danger of an explosion if the jar has not first been thoroughly exhausted of air.

Nutrient Media. It will be seen from what has been said concerning the food requirements of bacteria that many different sorts of culture media are necessary in order to study all of the known species. Actually well over a thousand different recipes have been published. Most of the well-known species will, however, grow upon a series of rather complex organic media which were developed quite empirically in the early days of bacteriology, which have been used almost routinely by bacteriologists ever since. The *cultural characters* of bacteria upon these *routine media* form a considerable part of the description of bacterial species. The cultural characters include, first, a sort of gross anatomy, i.e., the naked-eye appearance of the mass of bacteria upon the surface of solid media, or distributed in liquid media; and second, the chemical changes which the bacteria bring about in the medium. The routine media are nutrient broth, nutrient gelatine, nutrient agar, peptone solution, and litmus milk.

Broth. This is made either from fresh beef or from commercial beef extract. The latter is more convenient and is usually used, but some of the more delicate pathogenic bacteria grow much better in broth prepared from fresh meat, especially veal. To make broth from fresh beef, an equal volume of water is added to the ground meat and allowed to stand over night, so that all of the soluble matter is extracted. It is then heated to boiling, to coagulate the proteins, and strained through gauze. To the liquid is added 1% peptone, and usually 0.5% of common salt. Next a sample is tested for acidity with indicators, and sufficient alkali is added to make the solution neutral. The broth is again heated to boiling and while hot is filtered through paper to make it perfectly clear. It is then distributed in test tubes which are plugged with cotton, and sterilized. Meat extract broth is simply made by dissolving in water some Liebig's beef extract (0.3%), some peptone (1.0%), and salt (0.5%), by heating. The reaction is then adjusted, and further treatment is the same as above.

When grown in broth, bacteria show a characteristic distribution in the medium. They may float on the surface to form a scum, or *pellicle;* they may be diffusely scattered through the liquid to produce *turbidity;* or they may grow entirely at the bottom in the form of a *sediment.* The latter is usually the end result of all broth cultures, for pellicles will sink, and the bacteria dispersed through the liquid will also eventually settle to the bottom of the tube. Sedimentary growth is, therefore, significant only when it is present from the very beginning. Pellicles may be dry and wrinkled, or mucoid in character. Sediment may be granular, or sticky, twisting into a ropy mass when the tube is whirled. These characters, together with the color and odor of the culture, which are often characteristic, comprise the cultural characters to be observed in broth.

Agar. Nutrient agar is prepared by dissolving 1.5% of commercial agar in nutrient broth. It is filtered through cotton while hot, distributed into tubes and sterilized. Two sorts of tubes are prepared, *deeps* and *slants.* Agar deeps are tubes filled about one-third, and after sterilizing the agar is allowed to solidify with the tubes in a vertical position. They are sometimes used for stab cultures, the bacteria being introduced into the agar by stabbing the inoculating wire down through the middle. But mostly deep agar tubes are used in making plate cultures. Agar slants are prepared by putting less agar in the tubes (about one-fifth full), and, after sterilizing, the tubes are placed in a slanting position until the agar solidifies, so that a long sloping surface is provided upon which the bacteria may be grown. Agar slant cultures are inoculated by making a single stroke with the inoculating wire from the bottom to the top of the slant.

One notes, with agar slant cultures, first the form of the growth, whether confined to the stroke made with the wire, or spreading over the surface; whether the edges are smooth or irregular. Then one notes the density of the growth, whether abundant or scant, opaque or translucent; whether the surface is smooth and glistening, or dull, or wrinkled. The color is often striking. The bacteria themselves may be pigmented, so that only the growth on the surface is colored, or a diffusible pigment may be formed which spreads into the agar and colors the whole medium. Finally one determines the consistency of the growth by touching it with a wire. It may be sticky or buttery or brittle (breaking into flakes), or tenacious and adherent to the agar. Agar slants are used more widely than any of the other media for storing cultures, or for merely obtaining a good growth of organisms to be used in experiments, etc.

Gelatine. Nutrient gelatine is prepared in the same way as agar. Gelatine is added to nutrient broth, usually in 15% concentration, dissolved by heating, and then tubed and sterilized. It is practically always tubed as deeps, and inoculated by stabbing.

The principal fact to be learned from gelatine cultures is whether the organism being studied secretes *gelatinase;* if it does, the gelatine will be liquefied. While bacteria that liquefy gelatine will not necessarily attack other proteins, in general the putrefactive bacteria are gelatine liquefiers, and this character is important in identifying bacteria. Liquefaction usually begins at the top of the column and proceeds downward, and may be detected by tipping the tube, when the liquefied portion will run. If the gelatine is liquid over the entire surface exposed to the air, so that when the tube is tipped the solid part remaining has a flat upper surface, the liquefaction is said to be *stratiform,* i.e., it proceeds in layers. Often, however, the liquefied part is funnel-shaped or turnip-shaped.

If a special gelatine incubator is not available, the gelatine cultures may be incubated with the other cultures at some higher temperature. After growth occurs, the tube is set in cold water, below 20° C. If the gelatine hardens again, it has not been digested. If it has been acted upon by gelatinase, it will not set.

Stab cultures give some indication of the oxygen requirements of a microbe. If growth occurs only at the surface, the organism is strictly aerobic. If it is abundant in the depths of the medium, the organism is facultative.

Peptone. Peptone solution is made by dissolving 1% peptone and 0.5% salt in water. It is then tubed and sterilized. The reaction seldom needs adjustment. The growth of bacteria in peptone usually appears the same as in broth. The main purpose of peptone cultures is to test the organism's ability to form *indol*.

Indol. Indol is a complex nitrogenous compound produced by putrefactive bacteria during the decomposition of proteins. It can be derived only from the amino-acid tryptophane. Tryptophane may be derived from peptone. Indol is tested for, after growth has continued for several days, by a chemical reaction. Two reagents are used, one a solution of paradimethylamidobenzaldehyde, the other of potassium persulphate. These two solutions are mixed in equal parts just before testing, and an equal volume of this mixture is added to the peptone culture. The presence of indol is indicated by the development of a pink to red color. This color will develop better if the tube is shaken to insure aeration, and allowed to stand for about 15 minutes. The indol may be first concentrated by shaking the culture with a little chloroform or ether; the indol will dissolve in these.

Potato. Potato medium is prepared by cutting potatoes into cylindrical plugs with a cork borer. These are then sliced diagonally to give two pieces, each with a slanting surface. The pieces of potato are placed in running water over night; this washes out acid substances which tend to inhibit growth. The pieces of potato are then placed, slant side up, in culture tubes, in the bottom of which has been put a little wad of cotton saturated with water, to help keep the potato from drying up. The tubes are plugged with cotton and sterilized. Potato is inoculated in the same manner as the agar slant, by making a stroke over the slanting surface.

Potato cultures appear in general like agar slant cultures. But any tendency of the organism to form pigment is brought out better on potato, partly because of the light-colored opaque background, but also because some ingredient of the potato increases pigment production. Some of the pathogenic bacteria, which will grow readily on the other routine media, will not grow, or will grow only slightly, on potato. The failure of an organism to grow upon potato is therefore an aid to identification.

Litmus Milk. Litmus milk is the most important of the culture media for yielding information about the biochemical activities of bacteria. It is prepared from fresh skim milk, or from powdered skim milk dissolved in water, to which is added enough litmus solution to give the right color, a lavender. The milk is then tubed and sterilized. To understand the changes which may occur in milk cultures, one must know what ingredients may be acted upon by the bacteria and what reactions they may produce. In litmus milk medium the butter fat has been removed, as far as possible. The important substances are two sugars, lactose and glucose, and two proteins, lactalbumen and caseinogen. The litmus itself is a fifth important substance.

Carbohydrates in Milk. Sugar occurs in milk only in the form of the disaccharide, lactose. But when the milk is sterilized, a little of this is hydrolyzed to yield two monosaccharides, glucose and galactose. Galactose is fermented by very few organisms, which also ferment glucose; practically, the galactose may be ignored. For bacteriological purposes, then, milk may be considered as containing a large amount of lactose and a small amount of glucose.

If a bacterial species, which ferments *glucose* but not lactose, is inoculated into milk, the litmus will turn pink because of the acid formed. The change in color will not be great, because the amount of glucose is small. This color change is best observed by comparing the culture with an uninoculated tube of the same lot of litmus milk. Often the bacteria which ferment the glucose will also slowly produce basic substances from one of the protein constituents, usually the lactalbumen, so that the color eventually changes back to lavender, or even blue. An initial pink color, followed by a return to blue, is a sign that organisms may ferment glucose but not lactose. If the organism studied can ferment *lactose*, a larger amount of acid is formed (since lactose is present in greater quantity), and therefore the litmus will turn a deep red, instead of pink, and usually not enough alkaline material is formed by the organism to change this color. A permanent deep red color, therefore, shows that the organism can ferment lactose. Now the fermentation of lactose is brought about first by a hydrolysis to glucose and galactose, and then a fermentation of one or both of these monosaccharides. Therefore, if lactose is fermented, it may be safely assumed that glucose has been fermented, also.

Proteins in Milk. Lactalbumen is a protein, present in small quantity, which is coagulated by heat. It is the substance which appears as a scum when milk is boiled. It may be broken down by proteolytic bacteria to yield ammonia or basic amines, with a resultant change of the litmus to a distinct blue color. An alkaline reaction in the milk without other change may be taken as an indication that organisms may digest lactalbumen, but not the other protein, caseinogen.

Caseinogen is the main protein ingredient of milk. It occurs in the milk in the form of very finely divided particles suspended in the liquid. It is the caseinogen which gives the milk its opacity and white color. It may be acted upon by bacteria in two ways. It may be *coagulated,* in which case the milk becomes solid and will not run; or it may be digested, or *peptonized,* by proteolytic enzymes, in which case the milk becomes more transparent.

Curdling of Milk. Coagulation may be brought about through the action of *acids.* Caseinogen is chemically bound with calcium; it may be considered a calcium caseinate. The formation of lactic acid by fermentation of lactose will remove this calcium, forming calcium lactate, and leave behind the *casein,* or curd. The casein particles flocculate to form a semisolid substance, and so the milk is coagulated. *Acid coagulation* may always be recognized by the accompanying red color of the litmus; it is to be differentiated from another sort of coagulation due to the enzyme *rennin,* which occurs in milk with a basic reaction. The fermenting organism may also form gas from the sugar, and gas bubbles will be entrapped in the curd. Sometimes gas is formed so rapidly and abundantly as actually to blow the curd out of the milk to the upper part of the tube. This *"stormy fermentation"* is characteristic of the anaerobic bacillus, *Clostridium welchii,* one of the causes of gas gangrene.

Rennin is an enzyme, also called rennet, or the lab ferment. It is formed not only by various microörganisms, but is also one of the enzymes secreted by the stomach. Rennin from this source is used by cheese makers to produce the curd from which cheese is manufactured. The nature of the chemical change brought about by rennin coagulation is not clearly understood. It may be the condensation of caseinogen molecules to form a new substance called *paracasein,* or the change may be purely physical. Rennin coagulation may occur in a medium of neutral reaction. It is sometimes referred to as "sweet curdling." But usually the organisms which form rennin are also to some extent proteolytic, and so produce basic substances that give the medium an alkaline reaction, turning the litmus blue.

Peptonization. *Peptonization,* the digestion of the caseinogen or casein, is manifested by a *clearing* of the milk. It may occur with or without a previous coagulation, in an acid or alkaline reaction. The milk becomes more and more transparent, starting at the top of the tube and working downward.

Reduction. The litmus serves not only as an indicator of the acidity or alkalinity, i.e., the hydrogen ion concentration, but also as an oxidation-reduction indicator. In its oxidized form it is red, lavender, or blue according to the pH. In its reduced form it is colorless. If the organisms being studied are capable of bringing about reduction, the litmus in the bottom of the tube (where aeration is imperfect) will be decolorized, and the normal white color of the milk will reappear. This decolorization is usually more extensive when the milk has been previously coagulated, since the coagulated casein does not allow so rapid a diffusion of oxygen from the air. Sometimes a tube of litmus milk is completely reduced, so that no litmus color can be seen, and consequently the reaction may not be determined. In this case the color will return, and the acidity or alkalinity may be observed, if the tube is thoroughly shaken so that the milk becomes well aerated. If the casein has been peptonized and the litmus also reduced, the semi-transparent liquid will have a yellowish or straw color, due to the color of the products of digestion of the casein.

A consideration of these facts shows that a great deal may be learned about the biochemical characters of an organism by simply inoculating a tube of litmus milk, and after growth has occurred, noting: — 1, the color, whether pink, red, lavender, blue, or white; 2, the presence or absence of coagulation, determined by tipping the tube; 3, the presence or absence of peptonization, shown by increased transparency.

Sugar Media. The complete identification of many organisms requires a determination of what carbohydrates they may ferment, and, in some cases, of the products of the fermentation. This is accomplished by growing the organisms in "sugar broths," broth to which is added one or another fermentable substance, which is not always a sugar. The substances most widely used are the monosaccharide, *glucose*, the disaccharides, *lactose*, *sucrose*, and *maltose*, and the alcohol, *mannitol* (or mannite). Others less commonly used are the pentoses, *arabinose* and *xylose;* the hexoses, *fructose, galactose,* and *mannose;* the alcohols, *glycerol* and *dulcitol* (or dulcite); and the polysaccharide. *inulin.* The products of the fermentations of these substances are largely organic acids, with or without gas (carbon dioxide and hydrogen).

To be certain that the acid and gas have been derived only from the carbohydrate used, it is necessary to use a sugar-free base for the medium. Meat extract broth is sugar free, so the sugar broths are made by dissolving some of the carbohydrate to be tested in this medium. Generally 1% of the sugar or other substance is added. To show the formation of an acid, an indicator is added. *Andrade's indicator* is commonly used; this is the dye, acid fuchsin, to which sodium hydroxide is added until it is decolorized. When added to broth this indicator remains colorless when neutral or basic in reaction, but turns a deep red if acid. The broth is distributed in culture tubes, and to detect the formation of gas, a small test tube is placed upside down within the larger one. When the broth is heated for sterilizing, the air in this little tube, or "gas trap," is driven out and replaced by the broth when cool. If gas is formed from the sugar this broth in the little tube will be displaced, and the gas production is readily detected.

One cannot be certain that an organism does not ferment a sugar if a vigorous growth has not taken place in the sugar tube. To insure such a growth with certain of the pathogenic bacteria, especially the Streptococci, it is necessary to add some sterile blood serum to the sugar broths.

Special Media. The culture media which we have considered are those commonly used in the study of the majority of microorganisms. We shall have occasion in the following pages to refer to a number of special media of one sort or another, enrichment media, or selective media, or differential media used for isolating particular species, or special media used for determining some particular biochemical reactions. But we should mention here two other groups of culture media, which, while not in routine use, are of general value.

Blood Media. Many of the pathogenic bacteria grow very poorly or not at all unless the composition of the medium is somewhat similar to that of their natural habitat, the animal body. These bacteria may often be cultivated on media containing blood or blood serum. Serum is the clear liquid part of the blood that separates from the blood cells and fibrin in clotting. Its main ingredients are serum albumen and serum globulin. Whole blood is used in some media, only the serum in others.

Loeffler's blood serum is prepared from the serum of beef blood to which is added some beef extract, peptone, and glycerol or glucose. It is a very rich medium. The liquid is distributed in culture tubes, which are then placed in a slanting position and heated at 70° C. long enough to coagulate thoroughly the proteins of the blood serum. There results a solid, opaque, buff-colored medium arranged in the tube with a long slanting surface, like an agar slant culture. The medium is now heated further to sterilize it. This medium will yield a good growth of many bacteria which grow only poorly on plain agar. It is especially useful in cultivating the diphtheria bacillus.

The remaining blood media differ from Loeffler's blood serum in that the *blood cannot be heated.* It must be collected from the animal aseptically, i.e., in such a manner that no contamination with bacteria may occur; or, in the case of serum, it may be sterilized by filtration through a Berkefeld filter.

Blood agar is made by adding sterile whole blood to melted nutrient agar. The agar must be cool enough that the blood proteins will not be coagulated, below 60° C. The blood may be collected with a sterile syringe from a vein. It is thoroughly mixed with the agar, which is then poured into a Petri dish, or slanted. An opaque, red, solid medium results. Blood agar is used for the cultivation of certain bacteria which produce characteristic changes in the red blood cells or their pigment, *haemoglobin;* or for the growth of certain bacteria that require haemoglobin.

Serum agar and serum broth are made by adding sterile, unheated blood serum to agar and broth. Some of the more delicate microbes, such as the gonococcus and meningococcus, will not grow without the addition of this substance to the media.

Synthetic Media. With all of the culture media so far considered, it is impossible to determine the precise chemical composition. Meat extract and peptone, milk and blood, contain complex ingredients whose precise chemical structure has never been determined. For biochemical studies, such media are quite unsuitable, since to the difficulty of determining the products of growth is added the practical impossibility of knowing the conditions before growth has occurred. Therefore, there have been devised a number of media whose composition may be precisely known. Such media are commonly called "synthetic" media.

These media must provide the elements necessary for growth.

These are C, O, H, N, S, P, and K; many organisms also require traces of Mg and Fe, perhaps also Ca. With autotrophic organisms one may devise an appropriate medium of purely inorganic materials. With heterotrophic bacteria it is necessary to supply an organic carbon compound as a source of energy, though this may be very simple. A number of microbes will grow readily in a solution of ammonium sulphate, potassium phosphate, and glycerol. All of these ingredients may be readily obtained as pure chemicals. Sometimes an organic source of nitrogen is also necessary. This may be supplied as a chemically pure amino-acid; asparagin is commonly used.

The recent discovery of the accessory growth-promoting substances required by bacteria, and the isolation of some of these as pure chemicals, is opening the way for cultivation of the more fastidious pathogenic bacteria in synthetic media of known composition, which will in turn make it possible to learn more about their metabolism and chemical composition. Although of known composition, such media are often very complex. Thus it has been found possible to grow diphtheria bacilli, with the production of toxin, on a medium composed of the amino-acids obtained by the hydrolysis of gelatine, supplemented by methionine, cystine, tryptophan, minute amounts of pimelic acid, beta-alanine, and nicotinic acid, together with certain inorganic salts, lactic acid, glucose, and maltose.

Sterilization of Media. If cultures are to be maintained pure, the media in which they are grown must, of course, be free of all other microbes; they must be sterile before they are inoculated. Culture media, with few exceptions, are sterilized by steam heat. To kill bacterial spores the medium must be subjected to a temperature above the boiling point, 120° C. This requires steam under pressure. Agar, broth, and peptone solutions are sterilized in an *autoclave*, a sealed vessel in which they are subjected to the temperature of steam at 20-pounds pressure for 20 minutes.

Such a treatment, however, would injure other media by hydrolyzing certain of their constituents. Potato would get too mushy, gelatine would not harden again, while the sugars in milk and the sugar broths would be broken down. Such media must be sterilized by a less drastic method. They are heated at a lower temperature for a longer time, in an *Arnold* sterilizer, where they are subjected to the temperature of flowing steam not under pressure (100° C.) for an hour. This treatment will not, however, kill spores. To make the media completely sterile, they are allowed to stand over night. During this time any spores present, finding themselves in a favorable medium, will germinate. They are now not so resistant, and a second treatment in the Arnold sterilizer will kill them. To make doubly sure, this treatment is usually repeated again on the third day. Such a method is called *fractional sterilization*.

CHAPTER XIV

ECOLOGY OF BACTERIA: HABITATS

Since bacteria have become adapted to such a wide range of environmental factors, it is not surprising to find that they are almost universally distributed over the earth's surface. Probably, if a total census could be taken, it would be found that the majority of them occur in the soil; from the dried surface of the soil every wind storm carries great numbers into the air, from which they slowly settle down again. The sea, lakes, ponds, and streams all have a bacterial flora. Every mass of organic matter soon becomes inoculated and starts to decay. All plants and animals have their parasitic species. Queer places like salt lakes and hot springs and sulphur beds about volcanoes all serve as habitats for some sorts of bacteria. We cannot find space to discuss all of the habitats occupied by bacteria. We will have to limit ourselves to a brief consideration of certain more important ones — soil and water, milk, and the human body.

SOIL

Beebe, in his book *Jungle Peace,* has described in his fascinating manner the varied assortment of creatures sifted out from a cubic yard of jungle soil. He limited his investigation to animals which could be seen with the naked eye or a pocket lens. With a compound microscope and the methods of cultivation used by the bacteriologist, one could extract a greater number of species from a single teaspoonful of rich soil. The soil is populated by an unseen host of microscopic creatures — bacteria, molds, algae, protozoa, microscopic worms — so that the term "the living earth" is much more than a figure of speech. The soil breathes; it is dynamic and fertile through the activities of these microörganisms. Without the soil microbes the surface of the earth would be a lifeless desert.

Soil as a Culture Medium. We have already pointed out the similarity of the soil to a trickling filter type of sewage purification plant. The soil is made up of inorganic mineral particles coated with a layer of colloidal material, mainly of organic matter, and separated by air spaces. The layer of colloidal organic matter, holding moisture, is much like a layer of agar; it serves as a culture medium for the growth of bacteria. The mineral particles are derived from the bedrock of the earth, which becomes broken up and chemically altered by weathering agencies — wind, rain, freezing, and wave action. Even in this process, bacteria play a part. By forming acids, either organic or inorganic (sulphuric, nitric), they dissolve limestone and phosphates and similar materials. These mineral particles vary markedly in size, which to a large extent determines the texture of the soil. The size ranges from relatively coarse particles like pebbles or sand grains down to the microscopic particles forming clay. These particles are made up of minerals rather inert chemically, i.e., not easily dissolved. Silica and aluminum oxide are the most common.

The jelly-like film upon the soil particles is composed partly of very finely divided mineral matter, partly of residues of undecomposed organic matter, and of water, with of course bacteria and other microbes.

The relative amounts of the different constituents vary enormously in different soils, depending upon the nature of the mineral elements available and upon climatic conditions and other factors. A good average fertile soil is found to have about 25% of its volume air, 25% water, 45% mineral matter, and 5% organic matter. A desert sand will of course be almost entirely air and mineral, while peat is almost entirely organic matter with a great capacity for holding water. It will thus be seen that the suitability of the soil as a culture medium is quite different in different kinds of soil.

Methods of Studying Soil Microbes. The soil bacteria have been most extensively studied by making cultures of the soil in various culture media, usually in agar plates. These may be made quantitative; a weighed amount of soil is placed in a measured volume of sterile water, and after thorough shaking dilutions are made from this suspension for quantitative plate cultures. No one culture medium will, however, permit all of the soil bacteria to grow. If ordinary meat extract agar is used, the majority of the bacteria which grow will be the proteolytic species. If a starch medium is used, starch-splitting bacteria will grow. By varying the temperature, the pH, the aeration, and composition of the medium, one may make an almost infinite series of different sorts of plate cultures. It has been found that a very dilute agar medium containing organic nitrogen (sodium caseinate or albuminate) and glucose, neutral in reaction, and incubated aerobically at room temperature for a week or more, gives a higher count than any other single medium, and it has been widely used to estimate the relative abundance of bacteria in different kinds of soil.

Another method used to study soil bacteria is to prepare a series of selective media, usually in liquid form, which are then inoculated with samples of the soil to be studied. Thus one may make a special medium for nitrogen-fixing bacteria, for nitrifying bacteria, for ammonifying bacteria, and for bacteria which can digest cellulose or chitin or other particular organic substances. After incubation the cultures are examined for the particular organisms to which each medium is suited, either by a microscopic examination or by the use of chemical tests which will show the end products of the reactions caused by each species, and thus determine the presence or absence of different groups of soil microbes in the soil sample. This may be made quantitative by the method of extinction-dilution mentioned in the preceding chapter.

Culture studies of the soil give a sort of puzzle picture of the soil microflora; one must mentally put together the results from all of the different cultures in order to gain an impression of the whole, which is almost impossible. And so various investigators, especially Winogradsky, have tried to work out methods for a direct microscopic study of the soil. This is very difficult because of the large amount of opaque finely divided mineral and organic matter which obscures the field. Winogradsky suspended the soil in water, or in agar or gelatine, and then spread the liquid on a slide, which is stained with erythrosin. This acid dye will stain bacteria (though faintly) after a time, but does not stain most of the inert material in soils. Others have tried to get rid of the soil particles by adding salts to the water in which the soil is suspended, hoping to alter the electric charge on the bacteria, and thus cause them to be freed from the soil particles, which are then allowed to settle out. Cholodny puts microscope slides into the ground, and lets the soil bacteria grow upon the glass. Another investigator takes his microscope to the field, pokes the lens down to the surface of the soil, and by means of a vertical illuminator studies the soil bacteria and fungi and protozoa *in situ*. These methods, however, have not been used extensively enough to allow us to summarize the results in definite form.

Distribution of Soil Bacteria. All methods of study indicate that bacteria are most numerous in the top layers of soil, and that they decrease rather rapidly with depth. This is only natural, since organic matter is constantly being added to the surface, and here conditions of aeration are the best. The numbers also vary greatly in different soils. In a well-cultivated rich soil, direct microscopic counts may indicate several billions of bacteria per gram. Such a soil, using plate cultures for counting, might show about 50,000,000 bacteria, 20,000,000 actinomycetes, and perhaps 100,000 molds (spores or mycelial fragments) per gram. It would probably have from 100,000 to 300,000 protozoa and perhaps 50,000 to 100,000 algae. A gram of soil is less than a teaspoonful.

Environmental Factors in the Soil. The soil is subject to wide fluctuations in all of the environmental factors which influence the growth of bacteria. Probably the *moisture* content of the soil is the most important, and this of course depends mainly upon the average rainfall, but is determined also by the degree of water-holding capacity of the soil, and its drainage.

If water is inadequate, green plants cannot grow, and there is little organic matter added to the soil; consequently bacteria are few. If water is excessive, the air spaces between the soil particles become filled; oxygen cannot penetrate as rapidly as it is consumed, and conditions become anaerobic. Under these conditions, organic matter is incompletely decomposed, and accumulated products of decomposition (especially acids) tend to inhibit the growth of bacteria. Optimum conditions obtain when the colloidal film on the mineral particles is saturated with moisture, but the spaces between are still well aerated.

The *temperature* of the soil of course varies with the seasons, though not so much so as that of the air. Experimentally it can be shown that the activities of the soil bacteria increase when the soil is warmed, but counts through the seasons show that other factors than temperature (moisture, the growth of plants) influence the microbic population. The soil bacteria reach their peak in the spring.

The *reaction* of the soil varies; probably the range from pH 4 to pH 10 would include nearly all soils. The reaction depends upon many factors, of which the most important is the mineral composition of the soil. It is found that the numbers of bacteria decrease as the reaction departs in both directions from near neutrality. Probably slight alkalinity is most favorable. But the reaction alters greatly the proportion of different kinds of bacteria. Molds are more abundant in acid soils, while actinomycetes are almost absent. The nitrogen-fixing species, *Azotobacter chroöcoccum*, cannot live in soils much below pH 6.

Bacteria and Soil Fertility. In general those conditions in the soil environment which are most favorable to the growth of bacteria are also most favorable to the growth of higher plants. The activities of the bacteria in the soil provide, for the most part, the nutrients which the plant must absorb from the soil. It is not surprising, therefore, to find a rather good correlation between the numbers of bacteria in soil and its fertility. It is even possible to estimate, to some degree, the effect of liming or fertilizing or other soil treatments upon crop yield by first studying the effect upon the bacterial count of the soil.

Cultivated soils usually show higher bacterial counts than unculti-vated soils of the same type. It is interesting to note the effect of till-ing the soil upon the bacterial population. Plowing and harrowing carry dead plant matter from the surface down into the soil where it is protected from sunlight and drying, and so can be acted upon by the bacteria. But, more important, these operations break up the soil, loosen its texture, and so provide aeration. Aeration favors the complete mineralization of organic matter, favors nitrogen fixation, and favors nitrification, all of which are bacterial activities that tend to increase the fertility. If aeration is imperfect, these processes are inhibited, while denitrification, i.e., a reduction of the nitrates to atmospheric nitrogen, is favored, so there may be an actual loss of fertility.

WATER

A much larger portion of the earth's surface is covered by water than by land. Even a considerable proportion of the continents is covered by lakes and streams. It must be obvious that the activities of bacteria in the sea and fresh waters are of tremendous importance in the economy of nature. But it is only within the last few years that any very extensive studies have been made in this field. Most of our information about water bacteria has been obtained in investigations carried out from the standpoint of sanitation. These will be dis-cussed in a later section of the book, in connection with the intestinal diseases. In this chapter we will only summarize what little is known about water bacteria from the standpoint of ecology.

Methods for Studying Water Bacteria. A large part of the investigation of water bacteria has been carried on by the same methods used in studying soil bacteria, i.e., by making plate counts on various culture media, especially ordinary nutrient agar; and in inoculating water into various special media which reveal the activities of particular physiological groups. In the study of marine bacteria, it is important to use sea water instead of distilled water. In the study of lakes and streams, the investigation is confused by the fact that such waters are constantly having soil bacteria washed into them, many of which are not capable of living extensively in the water, but which will grow in the bacteriologist's artificial media.

The author has used a direct microscopic method for studying water bacteria. Glass slides are attached to a line suspended from a float. Bacteria soon attach themselves to the glass and grow there. These bacteria are often of interesting morphology — Chlamydobacteriales and Caulobacteriales and other striking types, types which will not grow in the ordinary culture media. They may be easily stained and observed and counted. The number of bacteria per square millimeter of glass per day of immersion serves as a measure of bacterial growth in the aquatic habitat. The microscopic method has several disadvantages. Many of the bacteria cannot be identified by their morphology alone; and one knows nothing about what sort of chemical transformations the bacteria on the slide are performing. Both microscopic and cultural methods are needed to get a complete picture.

Lakes. Lakes are of many types, so that it is difficult to generalize about them. They tend to fall into three main groups. *Eutrophic* ("well nourished") lakes support an abundance of aquatic life, fish and algae and shore plants. They usually occur in the course of a stream and receive considerable drainage. They are usually slightly alkaline in reaction, and contain relatively large amounts of organic matter in solution. If sufficiently deep, this high B.O.D. leads to anaerobic conditions in the lower parts of the lake during the summer. *Oligotrophic* ("poorly nourished") lakes are less productive. They are usually "spring-fed" lakes, sometimes without an outlet, often occurring in the high mountains. They are usually neutral or slightly acid in reaction, and do not have enough organic matter to become anaerobic in the deeper parts during the summer. *Dystrophic* ("abnormally nourished") lakes drain *Sphagnum* bogs, and have a very high content of peculiar organic matter. They are found mostly in northern climates. Their water is dark in color. The high content of organic matter makes them completely anaerobic a few feet below the surface. The color prevents the penetration of sunlight, and the water is very cold a few feet down. Their water is usually very acid in reaction. They are almost lifeless. There are, in addition to these three types, many lakes of peculiar type which will not fit such a classification.

Bacteria in Lake Waters. Bacterial activity is greatest in eutrophic lakes. The numbers are greatest near the shore, and decrease toward the middle. A very productive lake showed about 900 bacteria per cc. of water near the central part, with about 500 bacteria per sq. mm. per day on immersed slides; while a shallow, weed-choked bay near shore showed about 30,000 per cc. in plate counts, and about 3500 bacteria per sq. mm. per day on slide counts. Oligotrophic lakes contain fewer bacteria. An oligotrophic lake was found to have about 60 bacteria per cc. when plated, and about 110 bacteria per sq. mm. per day were deposited upon slides in the surface water. Dystrophic lakes, in spite of their high content of organic matter, have relatively small numbers of bacteria, probably because of low temperature and anaerobic conditions. A dystrophic lake was found to have 65 bacteria per cc., and about 180 bacteria per sq. mm. per day upon slides in the surface water.

Bacterial activities in lakes decrease markedly with depth in very deep lakes. This is not shown by plate counts, but is clear from microscopic observations of submerged slides. It is probably due mainly to the lower temperatures of the deeper layers. The bacteria in lakes also show marked seasonal fluctuations. These are due to several factors. Deep lakes "turn over" in the fall and spring, the deeper water coming to the surface. This tends to bring bacteria from the bottom mud into the water, and so cause a temporary increase. But probably more important is the seasonal fluctuation in the amount of *plankton*, the floating algae and other microscopic organisms which produce organic matter in the water. In one lake which the author studied, the bacteria were found to vary with the amount of plankton in the water.

Lake Bottoms. Lake waters usually have relatively small bacterial populations. When streams whose waters contain numerous bacteria empty into lakes, the bacteria tend to disappear a relatively short distance from the mouth of the stream. This is thought to be due mainly to *sedimentation*. The bacteria themselves do not readily settle, but they become adsorbed onto larger particles suspended in the water. If one tows a fine net of bolting silk through the water, it traps large numbers of algae and microscopic crustacea and other plankton organisms. Nearly all of these are found to have a coating of bacteria on their surface. When these organisms die, the bacteria also gradually settle to the bottom. Bacteria in the lake water are thus constantly settling to the bottom, and the bottom mud therefore has a much denser population than does the water.

The bottom deposit of lakes somewhat resembles the soil. It is composed of mineral particles and of organic matter. In most lakes it is of very fine texture, a soft black ooze. In oligotrophic lakes it may consist very largely of inorganic silt or sand. In eutrophic lakes it is richer in organic matter. In dystrophic lakes, it is a peculiar brown deposit composed largely of colloidal organic matter.

The numbers of bacteria in bottom mud vary with different kinds of lakes. In a shallow bay, plate counts as high as 500,000,000 per cc. were obtained, while near the middle of the lake the numbers were less than 1,000,000. This was a eutrophic lake. Dystrophic lakes show smaller numbers, and oligotrophic lakes very small numbers (about 2000 per cc. in one such lake). It will be seen that these are figures much higher than those for the water above, and comparable to those for soil. The bacteria are most abundant in the very surface layer of the mud, decreasing rapidly below the water-mud interface; on the average, they decrease by one-fourth for every centimeter of depth.

The activities of the bottom bacteria must then be restricted very largely to the surface of the mud. Life in the lake bottoms is quite different from that in other habitats. Conditions are quite anaerobic throughout, or at least a few millimeters below the surface of the mud, and usually the temperature is only a few degrees above freezing. The decomposition of organic matter must therefore proceed slowly and imperfectly. We have as yet little information, but it seems that the organic matter is eventually liberated largely as hydrogen and methane and carbon dioxide. The methane and hydrogen, diffusing through the upper water, are finally oxidized by autotrophic bacteria there.

Kinds of Lake Bacteria. Both microscopic and cultural studies of lake bacteria indicate that there is a characteristic bacterial flora of lakes, distinct from that of the soil or other habitats, but details regarding the species remain to be worked out. In plate cultures, about one-fourth of the colonies which appear are chromogenic species, colored yellow, orange, red, blue, or purple, the frequency of the different colors being in the order named. In the dark waters of dystrophic lakes, however, pigmented bacteria are rare.

By the use of specific media such as are used for soil bacteria, nearly all of the physiological groups found in soil are found to have representatives in lakes, though they may be represented by different species. Thus *Azotobacter agilis* appears to be the aquatic nitrogen-fixer. It is clear that the rôle of bacteria in the economy of lakes is a very complex one, and that only a start has been made toward understanding it.

Streams. Streams start in the highlands, often in the mountains, and in their upper reaches the water is usually clear, cold, and rapidly flowing. It receives relatively little organic matter from the surrounding land, which is often barren and rocky. As the stream flows on through its lower reaches, it becomes slower and deeper, and from the surrounding land there is brought in more and more soil with its hordes of bacteria, and it receives more and more organic matter. With most streams this organic matter consists in ever-increasing amounts of sewage and industrial wastes, and almost the only bacteriological studies of streams have been concerned with this pollution, its relation to disease, and means of controlling it. It is obvious that the numbers of bacteria in streams must increase steadily from the source to the mouth, but we know almost nothing about the microbes peculiar to running water, or their activities.

Self-purification of Streams. If sewage is discharged into a stream, and no other sewage is added downstream, the water tends to purify itself; both the concentration of organic matter and the numbers of bacteria decrease. Many studies have been made to determine the nature of the processes which occur in this self-purification, and it is found to be very complex, with many factors at work. If the flow of the stream is sluggish, sedimentation may be an important factor; both bacteria and organic matter settle to the bottom, leaving the water above more clear. But if the stream is deep and the flow too slow, purification is prevented; the mass of water becomes anaerobic, and putrefaction is continuous and incomplete. Such a situation is seen where a city discharges its sewage into a river immediately above a dam.

If the flow is rapid and the stream shallow, as in riffles, thorough aeration of the water leads to a rapid decomposition of the organic matter to inorganic substances. Lack of organic food then leads to death of the bacteria. In such situations an important factor is the carpet of attached algae and other organisms on the bottom and the sides of the stream. This carpet presents an enormous surface which tends to adsorb bacteria and other colloidal material. It has been found that without this carpet the purification rate is slower.

Other factors may be of importance. Many bacteria are destroyed by protozoa in the water, and these microbes of prey undoubtedly are important in limiting the bacterial population. There is some evidence that the cholera and related organisms are destroyed in rivers of India by the bacteriophage. Formerly the action of sunlight was considered important in destroying bacteria in the water, but this is considered unimportant now because it has been found that the ultraviolet rays, which destroy bacteria, do not penetrate deeply into the water.

The Sea. The vast areas of the oceans have hardly been touched by bacteriological explorations, but enough has been learned about marine bacteria to indicate that they are distributed much as are bacteria in lakes. The bacteria of the sea have been studied in the same manner as lake bacteria, save that heavier and more elaborate apparatus is required to obtain samples from the great depths.

Plate cultures indicate that bacteria are very numerous in the shallow waters near shore, especially about the mouths of streams, but become very few a relatively short distance from land; many samples yield less than 10 bacteria per cc. of water. Examination of plankton obtained with silk nets shows large numbers of bacteria attached to the plankton organisms, especially the diatoms. These plankton organisms are continually dying and settling to the bottom, carrying with them the bacteria. Bottom deposits of the sea, even at great depths and far from land, may contain a million or more bacteria per cc. They decrease with depth in the marine bottom ooze just as they do in lake mud.

The kinds of bacteria in the sea also resemble closely the kinds found in fresh-water lakes, save that they are for the most part halophilic, incapable of growing without some salt in the medium. Pigment-forming species appear to be more abundant than in lakes; they form nearly 70% of the bacteria cultivated from sea water in the vicinity of La Jolla. Bacteria concerned with the various phases of the nitrogen cycle, the decomposition of cellulose and chitin and other organic materials, have all been found in the sea. A noteworthy feature is the abundance of bacteria which can dissolve agar. Such bacteria are very rarely found from terrestrial or fresh-water habitats. It is also interesting to note that all of the luminescent bacteria, those which can emit light, have been obtained from marine habitats.

MILK

Milk is a favorable culture medium for the growth of many species of bacteria, including some which cause disease in man. It is more important, from a bacteriological standpoint, than any other food-stuff of man, and for that reason has been very extensively studied. A large share of the increased health and longevity of man which has been brought about in the past quarter century may be attributed to the better quality of milk and the improvements in its handling.

Numbers of Bacteria in Milk. Various methods are used for counting bacteria in milk. Most commonly quantitative plate cultures are made and the colonies are counted. Media which approach the composition of milk are often used, as whey agar or digested milk agar, since these yield higher counts than ordinary nutrient agar. Milk bacteria may also be counted by a direct microscopic method. A measured volume of milk is spread over a measured area of slide in a thin film which is then dried, fixed, stained, and examined through the microscope. The microscopic count is always higher than the plate count, because some of the bacteria in the milk are dead, many are in clumps which will form only one colony, and some will not grow on the plating medium. The use of both methods gives more information than either alone. A high microscopic count with a very low plate count might indicate that the milk had been produced under dirty conditions but had been thoroughly pasteurized.

The number of bacteria in milk depends upon a great variety of factors which can all be grouped under three divisions: 1. The degree of contamination of the milk. 2. The time between milking and collecting the sample for counting. 3. The temperature at which the milk was stored. There are some bacteria in the milk as soon as it is drawn, derived from the normal parasitic flora of the milk ducts. To this initial flora may be added many other bacteria from the air, the cow's coat, the dust of the stable, the hands of the milker, and the pail in which it is collected. Nothing can be done about the bacteria in the udder, but contamination from other sources can be greatly reduced by cleanliness in milking and handling the milk.

Many cities have established limits above which the milk cannot be sold. These limits vary with different communities. Milk is in some communities graded according to several qualities, among which the bacterial count is important. The U. S. Public Health Service has recommended the following grades:

	Bacteria per cc.	
	Raw milk	Pasteurized milk
Grade A	50,000	30,000
Grade B	200,000	50,000
Grade C	1,000,000	For cooking only
Grade D	For cooking only	

Many communities have a Medical Milk Commission which supervises the production of very clean raw milk for babies, called "certified" milk, which must not have more than 10,000 bacteria per cc.

Pasteurization. Pasteurization is a method of heating milk to a sufficient temperature for a sufficient length of time so that the disease-producing bacteria commonly spread by milk will be killed; and so that the bacteria which normally sour or spoil milk will be inhibited, and the milk will thus keep longer. The pasteurization temperature cannot be made too high, or the milk will have a cooked taste. Various methods of pasteurization are in use. The most common, or *holding* process, exposes the milk to a temperature of about 62° C. for 30 minutes. This will destroy tubercle bacilli in the milk, but not the milk-souring *Streptococcus lactis*.

Normal Fermentation of Milk. Milk contains proteins and sugars favorable to the growth of a great variety of organisms. Placed as it is, in a tall, relatively narrow bottle with a small surface exposed to the air, and with a layer of cream through which oxygen cannot readily diffuse, the first growth of bacteria soon renders the milk anaerobic, and those bacteria will grow best which can efficiently utilize the energy in the milk sugar by anaerobic fermentation. When milk stands, it sooner or later sours; sooner if it is raw milk or if it stands in a warm place, later if it is pasteurized or stands in a cool place. But almost every sample of milk undergoes a lactic acid fermentation as the first step in its spoilage.

There are a number of species of bacteria which can ferment lactose, but one is so much more efficient than the others in growing in milk that it almost invariably gets a head start and crowds the others out. This is *Streptococcus lactis*. Where it comes from is something of a mystery. It is not a human or bovine parasite. It has been found growing on certain plants, and probably gets into the milk from the air of the milking stable, where it is present on dust from dried plant matter. In any case, it is almost always present in the milk when it leaves the stable. It is admirably suited to its work of souring milk; it will grow at temperatures as low as 10° C., it is more resistant to heat than most bacteria without spores, and it will grow in acidities up to pH 4.

Lactobacilli are also concerned with the souring of milk in some cases. Three species, *L. casei*, *L. acidophilus*, and *L. bulgaricus* may be found. Of these, *L. casei* occurs more frequently. The Lactobacilli grow more slowly than *Streptococcus lactis*, and grow better at higher temperatures, but they can tolerate somewhat greater degrees of acidity, and may therefore continue the souring process after the Streptococci have stopped growing. *Aerobacter aerogenes* and *Escherichia coli* may also occur in milk, and ferment lactose. They sometimes get the upper hand, especially if the milk becomes warm. They do not produce as much acid as either *S. lactis* or the Lactobacilli, but produce gas from the sugar, and objectionable flavors in sour milk. They are considered undesirable organisms in milk.

Abnormal Fermentations. Under the term "abnormal fermentations" dairy bacteriologists list a series of changes in milk caused by bacteria, other than the normal souring, which are not all fermentations in a chemical sense. Among these may be mentioned gassy fermentation, often caused by lactose-fermenting yeasts; ropiness, caused by bacteria which form large amounts of gum, and so cause the milk to become slimy or mucilaginous; sweet curdling, caused by bacteria which secrete rennin; and various colors produced by chromogenic species of bacteria, especially blue milk caused by *Pseudomonas cyanogenes*.

Diseases Spread by Milk. Milk is much more important than other foodstuffs as an agent in the transmission of infectious diseases, because it is a favorable culture medium for many of the pathogenic bacteria. A very small number of bacteria, perhaps only one, gaining access to the milk, may multiply to such an extent by the time the milk is consumed that an overwhelming dose of the germs is taken into the body. The diseases of man which may be contracted by drinking milk fall into two classes: those transmitted from the cow, the germs being present in the milk as it is drawn from the udder; and those derived from persons handling the milk, the organisms multiplying in the milk before it is consumed. In the first group, undulant fever, caused by *Brucella abortus*, and tuberculosis are most important. In the second group, the Streptococcus infections, acute sore throat and scarlet fever, are the most important, but diphtheria, typhoid fever, and dysentery are also spread in this manner. Such diseases are transmitted by persons handling the milk who are convalescent from the disease, or who are normal carriers of the pathogenic germs. The organisms which cause these diseases are all killed by pasteurization.

The Human Body

The intestinal canals of all of the higher animals contain an enormous flora. Smaller numbers are found in the mouth and upper air passages, and on the skin. No extensive survey of these bacteria has been made for any animal save man, and our knowledge of the bacterial flora of man is still very incomplete. Such a survey is a problem of great complexity. Both direct microscopic studies and observations of bacteria isolated in cultures show that the microbic flora of a given part of the body varies greatly when different individuals are compared, or when different age groups are compared, or may even vary in the same individual from time to time.

When one compares the variety of morphological types observed in smears from the mouth, or the intestinal contents, with the small number of species which are obtained when cultures are made from these same materials, he is forced to conclude that a large number of the species of bacteria parasitic in man have not been grown in culture media, and this has been a great impediment to progress in learning about the normal flora of the human body. With the use of an increasingly greater variety of culture media and methods of cultivation, the number of species which may be studied in pure culture is steadily increasing.

Since bacteria are present in the air we breathe, the water we drink, the food we eat, and on nearly all surfaces with which the body may come in contact, it is not surprising that cultures made for the purpose of studying the normal flora of the body often yield a growth of bacteria which are only accidentally and temporarily present in the material being studied. It is only by studying many individuals, and repeatedly, and thus determining the microbes that are *constantly* present, that we can exclude from our data these accidental visitors.

The body of a new-born baby is sterile, i.e., free from microbes, except for a few in the mouth which are derived from the bacterial flora of the mother's vagina during its passage through the birth canal. Within a few hours, however, bacteria from its surroundings have begun to implant themselves, and within a day they have passed through the alimentary canal and have begun to appear in the stools. These bacteria, normal body parasites, are derived from the mother or from others who care for the infant.

Where Parasitic Bacteria Are Found. Parasitic bacteria may be found on all parts of the skin. They are very numerous in the mouth, less abundant in the nose and throat. They do not extend into the respiratory tract beyond the bronchi. They may be present in small numbers in the esophagus and stomach, becoming increasingly more abundant throughout the intestines. A large proportion of the bulk of the feces is made up of bacteria. Parasitic bacteria are present in great numbers in the vagina, but do not extend into the uterus or beyond. They are present about the glans penis, but do not extend into the urethra and bladder. The blood, the internal viscera, and closed body cavities (pleura, peritoneum, meninges), the muscles, and all other internal tissues are *normally sterile*.

The Skin. Continuously exposed to the external environment, all sorts of bacteria may be cultured from the skin. Only two groups, however, are constant or normal parasites, the *Staphylococci* and the *Corynebacteria*. Three species of Staphylococci occur as normal skin parasites, *albus*, *aureus*, and *citreus*, their frequency being in the order named. It is noteworthy that the latter two species are the only normal body parasites which are chromogenic, and that they occur on the skin which is exposed to light. Probably several species of diphtheroid bacteria occur, but their classification has not been worked out.

The Mouth. Bacteria are present in the mouth immediately or shortly after birth. In the baby's mouth the normal bacterial flora is relatively simple. Staphylococci and *Streptococcus salivarius* are the only constant species. With the eruption of the teeth, however, a marked change occurs. This is perhaps due in part to a change to a more varied diet, but more particularly to the formation of spaces and crevices where bacteria may grow undisturbed. While *Streptococcus salivarius* is still the dominant species which appears in aerobic plate cultures, and can be demonstrated in large numbers in smears made from the mucous membranes of the cheeks or gums, a great variety of microbes can be found in microscopic examinations of material from between the teeth, or the surface of the tongue, or from the crevices between the teeth and the gums.

Gram positive and Gram negative rods, spheres, and spiral forms may be found. Some are aerobic, some are anaerobic. Certain long, unbranched filamentous bacteria, *Leptotrichia buccalis*, occur. Rod forms with pointed ends, members of the genus *Fusobacterium*, are found, usually associated with Spirochaetes of the genus *Borrelia*. Among these a parasitic amoeba, *Entamoeba buccalis*, is normal.

The mouth flora is subject to considerable variation in numbers of both individuals and species. In people with digestive disorders or fevers, who develop a "coated tongue," the number of bacteria is increased, and in long-continued diseases, especially if the individual is unconscious for some time, a very heavy growth of bacteria may occur. If the teeth develop cavities, or if the disease pyorrhoea attacks the gums, the mouth bacteria increase in number. Since these mouth diseases occur in a large proportion of the population with increasing age, there is a general tendency for the mouth flora to become more extensive and more complex with age.

Nose and Throat. The flora of the nose and throat is less extensive and more simple than that of the mouth. Cocci are the dominant organisms, white Staphylococci, the *Streptococcus salivarius*, and especially Gram negative diplococci of the genus *Neisseria*. These latter are the most constant and characteristic bacteria of the nasopharynx. The crypts of the tonsils contain a mixture of bacteria similar to that found in the crevices of the gums.

Alimentary Tract. Bacteria are being constantly swallowed in food and water, and many mouth bacteria are carried to the stomach in swallowing. But the gastric juice is normally highly acid (pH 1 to

pH 2) due to the hydrochloric acid which it secretes. This is sufficient to kill many of the bacteria which reach the stomach, and the
normal gastric juice is almost sterile. In diseases where the gastric
juice is reduced in acidity, and especially in cancer of the stomach,
bacteria may be quite abundant in the stomach fluid.

The upper part of the small intestine also contains relatively few
bacteria, but these increase steadily in numbers, becoming unbeliev-
ably numerous in the large intestine. The intestinal flora of infants
and adults is markedly different.

Babies before they are weaned have an intestinal flora composed
almost entirely of fermentative bacteria of the same sorts as those
concerned in the souring of milk, namely *Streptococci* and *Lactobacilli*. In breast-fed infants a peculiar branched Gram positive rod-
shaped organism, *Lactobacillus bifidus*, is prominent. If fed on cow's
milk, *Lactobacillus acidophilus* is more numerous. These organisms,
strong acid formers and highly acid tolerant, keep the intestinal
contents acid and thus prevent much growth of putrefactive bacteria.
A normal infant's stool smells sour, not putrid.

When the baby is weaned and the diet becomes general, the intestinal flora is changed. It becomes more varied with regard to
species, and putrefactive bacteria become dominant in most cases.
Smears of the feces show a great mixture of Gram negative and Gram
positive rods, with some cocci. There may be a few Spirochaetes.
Not uncommonly a parasitic amoeba, *Entamoeba coli*, is found.

Since the intestines contain large amounts of organic matter and
large numbers of bacteria, all closed off from the air, conditions must
be entirely anaerobic, and the intestinal species are probably all either
strict or facultative anaerobic species. When plate cultures are made
from feces, and grown aerobically, the organisms which appear in
largest numbers are Gram negative rod-shaped species, *Escherichia
coli*, and related forms. Smaller numbers of *Streptococcus fecalis* and
Lactobacilli may occur. The strictly anaerobic species are mostly
fermentative or putrefactive spore-formers of the genus *Clostridium*,
but a number of asporogenous anaerobic species have been cultivated.

Intestinal Bacteria and Health. The influence of the enormous
intestinal flora upon the welfare of the human body which contains it
is a problem which has been considered from the earliest days of
bacteriology, but which has not yet been settled. On one hand it has
been claimed that the enzymes of the bacteria play an important part

in the digestion of our food, serving to complete the work done by the gastric and pancreatic and intestinal enzymes. There has been no clear proof of this, save that it seems clear that cellulose-dissolving bacteria are important to the herbivorous mammals. On the other hand, it has been claimed that the absorption of toxins or of products of putrefaction resulting from the activities of intestinal microbes causes various diseases. There is but little doubt that the general malaise resulting from constipation and the acute toxic state which follows intestinal obstruction are due to the absorption of poisonous substances produced by the intestinal bacteria.

Metchnikoff believed that hardening of the arteries and other tissue changes occurring in old age were due to the continued absorption from the intestines of indol, phenol, and other poisonous products of putrefaction. He suggested that the disintegration of old age might be postponed by replacing the putrefactive bacteria of the intestine with fermentative organisms. He supported this theory by the observation that in southeastern European countries a number of individuals lived to remarkable ages, and that in these countries fermented milk beverages formed a large part of the diet. He studied particularly a milk beverage of Bulgaria, milk soured by the fermentation produced by *Lactobacillus bulgaricus*, and suggested that the consumption of this milk or of cultures of the organism would lead to a replacement of the putrefactive intestinal flora with the beneficial Lactobacilli. But it was later found that the organism of Bulgarian buttermilk will not grow in the human alimentary tract. Even though voluminous cultures are consumed, the organisms do not become implanted. It was therefore proposed to accomplish the aims of Metchnikoff with another Lactobacillus, *L. acidophilus*, known to occur naturally in the intestines of infants. If cultures of this are consumed, and the diet is changed, it will become implanted in the intestines and will tend to replace the putrefactive flora. It requires the consumption of at least a quart of milk per day to maintain this changed flora. There is no clear evidence that the use of "acidophilus milk" is of any great benefit save possibly in certain cases of chronic constipation.

Life without Germs. Since it has been suggested that the parasitic bacteria of the alimentary tract take part in the digestion of food, and it has been considered that they might be essential to life in other ways, several experiments have been undertaken to attempt raising animals aseptically, i.e., completely shielded from bacteria. These experiments have been performed upon chicks, which may be removed from the shell with aseptic precautions when they are about to hatch, and upon guinea pigs which have been delivered by Caesarian section when they were about to be born. The animal must then be placed in a sterile chamber, fed with sterilized food, and handled in every way aseptically. Such an experiment is a veritable *tour de force* in aseptic technique, and most such experiments have failed or have been inconclusive. Recently, however, it has been reported that guinea pigs were successfully raised aseptically, and that they appeared to develop normally save that their lymph glands did not grow.

CHAPTER XV

THE DEATH OF BACTERIA; DISINFECTION

Since man's interest in bacteria has largely centered about the prevention of infectious diseases and the preservation of foods and other substances from decomposition, it is not surprising that a large amount of research has been concerned with the destruction of bacteria by various means. Aside from the very important practical applications of this part of bacteriology, the death of bacteria

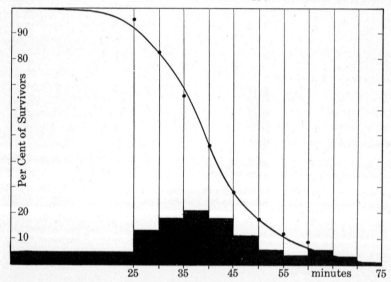

FIG. 70. The Order of Death of Mustard Seeds Killed by Bichloride of Mercury. The curve shows the percentage of seeds surviving at each time interval; the solid blocks show the relative numbers killed in each interval. Note that the largest number of seeds were killed in the interval from 35 to 40 minutes. (After Rahn, *The Physiology of Bacteria*, Blakiston & Co., Philadelphia.)

resulting from various agencies exhibits certain differences from the same phenomenon in higher organisms, which are of great interest from a scientific standpoint.

The Order of Death. When bacteria are subjected to heat or treated with a chemical disinfectant, the cells do not all die at once. This is, of course, not surprising, since one might foresee that the cells would not all be the same, that they would vary in their susceptibility, and that this variation might be distributed according to a normal chance distribution, with the majority of individuals succumbing at about the same time, but a number showing lesser or greater resistance to the killing agent. Such is found to be the case when higher organisms are killed, as shown in graph in Fig. 70. At first a few, and then more and more individuals are killed, until in one time unit a maximum number succumb, after which the number dying in each period falls off again.

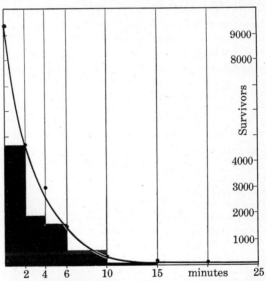

With bacteria, however, the order of death is different. The death curve may be determined by placing a suspension of bacteria in a water bath at a killing temperature, or by adding a poison to the suspension, and then, at regular short time intervals, by making quantitative plate cultures. Counting the number of colonies on these plates will show the number of bacteria surviving at each period. When such counts are made, it is found that the largest number dying in any time interval, die in the first interval, and that the number killed in each period is a constant proportion of the number alive at the beginning of that period. Starting with a suspension

FIG. 71. The Order of Death of Bacteria (Spores of *B. anthracis*) Killed by Bichloride of Mercury. The curve shows the actual numbers of survivors; the solid blocks show the relative numbers dying in each time interval. Note that the greatest number were killed during the first interval, from 0 to 2 minutes. (After Rahn, *The Physiology of Bacteria*, Blakiston & Co., Philadelphia.)

of 1,000,000 bacteria per cc., and taking samples every minute, it might be found that 900,000 were killed in the first minute; then, of the surviving 100,000, 90,000 would be killed in the second minute; of the surviving 10,000, 9,000 would be killed in the third minute, and so on. While the results of actual observations will not be so precise as this, the general results of a number of such observations agree closely enough to indicate that this is the rule in the death of bacteria. Death occurs at a constant rate; if the logarithms of the numbers of surviving cells are plotted against time, a straight line results.

This fact was discovered by Madsen and Nyman, and by Chick, who called attention to the fact that the curve for the death of bacteria is the same sort of curve as that which expresses the rate of a *monomolecular chemical reaction.* Such a reaction is one in which the rate of the reaction is determined by the concentration of but *one* of the reacting molecules. Since this substance is being constantly removed during the reaction, it follows that the greatest amount of substance must be changed at the very beginning of the reaction, that the amount changed in a unit of time must constantly decrease, and that the rate of this decrease is constant. The logarithms of the quantities of material remaining at each time interval fall on a straight line.

Theories. Various theories and views have been offered to explain the apparent monomolecular character of the bacterial death curve. Some authorities would deny that this death curve is different from that of higher organisms, claiming that the process is so rapid that the first part of the curve, showing an increasing death rate, cannot be followed. Rahn, however, in a careful review of many separate experiments, shows that this cannot be the case. With certain exceptions, the death curve is always monomolecular in character. These exceptions are in the case of Staphylococci and spore-forming bacteria, where the natural arrangement of the cells in clusters and chains makes the plate count an unreliable method for counting the surviving cells; in the case of cultures where growth is still continuing, the presence of young cells of high susceptibility and of old cells of greater resistance introduces a real element of variation in the cells themselves; and finally, in the case of death by starvation, where apparently the curve expresses a true chance distribution in the longevity of the cells. In all other cases which have been adequately studied, a monomolecular type of curve has been obtained.

It has been claimed that this death curve, peculiar to bacteria, may be explained by their small size, which approaches molecular dimensions. There is, however, ample room for a large number of molecules in a bacterial cell. Chick noted a great similarity between the curves for sterilization of cultures and the curves for the coagulation of proteins in pure solution, and came to the conclusion that the monomolecular character of the death curve may be best explained by assuming that the death of bacteria is due to the effect of the lethal agent upon one particular protein in the organism.

Bacteria Are Different. We have stressed this peculiarity in the order of death of bacteria because it is one more example of a fact which has been emphasized earlier in this book, namely, that with organisms so minute and simple as the bacteria, the ordinary biological laws do not necessarily apply. Rahn has ingeniously suggested that the reacting molecule responsible for the order of death peculiar to the bacteria is a *gene*, which in such small organisms may well consist of a single molecule. That this peculiarity is associated with the minute size of the bacteria is indicated by Rahn's observation that the slightly larger yeasts show curves indicating that sometimes one, sometimes two, molecules are reacting, while with the still larger protozoan, Colpidium, the curves are regularly dimolecular.

Susceptibility of Different Microörganisms. In any study of sterilization and disinfection, the species of bacterium used is an important factor; some are much more susceptible than others. In general, bacteria may be divided into two classes, the spore-formers and the non-spore-formers. Spores are much more resistant to all killing agents — heat, drying, and chemical poisons — than are vegetative cells, or bacteria without spores. The acidfast Mycobacteria, probably because of their waxy constituents, are peculiar; in their resistance to drying and chemicals they resemble spores, while they are little more resistant to heat than bacteria without spores.

Sterilization and Disinfection. It is customary to consider the destruction of bacteria under two headings. Killing by physical agents — drying, heat, light, various radiations, electricity — is called *sterilization,* and is distinguished from death by chemical poisons, which is called *disinfection.* This difference is more apparent than real, since probably in all cases death by physical agents involves a chemical reaction in the microbe, induced by the physical change.

Death by Drying. Since water is necessary for life, it follows that complete desiccation must result in death. There is, however, a wide difference in the susceptibility of microörganisms to this factor. Spores may remain alive in a dried state for years; some of the delicate pathogens may die in an hour or so when dried. The effect of drying varies widely with the conditions of the experiment. If dried on glass, bacteria will die much more quickly than if dried in sputum or similar material.

Bacteria will remain alive much longer when dried if they are kept in a vacuum, or if the air is replaced by an inert gas. It is quite evident that the death of organisms when dried is due to an *oxidation;* it is claimed that the rate of death is proportional to the square of the oxygen concentration. The rate of death by drying also proceeds more slowly at very low temperatures. One of the best methods for preserving bacteria alive is to dry them rapidly on filter paper in a vacuum kept in a refrigerator. Such specimens may remain alive for years.

Light. It has long been known that exposure of bacteria to intense direct sunlight will rapidly kill them. A study of the action of different parts of the spectrum upon bacteria showed that it is mainly the invisible ultra-violet light which is the most destructive; actually, those waves which lie between 2800 and 2540 Ångström units are most efficient. Ultra-violet light has been used in a practical way to destroy bacteria, particularly in the purification of water. But the very short ultra-violet rays have little power to penetrate substances which are quite transparent to visible light, such as glass and water. It follows that, for efficiency, the substance radiated must be spread in an exceedingly thin film.

There is some evidence that light kills bacteria also through oxidation, by the production of either peroxides or ozone. It is more likely, however, that the action is a direct one upon some constituent of the cell.

It has been found that Roentgen rays and radium emanations are also destructive to some organisms.

Heat. The death of bacteria by heat is greatly affected by their moisture content. It requires a higher temperature for a longer time to kill dried bacteria than is the case if they are moist. This is probably due to the fact that death by heat is due to coagulation of some protein within the cell. It requires a higher temperature to render proteins insoluble when dried than when in solution. It is evident that water enters into this coagulation process.

Dry heat is used in the laboratory to sterilize glassware. Generally a temperature of 160° C. for one hour is used.

The resistance of bacteria to moist heat varies considerably. It is usually expressed as the *thermal death point,* which is the temperature necessary to kill bacteria in ten minutes when moist. To determine this value it is necessary to place a number of tubes containing the same suspension of the bacteria in several different water baths heated to different temperatures, and to make subcultures from all of them at the end of ten minutes. This value will vary from 45° C. to about 60° C. with non-spore-forming bacteria, and is over 100° C. with most spore-formers. To attain the latter temperatures with moist heat requires the use of steam under pressure.

Moist heat may be applied in several ways. *Pasteurization* is a process by which certain bacteria are killed and others are inhibited for a considerable period of time. Pasteurization is used in the preservation of foodstuffs which would be injured by higher temperatures, particularly milk. Two methods are in use in the pasteurization of milk, the *flash* method, in which the milk is heated to 75-80° C. and immediately cooled again; and the *holding* process, in which it is heated to 60-65° C. for thirty minutes. Boiling will, of course, almost instantly kill all bacteria except those in the form of spores. It is the usual method for sterilizing surgical instruments and hypodermic syringes. The use of flowing steam, at air pressure, has the same efficiency as boiling. It is used in the fractional sterilization of culture media, and in the "cold-pack" process of home canning of food. Steam under pressure in the autoclave is efficient not only in sterilizing culture media, but also in sterilizing surgical dressings, and in the commercial "processing" of canned foods.

The dairyman and the canner are limited by the material they have to heat, as regards the temperatures they may use in attempts at sterilization. It has been pointed out that for their purposes the thermal death point is not so useful a measure of the susceptibility of bacteria as the *thermal death time,* i.e., the time necessary to kill all the bacteria in a given suspension at a given temperature.

Disinfectants. A great variety of different substances have been used or are used as disinfectants, and new ones are continually being brought forth. Unfortunately many of these are but patent nostrums, worthless, or at least no better than well-known cheaper substances. We cannot take space to describe all the different sorts of disinfectants and their uses. The student is referred to works on hygiene and pharmacology for detailed information. The various disinfectant substances may be classified into groups of related compounds having a similar action. We will briefly list the more important of these groups with their characteristics.

Acids and Alkalies. Strong acids and alkalies may kill bacteria by virtue of the hydrogen or hydroxyl ion concentration of their solutions. Such solutions, however, are too caustic or destructive to be used as practical disinfectants. The weaker organic acids apparently have an antiseptic action independent of their hydrogen ions, since the injury to bacteria seems to be proportional to the concentration of undissociated acid.

Oxidizing Agents. Among the most efficient of the disinfectants are those that act through oxidation, especially if they liberate *nascent* oxygen. Among these are hydrogen peroxide, sodium perborate, potassium permanganate, and the halogens, iodine and chlorine.

Iodine, because of its penetrating power, is probably still the best substance to apply to the skin before a surgical operation, or to disinfect a fresh wound. Chlorine is widely used as a disinfectant in the purification of water supplies, either as the gas, or in the form of a hypochlorite.

Coagulants. Many of the disinfectants are substances which are known to coagulate proteins, and which probably kill bacteria by so acting upon some protein within the cell, i.e., their action is the same as that of heat. In this group would be placed certain salts, as bichloride of mercury, and silver nitrate; carbolic acid and related substances (cresol, lysol); formaldehyde; and alcohol.

To serve as an antiseptic of this sort, the substance must be able to penetrate the cell. Pure alcohol is not a good disinfectant, probably because it cannot diffuse through the cell membrane. These coagulants will, of course, be bound by other proteins. They are not nearly so efficient, therefore, in albuminous solutions (sputum, for instance) as in pure solutions.

Carbolic acid, or phenol, is the oldest of the disinfectants, dating since Lister's time, and for some purposes is still the best. It is taken as a standard with which to compare all other disinfectants.

The Dyes. Certain of the aniline dyes have an injurious effect upon bacteria. This fact was pointed out by Churchman, who showed that if small quantities of gentian violet are added to broth cultures of Gram positive bacteria, after a time subcultures from these tubes will not grow, while under identical conditions the Gram negative bacteria will grow. On the other hand, Gram negative bacteria may be inhibited by acid dyes, such as acid fuchsin, while Gram positive species are not affected. Further studies indicated that the action of the dyes consists more in an inhibition of growth than an actual killing of the cells; they are said to be *bacteriostatic* rather than bactericidal. The results are not entirely consistent, some of the Gram positive species (notably the acidfast group) being resistant to the violet, while some of the Gram negative forms are resistant to the fuchsin. But in general the results are consistent enough to warrant the general conclusion that Gram positive bacteria are injured by the basic dyes, while Gram negative species are inhibited by the acid dyes. This is interesting when considered in relation with the fundamental differences between Gram positive and Gram negative bacteria noted in Chapter II. These differences are probably dependent upon a difference in the iso-electric points of the proteins in the two groups of microbes, and on this basis the action of the dyes may be considered as due to a union with proteins within the cells. In addition to gentian violet, other basic dyes (malachite green, safranin) will inhibit Gram positive organisms, while the flavines are acid dyes similarly affecting the Gram negative group. These dyes have been used in various combinations in the treatment of wound infections, but with disappointing results.

Surface Tension Depressants. The antiseptic action of soaps and certain other substances has been attributed to their action in reducing the *surface tension* of water. Larson has shown that castor oil soap (sodium ricinoleate) will inhibit most of the Gram positive bacteria, but not the Gram negative ones. The cells of the pneumococcus and of the bacillus of tularemia are completely dissolved by solutions of the castor oil soap, while the pneumococcus is also dissolved by bile salts. This dissolution of the cells is considered to be due to a depression of the surface tension similar to the action of saponin upon red blood cells. Hexyl-resorcinal is an antiseptic whose action is said to depend, in part at least, upon its ability to reduce surface tension. A difficulty involved in all of these studies is the impossibility of measuring the surface tension at the cell-liquid interface.

Standardization of Disinfectants. Since there are so many different kinds of disinfectants, it would be very desirable to have some standard method for measuring their efficiency, so that they might be compared. There are, however, certain difficulties involved in such a comparison. The *rate* at which bacteria are killed by a chemical poison varies with a number of factors, such as the concentration of the bacterial suspension and the susceptibility of the particular strain of bacteria used; the concentration of the disinfectant, and a value for this particular disinfectant called its concentration coefficient; the temperature of the test and the temperature coefficient of the disinfectant; and the effect of the presence of organic matter. None of the methods for standardization in use control sufficiently these various factors.

The Phenol Coefficient. The efficiency of a disinfectant is expressed in terms of the efficiency of phenol, the standard disinfectant. The efficiency is given a value called the *phenol coefficient*. A phenol coefficient of 2 would mean that the disinfectant given this value is twice as powerful as phenol. There are several methods in use for measuring this phenol coefficient. The procedure given below is the method of the National Institute of Health.

A series of dilutions of pure phenol, 1–80, 1–90, 1–100, and 1–110, are prepared. A series of dilutions of the unknown disinfectant whose value is to be determined are also prepared. The degree of dilution will of course vary greatly with the potency of the disinfectant, and if this is entirely unknown, several preliminary tests will have to be made for orientation. Knowing roughly the potency of the unknown, dilutions are made whose killing power will be somewhat near that of the standard phenol dilutions given above. These various dilutions are now distributed in 10 cc. lots in test tubes placed in a water bath kept constantly at 20° C.

To each tube of diluted disinfectant, phenol and unknown, is added 0.2 cc. of a 24-hour broth culture of a standard test organism — a particular strain of typhoid bacilli, or of Micrococci, whose susceptibility to disinfectants is known to be relatively constant. At intervals of $2\frac{1}{2}$ minutes, a loopful from each tube is transferred to a tube of sterile broth. When the bacteria have been killed, these subcultures will of course show no growth. After 24 hours' incubation, the subcultures are examined, and the time required by each dilution of both disinfectants to kill the test bacteria is determined.

It is necessary to *compare dilutions*, i.e., find a dilution of phenol and a dilution of the unknown which will both kill all of the test organisms in the same period of time.

Thus if phenol killed the bacteria in $2\frac{1}{2}$ minutes when diluted 1–80, and the unknown disinfectant killed in the same period when diluted 1–400, the phenol coefficient of the unknown would be 400/80 or 5. But since the rate of death is not a straight line relation, the results are more accurate if several time intervals are compared. The National Institute takes the average of the ratios of the two dilutions that kill at $2\frac{1}{2}$ minutes and at 15 minutes. Thus, continuing the hypothetical case considered above, it might be found that phenol killed the bacteria in 15 minutes when diluted 1–100, while in the same period the unknown destroyed all the bacteria in a dilution of 1–700. This would give a value of 7. The average of 7 and 5 is 6. This would indicate that the unknown disinfectant is six times as potent as carbolic acid.

Chemotherapy. Since the very earliest days of bacteriology, scientists have sought to discover a substance which could be introduced into the body, that would kill the bacteria in the tissues without injuring the latter. In the first edition of this book it was stated that this search "has been to the bacteriologist what the search for the philosopher's stone was to the ancient alchemists — a never-ceasing, but apparently hopeless, task." But, just as the physicists eventually discovered how to transmute the metals, so the bacteriologists have apparently made a good beginning toward developing drugs that will cure infectious diseases.

Such drugs had been known for some time in the case of certain protozoan and spirochaete infections — quinine for malaria, ipecac in amoebic dysentery, and salvarsan in syphilis. The term *chemotherapy* is applied to the treatment of infectious diseases with specific drugs that act directly upon the parasitic germs. But no chemotherapeutic agents for bacteria had been found until very recently.

Sulfanilamide is such a drug which has been found to have a curative value in certain infectious diseases, especially acute streptococcus infections. It was first introduced as a dye, commercially labelled *Prontosil*, but it was soon found that this dye is broken up in the body, releasing a substance (para-amino-benzenesulfonamide), which is the actual substance that acts upon the bacteria. This substance, under the name sulfanilamide, is now used instead of the dye.

Both experimentally and in clinical use this drug is found to be efficient only in *acute* infections caused by *Streptococcus pyogenes*, the meningococcus and the gonococcus. There is also clinical evidence that it is of value in pneumococcus meningitis (but not in other pneumococcus infections), in undulant fever, and in trachoma. It appears to act directly upon the bacteria. When given in amounts sufficient to cure the infection, the drug reaches a concentration in the blood (about 10 mgm. per 100 cc.) which is sufficient to completely inhibit the growth of the bacteria; it is *bacteriostatic*. The bacteria which have been acted upon by the sulfanilamide are then taken up by the leucocytes and destroyed. Sulfanilamide is excreted in the urine, and may reach a concentration in this fluid sufficient to inhibit the growth of other species of bacteria. It has been found to be of value in the treatment of infections of the bladder (cystitis) caused by *Escherichia coli* and other species of bacteria.

At the present time numerous investigators are modifying the structure of sulfanilamide, producing new but similar compounds, and it seems probable that more efficient drugs of this sort, capable of inhibiting other kinds of pathogenic bacteria, will be shortly discovered.

CHAPTER XVI

INFECTION

When Pasteur discovered, and Koch proved, that bacteria are causes of disease in man and animals, this fact was seized upon by a host of researchers as the starting point for an intensive investigation of the nature of infectious diseases and of the phenomena which occur when bacteria invade the tissues of the body. The results of these researches cannot, strictly speaking, be considered part of the subject matter of microbiology, since they deal not so much with the action of the invading bacteria as with the reactions of the invaded animal, and are more properly a part of the science *pathology*, which deals with disease. Nevertheless these studies have played such an important part in the history of microbiology, have exerted such a profound influence upon its development, that the student's knowledge of the subject would be quite incomplete if he did not have at least a speaking acquaintance with the essential data of infection and immunity.

Infection. *Infection* is the invasion of the body tissues by microorganisms, resulting in disease. The disease-producing power of bacteria, i.e., their ability to invade and injure the body, is called *virulence*. When disease-producing bacteria come in contact with, or invade, the body, they are opposed by certain protective mechanisms which collectively are known as *resistance* or *immunity*. Both the virulence of the microörganisms and the immunity of the body are subject to fluctuations. When organisms and body come in contact, the occurrence or non-occurrence of infection is determined by the *balance* established between the virulence of the microörganism and the immunity of the body.

Parasitic Bacteria. Not all species of bacteria are *pathogenic*, i.e., capable of producing disease; the great majority are not. There are many species of bacteria which are parasitic on the body surfaces, either internal or external, which are not pathogenic; they are either unable to invade through the skin or mucous membranes,

259

or if they do invade in small numbers from time to time, are unable to cause an injury.

Parasitic Bacteria May Become Pathogenic. Some of these parasitic bacteria may, however, acquire virulence and cause infection, or, more properly speaking, the immunity of their host may be so lowered that they are able to manifest their virulence. Other species of bacteria may be strictly pathogenic organisms, never found in or upon the body except in disease. Their existence is dependent upon a continual transfer from one susceptible individual to another. Finally, there are pathogenic bacteria which may cause disease in some individuals, may grow as harmless parasites in others, while they cannot maintain a foothold at all in still others. When, for instance, an epidemic of cerebrospinal meningitis occurs in a community, we find that a small proportion of the population will develop the disease; we can demonstrate the presence of the meningococci in the throats of a larger number of individuals who are perfectly healthy; but they cannot be found in the throats of the great majority of the population. Individuals of the second group, who, *while themselves healthy*, harbor in their bodies as parasites organisms which are pathogenic to others, are called *carriers*. Carriers are of great importance in the spread of epidemic diseases.

Specificity. Pathogenic microörganisms exhibit a certain degree of *host specificity*. As far as is known, none of the organisms which cause disease in plants will infect animals. In general, bacteria pathogenic for warm-blooded animals will not produce disease in cold-blooded animals. The majority of microörganisms which will infect mammals fail to infect birds, though here we begin to find some overlapping. Many species of bacteria will infect only a limited number of species of mammals, and some are strictly species-specific, able to invade only one host species. It should be noted in this connection that some of the bacteria pathogenic to man will not produce *infection* when inoculated into lower animals, but will manifest *toxicity* if injected in large quantities. The organisms are incapable of multiplying in the experimental animal, but are capable of injuring its tissues or causing death when introduced in sufficient numbers.

Factors of Virulence. The virulence of microörganisms depends upon two independent factors, their ability to *invade* and multiply within the tissues, and their ability to injure the invaded tissues by the secretion of poisons or *toxins*. These two properties vary widely with different kinds of pathogenic bacteria, and specific characters of the various infectious diseases may be attributed to specific modes of invasion and specific sorts of poisons characteristic of the infecting organism.

Invasive Power. The *invasive power* of pathogenic bacteria also involves two more or less independent properties, viz., their ability to break through the epithelial covering of the body tissues, and their ability to multiply within and spread through the tissues once this epithelial barrier has been traversed.

The body tissues are separated from the external world by the skin and mucous membranes, two different kinds of epithelium. We find bacteria living in enormous numbers on the outer surfaces of these tissues, but rarely penetrating them. The reasons are not clear. The outer layers of the epidermis of the skin are hardened, or cornified, and bathed with an oily secretion which must offer resistance to the penetration of bacteria. The mucous membranes secrete a continuously outward-flowing fluid, the mucus, which is supposed to offer some mechanical resistance to bacteria on their surface, and some of the mucous membranes are lined with ciliated cells which tend to sweep away solid particles that lodge upon them. But it is very difficult to understand how the thin layer of epithelium in the intestines, for example, is able to keep out the vast hordes of microörganisms which fill the lumen.

Portal of Entry. Certain species of pathogenic bacteria are never able to break through the epithelial barrier; they produce infection only when this barrier has been broken by wounds or by the actions of other species of bacteria. In other cases we find that the invading organisms may break through this armor at some particular spot, but not at others. For each of the disease-producing microörganisms there is some special part of the body which is to it the Achilles' heel, the point of vulnerability. This vulnerable portion of the epithelial coating is the *portal of entry* for that organism.

The meningococcus invades the body through the mucous membrane of the nasopharynx. The diphtheria bacillus usually finds the weak spot in the tonsils. The organism of pneumonia invades the respiratory tract. The gonococcus, while capable of infecting other mucous membranes, usually invades through the urethra. The organisms of typhoid, dysentery, and cholera cannot produce disease unless they reach the intestines.

At this point it might be mentioned parenthetically that pathogenic bacteria are discharged from the body in a characteristic manner in various infectious diseases. In infections of the respiratory tract they leave the body in sputum or in droplets of moisture discharged into the air in talking, coughing, or sneezing. In the intestinal diseases they leave the body only in the feces (or occasionally in the urine). A knowledge of the specific portals of entry and specific modes of discharge of the bacteria in the infectious diseases forms to a large extent the scientific basis for preventive medicine. In typhoid fever, for example, the bacteria can produce the disease only if swallowed, and leave the body only in the excreta. The prevention of this disease consists almost entirely in preventing the contamination of food and water with urine and feces.

Resistance of the Bacteria. If one injects harmless bacteria into the tissues of an experimental animal, these bacteria are quickly killed by the body fluids, quickly removed and destroyed by the cells. The ability of pathogenic bacteria to grow and spread within the tissues must be due in large part to some resistance which they offer to these defense mechanisms of the body. We have already seen how the gums or capsules secreted by at least some of the pathogenic bacteria may function in this way.

Local Infections. After bacteria have invaded the tissues, and have begun to multiply there, the further course of the disease depends upon the balance established between the opposing forces of virulence and immunity. In the majority of cases, after a short struggle, the body resistance gets the upper hand, and prevents any further spread of the organisms through the tissues. A new barrier is established by the body cells, a layer of tissue which the pathologists call granulation tissue, which serves to wall off the area of infection and keep the disease process *localized*. If, however, the organisms are sufficiently virulent, the infection will spread, and it may extend in several ways.

Spreading Infection. The invading bacteria may occupy new territory simply by continuously growing through the tissues. Multiplying rapidly, laying down one new cell after another, they extend outwards from the portal of entry. Such an infection is said to extend *by continuity*. Often, however, infection is extended to new territory by way of the lymph vessels or the blood stream. Not infrequently, after a wound infection has been established in the hand, we may find red lines of inflammation extending up the forearm, following the course of the subcutaneous lymph vessels. The bacteria have invaded these vessels, probably having been carried there by certain of the body cells. As this occurs, the *lymph glands* first at the elbow, and later under the shoulder, become swollen and tender, due to the action of bacteria and their poisons which have been carried to these glands by the lymph stream. Frequently the bacteria are overcome by the body defenses in these glands. Sometimes a new area of infection is established, and abscesses develop in the glands.

Invasion of the Blood. Probably in many infections small numbers of bacteria invade the blood from time to time, but there they are rapidly overcome, for the defense mechanisms of the body are largely concentrated in the blood. If of sufficient virulence, however, they may remain alive in the blood, and two possible sequels may result. If they are unable to multiply in the blood, they may lodge in the tissues of some other part of the body and there set up a new localized infection. Such a localized infection arising at a distance from the primary areas of disease is called a *metastatic* infection. Several such areas may develop in various parts of the body simultaneously, or the process may occur repeatedly, bacteria invading the blood from the original point of infection over a period of time, giving rise continuously to new metastatic infections. Such a condition is known to surgeons as *pyaemia*.

Septicaemia. The second possibility is that the bacteria may actually multiply in the blood without localizing. This implies an infection of the whole body simultaneously. If the invading organisms are also capable of producing serious injury, if they are toxic, the condition of the patient is very grave indeed. There occurs a characteristic fluctuating fever curve. Such a state is known to the surgeons as *septicaemia*.

The term *bacteraemia* is used sometimes to indicate the mere presence of bacteria in the blood, sometimes to indicate their actual multiplication there. It is rather confusing.

Toxins. The second factor in virulence, the ability of the invading organism to injure the tissues, is clearly dependent in some cases upon their ability to secrete specific poisons or toxins. In other cases this is not so clear. Two kinds of toxin are known. *Exotoxins* are thrown off by the bacterial cells into their surrounding medium and can be readily separated from the bacteria. *Endotoxins* are supposedly toxic substances formed by the bacteria which are retained within their cells, and which cannot easily, at least, be separated from the organisms.

Toxaemia. In the disease diphtheria, the organisms grow in the superficial tissues of the tonsils. They may extend by continuity over the soft palate, into the pharynx, thence up into the nose or down into the larynx, but do not invade deeply into the tissues and practically never invade the blood stream. Ordinarily, the local infection is no more extensive than a boil on the neck, yet frequently the child is desperately ill. This illness is due to an absorption into the blood of a toxin secreted by the bacteria in the throat. Diphtheria is a local infection with a *toxaemia*.

Exotoxins. We may prove this experimentally. If we grow virulent diphtheria bacilli in broth of a certain kind, and then filter this broth through a Berkefeld or Chamberland filter, which will remove all the bacterial cells, we may separate the toxin from the bacteria. If now we inject some of this filtrate into a guinea pig, which is susceptible to diphtheria, the guinea pig will die. Upon post mortem examination we shall find at the point of inoculation and in the internal organs exactly the same sort of changes in the tissues which occur when we inoculate the living diphtheria bacilli. There is something that has been formed in the broth which can be separated from the bacteria, which will produce all the symptoms and tissue changes of the natural disease. This something we call the exotoxin of the diphtheria bacillus.

When we try similar experiments with other species of bacteria we succeed in only a limited number of cases. Exotoxins are formed by the bacteria responsible for the following diseases:

Diphtheria	Tetanus
Gas gangrene	Botulism
Scarlet fever	

In these diseases the symptoms of the natural disease may be accurately reproduced by inoculation of the pure toxin, i.e., the disease is almost entirely due to the effect of this toxin. Exotoxins have been discovered in cultures of other species of pathogenic bacteria, but they are clearly not entirely responsible for the symptoms of the diseases they produce. Thus a number of species of bacteria form a toxin-like substance, *haemolysin*, which will destroy red blood cells. But anaemia is not a prominent feature of the diseases which these bacteria cause. Several different exotoxins are secreted by *Staphylococcus aureus*, but it is as yet uncertain what part these play in the natural infections.

Nature of Exotoxins. The exotoxins of bacteria belong to a group of poisons having very characteristic qualities. Similar poisons are found in the castor bean and in the venoms of certain snakes. These poisons are far more powerful, as measured by their minimum fatal dose, than such poisons as bichloride of mercury, or arsenic, or strychnine. The bacterial exotoxins are complex compounds of a protein-like nature. They may be precipitated by certain chemicals, and thus concentrated, though they have not been obtained in a pure form. They are extraordinarily unstable, easily destroyed by light, by various chemicals, and by heating to moderate temperatures (excepting the scarlet fever toxin, which is quite heat resistant). They may be inactivated by treatment with certain substances that reduce the surface tension of liquids, especially castor oil soap (excepting the toxin of botulism). Another character which serves to distinguish the bacterial toxins from other poisons is the fact that they require an *incubation period* before their action is manifest, i.e., they do not begin to produce symptoms as soon as they are introduced into the body tissues. This incubation period varies with the different kinds of toxin. But the most important general character of the toxins, including those of the castor bean and the snake venoms, is their ability to give rise to *antitoxins*. If one injects a sub-fatal dose of one of these poisons into a susceptible animal, after it has recovered from the effects it is found to be refractory to even much larger doses. And, by repeated inoculations, it can be made so immune that it will withstand an injection of many normally fatal doses. This immunity is due to the formation of a specific neutralizing substance in the blood.

Endotoxins. Some years ago, a German bacteriologist, Pfeiffer, in the course of some experiments on cholera, discovered the following facts. If guinea pigs are inoculated with dead cultures of the cholera vibrio in small doses, they eventually become immune to the injurious action of inoculations with living bacteria. This immunity, he showed, was due to the development in the guinea pig of a substance, *bacteriolysin*, which has the property of completely dissolving the cells of the injected cholera germs. If, however, one inoculates such an immunized guinea pig with a very large dose of the cholera organisms, the animal will shortly die. Upon examination, however, it is found that even in these animals the inoculated bacteria have been completely destroyed. The death of the animal is due entirely to some injurious action of the bacteria, not to their multiplication in the inoculated animal. Following the idea of the endoenzymes, which had recently been discovered in yeasts by Buchner, Pfeiffer postulated that the death of the guinea pig was due to some poisonous product formed within the cells of the bacteria, which is not active until it has been liberated into the tissues by the death and disintegration of these bacteria. These hypothetical poisonous substances he designated as *endotoxins*, and this theory offered for a time a satisfactory explanation of the injury to the body produced by all those pathogenic microörganisms which do not form exotoxins. If this theory is true, we are faced with the paradoxical condition that such invading bacteria will be harmless to the body as long as they are kept alive and multiplying!

Many of the pathogenic bacteria which do not form obvious exotoxins behave in the animal body like the cholera vibrio. They do not multiply, but cause death if a large enough dose is inoculated. In some instances the cells killed by heat are equally poisonous. But there has not been any clear and unequivocal demonstration that these bacteria contain a toxin within their cells; it has not been possible to separate the endotoxin from the cells. It is true that various poisonous substances have been obtained from the cells of bacteria by extraction with acids or alkalies or other chemicals, or by digestion with enzymes, or by dissolving the cells with bile or soaps, or by simply allowing the dead cells to digest themselves (autolysis). But there is no clear evidence that these poisonous substances are the same as those which cause the injury in the infected animals — they do not cause the same symptoms, the same tissue changes, as is so clearly the case with the exotoxins. In the case of the various chemical extractions, one suspects that we are dealing here with poisons artificially produced in the laboratory, which have nothing to do with the natural disease.

It would be very interesting if one could squeeze the cell sap out of bacteria, as Buchner did with yeasts, and determine its effect upon animals. Because of their minute size this has, so far, been impossible. But there are some molds which produce infections in animals that present the same general characters as bacterial diseases, notably *Aspergillus fumigatus*. The author has recently demonstrated that this mold contains in its cell sap a potent toxin which has many of the characters of the exotoxins of bacteria, including the ability to form antitoxin in the blood. This is a true endotoxin, since no effects result from injecting the filtered broth in which the mold has been growing.

Botulism. Let us revert for a moment to a statement considered previously. The invasive power of pathogenic bacteria is a property independent of their toxicity. This may be clearly illustrated in the case of botulism. This disease is a food poisoning, contracted by eating certain foods, particularly canned goods, in which the *Clostridium botulinum* has been growing. The symptoms are due to the action of an exotoxin secreted by this organism. In its general properties, this toxin is not very different from other exotoxins formed by bacteria except that it may be absorbed through the intestinal tract, which is not true of any other toxins. But in the disease botulism, the symptoms are due entirely to a toxin which was preformed outside the body (in the foodstuffs); *the organisms do not invade the tissues.* Here is an organism which is really a saprophyte, which has no invasive power at all, yet is capable of producing disease. Properly speaking, botulism is not an infection.

Pathogenic Saprophytes. The organisms of gas gangrene and tetanus are widespread and abundant in soil, where apparently they lead a saprophytic existence. They produce disease in man following wounds which become contaminated with soil. Tetanus occurs, now and then, following various sorts of wounds, particularly deep punctured wounds in which dirt becomes forced into the tissues, such as might result from stepping on a rake, or following gunshot wounds. But gas gangrene is rarely seen in civilian life except in certain types of very severe industrial accidents. Both of these diseases are common and serious sequels of war wounds, particularly the extensively lacerated wounds made by pieces of bursting shells. The reason is to be found in the fact that these organisms *will not invade healthy living tissue.* Where there has been extensive injury, where tags of muscle or other tissue have been torn from their blood supply, and are dead, then there is provided a situation in which these essentially saprophytic organisms may grow. In the case of tetanus the organisms multiply only to a slight extent locally, for the tetanus toxin has little effect upon tissues other than those of the nervous system. But the gas gangrene bacilli secrete powerful general toxins which diffuse ahead of the organisms, into the healthy tissue, killing the cells and causing gangrene. Into these areas of dead tissue the bacteria may now advance, there to secrete more toxin and so continue the process. Thus there results a rapidly advancing gangrene, although the organisms have very little ability to invade living tissues.

Invasive Power and Toxins. We have already noted that in diptheria the bacteria are limited to a very small area of the throat, showing no tendency to invade deeply. In scarlet fever the case is somewhat different. Here also the organisms grow in the throat. In a certain proportion of cases, however, the Streptococci of scarlet fever invade the blood stream, and may give rise to metastatic abscesses, or to a septicaemia. Such an invasion, however, occurs only in a minority of the cases and is not necessary for the development of the disease. The scarlatinal rash may be produced entirely by the absorption of toxin from a limited localized infection in the throat.

In short, all of those bacteria which form exotoxins show a very limited invasive power, and usually multiply only slightly within the living body tissues. How different is the case with the other pathogenic bacteria! Wherever the disease is acute, severe, extensive, we find that the organisms have invaded widely, have multiplied extensively in the living tissues. In sections of the lungs from cases of lobar pneumonia one finds hundreds of pneumococci in each little alveolus. A drop of blood from any part of the body may yield hundreds of organisms in cases of Streptococcus septicaemia, or typhoid fever, or plague, or anthrax. If the organisms do not invade widely or multiply extensively, then the infection remains mild and localized.

The actual presence of large numbers of bacteria, of large amounts of bacterial protoplasm, within the body tissues or fluids seems to be the prime factor in producing injury with those organisms which do not secrete exotoxins. The bacteria need not be alive. We may produce intoxication, death, even the development of the characteristic tissue changes of the disease, by injecting animals with dead cultures, if the dose is large enough. These facts will fit the endotoxin theory, but the complete failure to obtain such endotoxins free from the bacteria has cast considerable doubt upon the theory. We may explain these facts in another way. It may be that the injury results not from a toxin formed by the organism itself, but from *a poisonous substance produced by a reaction of some agent in the body fluids or tissues upon the bacterial protoplasm.* We will discuss this viewpoint further in a later chapter.

Incubation Period. Many of the infectious diseases present a characteristic *incubation period.* A definite time elapses between the introduction of the bacterium into the body and the development of symptoms. This is probably to be explained in several ways. We have already noted that when exotoxins are injected into an animal, some time must elapse before symptoms appear. This may be due to the necessity for the toxin to diffuse to and be absorbed by particular cells. Tetanus toxin affects only motor nerve cells, and is absorbed by and diffuses through the peripheral nerve fibers. It may take some days for this toxin to reach the central nervous system, and there act upon the motor nerve cells, to produce the characteristic spasms of tetanus. In the case of the bacteria which do not form exotoxins, the incubation period is probably dependent upon the rate of growth of the bacteria within the body. If they multiply rapidly within the tissues, immediately upon invasion, the incubation period will be short. Thus one may find signs of inflammation within an hour after pricking the finger with a needle contaminated with virulent Streptococci. In typhoid fever, a week elapses between the swallowing of the bacteria and the development of symptoms. The similarity between the incubation period in an infectious disease and the lag phase in the growth of a culture is striking.

Variations in Virulence. The virulence of pathogenic bacteria is subject to fluctuations. When growing continuously on artificial culture media, virulence decreases and ultimately disappears, rapidly with some organisms (such as Streptococci), slowly with others (as the tubercle bacilli). On the other hand, rapid transfer from animal to animal exalts virulence. One may thus increase the virulence of a culture of Streptococci so that, whereas at the beginning perhaps 5 cc. of a broth culture was necessary to kill the animal, after a number of animal passages a drop will suffice. One may alter the species specificity by animal passage. A strain of Streptococci passed simultaneously through rabbits and rats will increase in virulence for each species, but at the end of the experiment the substrain which has been passed through rats will have lost its virulence for rabbits, and conversely.

These variations in virulence are to be explained as modifications of the invasive power rather than of the toxicity. While exotoxin-forming organisms may sometimes lose their toxicity in artificial cultures, they cannot be increased in virulence by animal passage. Moreover, maintained on the proper media, toxin-forming bacteria will maintain their potency for many years. The loss of virulence in artificial cultures and its increase by animal passage are to be looked upon as the effects of artificial selection. When we inoculate media, those cells of the inoculum which are best equipped for saprophytic life will grow first, and will produce offspring tending toward the same characters. When we inoculate animals, we select those cells best equipped for parasitic existence.

CHAPTER XVII

IMMUNITY

Long before it was discovered that bacteria cause disease, it had been known that people vary in their susceptibility. Even in a severe epidemic, not all of the persons exposed to infection take sick; a large proportion are resistant. But no one knew just what caused this variation in resistance or susceptibility. It had been supposed that various factors which impair the general health, such as undernutrition, exposure to cold, bad ventilation, or alcoholic intoxication, might break down one's resistance. But with the advent of scientific investigation of infectious disease, it has not been possible to prove the effect of such factors save in a few instances.

One way by which resistance to disease could be established was definitely known. Long before the bacteriological era it had been observed that people who had recovered from an attack of certain contagious diseases would not be subject to that disease if again exposed to it. This is particularly true of the eruptive fevers, such as smallpox, scarlet fever, and measles. Children were deliberately exposed to mild cases of these diseases in the hope that they would also develop a mild case, and on recovery, would become *immune*.

Vaccination. A safer and more certain way of producing such an immunity was introduced by Jenner. Observing that dairymaids who had contracted the disease, cowpox, or *vaccinia*, from their cows were not susceptible to smallpox when the latter disease was prevalent, he deliberately inoculated fluid from the blisters of cowpox into the skin of children. The result is a mild localized disease which is without any danger, and which definitely *immunizes* the individual so treated against a later infection with the dangerous disease, smallpox. This process is called *vaccination*, and the substance used to inoculate is *vaccine*.

Now smallpox is not a bacterial disease. It is one of those diseases caused by an invisible ultramicrobe, or filterable virus. We now know that smallpox in man and cowpox in cattle are caused by the same virus. But when this virus is transferred from man to cattle, it is somehow altered so that when transferred back to man again it does not produce the generalized disease smallpox, but the mild localized disease, vaccinia. Just what happens to the virus in this transfer is not clearly known, but it is quite evident that it has lost in disease-producing power, or virulence. We say that the virus has been weakened or attenuated, and when we vaccinate against smallpox, we inoculate with an *attenuated virus* of that disease.

Other Vaccines. This was all that was known about immunity to infectious diseases until Pasteur and Koch discovered that bacteria cause disease. But in 1880 Pasteur found another way to produce immunity. Working with the bacterium that causes chicken cholera, he showed that when a fowl was injected with a pure culture of this bacterium, which was some weeks old, the bird did not die; it developed only a mild temporary illness. But a subsequent inoculation of this same bird with a fresh, fully virulent culture produced no effect; although the same dose injected into a control bird that had never been inoculated previously proved fatal over night. By allowing the microbes of chicken cholera to age in artificial cultures, they become *attenuated in virulence*, so that they produce only a mild disease. Recovery from this mild infection leaves the animal immune.

Pasteur discovered other ways of producing immunity by inoculation with attenuated organisms. He found that when anthrax bacilli are grown at a temperature of 42° C., which is above their optimum, they lose in virulence. Injecting these cultures into animals does not produce anthrax, but it does produce an immunity to a subsequent injection of virulent anthrax germs. He also discovered that the virus of rabies, or hydrophobia, could be attenuated by drying, so that it will not cause disease but will still produce immunity. And later workers have found a variety of other methods serving the same purpose. We may immunize against typhoid fever by inoculating cultures of typhoid germs that have been killed by heat. We may immunize against diphtheria and scarlet fever by inoculating, not the bacteria, but minute doses of the exotoxins of these bacteria. These toxins themselves are attenuated, or weakened, by mixing them with antitoxin, or by chemical treatment.

The word "vaccine," originally derived from the Latin name for cowpox, is now applied generally to all of these immunizing agents. A vaccine is any substance used to immunize artificially, actively, against disease, and may be composed of bacteria or viruses, attenuated or killed, or their toxins.

Active Immunization. The production of immunity by recovery from disease or by *vaccination* is called *active* immunization, to distinguish it from another kind of immunization which results from the injection of *serums:* the latter is called *passive* immunization. In active immunity the resulting protection against disease is brought about by an active response upon the part of the body to the agent of the disease. The body itself builds up its defense mechanisms. .

Vaccination is successful only with those diseases in which recovery from the natural infection leaves the individual immune. In the case of human diseases, the use of vaccines is limited to a few. Vaccines are given as a *preventive* measure, before disease has developed. We vaccinate children against smallpox and diphtheria before they start to school, soldiers against typhoid before they take to the field. It usually requires some weeks for immunity to develop; therefore it is useless to administer vaccines after a person has been exposed to the disease. In hydrophobia, the incubation period of the disease is long, and in this case we start to vaccinate a person who has been bitten by a mad dog, knowing that usually immunity may be built up before the disease has developed. But with one or two exceptions, vaccines are useless *after* disease has developed. In certain mild, recurrent, localized infections, as pimples and boils, the injection of vaccines may have a curative value in some cases. In general, however, vaccines are dangerous things to use in the *treatment* of disease; their sole value is in prevention.

Antitoxins. Although means had been developed for producing immunity, nothing was known about the mechanism of this immunity, about the way in which the body defends itself against infection, until the discovery of diphtheria antitoxin by von Behring in 1890. Roux, working in Pasteur's laboratory, had already discovered the exotoxin, had shown that the disease diphtheria is due to an absorption of this poison, rather than to an invasion of the bacteria. Von Behring, in Koch's laboratory, now found that guinea pigs which recovered from diphtheria are immune; that this immunity is due to some substance in the blood; and that immunity *may be transferred* to a susceptible guinea pig by inoculation with the immune blood.

This last fact was a very important discovery. The blood of an immune guinea pig, injected into a normal guinea pig, makes the latter immune so that it will withstand an inoculation of many fatal doses of virulent diphtheria bacilli. Further, the blood of an immunized animal, injected into a guinea pig already sick with diphtheria, will save its life, will cure the infection.

The substance which confers this immunity is present in the blood *serum*, the liquid which is squeezed out when blood clots. It is something in solution. It does not kill or injure the diphtheria bacilli themselves; they will grow in it! Its action is solely upon the exotoxin, making it, somehow or other, innocuous. We say that it *neutralizes* the toxin, as though it were something like the action of an acid upon an alkali, but this is largely imaginative; we really don't know just what it does. To this substance in the immune blood serum von Behring gave the name *antitoxin*. Since the immunity in diphtheria is due entirely to this antitoxin, and not to any action upon the bacteria, we may produce this immunity more safely and certainly by inoculating animals with the bacteria-free toxin rather than with the whole bacterial cultures.

Serums. It did not take long to apply this discovery to the treatment of human diphtheria, and, as every one knows, with great success. By the use of antitoxin, the mortality from diphtheria has been so greatly reduced that it is no longer the dreaded scourge it used to be. Diphtheria antitoxin is the blood serum of a horse which has been *actively* immunized by many repeated small doses of diphtheria exotoxin. Injected into a human being it confers a transient immunity. It may be used as a *preventive*, inoculated into persons who have recently been exposed to diphtheria; but it is more important as a *curative* agent, causing a prompt disappearance of the symptoms of the disease when injected early enough and in sufficient quantities.

Such antitoxic serums have been developed against all of the bacterial exotoxins — tetanus, scarlet fever, gas gangrene, and botulism, as well as diphtheria — and also against the related poisons, snake venoms, and the ricin of the castor bean. But none of these other antitoxins has been so successful as diphtheria antitoxin. In the case of tetanus and botulism, this is due largely to the fact that the antitoxins cannot neutralize the toxins after the latter have combined with the protoplasm of the nerve cells which they injure. After symptoms of the disease appear, it is already too late for much success with the serum treatment. Tetanus antitoxin is, however, a proved certain preventive, if administered before symptoms appear. We cannot state the value of gas gangrene serum because of a lack of sufficient experience with it, and the same is largely true of the very recently discovered antitoxin for scarlet fever.

Passive Immunity. When we inject a serum, the resulting processes are quite different from those obtained by injecting a vaccine. A *vaccine* contains bacteria or their poisons; it causes a mild, controllable attack of the disease; it causes the body to react by producing immune substances — antibodies. Generally several inoculations and considerable time are required for the development of immunity, but once developed it will last for months, in some cases for years. A *serum* contains, not the germs or their products, but *antibodies* against these germs or their products; the resulting immunity is due, not to any reaction upon the part of the body, but simply to the presence of these ready-made antibodies introduced from without. The immunity is conferred immediately upon injection but lasts for but a short time, a few weeks at most. Since the body itself takes no part in the process, immunization with serums is called *passive immunization*.

Antibacterial Serums. Many attempts have been made to apply the principle of passive immunization to other kinds of pathogenic bacteria, to those which do not form exotoxins. It was hoped that by inoculating horses with the whole bacteria, rather than toxins, there would develop antibodies against these bacteria which would cure their respective diseases. Such a serum is called an *antibacterial* serum, to distinguish it from an *antitoxic* serum. Practically, however, all such antibacterial serums have proved to be failures, with the exception of those used in the treatment of epidemic meningitis and of pneumonia.

Serum and Vaccine. The terms "serum" and "vaccine" are used so loosely by the laity and even by a large part of the medical profession that it seems worth while to recapitulate briefly their differences. A vaccine contains microbes or their products; a serum contains antibodies. A vaccine produces active immunity, slow in development, but fairly permanent; a serum produces passive immunity, immediate but transient. A vaccine is used almost exclusively in preventing disease, before exposure; a serum is used as a preventive after exposure to infection or as a cure after disease has developed.

Phagocytosis. With the discovery of diphtheria antitoxin it was believed that a start had been made toward explaining all immunity. It was hoped that an antitoxin might be developed for each of the bacteria that cause disease. We have seen how such hopes were dashed. Tetanus antitoxin was shortly discovered, but for the remaining diseases there could be found neither toxin nor antitoxin. And yet Pasteur had shown how one might produce an immunity to these other diseases. What, then, is the mechanism of immunity where there is no exotoxin?

One such mechanism was the discovery of Metchnikoff, who did the greater part of his experimental work in the Pasteur Institute at Paris. Unlike the chemists and physicians who were his contemporaries in bacteriology, Metchnikoff was a biologist, and he attacked the problem of immunity with the training and mental attitude of a comparative morphologist.

In our discussion of the amoeba in an earlier chapter, we have noted how this organism feeds by sweeping a pseudopodium around a bacterium or an alga, and taking this foreign microbe into its cell substance. The amoeba is apparently quite indifferent as to what it takes in. If it is digestible, well and good; if not, it is cast out again. Now Metchnikoff became interested in tracing the occurrence of this sort of feeding in the higher organisms. In some of the lower multicellular animals, the Coelenterata, this mode of nutrition persists, the cells of the digestive tract taking solid particles into their interior, there to be digested. But with higher animals, this method of feeding disappears. Food is digested outside the cells by secreted enzymes, and absorbed in solution. Nevertheless, in such higher organisms, there are still found cells in the body which possess the power of ingesting solid particles. Metchnikoff particularly studied the action of certain wandering cells, cells with amoeboid motion, that occur in the body cavity of larval starfish, and observed their ingestion of particles of carmine which he injected into the body cavity.

Such cells, either fixed or moving, which will ingest foreign particles, occur in all animals, including man. Metchnikoff had the brilliant idea that invading bacteria would be ingested and destroyed by such cells. He designated these cells *phagocytes*, and the process phagocytosis. The name is derived from the Greek, meaning " cells which devour." The actual part which these cells play in immunity was first observed in a water-flea, Daphnia, which is subject to infection with a yeast. This yeast forms long, sharp, needle-like spores. When swallowed by Daphnia they may perforate the digestive tract and gain entrance to the body cavity. Here they are usually engulfed by a wandering phagocyte, and destroyed. If they are not, they will germinate, giving rise to a yeast cell. This yeast cell apparently forms a poison, for its presence and multiplication are followed by death of the Daphnia. Moreover, after a spore has germinated, the wandering cells make no effort to engulf it. Daphnia is a transparent microscopic organism in which the whole process may be readily followed under the microscope. Here the occurrence of infection, or its failure to occur, appeared to depend entirely upon the phagocytes. If successful in devouring the spore, the animal might be considered immune to the yeast; a failure of phagocytosis meant susceptibility to infection.

Phagocytosis in Higher Animals. It is not so easy to follow the process in higher animals, but by the use of various procedures we may gain a comprehensive picture of what goes on. If bacteria, say a culture of Staphylococci, are injected under the skin of a rabbit, there occurs first of all a dilatation of the blood capillaries. As a result, this part of the skin has more than a normal blood supply, and it becomes red and warm, two of the important symptoms of inflammation. Also, the flow of blood through these capillaries becomes much slower. Certain of the white blood cells, or *leucocytes,* now come to rest on the thin walls of the capillaries. These leucocytes are capable of amoeboid movement. They slip a pseudopodium between two of the lining cells of the capillary, and gradually worm their way through, until they come to lie outside the capillary in the tissue spaces. Now by amoeboid motion they work their way toward the bacteria. It is quite evident that somehow or other they are attracted toward the germs. We must assume that this is a response to some chemical substance emanating from the invading microbes. The response of the leucocyte to this substance is called *chemotaxis.*

The remaining steps of phagocytosis are precisely the same as the feeding of an amoeba. The protoplasm of the leucocytes flows around the Staphylococcus; it is *ingested* into the cell substance. There it becomes enclosed in a vacuole, and if the leucocyte is victorious, the germ is finally killed, and *digested,* or completely dissolved.

Pus. We have followed but a single leucocyte. But if we have injected enough Staphylococci, and if they are sufficiently virulent, great numbers of these leucocytes will emerge from the many capillaries, and all migrate toward the bacteria. They will not, all at once, succeed in destroying the bacteria. In fact, many of the leucocytes will themselves be overcome. Now these dead leucocytes liberate an enzyme, trypsin, that digests proteins. This trypsin will digest not only the dead bacteria, but also the dead leucocytes, and the tissue cells which have been killed by the bacteria. The total result is a great mass of leucocytes contained in a fluid resulting from the digestive action of this trypsin, a thick creamy or yellowish fluid which is called *pus*. This collection of pus, under tension, is an *abscess*. Eventually the skin over the abscess will be digested, the pus will burst forth, the abscess will empty and then heal.

Different Kinds of Phagocytes. The leucocytes which gather at the site of infection are only one kind of phagocytic cell. There are others. The leucocytes are called *microphages*, because they are smaller than the other kind. *Macrophages*, the larger phagocytic cells, are not present in the blood save in small numbers, but are present in the tissues, either as wandering cells or as fixed cells. While both kinds of phagocytic cells may take part in a single infection, in general bacteria call out one or the other sort, depending on the species of bacterium. Thus the Staphylococci are attacked mainly by the microphages, tubercle bacilli by the macrophages.

Those species of pathogenic bacteria which call forth the leucocytes of the blood, or microphages, regularly give rise to the formation of pus in the invaded tissues. They are called pus-producing, or *pyogenic* bacteria. Mostly they are the spherical bacteria.

Leucocytosis. If the infection is severe, the body is not satisfied with mobilizing the leucocytes in the circulating blood at the site of infection. It calls out the reserves, so to speak, pouring great quantities of newly made leucocytes from the bone marrow into the circulating blood, so that the number of white blood corpuscles in a cubic millimeter of blood will rise from eight or ten thousand to twenty or thirty thousand. This increase in the number of circulating white corpuscles, or *leucocytosis*, as it is called, is a valuable diagnostic sign. It tells the physician that somewhere in the body there is a severe infection by pyogenic bacteria.

Phagocytosis and Immunity. This, briefly, was Metchnikoff's idea of immunity. Infection is a battle between microbes and phagocytes. Immunity implies victorious phagocytes; susceptibility, victorious microbes. He showed that when the bacteria are extremely virulent, the leucocytes do not attack; in fact, they run away, they exhibit a *negative* chemotaxis. This picture of a visible, protective army of phagocytes took hold of the imagination; it was an attractive theory, it seemed at first glance to fit the facts. But eventually it was found that phagocytosis is only a part, and perhaps a minor part, of the protective mechanism against infection.

Serum Reactions. For while Metchnikoff had been investigating the action of the phagocytes, there had been accumulating more information about the properties of the blood *serum*. Briefly, it was discovered that, while antitoxins could be obtained in only a few

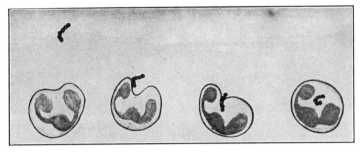

Fig. 72. Phagocytosis. Diagram showing the ingestion of a chain of Streptococci by a microphage. (After Thomas, *Bacteriology*, McGraw-Hill, New York.)

cases, other types of antibodies, acting upon the bacterial cells themselves, could be commonly demonstrated in the blood serum of immunized animals. As early as 1888 an Englishman, Nuttall, found that blood had the power of *killing* certain kinds of bacteria, and in 1893 Pfeiffer discovered that the blood serum of an immunized guinea pig would not only kill the cells of the cholera vibrio, but would actually *dissolve* these bacteria, causing them to disappear. Shortly later, Gruber and Durham discovered another peculiar property of immune serum, that of causing the cells of bacteria to clump together, or *agglutinate*, while a year after, Kraus observed still a fourth property, that of forming a *precipitate* when the immune serum was added to a filtered broth culture of bacteria.

In short, it began to be apparent that in addition to the phagocytes, there were other factors in immunity, in the form of substances dissolved in the blood serum, that exert a direct action upon the bacteria or their products. Metchnikoff, jealous for his own discoveries, tried to pooh-pooh these new observations; tried to show that the various antibodies were but secretions of his phagocytes. On the other hand, the students of serum reactions, particularly in Germany, were convinced that the activity of the phagocytes is quite secondary in importance to that of the antibodies. And so there developed a controversy between the supporters of the *cellular* theory of immunity, who sought to explain resistance to disease entirely upon the basis of phagocytosis, and the proponents of the *humoral* theory, who emphasized the importance of chemical substances (antibodies) dissolved in the blood serum.

Opsonins. This controversy was finally settled by the discovery of still another sort of antibody. By an appropriate technique, white blood cells may be obtained free from blood serum. This is done by whirling the blood in an instrument called a centrifuge, and so throwing the cells to the bottom of the vessel. The liquid blood serum is poured off and replaced with physiological salt solution. By repeating this process several times, the white blood cells may finally be washed free of all traces of the serum. If, now, we add some of these washed white blood cells to a suspension of bacteria in a test tube, they will show no phagocytic activity. But if we add to the tube a little of the original blood serum, at once the leucocytes begin actively to engulf the bacteria. This means that leucocytes alone cannot carry out phagocytosis of bacteria; there is required an additional substance, present in the blood serum, an antibody. This antibody, called *opsonin*, acts upon the bacteria, not upon the leucocytes. Just what it does to the bacteria is not clearly known, but somehow or other it prepares them for phagocytosis. Without this antibody there will be no phagocytosis. It would seem that instead of being the protecting soldiers that Metchnikoff pictured them, the phagocytes merely remove the invading bacteria that have been overcome by antibodies; they are scavengers.

Immunology. These investigations of the peculiar properties of blood serum with regard to foreign cells and their products, begun some forty years ago, have progressed with great intensity ever since, and have developed into what may be considered a separate branch of biological science, *immunology*. It must be frankly admitted that, so far as fulfilling their original aim of providing cures

and preventives for all the infectious diseases is concerned, these researches have proved very disappointing. The vaccines and serums
listed on preceding pages constitute the total achievement in this direction. But immunology has unearthed a whole series of curious
and perplexing facts which have greatly extended the biological hori-
zon, and has provided for the bacteriologist some very valuable diagnostic tests.

Antibodies. We have mentioned a variety of different activities
of the blood serum which may be ascribed to the action of particular
substances in the blood called *antibodies*. It was at first believed that
each activity was due to a separate substance, and so names were
applied to the various antibodies to indicate their particular actions.

Antitoxins act upon those poisons, exotoxins, snake venoms, etc.,
which are of a protein nature. Their sole action is to neutralize the
poisonous power of these toxins.

Agglutinins act upon foreign cells which are suspended in a
liquid, and cause these cells to gather together in clumps, or agglutinate, and to settle out of the liquid.

Precipitins react with foreign proteins in solution to form a
precipitate.

Lysins act upon foreign cells, causing them to dissolve or disintegrate.

Opsonins act upon foreign cells, causing them to be ingested by
the phagocytes.

Bactericidal substances act upon bacteria, killing them, or at
least inhibiting their growth.

More recent investigations indicate that probably there are not
so many different antibodies, but that rather these names indicate
different activities of but a single substance. Nevertheless it is convenient to study each of these activities separately, and the various
names applied are still in general use.

Antibodies of various sorts may be demonstrated in small quantities in *normal* blood. Whether these result from previous infections or are part of the normal composition of the blood is not
altogether clear. Possibly minute traces of all the antibodies are
present normally. But all of the antibodies may be tremendously increased by immunization, by repeated inoculations of the appropriate substances. There is no evidence that these *immune* antibodies
are different from the normal antibodies, save quantitatively.

282 THE BIOLOGY OF BACTERIA

The exact chemical nature of antibodies is not known. They may be concentrated by precipitation of that part of the serum proteins called the *globulin* fraction, and it is generally believed that the antibodies are modified serum globulins. The molecules of the antibodies are apparently larger than those of the normal serum globulins. In some cases a lipoid component appears to be necessary for antibody action. The antibodies produced by different species of animals against the same foreign substance may be chemically different. It is certain that the antibodies are large complex molecules, probably proteins.

Antigens. It was shortly found that antibodies might react with harmless bacteria as well as the pathogenic ones; and with many types of cells (or their products) other than bacteria. The antibodies do not constitute a purposeful protective mechanism against dangerous microbes. On the contrary, they constitute a peculiar system capable of reacting with all sorts of cells which are *foreign* to the body, harmful or not. We may obtain antibodies against blood cells as well as against bacteria, against harmless proteins (like egg albumen) as well as against toxins.

A host of laboratory animals have been inoculated with all imaginable substances, and their response, if any, in the production of antibodies has been determined. As a result of such innumerable experiments, we have a clear idea as to what sorts of materials may give rise to antibodies. A substance which, when introduced into the blood or tissues of an animal, gives rise to antibodies is an *antigen*.

Most authorities believe that only *foreign proteins* may serve as antigens. There is some evidence that lipoid or carbohydrate substances may give rise to antibodies, but it is not certain that these have not been bound to a protein. The ability to give rise to antibodies is common among the proteins, and rare with other kinds of substances. It is quite certain that only large complex molecules may serve as antigens.

By a foreign protein we mean one which does not occur naturally in the body of the animal immunized. We cannot produce in rabbits antibodies against the proteins of rabbits' blood; but we may obtain antibodies against proteins from the blood of some other species, as sheep.

The foreign protein must gain access to the body tissues unchanged. With possibly a few exceptions, antibodies do not result from feeding the foreign protein, since the protein will be digested before it is absorbed, i.e., it will no longer be a protein. Antibodies may result from an inoculation of either whole cells or of proteins extracted from these cells. To demonstrate certain types of antibody action, as agglutination or dissolving (*lysis*), it is of course necessary to have the intact cell. But it is not necessary to inoculate the whole cells in order to obtain these antibodies. We may produce agglutinins, which will cause typhoid bacilli to clump, as well by inoculating proteins extracted from typhoid bacilli as by inoculating the bacteria themselves.

While, in general, the substance with which an antibody reacts is the same as the antigen which called it forth, this is not always the case. The serum of an animal which has been immunized against pneumococci will produce a precipitate when brought together with fluid in which pneumococci have been growing. Now it has been found that the substance with which the antibody reacts to form this precipitate is that polysaccharide gum which, we noted in an earlier chapter, forms the capsule of this microbe. This polysaccharide, inoculated in pure form, will not give rise to precipitin. One must inject the whole pneumococci to get this antibody. There are other cases known where the antibodies react with such polysaccharides. But these polysaccharides are *not antigens;* they will not themselves give rise to antibodies.

Haptens. Such a substance, unable to give rise to antibodies, but capable of reacting with them, is a partial antigen or *hapten.* These haptens are just as important as antigens in understanding what occurs in infection and immunity. It is probable that in the pneumococcus the polysaccharide is chemically bound to proteins, and that this compound substance serves as an antigen, producing antibodies. But the polysaccharide alone, which has been chemically freed from the protein, will react with the antibodies.

Artificial antigens may be made by attaching, chemically, various compounds to proteins. These new compounds give rise to antibodies which will react with the particular chemical compound which was linked with the protein to form an antigen. It has been possible in this way to prepare an entirely artificial antigen, a laboratory-prepared polysaccharide linked to serum globulin, which when used to immunize rabbits gave rise to an antibody that formed a precipitate with the gum from pneumococci, and which protected mice against infection with that microbe.

Specificity of Serum Reactions. If one immunizes a rabbit with repeated inoculations of typhoid bacilli at short intervals over a considerable period of time, the rabbit's blood will develop a high antibody content. It may cause an agglutination of typhoid bacilli when diluted up to 1–10,000 or even 1–100,000. Now if this serum, properly diluted, is added to suspensions of other species of bacteria, no agglutination results. The agglutinin is *specific* for the species of bacterium used to call it forth.

This specificity is equally true of other antibodies. Diphtheria antitoxin has no effect upon tetanus toxin. The serum of a rabbit inoculated with sheep's red blood cells will cause those cells to dissolve but will have no effect upon the blood cells of a dog. And so on. Each antibody reacts with its own specific antigen.

Group Reactions. But a typhoid immune serum may agglutinate other species of bacteria when not sufficiently diluted. If we have a serum that will agglutinate typhoid germs when diluted to 1–10,000, and we try this serum in various dilutions against a variety of organisms, we may find that it will agglutinate

> Typhoid bacilli at 1–10,000,
> Paratyphoid bacilli at 1–500,
> Dysentery bacilli at 1–500,
> Colon bacilli at 1–100,

and Micrococci or other bacteria not at all. Now the paratyphoid and dysentery and colon bacilli are very similar to the typhoid bacilli; we consider them to be closely related species of bacteria. Our typhoid agglutinin will, then, give some agglutination of *closely related* bacteria, but in a much lower dilution.

This reaction of an antibody with antigens derived from species different from that used to call forth the antibody is called a *group reaction*. Group reactions may be observed with other types of antibodies. One may produce a precipitin against proteins present in the blood serum of, say, a dog. The precipitating serum will form a precipitate with dog serum when the latter has been highly diluted; it will form a precipitate with fox or wolf serum in lower dilution; but it will not form a precipitate at all with the blood of distantly related mammals, as a sheep or guinea pig.

When we inoculate an animal with bacteria, or blood cells, or blood serum, or extracts of bacteria, we introduce a number of different kinds of proteins, for none of these substances consists of but a single protein. We may, however, produce an antibody against a single pure protein in solution. Such an antibody is found to react with this pure protein alone, no matter from what source the protein is derived. Therefore the species specificity is to be explained on the basis that each species of bacterium, or each kind of blood serum, etc., contains one or more dominant proteins which are characteristic of that species, while the group reactions may be explained by assuming that certain proteins are common to a group of closely related species. In the case of the typhoid agglutinating serum just considered, we may explain the results obtained by assuming that in the typhoid germs used to immunize the rabbit, for every 10,000 molecules of protein peculiar to the typhoid bacillus, there were also present 500 molecules of a protein which also occurs in the paratyphoid and dysentery bacilli, and 100 molecules of a protein which also occurs in colon bacilli.

Antigenic Structure of Bacteria. Immunize a rabbit so that its serum will agglutinate typhoid bacilli. Now to this typhoid-immune serum, add an excess of typhoid bacilli. After standing for a time, remove the typhoid bacilli, and test the serum against another suspension of typhoid bacilli. It will be found that the serum has lost its ability to agglutinate the typhoid germs. The antibody has been *absorbed* from the serum by the excess of typhoid bacilli originally added. This serum will also have lost its group agglutinins, those for paratyphoid and other related organisms. But if the serum is absorbed with paratyphoid bacilli, only the agglutinins for paratyphoid bacilli will be removed, because these bacteria contain an excess of antigens peculiar to themselves, but only slight amounts common to the other species. By such *cross-absorption* tests one may determine very precisely what antigens or haptens bacterial species have in common, and which ones are peculiar to each species.

If one immunizes a rabbit with a strain of the pneumococcus, and then tries this serum against many other strains, it will be found to be specific for only some of them, while it fails to agglutinate others. This is due to the fact that the polysaccharide haptens are not identical in all of the pneumococci. By cross-immunization experiments it may be shown that there are at least 32 different kinds of pneumococci. These are all alike as far as their morphology or cultural characters are concerned, almost identical as regards their ability to produce disease. They are called *types*, a term used by immunologists to indicate varieties of a species which differ only in their antigenic structure. A number of other species of bacteria have been found to be divisible into antigenic types.

The type-specificity of the different strains of pneumococci is determined entirely by the polysaccharide haptens that form their capsules. When pneumococci dissociate, and produce rough forms, the latter are found to have lost their virulence and their capsules. When such rough forms are used to immunize rabbits, there is obtained another kind of antibody, which will agglutinate indiscriminately rough forms of all pneumococci, regardless of the smooth type from which they were derived. This can be explained only by the fact that all pneumococci have a common antigen in the interior of their cells, and a type specific antigen in their capsules. Similar experiments have been performed with non-motile variants of motile species of bacteria. Here it has been found that one antigen is contained in the flagella, and another one in the interior of the cells. Antigens contained within the cell are called *somatic* antigens. Flagellar and capsular antigens are sometimes referred to as *surface* antigens. There is evidence that bacteria which have neither capsules nor flagella have surface antigens which are different from their somatic antigens.

So by cross-immunity tests and cross-absorption tests with different species and strains of bacteria and with different variants of a single strain, and by chemical extraction, purification, and identification of the antigens and haptens of bacteria, we are slowly arriving at a very complete picture of the complex structure of bacteria. This is highly important in explaining not only the relationships of bacterial species, but also the complex reactions that take place in infection and immunity. But, more important still, such studies offer a new approach to the determination of the structure of protoplasm itself. It seems to the author that the researches of the past decade on the nature of filterable viruses, on the antigenic structure of bacteria, and on the enzymes of microbes have brought us closer to a realization of the nature of living matter than any other biological researches.

Applications. The delicate specificity of the serum reactions has provided some valuable diagnostic methods. We may, for instance, rapidly and certainly identify cultures of unknown bacteria by means of agglutination. Let us suppose that we have isolated from a patient an organism which we suspect is a typhoid bacillus. To make certain, we must make a stained slide, observe its morphology; prepare a hanging drop and note its motility; and inoculate it upon a series of culture media, including various sugar broths, and study all of its cultural characters. This requires considerable time.

But if we have on hand some known typhoid agglutinating serum, the identification is much simpler. All that is needed is to add some of the serum, properly diluted, to a suspension of the unknown bacteria. Clumping of the bacteria may be observed under the microscope within an hour, by the naked eye after standing over night. If the serum has been properly tested, if the test has been properly controlled, then clumping of the unknown bacteria means that they are typhoid bacilli, that they can belong to no other species. The same method may be used to identify any other species of bacteria which will form stable, uniform suspensions in liquids. The modern diagnostic laboratory keeps on hand a variety of agglutinating serums, each specific for some particular species of bacterium.

The serum reactions may be used as diagnostic tests in a manner just the converse of the above. Having on hand identified cultures of bacteria, we may search for the presence of antibodies in the patient's blood. Such a procedure is the *Widal test* for typhoid fever. In this disease, after a week or more, agglutinins appear in the patient's blood in response to an invasion by the typhoid bacilli. If we collect a little of the patient's blood, allow it to clot, remove the serum, and add this (properly diluted) to a suspension of *known* typhoid bacilli from a culture kept on hand in the laboratory, the occurrence of clumping signifies that the patient is suffering from typhoid fever.

The precipitin test may be used to identify minute traces of unknown proteins. A potent precipitating serum will detect the presence of proteins which are present in quantities too small to be demonstrated with certainty by ordinary chemical tests, and will distinguish proteins which cannot be separated by chemical means. One of the most important applications of the precipitin reaction is the identification of blood stains. The serum of a rabbit that has been intensively immunized with human blood will form a precipitate when added to human blood when the latter has been diluted up to 1–100,000 or more; will not form a precipitate with the blood of any other species save some of the higher apes; and will react with blood which has been dried on cloth or wood or other material for years. This is a reliable means of proving the identity of doubtful stains in murder cases.

We have seen that agglutination and other serum reactions serve to distinguish not only between closely related species, but also between races or strains or types of a single species. Conversely, by means of the group reactions, it has been possible to demonstrate relationships between organisms which sometimes are morphologically quite dissimilar. With groups of organisms whose relationships are quite clear, we have seen that the group reactions follow closely this relationship. Therefore we may use the group reactions to indicate blood relationships in groups of organisms where these relationships are not so clear. This has been done with mammals and with many of the higher plants. Thus the serum reactions have proved valuable in that branch of biology which deals with classification of living organisms, *taxonomy*.

Serum reactions are not, however, always perfectly specific. A number of anomalous reactions have been observed, sufficient to warn against a too complete reliance upon the results of these reactions in all cases. After all, the specificity of serum reactions is based upon the constitution of protein molecules, and it is possible for an identical configuration to occur in proteins synthesized by widely diverse species. There is still a great deal to be learned about the mechanism of these antibody reactions and their significance.

Complement. Antitoxins, agglutinins, and precipitins are stable antibodies. Immune serums showing these properties will remain active for a long time, and they do not lose their potency if heated to a moderate degree, to temperatures below the coagulation point of the proteins in the serum. On the other hand, the lysins, opsonins, and bactericidal substances are very unstable. Serums exhibiting these activities may lose their potency on standing, and are completely inactivated by heating for a short interval at 56° C., well below the coagulation temperature. This is an important and fundamental difference.

If one injects a rabbit repeatedly with sheep's red blood corpuscles, the rabbit's blood serum develops an antibody, *haemolysin*, which will dissolve sheep's red corpuscles. A little of the fresh immune rabbit's serum added to a suspension of the red cells in salt solution will cause the turbid fluid to clear, showing that the cells have dissolved. If, however, the immune rabbit's serum is first heated to 56° C. for half an hour, it will no longer dissolve the sheep's blood cells. But by adding a little bit of the fresh unheated rabbit's serum, the blood-cell-dissolving power is returned. It need not be immune blood; the inactivated immune serum may be reactivated by unheated *normal* blood serum. And it need not be rabbit's blood serum; the inactivated immune serum may be reactivated by the fresh serum of *any animal*. Guinea pig's blood serum is especially potent in reactivating the heated rabbit's immune serum.

These experiments may be explained only by assuming that for the dissolving of red blood cells there are required two distinct substances. One, the antibody proper, is not destroyed by heat. It results from the immunization, and is not present (unless in very minute quantities) in the normal blood. The other substance is easily destroyed by heat, and is not the result of immunization, but is present in the normal blood of all animals. It is called *alexin*, or more commonly, *complement*, since it completes the action of the antibody proper.

Further experiments have revealed other properties of complement. While the amount of complement varies in different species of animals, or in different individuals, it cannot be increased by immunization, as can the antibody proper. Moreover, complement is *not specific*. The same complement that completes the action of a haemolytic antibody will also serve to reactivate a bactericidal or opsonic serum. The same complement which completes the action of an antibody against one species of bacterium will serve to activate a serum against any other species. It can be shown that the antibody proper combines directly with the blood cell, or bacterium, or other antigen, but that complement will not unite with antigen save in the presence of the antibody proper.

Complement is itself a complex protein constituent of the blood. It is thought to be something like an enzyme, which brings about the actual dissolving of the blood cell, or death of the bacterium, or preparation for phagocytosis. It cannot, however, produce this effect until the antigen has first combined with the antibody proper. The antibody serves to *sensitize* the blood cell or bacterial cell, making it susceptible to the enzyme-like action of the complement.

Complement Fixation. Complement may combine with sensitized bacteria or other antigen (i.e., antigen combined with the antibody proper) even without showing any visible change in the bacteria. This may be demonstrated by showing that the complement has been bound or *fixed* by the sensitized antigen. To do this, we must utilize an indicator for the presence or absence of complement. Since the same complement serves for all of the sensitized antibodies, we may use as our indicator another sensitized antigen which *will* give a visible change in the presence of complement, such as blood cells which have been treated with immune serum against such blood cells. This is the principle upon which the *complement fixation test* is based.

The complement fixation test is another and more delicate way of using the specificity of the serum reactions in diagnosis. As with agglutination, we may employ it either to identify bacteria, using a known serum, or to diagnose disease, using a known bacterium. The use of this test was introduced by Bordet and Gengou. These investigators also discovered the bacillus of whooping cough, or pertussis, and to show how the complement fixation test works, we may take as an example its use in the diagnosis of that disease. Some blood of the patient is collected and allowed to clot. The serum is removed, and inactivated by heating to 56° C. Then, in a little test tube, we mix

> Patient's serum,
> Pertussis bacilli,
> Complement (fresh guinea pig serum).

The mixture is allowed to stand at body temperature for an hour. If the patient has whooping cough, he should have sensitizing antibodies in the blood which should combine with the bacteria. The sensitized bacteria should now combine with, or fix, the complement, so that the latter can no longer act upon any other sensitized antigen. To see if this has occurred, we now add

> Sheep's red blood cells,
> Rabbit's serum immunized against r.b.c.

If the complement has been fixed, no change will occur in the red blood cells; this would indicate that the patient actually has whooping cough. If the complement has not been fixed, it will dissolve the sensitized red blood cells, and the tube will clear; this would indicate that the patient does not have whooping cough.

The complement fixation test is a very delicate one, perhaps too much so to be entirely reliable. Bacteria alone will often inactivate complement; the same is sometimes true of the patient's serum. This requires careful controls. The quantities of the various reagents must be very carefully adjusted for each test.

Theories of Serum Reactions. Two general theories have been proposed to explain the reactions of the antibodies with their antigens.

Ehrlich's side-chain theory attempted to explain these phenomena as purely chemical reactions. He was particularly impressed by the specificity of the antibodies for their respective antigens. This, he thought, could be explained by assuming that each complex antibody molecule possesses a particular radicle, or atom complex attached to it like a side chain on the benzol molecule. Similarly, each antigen must possess a "side chain" capable of uniting chemically with the "side chain" of the antibody molecule. The two groups of atoms would fit each other as a key fits a lock. To explain all the varied reactions of the different sorts of antibodies required an extremely elaborate development of this theory. A number of different symbols were required to make it possible for one to visualize the various combinations of these hypothetical side chains. For example, to show what happens when red blood cells are dissolved by immune serum and complement:

We must first assume that the red blood cell has a "side chain" peculiar to itself, thus —

The sensitizing antibody must have two side chains, one to unite with the blood cell, one to unite with the complement —

and the complement must have a side chain capable of uniting with the sensitizing antibody, and another portion which exerts an enzyme action upon the sensitized blood cell. This latter portion of the molecule is represented by a fringe, the whole complement molecule appearing thus —

When these three reagents — blood cells, sensitizing antibody, and complement — are brought together, they combine,

the sensitizing antibody serving to establish a chemical union between the complement and the red blood cell. The enzyme portion of the complement molecule may now bring about a dissolution of the red blood cell.

Bordet vigorously opposed Ehrlich's theory on the grounds that the *quantitative* relationships between antibody and antigen did not follow the laws of chemical reactions, but rather indicated that the union between these reagents is that looser sort of a physical binding of colloidal substances which is called *adsorption*. To explain away these quantitative discrepancies, Ehrlich was forced to postulate more and more different sorts of chains, to assume that in each reaction we are not dealing with *one* antibody uniting with *one* antigen, but a whole series of substances having varying affinities for each other, until finally the whole theory became so complex that it was unacceptable. Bordet's adsorption theory is now generally accepted, but leaves unexplained the specificity of the reactions.

The recent work on haptens and on artificial antigens has led to something of a revival of Ehrlich's side-chain theory. When compounds are linked to proteins, and these new substances are used as antigens, they show a specificity different from that of the original protein. The resulting antibody reacts with the substance linked to the protein. Now this is much like Ehrlich's conception. The substance linked to the protein molecule may well be conceived of as a "side chain."

Ehrlich's and Bordet's theories may perhaps be reconciled. Both antigens and antibodies are very large complex molecules, which probably present on their surfaces *polar groups*, i.e., atom-complexes which, while neutral as a whole, exhibit a difference in electric charge in different portions of the group. Such polar groups may then give rise to a characteristic pattern of electric charges on the surface of the antigen or antibody molecule. It is possible that such patterns are complementary to each other, thus:

Antigen $\quad -+--+++-++---+--$
Antibody $\quad +-++---+--+++-++$

Such a theory explains at the same time the union of the antigen and antibody as an adsorption phenomenon, and the specificity of the reaction, the two reagents fitting much as a key fits a lock.

Antibody Reactions Are Colloidal Phenomena. In considering the mechanism of the serum reactions, it is now clear that we must sharply differentiate between the *union* of antigen with antibody, and the occurrence of a demonstrable *change* in the antigen. We may cause antibodies to combine with their antigens without producing any change at all, and we may bring about the various reactions — clumping, precipitation, dissolving of cells, etc. — without the intervention of an antibody. In each case the reaction occurs in two stages, first a union of the antibody with the antigen, then a change in the latter; and these two steps may be separated — they are not necessarily dependent upon each other.

When antitoxin unites with toxin, a precipitate may be formed. But this is not essential to the neutralization of the poisonous effect of the toxin. As far as can be determined, the mere union of the antibody with the poison is sufficient to render it innocuous. By certain means the two may be separated again, and the toxin is found to be as toxic as before.

The phenomena of agglutination and precipitation are almost identical in all respects. In one case, it is the minute cells in suspension which are flocculated; in the other, the molecules, or fine aggregates of molecules, of the proteins, in the form of colloidal solutions. In the *absence of immune serum*, one may produce the same flocculation by adding electrolytes — ionizable salts or acids — to the suspension of the bacteria or proteins. In the *absence of electrolytes*, the antibody will unite with the antigen, but no agglutination or precipitation occurs. It is apparent that the union is independent of the flocculation, and that the effect of the antibody (agglutinin or precipitin) upon the antigen (bacteria or protein) is merely to render the latter more susceptible to the flocculating action of electrolytes.

In the case of the sensitizing antibodies, we have already seen that it is the complement, not the antibody, which produces the observable effect upon the antigen. Antibody may *unite* with the antigen independent of the complement. Complement is essential for the *change* in the antigen. The nature of this change is not entirely clear. In the case of lysis of cells, this may be a surface tension effect, similar to the dissolving of blood cells or bacteria by soap or bile salts or saponin.

It would appear, then, that the phenomena of immunity may be largely explained on the basis of physical chemistry as colloid phenomena. The union of antigen with antibody is an adsorption; the changes occurring in the antigen are also colloidal phenomena. But that remarkable specificity is not at all clear.

Hypersensitivity. In the earlier days of antitoxin treatment of diphtheria, it occasionally happened that immediately following the injection of the immune horse serum the patient would exhibit a marked unfavorable reaction — sudden collapse, perhaps sudden death. An investigation of these untoward results showed that they are independent of the *antitoxin* content of the serum, and are due to a peculiar sensitivity of some people to *horse serum*. With improved methods for concentrating antitoxin, and greater care in its administration, such reactions, never common, have become so rare as to be practically negligible.

But researches upon the mechanism back of these reactions have unearthed a whole category of phenomena, which, we now know, have an important bearing upon infection and immunity. Our knowledge of these phenomena is still very incomplete, rather vague, and, as is so often the case where things are imperfectly understood, hampered by a confused terminology. It is evident that we have to deal here with several different, but closely related, phenomena; though to what extent they are different and to what extent they are related we cannot say. Collectively we may designate these phenomena as *hypersensitivity*, by which we mean an abnormal susceptibility to substances which are normally either harmless or at least not so harmful to a normal individual as to the hypersensitive individual.

Varieties of Hypersensitivity. Under this general term are included what appear at the present time to be six different categories of phenomena: — *anaphylaxis, serum sickness,* the *allergy of infection, atopy, ivy poisoning,* and the *drug idiosyncrasies.*

By *atopy* is meant an inborn or hereditary hypersensitivity to certain substances, which cannot be produced experimentally. Hay fever is such a condition, due to susceptibility to the proteins of pollen. Asthma is another atopic disease, caused by dandruff or mold spores or other materials floating in the air. Food idiosyncrasies, resulting in digestive disturbances and hives (or urticaria) when some particular food is eaten, form still a third type.

Poisoning with ivy or poison oak and certain other plants affects only some susceptible individuals. The violent reaction of certain people to small, medicinal doses of certain drugs indicates a similar sort of hypersensitivity. These types will not be discussed further since they do not appear to be related to bacterial infections.

Anaphylaxis. If one inoculates into a guinea pig a minute quantity of horse serum or white of egg or other protein substance, and then, after waiting about two weeks, makes a second injection of the same material, this second injection will be immediately followed by severe symptoms of illness, and will usually result in sudden death of the animal. These are the essential facts about *anaphylaxis* — a preliminary injection of a *sensitizing dose* of a protein, after a proper incubation period, renders the animal hypersensitive, so that a second injection, the *shock dose,* suddenly kills. A substance which is in itself bland and harmless becomes a violent poison to the sensitized animal.

The symptoms of anaphylaxis are the same regardless of the substance used to induce the shock. Thus a guinea pig sensitized to white of egg will show the same sort of symptoms when reinoculated with that protein, as will another guinea pig sensitized to horse protein when injected with a shock dose of that protein. But the symptoms vary with different animals. The symptoms of anaphylactic shock in a guinea pig are due very largely to a constriction of the involuntary muscles of the bronchi, interfering with breathing. Death is caused by suffocation. In the rabbit, the symptoms are those of heart failure, and this is due to a spasmodic contraction of the muscles of the pulmonary arterial system, causing a dilatation of the right side of the heart. It appears that in all cases the reaction of the animal is largely due to a change in the involuntary muscles of one part of the body or another.

Anaphylaxis shows many features which indicate that it is somehow related to the antibody reactions. Only those substances, proteins, which will serve as antigens, will also serve to sensitize and give rise to a shock. The reaction is specific, i.e., the sensitized guinea pig will respond to a second injection of the same protein as was used in sensitization, but to no other. It is a very delicate reaction, extremely minute quantities of a protein being sufficient to sensitize, although considerably larger doses are necessary to produce a fatal shock.

This parallelism with the serum reactions led to the conclusion that anaphylaxis is due to the formation of an antibody of some sort, and this view gained support when it was found possible to transfer the anaphylactic state from a sensitized guinea pig to a normal guinea pig by inoculating the latter with the blood serum of the former. This *passive anaphylaxis* is accomplished as follows: A guinea pig is sensitized by injecting a small dose of some protein, say egg white. After a proper incubation period, about two weeks, this guinea pig is bled. The serum is now injected into a second guinea pig which has never been inoculated with egg white. This second guinea pig is now sensitized so that when injected with egg white (the first time) it will show typical symptoms of anaphylaxis.

These facts supported a *humoral* theory of anaphylaxis. It was assumed that the sensitizing dose leads to the formation of an antibody; that when the shock dose is administered, this antibody reacts with it in the blood to form a poison, which then causes a reaction on the part of the smooth muscle cells. But later investigations indicate that the seat of the reaction is not in the blood, but in the cells, and the *cellular* theory now receives greater support.

In passive anaphylaxis the guinea pig which has received the blood serum of the sensitized guinea pig does not become sensitive immediately. A period of at least four hours, generally longer, is required before it will respond to the shock dose. This is interpreted as indicating that the animal will not become sensitive until the antibody injected has become bound to, or has somehow or other become integral with the cells. And anaphylaxis is probably due to a reaction between the sensitizing substance and so-called "sessile" antibodies, those within the cells, rather than circulating antibodies in the blood.

Serum Sickness. Those occasional rare cases of sudden death following the administration of antitoxin or antibacterial serum are probably to be explained as cases of anaphylactic shock in individuals who have scmehow or other become sensitized to the proteins of horse serum. This view is supported by the observation that such accidents are more frequent when *second* injections are given.

There occurs fairly frequently, however, another sort of reaction called *serum sickness*. This is, fortunately, much less alarming and without danger to life. It appears, not immediately after the injection of the serum, but about ten days later. The symptoms are those of a fever — elevation of temperature, pains in the joints, and general discomfort — together with the occurrence of an itchy rash ("hives"). It is noteworthy that the incubation period for this reaction to develop is about the same as that required to produce anaphylactic sensitization, and that this incubation period is much shorter in cases of second injections of serum. It is clear that serum sickness is somehow related to anaphylaxis, but not the identical phenomenon.

Allergy of Infection. The term *allergy* is somewhat confusing, since it has been used in a broad sense for all forms of hypersensitivity, and in a narrow sense to designate a particular sort of hypersensitivity resulting from bacterial infections, of which the *tuberculin reaction* is a well-known example. This particular sort of hypersensitivity may be called the *allergy of infection* without confusion.

Tuberculin, or, more specifically, Koch's old tuberculin, is a product of the tubercle bacillus obtained as follows: Tubercle bacilli are grown in 5% glycerine broth for some weeks until no further growth occurs. The culture is heated to boiling, to kill the bacteria, filtered, and the bacteria-free liquid is evaporated to one-tenth its original volume. The resulting dark brown syrupy liquid contains, among other things, products derived from dead and disintegrated tubercle bacilli.

If this tuberculin is injected into a normal guinea pig, nothing happens. But if injected into a guinea pig which has previously been inoculated with tubercle bacilli, and in which the disease tuberculosis has developed, there occurs a rapid development of marked symptoms, and if the dose has been large enough, death. If tuberculin is inoculated in a small dose into the tissues just beneath the skin of a normal person, who has not had tuberculosis, again nothing happens. But if injected in a small dose into the subcutaneous tissues of a person suffering from tuberculosis, there occurs a definite reaction, manifested in several ways. At the site of inoculation, there occurs a *local* reaction, consisting of redness, heat, and some tenderness of the skin. At the site of the natural infection, there occurs a *focal* reaction; if the disease is in a joint or lymph gland, these areas become swollen and painful for a time; if in the lungs, there is an increased cough and expectoration. And finally, there occurs a *constitutional* reaction, consisting of an elevation of temperature, and those vague symptoms of discomfort which accompany a fever.

It is evident that this reaction is very similar to anaphylaxis. The substance, tuberculin, is harmless to the normal animal or person, but acts as an irritant or poison when introduced into the tissues of an animal or person that has been *sensitized* by the growth of tubercle bacilli in the body.

For a long time, however, it was believed that the tuberculin reaction is something quite distinct from anaphylaxis, because the reactions in the animal are quite different from those occurring in anaphylactic shock caused by egg white and similar substances, and especially because animals could not be sensitized with tuberculin. It was only possible to produce sensitivity by producing tuberculosis in the animal. It seemed, therefore, that the substance which elicited the shock when injected into the tuberculous guinea pig must be different from the substance which causes the sensitization. Moreover, the tuberculin reaction cannot be passively transferred.

The substance in tuberculin which produces the tuberculin reaction has been isolated in pure form. It is a peculiar protein which is not coagulated by heat. With this purified tuberculin protein, it has been possible to sensitize guinea pigs without giving them tuberculosis. It is beginning to appear that the difference between the tuberculin reaction and anaphylaxis is quantitative rather than qualitative. There is some evidence that the tuberculin type of hypersensitivity is just a lower degree of the same process that occurs in anaphylaxis.

A similar allergy of infection may be demonstrated in other bacterial diseases. If extracts of the causative organisms are injected into the skin, an area of redness and swelling occurs in individuals who have or have had the disease, not in normal persons. Such reactions are more striking in the more chronic kinds of infection, as glanders and fungous diseases.

Hypersensitivity and Infection. In our discussion of the nature of endotoxins in the preceding chapter, it was pointed out that the injury to the tissues exerted by those bacteria which do not form exotoxins might be explained, not by the secretion of a poison by the bacteria themselves, but by the formation of a poison through some reaction between the body and the bacterial protoplasm. The phenomena of anaphylaxis and allergy provide the basis for such a hypothesis.

There is a great deal of difference of opinion among authorities as to whether the tuberculin sensitivity represents a protective mechanism or leaves the individual more susceptible to infection. It may be that the bacteria do not injure the body tissues until after these have become sensitized. There is considerable experimental evidence that this is the mechanism of infection in some of the more chronic diseases, especially some of the fungous infections. The rather long incubation period characteristic of some of the infectious diseases has been explained as the time necessary for the tissues to become sensitized.

Skin Tests. Since tuberculin produces a reaction only in individuals who have (or have had) active tuberculosis, it may be used as a diagnostic method. We no longer inject the tuberculin into the tissues under the skin, since this gives a disagreeable general reaction if the test is positive. Instead, a minute quantity of the tuberculin is injected with a fine needle directly into the very superficial layers of the skin itself. This is called an *intracutaneous* injection. It gives rise to a local reaction only, without any general symptoms. This test is called the *Mantoux* test when used to diagnose tuberculosis. It is conclusive only when negative, since a positive reaction may occur in individuals in whom the disease is no longer active.

Similar skin tests may be used in the diagnosis of other infectious diseases, injecting intracutaneously minute doses of extracts of the appropriate microbes. They are also used to diagnose other sorts of hypersensitivity. Thus it is customary, before administering antitoxin, to give an intracutaneous injection of a minute dose of the serum to see if the patient is sensitive to horse protein. And in a similar manner we may find out what pollens are responsible in cases of hay fever, or what foods will cause disturbances in cases of food idiosyncrasy, and so on.

In all these skin tests the substance inoculated is one which will not give rise to an inflammatory reaction in a normal individual. A *positive* reaction means that the person tested has somehow or other become *hypersensitive* to the test substance. But there is another kind of skin test in general use. If we wish to determine whether a given person is immune or susceptible to diphtheria, we inject into the skin a minute dose of the exotoxin of the diphtheria bacilli. If the individual is susceptible, this toxin will irritate the tissues, and an area of redness or inflammation results. If the individual has become immune, either from the natural disease or from vaccination, no irritation will occur because the toxin injected has been neutralized by antitoxin in his blood. Here a *positive* reaction means *susceptibility*, a *negative* reaction means *immunity*. Such a test for diphtheria susceptibility is called the *Schick* test. A similar test for susceptibility to scarlet fever is the *Dick* test.

CHAPTER XVIII

BACTERIAL DISEASES OF PLANTS

It is a rather curious and interesting fact that the importance of bacteria in causing diseases of plants was not recognized until some years after the microbic diseases of man and animals had been intensively investigated. This was due to the fact that a larger proportion of plant diseases are caused by parasitic higher Fungi than by bacteria, and the plant pathologists were too much occupied by studies of these Fungi to be concerned with the bacteria. It is true that a bacterial plant disease, fire blight of pears, was clearly described by Burrill in 1878, and the proof that this disease is caused by bacteria was furnished by inoculation experiments reported by Arthur in 1885. But these reports were not generally accepted, and as late as the beginning of this century, botanists were generally of the opinion that bacteria could not invade plants, and that no plant diseases were caused by bacteria.

Erwin F. Smith. It was not until about 1900 that this rather narrow-minded skepticism was overcome by the clear and vigorous publications of Erwin F. Smith. We now know that there are probably as many bacterial diseases of plants as of animals, involving many different families, and the list is rapidly growing larger. A number of these diseases were first investigated and described by Smith and his associates, and indeed his name occupies in this field of bacteriology a position comparable with that of Koch in the field of medical bacteriology.

Plant-Disease Bacteria. The bacteria which cause plant disease are not greatly varied in morphology. There is a disease, scab, of potatoes and some other root crops, caused by certain species of Actinomycetes. But with this exception, the bacteria that cause plant disease are Gram negative rod forms without spores. A number of them produce yellow pigments. Some are non-motile. Of the motile forms, some have but a single polar flagellum, others are peritrichous. The non-motile and monotrichous species are included

301

in one genus, *Phytomonas*. The peritrichous species are placed in another genus, *Erwinia*, named to honor Erwin Smith.

Virulence *vs*. Resistance. It is quite evident, then, that the ability to invade living plant tissues is a property exhibited by only a limited and highly specialized group of bacteria. Plant-disease bacteria show the same sort of specificity as the animal pathogens — some may infect only certain species, others may produce disease in a wide variety of plants; some may invade through one particular portal of entry, or may produce one particular sort of tissue change. In short, the bacteria causing plant disease possess a virulence made up of invasive power and ability to injure the tissues of the host plant, similar to the virulence of the bacteria causing animal diseases.

Also we find that some species or strains or individuals among the plants will be resistant to invasion by a bacterium that will cause disease in another plant, or variety, or related species. And so, plants must have some sort of resistance or immunity to infection, and we may well postulate that with plants as with animals the occurrence of infection is determined by the balance established between the virulence of the bacteria and the resistance of the plant.

But here our analogy breaks down, for when we come to inquire as to the mechanisms of virulence and resistance in plant diseases, we find that these are apparently quite different from those brought into play in animal diseases.

Mechanism of Virulence. For the injury produced by these bacteria is apparently not due to specific toxins which affect the protoplasm directly, but rather to enzymes having the power to attack this, that, or another constituent of the plant structure. As Smith states,* the bacteria produce "enzymes converting starches into sugars, complex sugars into simpler ones, and so on, for their nutrition. They also neutralize and consume plant acids, and feed upon amino bodies and other nitrogenous elements of the host. As a result of their growth, many of them liberate both acids and alkalies, to the detriment of the plant. The solvent action of their products on the pectin compounds of the middle lamellae separates cells and leads to the production of cavities in the cortex, pith, phloem and xylem. There is also, or may be, a mechanical splitting,

* Smith, Erwin F.: *An Introduction to Bacterial Diseases of Plants* (Philadelphia, 1920).

tearing, or crushing due to the enormous multiplication of the bacteria within confined spaces."

Such a conception of the mechanism of injury to the host indicates very little difference indeed between disease and decay, and implies that the sole difference between pathogen and saprophyte is ability to invade the tissues of the host plant. Such invasive power implies an ability to overcome the defensive mechanisms of the plant.

Resistance of Plants. It has recently been stated that in certain plants affected with chronic bacterial infections, agglutinins and precipitins could be demonstrated in the plant's sap. But aside from this single observation which awaits confirmation, there is nothing known in plants of an immunity comparable with that of animals. A natural immunity is well known — the resistance of certain species or races, occurring naturally or developed by breeding experiments. But there is no evidence that plants acquire immunity by recovery from disease, or that they may form antibodies, or that they have any mechanism comparable with phagocytosis. The natural immunity of plants is due rather to the mechanical resistance offered by the outer cuticle with its waxy coating, and by the walls of the cells themselves, and by the chemical nature of substances dissolved in the sap — certain acids and glucosides, essential oils, thymol, camphor, etc. — which are known to inhibit the growth of bacteria.

Portals of Entry. The bark and the waxy cuticle are practically impermeable to bacteria. To invade the plant they must therefore gain entrance to the plant tissues through wounds, or through the natural openings of the plant — the stomata, the water pores, or the nectaries of flowers.

Wounds may result from wind or hail, or may be produced in cultivating or by pruning. In some cases the disease is transmitted from plant to plant by pruning knives. Another type of wound infection is that produced by insects which feed upon the plant, and also serve to transmit the bacteria from one plant to another. The wilt of cucumbers and related plants is such a disease, transmitted by the cucumber beetle. Bacteria may be carried into the interior of the plant by droplets of moisture passing through the water pores; the black rot of cabbages arises in this way. Fire blight of pomaceous fruits gains entrance to the plant through the nectaries, and is carried from tree to tree by insects visiting the flowers.

Types of Plant Diseases. The bacterial diseases of plants vary in their symptoms and the sort of lesions developing, in a manner somewhat analogous to the diseases of animals. The nature of the disease process depends upon a number of factors — the portal of entry, the invasive power of the organisms, the mode of spread through the plant, and especially the degree of "toxicity," or tissue-destroying power of the organism.

Leaf spots are localized infections, the causative bacteria being unable to spread very far from the portal of entry. The angular leaf spot of cotton (due to *Phytomonas malvaceara*) and the blight or bacterial spot disease of bean (caused by *Phytomonas phaseoli*) are examples of such diseases. Infections of this type generally begin by an invasion of stomata, which form the center from which the lesion radiates.

Blights are diseases with more extensive injury to the tissues, the infection spreading through the tissues to involve a whole twig or branch, or eventually the entire plant. The fire blight of apples, pears, and quinces previously mentioned is an example. It is caused by *Erwinia amylovora*. Leaf spots might be considered analogous with localized abscesses, such as boils, in man; and similarly blights might be compared to such a spreading disease as erysipelas.

The *rots* are more rapidly extending diseases, in which, in addition to death of the tissues, decomposition also results. Gas gangrene in man might be considered an analogous condition. The soft rot of carrots and other stored vegetables, caused by *Erwinia carotovora*, is a well-known example. Here the distinction between pathogen and saprophyte becomes very tenuous indeed.

Vascular diseases are those in which bacteria spread rapidly and extensively through conducting vessels of the plant, often to such an extent that the vessels are plugged, the flow of sap cut off, and the plant consequently *wilts*. Cucumber wilt, due to *Erwinia tracheiphila*, and Stewart's disease of sweet corn, caused by *Phytomonas stewarti*, are representatives of this group of diseases.

Finally, there is a group of bacterial diseases characterized by the formation of *tumors* or *galls*. The bacteria do not cause a destruction of the tissue; instead they merely irritate the cells, causing overgrowth. The nodules that develop on the roots of leguminous plants, which harbor the nitrogen-fixing bacterium, *Rhizobium leguminosarum*, are examples of such tumors. Another is the disease called *crown gall*, occurring in a variety of plants, and due to *Phy-*

tomonas tumefaciens. This latter disease is a very remarkable one, imitating in some respects cancerous disease in man. The lesions are usually warty or nodular outgrowths on stems or roots, but at times the presence of the bacterium may give rise to *teratological* growths, i.e., to abnormalities of development, such as the occurrence of roots where leaves should be formed, or the formation of large numbers of new shoots crowded at one point on the plant. Erwin Smith believed that this disease in plants was in every sense analogous with cancer in man, but this view has not been accepted.

Control of Bacterial Plant Diseases. By careful study of the mode of spread and biological character of the causative bacteria it has been possible in some cases to introduce control measures tending to limit or completely check bacterial plant diseases. Thus it has been found that fire blight begins in the spring from bacteria oozing from certain "hold-over" patches on trunks or limbs. By carefully removing and burning these infected parts of the trees, the disease may be eliminated. In some cases the disease is carried from one season to the next on seeds or bulbs, and may be prevented by selecting seeding material from disease-free stock, or in some cases by treating the seed with antiseptics. Cucumber wilt may be controlled by measures tending to reduce attacks by the cucumber beetle. Crown gall is often transmitted by pruning implements, and sterilization between prunings will tend to eliminate the disease. In greenhouses it is practical to sterilize the soil itself, either by heat or antiseptics.

CHAPTER XIX

CLASSIFICATION OF BACTERIA

When biologists classify living organisms they have two ends in view — two ends which are fundamentally different, and at times incompatible. One is to arrange living beings in groups of related forms: — to take all individuals which appear to be alike and group them as a Species; to gather together all the species which appear sufficiently related and place them in a Genus; to lump together the related genera in Tribes, similar tribes in Families, families in Orders, orders in Classes, and classes in Phyla, the major subdivisions of the plant or animal kingdom. Further, it is hoped to arrange these divisions so that they will actually represent "blood" relationships, that they will express the course of evolution — to place in one genus all those species which have been derived from a common ancestral type, to place in one family all those genera which have had a common origin, and so on. The *systematic* biologists, or *taxonomists*, are thus interested primarily in *similarities* between forms, in finding connecting links, transitional species, which will indicate relationships.

The other aim in classification is to arrive at a differentiation of species — to arrange all organisms in clearly understandable *keys*, by reference to which any unknown species may be readily identified; and to *name* definitely the species which are known, by a standard, universally used name so that every other biologist will know precisely what kind of an organism is meant when this name is used. Thus it is a great advantage from a practical standpoint to be able to say "*Eberthella typhi*," and to know that everyone will understand that by these words we mean a Gram negative, rod-shaped, motile bacterium which does not liquefy gelatine nor produce gas from sugars; which does, however, form acid from glucose, maltose, and mannitol. And it is also a great advantage from a practical standpoint, having determined the above morphological and cultural characters of an unknown organism, to then turn to a book, and looking through the various keys, find out that this organism can be no other than " *Eberthella typhi.*" Biologists interested in classification from this standpoint direct their attention more to *differences* between species than to similarities. To them the transitional forms which will not fit a neatly arranged artificial key are an abomination.

Conflicting Aims. It would be highly desirable if a single classification could serve both ends — if all organisms could be grouped into a system which would provide at the same time a plan of their family tree and a key to their identification, and sharply separate all existing species. With some of the higher plants and animals, such an ideal system may be approached, but with more primitive forms, where gradations between species or other categories are continuous, and relationships are obscure, there is necessarily a conflict between the two aims, between the theoretical and practical.

The nature of this conflict may be illustrated by an example from the bacteria. It so happens that practically all the bacteria which cause plant diseases are Gram negative rod forms without spores, mostly motile, some with a single polar flagellum, others peritrichous. It is obvious that the habitat, plants, is suitable for only a limited group of bacteria. The plant pathogens form thus a homogeneous natural group, which are undoubtedly closely related, derived from a common ancestral type. From a theoretical standpoint it would be desirable to recognize this fact by setting aside these organisms as distinct from others. This has been done by a committee of the Society of American Bacteriologists, which placed all these plant pathogens in a tribe, *Erwineae*, with two genera, *Erwinia* with peritrichous flagella, and *Phytomonas* with polar flagella. But not all the motile Gram negative rods are causes of plant diseases, by any means. And also, one might readily isolate a plant pathogen from some other habitat than plants. Having on hand an unknown Gram negative peritrichous rod, one has no way of determining whether it belongs to the genus Erwinia, or to some other genus, save by inoculating the culture into all possible species of plants, a task which is obviously impossible! Such an arrangement, no matter how desirable it might seem from a theoretical standpoint, makes the classification useless from a practical standpoint.

A Compromise Is Necessary. To be of any use at all, a classification must be generally accepted so that different workers will employ the same names for the same kind of organisms. This requires the establishment of a *compromise* between the viewpoints of different scientists or groups of scientists. The botanists and zoölogists have adopted rules or codes to govern the naming of organisms, and maintain international committees and congresses to bring about the necessary compromises.

It is only within the last few years that bacteriologists have established an international organization. This organization has agreed to follow the codes of the botanists and zoölogists in so far as they may be applicable and appropriate, and has appointed a committee which has begun to work upon an internationally acceptable nomenclature and classification of bacteria. But as yet the classification of bacteria is in a very unsatisfactory state. The early bacteriologists were mostly physicians and chemists, with little biological training or interest. They were concerned entirely with the relationships of bacteria to disease or fermentation or soil fertility. Each needed an acquaintance with only a few species important in his particular field. Medical bacteriologists had no interest in the organisms important in industry, and conversely, industrial bacteriologists had no interest in pathogens. And so there was no great need for a classification from the practical side, and very little interest in the matter on the theoretical side.

Bacteria Require Special Treatment. Moreover, the problem of classifying bacteria presents difficulties not encountered with higher organisms. The botanists and zoölogists differentiate and group their species entirely by *morphologic* characters. Physiologic differences exist, but they are always so well correlated with structural differences that it is sufficient to utilize the latter alone. And a classification based entirely upon morphologic characters has the great advantage that it may be used as well in the study of dead museum material as of living organisms in the field or laboratory.

The bacteria also show, to a limited degree, this correlation between physiologic and morphologic characters. We have noted in a former chapter that the main types of fermentation of sugars are carried on by morphologically different groups. But this correlation is very limited indeed. We may recognize only a few fundamental morphologic forms, but a great variety of physiologic activities, and in many cases bacteria which are morphologically identical exhibit important differences in their activities. For example, the colon bacillus and the typhoid germ cannot be distinguished under the microscope, yet one is a normal intestinal parasite, the other a cause of severe disease. It is therefore impossible to base the classification and identification of bacteria entirely upon morphology. We must use to a large extent *physiologic* characters, as biochemical activities, ability to produce disease, etc.

Then it was discovered further that bacteria might be morphologically and culturally identical, but different in their immunity reactions. One may isolate two strains of meningococci from two different cases of epidemic meningitis which will appear precisely the same under the microscope and in all artificial cultures. And yet an immune serum against one will not agglutinate the other, nor can a therapeutic serum against one be used successfully in the treatment of an infection by the other. Now this difference in serum reactions may not be of sufficient importance to warrant creating new species, but it is of tremendous importance in the treatment of disease.

Thus we may distinguish bacterial species by

> Morphologic characters,
> Cultural characters and biochemical activities,
> Pathogenicity for plants and animals,
> Serum reactions.

What Is a Species? One of the great difficulties involved in classification is the determination of the limits of the various categories — species, genus, family, etc. These categories are sharply divided from each other, yet in nature such sharp divisions do not occur. This difficulty is greater with the lower divisions, genera and species.

At first glance it would seem that the term "species" indicates a perfectly definite concept. When one speaks of the species man, there can be no question as to what is included under this term. It is true that not all men are alike. We recognize different races of men, and within the races different types, and we may readily distinguish all the individuals of one type. And yet the most extreme differences observed in men are not so great as the difference between mankind and the nearest other species, the anthropoid apes. There is a gap, there are no living intermediate types to furnish a *continuous* gradation between men and apes. But as we descend in the evolutionary scale we find that such gaps become less and less apparent, and the variation becomes more and more continuous. And it is obvious that with these more primitive forms, the use of the term "species" involves an artificial division which does not actually exist. What shall be the limits of a species, where the lines shall be drawn, is again a matter which must be settled by arbitration and compromise between authorities. And we find that the criteria of species vary widely with different groups of organisms. Differences which are considered sufficient to warrant separating genera in one group would not be considered important enough to create varieties in another.

Principles to Follow. And yet there are certain fundamental principles which may be used as a guide for classification. It is not

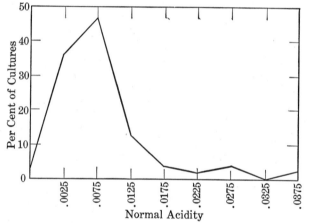

Fig. 73. Frequency Distribution of Orange Staphylococci according to Production of Acid in Glucose Broth. (Replotted from C.-E. A. and Anne Winslow, *Systematic Relationships of the Coccaceae*, John Wiley and Sons, New York.)

entirely a matter of opinion. Whether a given character shall be considered of taxonomic value depends upon whether it varies in a perfectly continuous manner or shows a tendency to discontinuous variation, and whether it is correlated with changes in other characters, or varies independently of other characters. These things may be learned by the use of *statistical methods*.

The common orange-colored Staphylococci produce acid from the sugar, glucose. But if one examines a large number of strains of orange-colored Staphylococci from all sources, some will be found which produce no acid, some which produce a great deal of acid, and others producing amounts in between. Are we justified in separating the orange Staphylococci into species based upon acid production? First let us see how these different strains vary on a percentage basis — how, literally, they "stack up" with regard to the amount of acid formed. Figure 73 presents a curve which shows the amount of acid formed by a large number of strains of orange Staphylococci when grown in glucose broth. The acid has been measured by titration, and the percentage of strains producing certain amounts of acid has been calculated. It is seen that more strains

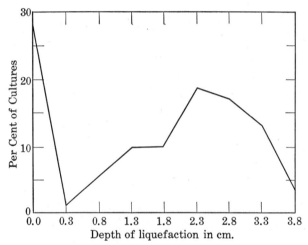

FIG. 74. Frequency Distribution of Orange Staphylococci according to Liquefaction of Gelatine. (Replotted from C.-E. A. and Anne Winslow, *Systematic Relationships of the Coccaceae,* John Wiley and Sons, New York.)

produced .0075 normal acidity than any other degree, that the curve forms a peak at this quantity. This peak is called the *mode*. On either side of this peak, the curve descends uniformly, a few producing no acid and a few producing much acid, with perfectly graded percentages in between. This means that as far as the amount of acid formed from glucose is concerned, the variation of these Staphylococci follows a perfectly normal or *chance* distribution, and that this character is of no significance in trying to discover species.

Discontinuous Variation. But when we plot a similar curve for the digestion of gelatine by orange Staphylococci, we find a different condition. A curve showing the percentage distribution of this

312   THE BIOLOGY OF BACTERIA

character is found in Fig. 74. The degree of digestion is measured
in terms of centimeters of a column of gelatine liquefied in thirty
days. Again we find a peak, or mode, at 2.3 cm., and the curve
descends uniformly on either side of this peak until we come to the
column for no liquefaction, where there is a very sharp rise. There
are *two* peaks, or modes, to this curve, one at 0 and one at 2.3 cm.
of liquefaction. And, although qualitatively there is a continuous
gradation from no liquefaction to rapid liquefaction, quantitatively
this variation tends to become *discontinuous*. If the distribution
were normal, the percentage of strains showing no liquefaction should
be very small; instead, 30% of all the strains failed to digest the
gelatine. This *bimodal* curve indicates that with regard to gelatine
liquefaction, the orange Staphylococci tend to divide into two groups,
those that do and those that do not. And if it is considered desirable
to split the orange Staphylococci into species, it is obvious that
liquefaction of gelatine is a better character for this purpose than the
production of acid from glucose.

Correlated Characters. It is doubtful, however, whether it is
ever desirable to separate species upon differences in but a *single*
character. In the case of the orange Staphylococci, there is some
slight evidence that those strains which liquefy gelatine are more
pathogenic than those which do not, and this might be considered
supporting evidence that there are fundamentally two species. Most
authorities, however, consider this evidence insufficient, and recognize but one, the *Staphylococcus aureus*. But with many organisms
we find that a variation occurs simultaneously in two or more characters, that there is a *correlation* between the degree or kind of variation in two or more characters. The occurrence of such correlated
variations provides a much stronger justification for the separation
of species.

A number of strains of Staphylococci were examined with regard
to the color of the pigment they produced, and, among others, two
groups were recognized, one which formed tints of cadmium yellow,
and another which produced tints of cadmium orange. These strains
had been gathered from all sorts of sources, some from skin or mouth,
abscesses or other lesions, some from air, water, soil, and so forth.
Now, when each of these two color groups was examined with regard
to source of the strain, i.e., as to whether it came from a parasitic or
saprophytic habitat, the following results were obtained:

	Yellow	Orange
Parasitic	22 strains	114 strains
Saprophytic	73 strains	25 strains

It is clear that while not all yellow Staphylococci are necessarily saprophytic or orange ones necessarily parasitic, this is true in the *majority* of cases. A correlation of specific characters with habitat might well be expected, since the selective action of a habitat is one of the factors which produce species. We may consider another example of correlated characters with these Staphylococci, comparing pigment production with the liquefaction of gelatine. Some of the Staphylococci produce red pigments. Comparing these with the orange strains from the standpoint of gelatine liquefaction, we find:

	Orange	Red
Liquefied	126 strains	4 strains
Did not liquefy	55 strains	21 strains

Here it is obvious that, as a rule, orange Staphylococci will liquefy gelatine while red ones will not. These positive correlations indicate that pigment production is a good character to be used in dividing species of Staphylococci.

So, by a judicious use of the *frequency distribution* of characters in a large number of individuals or strains, and by the determination of *correlations* between characters, one can arrive eventually at a conception of what constitutes "good" species in different groups, and as to what are good characters to be applied in the differentiation of species in each group. One discovers thus that characters which are important in differentiating members of the colon-typhoid group are of no use with the Staphylococci, and so on. Unfortunately, very little systematic work of this sort has been carried on with the bacteria. The above examples of the Staphylococci have been taken from *Systematic Relationships of the Coccaceae*, by the Winslows, one of the first studies of systematic bacteriology. There is great need for much more work of this character in bacteriology.

Early Classifications. The earliest microbiologists did not, of course, know the differences between bacteria and protozoa and algae. And yet some of these early investigators applied names to microbes which we can now recognize as bacteria. Thus, as far back as 1786, Mueller named two genera of "animalcules," Monas and Vibrio, which contained bacterial species. In 1838 Ehrenberg recognized five genera of bacteria, which were still considered to be animals:

1. *Bacterium*, inflexible rod forms,
2. *Vibrio*, flexible rod forms,
3. *Spirillum*, spiral, inflexible,
4. *Spirochaeta*, spiral, flexible,
5. *Spirodiscus*, flattened spirals.

It was not until 1872 that Cohn clearly recognized that bacteria are plants. Cohn included six genera, as follows:

1. *Micrococcus*, cells spherical,
2. *Bacterium*, isolated short rods,
3. *Bacillus*, long rods or filaments, rigid,
4. *Vibrio*, long rods or filaments, flexible,
5. *Spirillum*, cells spiral, rigid,
6. *Spirochaeta*, cells spiral, flexible.

Note that in Cohn's classification the term "Bacillus" appeared for the first time, and that the cocci were recognized.

There followed a number of arrangements proposed by various botanists. None of these received very wide acceptance. Two classifications which did come into general use were those of Lehmann and Neumann, and of Migula, both published at about the beginning of this century.

Lehmann and Neumann. Lehmann and Neumann divided the bacteria into three families, based upon the shape of the cells, and added an "appendix" to contain what they considered mold-like bacteria.

I. *Coccaceae*, spherical forms
   1. *Streptococcus*, in chains,
   2. *Sarcina*, in packets,
   3. *Micrococcus*, scattered or irregularly clustered.

II. *Bacteriaceae*, rod forms
   1. *Bacterium*, without spores,
   2. *Bacillus*, with spores.

III. *Spirillaceae*, curved forms
   1. *Vibrio*, slightly curved, with 1 or 2 polar flagella,
   2. *Spirillum*, long rigid spiral cells with lophotrichous flagella,
   3. *Spirochaeta*, long flexible spiral cells with no flagella.

The mold-like bacteria included:

1. *Corynebacterium*, slender rods, club-shaped, non-motile, not spore-forming, not acidfast,
2. *Mycobacterium*, acidfast rods,
3. *Actinomyces*, long threads showing true branching.

This classification proved satisfactory to many bacteriologists, especially those dealing with the pathogenic bacteria. It took account of the main morphologic differences, and was relatively simple. Note that the club-shaped diphtheria bacillus group (Corynebacterium) and the acidfast tubercle bacillus group (Mycobacterium) were separated from the other rod forms, which were themselves divided on the basis of spore formation.

Migula's Classification. Migula's classification was more elaborate and comprehensive. Bacteria were divided into two orders, the *Eubacteria*, or true bacteria, and the *Thiobacteria*, or sulphur bacteria. The latter were subdivided into several families and a number of genera, based on morphologic characters. As was pointed out in the discussion of sulphur bacteria in a previous chapter, now that these organisms have been grown in pure culture it is doubtful whether such morphologic distinctions are valid. We shall consider the Eubacteria only:

   I. *Coccaceae*, spherical forms

      Cells non-motile

Dividing in one plane	1. *Streptococcus*
Dividing in two planes	2. *Micrococcus*
Dividing in three planes	3. *Sarcina*

      Cells motile

Dividing in two planes	4. *Planococcus*
Dividing in three planes	5. *Planosarcina*

  II. *Bacteriaceae*, rod forms

Non-motile	1. *Bacterium*
With monotrichous flagella	2. *Pseudomonas*
With peritrichous flagella	3. *Bacillus*

 III. *Spirillaceae*, curved forms

Non-motile	1. *Spirosoma*
One or two polar flagella	2. *Microspira*
Tuft of polar flagella	3. *Spirillum*
Flexuous mobility	4. *Spirochaeta*

IV. *Chlamydobacteriaceae*, ensheathed filaments
    Filaments unbranched
    Filaments uniform in diameter   1. *Chlamydothrix*
    Filaments swollen toward tip
        Sheath thick   2. *Crenothrix*
        Sheath thin   3. *Phragmidiothrix*
    Filaments branched   4. *Sphaerotilus*

In Migula's classification, greatest emphasis is placed upon motility and the types of flagellation. Note particularly that spores are given no recognition. *Bacillus* and *Bacterium* are separated by the peritrichous flagella of the former, not on the basis of spores. While Migula's classification was widely followed, especially by the non-medical bacteriologists, it was never very satisfactory because of the practical difficulties involved in staining and observing flagella.

Orla-Jensen's Classification. So far, morphologic characters alone had been used for the major subdivisions, families and genera. But the classification proposed by Orla-Jensen in 1909 was an important departure, in that biochemical activities were stressed. Of morphologic characters, the type of flagellation was considered most important. Two orders were separated on this basis, under each of which a number of families and genera were placed. We shall consider the orders and families only.

Order *Cephalotrichinae*. If motile, flagella are monotrichous or lophotrichous; deriving energy mostly from oxidation without notable amounts of unoxidized split products.

  I. *Oxydobacteriaceae*, oxidizing carbon, hydrogen, or nitrogen compounds.
 II. *Actinomycetaceae*, tending to form branched mycelium, not typically water forms.
III. *Thiobacteriaceae*, the colorless sulphur bacteria.
 IV. *Rhodobacteriaceae*, the red sulphur bacteria.
  V. *Trichobacteriaceae*, the filamentous water bacteria, mostly iron bacteria.
 VI. *Luminibacteriaceae*, the phosphorescent bacteria.
VII. *Reducibacteriaceae*, actively reducing bacteria.

Order *Peritrichinae*. If motile, flagella are peritrichous. Splitting of carbohydrates or amino acids the primary rôle in metabolism, rather than oxidative processes.

I. *Acidobacteriaceae*, aerobic forms active in fermenting carbohydrates, forming acids.
II. *Alkalibacteriaceae*, aerobic forms producing ammonia from proteins.
III. *Butyribacteriaceae*, anaerobic bacteria which actively ferment carbohydrates, particularly forming butyric acid.
IV. *Putribacteriaceae*, anaerobic forms decomposing proteins.

In 1916 and 1917 Buchanan published an important series of papers on the classification of bacteria, and proposed a division of this group of microbes into six orders. In 1919 Castellani and Chalmers brought forth another classification which was important especially in subdividing the non-spore-forming rods into a number of new genera.

The S.A.B. Committee. The Society of American Bacteriologists is composed of members working in all possible fields of bacteriology, pure and applied. This comprehensive organization some years ago appointed a committee to work out some sort of classification which might be followed by all bacteriologists, which would bring some order out of the chaotic state of classification and nomenclature from which the science suffered at that time. This committee made a final report in 1920, and outlined a classification which is in general use in America at the present time. In 1923 the Society published, under the authorship of Dr. Bergey, a *Manual of Determinative Bacteriology*, in which, as far as possible, all known species of bacteria were described, arranged according to the classification recommended by the committee. Three further editions of this book were sponsored by the Society, with the following statement on the flyleaf:

"Published at the direction of the Society. In publishing this Manual the Society of American Bacteriologists disclaims any responsibility for the system of classification followed. The classification given has not been formally approved by the Society, and is in no sense official or standard."

Following the publication of the fourth edition the Society of American Bacteriologists relinquished sponsorship for Bergey's *Manual*. After the death of Dr. Bergey, the preparation of a fifth edition was undertaken by Dr. R. S. Breed and Dr. E. G. D. Murray. This edition is just going to press as this is being written. The author is greatly indebted to Dr. Breed for a preview of the classification used in this edition.

As this work has grown through its various editions it has become increasingly more voluminous and more complex. Bacterial species have been shifted from one genus to another, and differences between species and genera have been split more and more finely. Old species have been made into genera, genera into tribes and families. This has given rise to a great deal of criticism. Bacteriologists would like to see the classification and nomenclature of bacteria become stabilized.

This, however, cannot be accomplished for some time. New facts are continuously being learned about bacteria, which throw new light upon their relationships. New species are being continuously discovered. Probably something over a thousand valid species have already been described, but this is clearly only a small proportion of the number actually existing. We have studied only those habitats which are of some practical importance. As new species are discovered they often give a clue to relationships not known before. And so taxonomy must continue to grow along with the other branches of bacteriology.

The author has followed in this book the classification of bacteria presented in the latest edition of Bergey's *Manual*, because, while he does not agree with some of its details, he believes that it represents well the present state of our knowledge. Although not in any sense official, it comes nearer to being a standard and generally accepted classification than any other.

We have already described, in Chapter VI, the orders of this classification, and the families of two of these orders — the Eubacteriales and the Actinomycetales. The Chlamydobacteriales, the Caulobacteriales, the Thiobacteriales and the Myxobacteriales have not been sufficiently investigated, nor are they important enough, to warrant further discussion in this book. In the following pages, the Eubacteriales, the Actinomycetales, and the Spirochaetales will be considered in greater detail.

CHAPTER XX

EUBACTERIALES: NITROBACTERIACEAE, RHIZOBIACEAE, AND AZOTOBACTERIACEAE

The family of *Nitrobacteriaceae* contains those species of true bacteria which are autotrophic in their nutrition. This family is divided into three tribes. Tribe I, the *Nitrobacterieae*, includes species which obtain their energy by oxidizing ammonia or nitrites. Tribe II, the *Protobacterieae*, includes those which oxidize hydrogen, methane, or carbon monoxide. Tribe III, the *Thiobacilleae*, includes those which oxidize sulphur or sulphur compounds.

Bacteria Oxidizing Ammonia and Nitrites. We have already briefly considered, on page 189, the part which the nitrifying bacteria play in the nitrogen cycle, the conversion of the ammonia produced by putrefaction to nitrates, in which form nitrogen is usually assimilated from the soil by green plants. We have noted that this occurs in two steps, the oxidation of NH_4- compounds to $-NO_2$ compounds; and of $-NO_2$ salts to $-NO_3$ salts. The first step is accomplished by bacteria of the genera *Nitrosococcus* and *Nitrosomonas*, the second by bacteria of the genus *Nitrobacter*. While nitrifying bacteria may be readily grown in crude cultures, it is very difficult to isolate them in pure cultures. Crude cultures are obtained by inoculating soil into media containing various inorganic salts, such as potassium phosphate, sodium carbonate to furnish carbon, and ammonium sulphate for Nitrosomonas and Nitrosococcus, sodium nitrite for Nitrobacter. Note that these media are purely inorganic, the organisms absorbing carbon as carbonates, and obtaining their nitrogen from ammonia or nitrites, while energy is obtained entirely from the oxidation of the inorganic nitrogen compounds. The nitrifying bacteria are strictly autotrophic.

Nitrosomonas species may appear in cultures in two forms — as zoögloeal masses which rest at the bottom of liquid cultures, in which the cells are non-motile; and as motile "swarmers." In some strains or species the zoögloeal type of growth is more prominent, and Winogradsky refers to the masses of cells enclosed in slime as "cysts," and proposes a new genus for such species, *Nitrosocystis*. In both the zoögloeal and motile phases, the cells are oval to rod-shaped, not spherical. The motile swarmers are looked upon as active organisms, the "cysts" as resting forms.

Nitrosococcus species have been found less frequently. The cells appear as large cocci which grow free in liquids, i.e., do not form zoögloeae, and which are non-motile.

Nitrobacter is a non-motile rod-shaped organism, tending to be pointed at the ends, and staining more deeply in the center. While not growing in zoögloeae, there is some evidence of a capsule about the cells.

Bacteria Oxidizing Hydrogen, Methane, and Carbon Monoxide. These gases may appear as products of the decomposition of various organic compounds by heterotrophic bacteria. Methane is formed during the decomposition of cellulose by certain anaerobic bacteria. Such gases will appear in nature wherever organic matter is undergoing decomposition, especially under conditions of poor aeration, as in bogs and swamps and decomposing manure heaps. Autotrophic bacteria may utilize these gases, forming water and carbon dioxide.

These bacteria may be demonstrated in soil. To cultivate them, the soil is inoculated into a medium containing such salts as ammonium sulphate and potassium phosphate, providing all the elements necessary for life, but with no source of energy. The cultures are then placed under a bell jar through which is passed hydrogen, methane, or carbon monoxide. Some of these bacteria are apparently not obligate autotrophs; they may utilize an organic compound for energy, as well as one of these gases.

Bacteria which oxidize hydrogen belong to the genus *Hydrogenomonas;* those which oxidize methane fall in the genus *Methanomonas;* while those that oxidize carbon monoxide are called *Carboxydomonas.* These bacteria are all very minute rod forms, rarely over 1 μ in length, tending to become spherical in old cultures. As the suffix "*-monas*" signifies, they have, when motile, a single polar flagellum.

Bacteria Oxidizing Sulphur. The sulphur bacteria which belong in the family Nitrobacteriaceae of the order Eubacteriales are to be distinguished from the sulphur bacteria of the order Thiobacteriales. They are minute cells which do not store sulphur, and which do not have red or green pigments for photosynthesis. They are truly autotrophic bacteria, oxidizing elementary sulphur or thiosulphates or sulphides, forming sulphuric acid or sulphates. They are minute rod or oval forms; some species are motile.

We have previously considered one of these, *Thiobacillus denitrificans*, in connection with intermolecular respiration. Another interesting species is *Thiobacillus thioxidans*. This is a very minute rod form occurring in soil. It may be grown in liquid media containing various inorganic salts, but with no source of energy save elementary sulphur, which in the powdered form floats on the surface of the liquid. The bacteria grow about the particles of sulphur, which gradually decrease as sulphuric acid accumulates in the medium. A remarkable feature of this bacterium is its tolerance of high concentrations of hydrogen ions; the optimum is pH2 to pH4 while some growth continues at pH1!

Rhizobiaceae. This family includes three genera, *Rhizobium*, *Chromobacterium*, and *Alkaligenes*. *Rhizobium* contains the nitrogen-fixing bacteria which grow in the roots of leguminous plants. *Chromobacterium* contains certain bacteria which form a purple pigment. *Alkaligenes* contains certain species of rod-shaped bacteria which form alkali in culture media. The latter two genera have been placed in this family on the somewhat doubtful basis that they show flagellation similar to that of the root-nodule bacteria; they have sometimes one, sometimes two to four flagella, but are not definitely either monotrichous or peritrichous.

Rhizobium. Perhaps no part of the fascinating story of microbiology is more interesting than that which deals with the little partners of the leguminous plants that live in the roots, and in return for sugar and other material obtained from their host, supply it with nitrogen taken from the air.

If one carefully digs up a clover or pea or alfalfa or other leguminous plant, and gently washes the soil away from the roots, he will usually find attached to the finer rootlets tumor-like masses of varying size. They may be as large as a pea, usually smaller, and round or lobulated, sometimes with a number of finger-like processes. Place one of these nodules on a slide and crush it by pressure of another slide on top. Spread the juice which exudes in a thin film, and fix and stain it. You will find the bacteria present in several forms, but the most striking are large bodies with irregular staining. They will vary according to the species of legume studied. Some are oval or even spherical, but mostly they are large plump rods.

In many cases the cells are branched, Y-shaped or X-shaped, or with little bulgings here and there. These are called the "bacteroids" of Rhizobium. When first discovered they were recognized as resembling bacteria, but were not known to be such.

If such a nodule is carefully washed, first in water, then in an antiseptic solution, and finally in sterile water, it may be crushed in a tube of sterile water, and from this suspension of the bacteria cultures may be obtained. Like Azotobacter they may be grown in a medium containing only mannitol and inorganic salts, but in cultures they do not fix nitrogen so readily as in the host plant and growth is much better if they are supplied with a source of nitrogen. The addition of yeast extract or of a plant extract (asparagus) gives a better growth. In such cultures one does not find the bacteroids. Instead there usually appear very much smaller, slender, rod forms which in young cultures are actively motile. But as the culture grows older, a great deal of slimy gum is formed, and motility decreases or disappears.

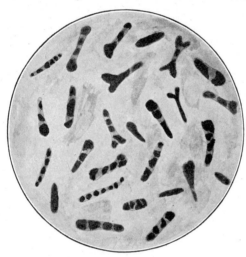

Fig. 75. Bacteroids of *Rhizobium leguminosarum*. Barred and branched forms are prominent. The types shown are found particularly in nodules from alfalfa and sweet clover.

As with Azotobacter, it is difficult to obtain pure cultures, and plating should be resorted to several times. When a pure culture has been obtained, it may be used in interesting inoculation experiments. Some seeds of the host plant are dipped in an antiseptic solution and then in sterile water. They are planted in two pots of sterile sand. One pot is then inoculated with a suspension of the nodule bacteria. The other is held as a control. Both pots are then watered frequently with a dilute solution of mineral salts containing all the elements necessary for plant life save nitrogen. The plants inoculated with the bacteria will show a normal development, and when dug up their roots will have nodules. The control plants will stop growing after the nutrient in the seed has been used up, will turn yellow, and eventually die. Their roots will show no nodules. They will have starved from lack of nitrogen.

The bacteria invade the root hairs from the soil. In the soil they occur either as non-motile spherical cells, or as oval motile cells with monotrichous flagella. The latter are the "swarmers" which invade the root hairs. The presence of the bacteria causes an over-production of cells in the invaded root, forming the nodule. Within the root the bacteria undergo a progressive development, forming first motile rods with peritrichous flagella. These lose their flagella, forming larger, slender, non-motile rods. Then comes further increase in size, and development of branching or other unusual cell forms, a transformation into the "bacteroids." Bacteroids are prominent only in the fully developed nodule. Within the bacteroids the protoplasm now is broken up into several deep-stained areas. With further age these break up into a series of very minute coccoid bodies which are eventually liberated into the soil (Fig. 64, p. 147).

When bacteria isolated from one species of legume are used to inoculate other species, it is found that cross inoculations are not always successful. There are a number of different species or types of Rhizobium. Bacteria isolated from alfalfa will produce nodules on sweet clover, both yellow and white, but not on red clover or white clover. Bacteria from red clover will form nodules on white clover and alsike clover, but not on alfalfa and sweet clover. In this way twelve distinct groups of Rhizobia have been established, and more will probably be discovered as more species are investigated.

The root nodule bacteria are rather widely distributed in soil, and usually where legumes will grow there will be bacteria to form nodules on the roots. But it is found that if the soil or the seed is heavily inoculated with a culture of the bacteria, nodule formation, nitrogen fixation, and crop yield are all increased. As with other valuable bacterial activities, it is better to use a pure culture "starter" than to depend on a chance inoculation from nature. Such cultures are distributed by various agricultural experiment stations and by commercial laboratories. It is important to know that the culture used for inoculation will produce nodules on the species of legume cultivated, i.e., that it belongs to the proper cross-inoculation group.

Different strains or races vary in their nitrogen-fixing power, and commercial cultures should be selected from this standpoint also.

Azotobacteriaceae. This family contains but one genus, the peculiar free-living, nitrogen-fixing bacteria of the soil, which have been given the name *Azotobacter.*

Azotobacter. The aerobic non-symbiotic nitrogen-fixing bacteria were discovered by Beijerinck, who inoculated soil into flasks con-

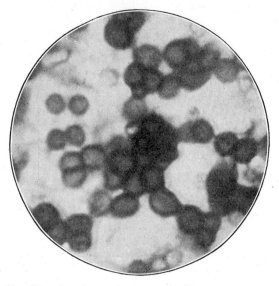

Fig. 76. *Azotobacter chroöcoccum.* Photomicrograph of a smear from an old culture on dextrin agar, showing thick-walled pigmented cells.

taining mannitol and potassium phosphate. This medium contained an organic carbon compound which could be used as a source of energy, and all the other elements necessary for life except nitrogen, which is available in the air for those organisms which can use it in elemental form. Upon this medium the Azotobacters develop as a pellicle floating upon the surface.

The Azotobacters are much larger than the majority of true bacteria, being nearly as large as many yeasts. They vary from spherical to rod shape, but the round or oval types predominate. A mucoid material is secreted by the cells, which are held together to form a rather firm pellicle on liquid media. At times this mucoid material forms distinct capsules, and one may occasionally find capsules within capsules. Two cells arranged in a pair may have each a distinct capsule, with a second capsule surrounding both, and so on. The members of this genus are subject to considerable variation in morphology. There has been considerable study and speculation concerning the life cycles of this group. It was largely from studies of Azotobacter that Löhnis postulated his complex life cycles of bac-

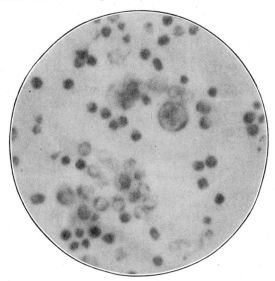

FIG. 77: *Azotobacter chroöcoccum.* Photomicrograph of a smear from dextrin agar.

teria. It now appears probable that spore formation does not occur. A nucleus has not been definitely demonstrated.

Azotobacter chroöcoccum is the most common species. It is characterized by the formation of a dark brown to black pigment, especially on media containing dextrin. Other species are *A. agile,* actively motile by means of lophotrichous flagella; *A. vinelandii,* forming a bright yellow soluble pigment in mannitol solution; and *A. beijerincki,* which is colorless in liquid media, but may show some yellow color on solid media.

The Azotobacters are widely distributed in soil, being almost universally present if the soil is not too acid. They cannot develop if the soil reaction is on the acid side of pH6.

CHAPTER XXI

EUBACTERIALES: ACETOBACTERIACEAE AND PSEUDO-MONADACEAE

The family of *Acetobacteriaceae* contains but one genus, *Acetobacter*, which includes all of the bacteria that oxidize ethyl alcohol to form acetic acid. They are the vinegar bacteria.

Vinegar Bacteria. While acetic acid may be produced directly from sugar by fermentation under anaerobic conditions, caused by several species of bacteria, the amount formed is small. Commercially, vinegar is produced by the fermentation of fruit juices, in two stages. A preliminary fermentation of the sugar to alcohol is brought about by yeasts. The alcohol so formed is then oxidized by vinegar bacteria to form acetic acid, according to the equation:

$$C_2H_5OH + O_2 = CH_3COOH + H_2O.$$

Since this is a direct oxidation process, it is obvious that such bacteria must be aerobic. If alcoholic beverages are tightly sealed, they will keep; if exposed to the air, they will turn to vinegar.

Manufacture of Vinegar. While any alcoholic solution of proper strength may be acetified, vinegar is usually made from either cider or wine. The alcohol content should not be over 15%, since the vinegar bacteria cannot tolerate higher concentrations. Vinegar may be made in several ways. A simple method is to place the cider or wine in a covered vat or barrel with air inlets at the top and an outlet at the bottom to draw off the finished product. The vinegar bacteria will grow over the surface as a thick, mucoid pellicle, the "mother of vinegar." When the conversion of alcohol to acetic acid is complete, the vinegar is drawn off, leaving the pellicle behind. In the "Orleans" method of commercial vinegar making, new wine is added to the vats continuously as the vinegar is drawn off. Since the formation of acetic acid occurs only where air is supplied, it is important that the pellicle be maintained. Pasteur improved the process by providing a floating lattice-work to support the pellicle. In the "rapid" method, the process is continuous. A cask is filled with beechwood shavings, and the cider or wine is allowed to trickle through. The tank is not allowed to fill, since the essential feature of this method is to provide a large surface constantly moistened with the alcoholic liquid which is exposed to the air. The bacteria grow upon the surface of the wood shavings, and there oxidize the alcohol to acetic acid as fast as it is supplied.

The bacteria of the genus Acetobacter are rod forms tending to grow in chains. In the pellicle which forms in the vinegar vats they are bound together by the slime or gum which they secrete to form a zoögloea. Most species are non-motile. Their most striking morphologic character is a pronounced tendency to extreme variation in form and size — they are very "pleomorphic." Certain cells in a chain may be greatly elongated, or swollen in the middle, or show bud-like bulgings.

Species of Acetobacter. There are apparently a number of species of Acetobacters, not all of which are desirable for vinegar making. Some of them oxidize the acetic acid which they form, and so reduce the yield. Others do not form a good pellicle, but grow through the liquid and so produce a cloudy vinegar, while others may carry on other sorts of chemical reactions that give the vinegar an undesirable flavor or odor. It is therefore best to use a pure culture starter in making vinegar, using a selected, cultivated species of vinegar bacterium.

Acetic acid bacteria have been subdivided, upon a practical basis, into four groups, as follows:

1. *Wort or mash acetic acid bacteria.* These will produce acetic acid in small quantities directly from sugar, especially maltose. They are not used in vinegar making, but appear in breweries and pressed yeast factories. *Acetobacter oxydans* and *A. industrium* are two species of this group.

2. *Beer acetic bacteria.* This group includes all those species whose growth is not inhibited by the extract of hops, and can therefore grow in beer. *A. aceti* is a species used in making vinegar from beer.

3. *Wine acetic bacteria.* Here are grouped all those species which occur spontaneously in the acetic fermentation of wine. Not all are good for vinegar making — there are "cultivated" and "wild" wine-vinegar bacteria. An undesirable species is *A. xylinum*, which is widely distributed, oxidizes the acetic acid, and produces undesirable flavors and odors.

4. *Rapid acetic bacteria.* These species show a minimum tendency to pellicle formation, but produce acetic acid very rapidly, and are therefore adapted to the rapid process of vinegar manufacture.

Pseudomonadaceae. This family contains a large number of species of bacteria which show terminal flagella, either monotrichous or lophotrichous. They are nearly all free-living saprophytic species found in soil or water. All are Gram negative and have elongated cells. The family is divided into two tribes, the *Spirilleae* with curved cells, and the *Pseudomonadeae* with straight cells.

Spirilleae. The Spirilleae contain four genera, *Vibrio, Cellvibrio, Cellfalcicula,* and *Spirillum.* *Cellvibrio* and *Cellfalcicula* are two genera created by Winogradsky to include certain aerobic cellulose decomposing bacteria of the soil, which are striking in morphology. In *Cellvibrio* the cells are slender curved rods with rounded ends, while in *Cellfalcicula* they are shorter and pointed at the ends, i.e., sickle-shaped.

The well-known species of this tribe are contained in the genera *Vibrio* and *Spirillum.* The difference between these genera is somewhat difficult to describe. In *Vibrio* the cells are but slightly curved, and usually show but a single turn. Many of the cells are fairly straight and the morphology shades off in one direction toward the rod forms, in the other toward the true spirals. In *Spirillum* the majority of the cells are truly spirally twisted, forming at least S-shaped cells, and often with more than one complete spiral. One is not likely to confuse them with true rod forms, as is the case with the Vibrios.

Vibrio. A number of species of Vibrio have been described. They occur as intestinal parasites in man and various animals and as saprophytes in water. Some saprophytic species are marine, and of these some are phosphorescent. This group of bacteria has been studied but little, except in relation with the one species pathogenic to man, the *Vibrio comma,* which causes Asiatic cholera.

Cholera. Cholera is an intestinal disease which occurs in *endemic* form in certain parts of the world, particularly India, but which has spread over large parts of the world in *pandemics* that have developed with great suddenness. Cholera is spread by drinking water and by carriers. With modern methods of water purification epidemics have disappeared, but endemic foci of this disease are maintained by carriers.

Koch announced his discovery of the cholera vibrio in 1884. His conclusions were based upon the constant finding of the peculiar "comma bacillus" in the stools of cholera patients, and the failure to demonstrate this organism in the feces of other persons. It was not possible to reproduce typical cholera in laboratory animals. At this time the "germ theory" of disease had not yet obtained general acceptance, and Koch's announcement was received with considerable skepticism, particularly after it was found that similar "comma bacilli" could be found at times in the feces of persons not suffering from cholera, and often in all sorts of other environments — well and river waters, cheese, etc. We now know that these were saprophytic species of Vibrio, which may be differentiated from the cholera vibrio by cultural and immunological methods. But the correctness of Koch's opinion was dramatically demonstrated by von Pettenkofer and Emmerich who, doubting the etiological relationship of Koch's organism, deliberately drank cultures of it. Von Pettenkofer developed merely a transient diarrhoea, but Emmerich suffered from a typical and severe attack of cholera.

A famous epidemic of cholera occurred in Hamburg in 1892 which strikingly illustrated the manner in which intestinal diseases are spread by water, and the value of water purification. The city of Hamburg was at this time supplied by the unpurified water of the river Elbe. A suburb, Altona, geographically continuous with Hamburg, also obtained its water from the Elbe, the intake being downstream from Hamburg, and the water therefore contaminated by the sewage of that city. But Altona's water was purified by filtration. In the epidemic, Hamburg developed 18,000 cases of cholera with over 8000 deaths, while in Altona there were but 516 cases, and there were good reasons for believing that most of these acquired the infection in Hamburg.

Morphology of Vibrio comma. The cholera vibrios may be found in enormous numbers in bits of mucus in the "rice-water" stools characteristic of the disease. They appear as small, slender, curved rods. A peculiarity is their parallel arrangement, like fish all headed upstream. In artificial cultures the organisms show a striking cytomorphosis. In young, actively growing cultures the cells are relatively straight, and larger than the "normal" form. In the resting stage the cells appear as typical curved vibrios, while as the culture ages, these differentiate into a large group of spherical or "coccoid" forms, and a smaller number of long, slender, filamentous or twisted forms. The morphology is subject to considerable variation in different sorts of culture media. These facts have led to considerable speculation regarding life cycles in this group.

The *Vibrio comma* is Gram negative, without spores or capsules, and motile by means of a single polar flagellum. The saprophytic vibrios do not differ markedly in morphology from the organism of cholera.

Cultural Characters. The *Vibrio comma* grows readily on ordinary culture media, forming a moist, greyish growth on solid media

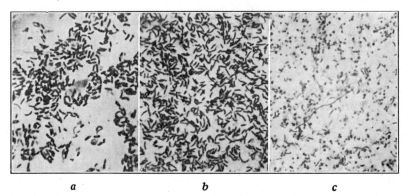

a   b   c

FIG. 78. Cytomorphosis of the Cholera Vibrio. *a,* from an agar slant culture 4 hours old, showing mainly bacillary forms; *b,* from a culture 48 hours old, showing curved vibrio types; *c,* from a culture 3 weeks old, showing faintly stained coccoid forms and occasional long filaments.

and turbidity in liquid media. A pellicle may form. Gelatine is liquefied, and milk undergoes alkaline peptonization. Acid without gas is formed from glucose, maltose, sucrose, and mannitol, but not from lactose.

Two peculiarities of the organism are taken advantage of in its isolation. It is aerophilic, growing best at the surface of liquid media, and it prefers an alkaline reaction. It will grow well with peptone as the sole nutrient. To isolate the organism from water or feces, one first prepares an enrichment culture by inoculating alkaline peptone solution. At the surface of this medium the vibrios will be numerically more abundant than the accompanying organisms. From the surface of this medium, after incubation, a loopful is removed and streaked on alkaline blood agar plates.

The **"Cholera Red" Reaction.** The comma bacillus forms indol from peptone. It also reduces nitrates to nitrites. In the presence of strong sulphuric acid, nitrites combine with indol to form a compound having a rose-red color. Commercial peptone contains small quantities of nitrate. If one adds a little concentrated sulphuric acid to a culture of the cholera vibrio in peptone solution, the characteristic red color appears very quickly. This is the "cholera red" reaction. Other bacteria, including saprophytic vibrios, may give the reaction. But a negative test is of value in ruling out cholera.

Other Vibrios. A number of other species of Vibrio are known, differing from the cholera vibrio in pathogenicity and in certain cultural characters. *Vibrio metchnikovi* was isolated from a diseased chicken. It is very pathogenic to pigeons. Mostly they are saprophytic species which have been isolated from water while searching for the organism of cholera. Several species have been named for the river from which they were obtained, as *V. schuylkiliensis* and *V. danubicus.*

Spirillum. The Spirilla are not readily cultivated and are of no economic importance. Therefore they have not been studied extensively. They are essentially water saprophytes, and appear frequently in hay infusions or other crude cultures of Protozoa or Algae. They are usually outnumbered by other more rapidly growing bacteria and are therefore isolated with great difficulty. Some species have never been grown in pure culture.

Spirillum volutans. *S. volutans* is one of the largest of bacteria, being 2 to 3 μ in diameter and up to 30 μ in length. It may often be found in hay infusions. Because of its large size it has been a favorite subject of morphologic studies.

The cells are rigid and spirally twisted, usually showing $2\frac{1}{2}$ turns. It is very actively motile by means of a tuft of polar flagella. Three or four flagella appear in stained preparations, but each of these is undoubtedly composed of a number of finer flagella which have become adherent to each other. These fused flagella may be seen in unstained preparations, especially if dark field illumination is used. The protoplasm is granular and vacuolated, due to the storage of fat and other reserve materials, including metachromatic granules. The term *volutin* applied to such material was derived from the specific name of this microbe.

Spirillum volutans possesses a distinct cell wall which may readily be demonstrated by the plasmolysis which occurs when the cells are dried on a slide. The protoplast shrinks markedly from the cell wall, and may be twisted quite free from it.

The Tribe *Pseudomonadeae* comprises the genera *Pseudomonas, Phytomonas, Protaminobacter,* and *Mycoplana.* These are all straight, rod-shaped bacteria with single polar flagella.

Pseudomonas. The best known species of this genus is *Pseudomonas aeruginosa,* formerly called *Bacillus pyocyaneus.* It is a common saprophyte, but also occurs at times as a secondary invader in suppurating wounds, and at times in the feces. This organism forms two soluble pigments which give a striking bluish-green color to the media in which it is cultivated. One, *pyocyanin,* is blue in color. It can be extracted from liquid media by shaking with chloroform. The specific name "pyocyaneus," formerly applied to this bacterium, means "blue pus," and indicates its activity in wound infections. The other pigment is a greenish fluorescent pigment, not extractable with chloroform.

Pseudomonas fluorescens is a name given to species which form the fluorescent pigment but not the blue pigment. *Pseudomonas syncyanea* and *Pseudomonas cyanogenes* have been found in milk, where they cause a bluish discoloration.

Phytomonas. This genus includes the plant-disease bacteria with monotrichous flagella. There are many species, distinguished mainly by their host specificities. Many produce yellowish pigments.

Protaminobacter. This genus has been created to include certain bacteria which grow poorly on ordinary peptone media but can utilize the lower alkylamines. They are soil and water forms, and some species form red and yellow pigments.

Mycoplana. This genus contains certain motile soil bacteria which use hydrocarbons like paraffin or gasoline as sources of carbon.

CHAPTER XXII

EUBACTERIALES: MICROCOCCACEAE AND NEISSERIACEAE

The *Micrococcaceae* are Gram positive spherical bacteria which do not form chains of cells. In the genera *Micrococcus* and *Staphylococcus* the cells occur singly or in irregular clusters. In *Gaffkya* they occur regularly in squares of four; in *Sarcina,* in regular cubical packets of varying size.

The distinction between *Micrococcus* and *Staphylococcus* is not easily made. The former genus includes saprophytic species, the latter parasitic. But with individual strains of unknown origin, there is little in the way of morphological or cultural characters to help in determining the genus. The cells of species of Micrococcus are on the average somewhat larger than those of Staphylococcus, not so firmly Gram positive, and show less of a tendency to occur in clusters; but these are highly variable characters.

Members of these two genera form heavy, opaque growths on agar, often colored (red, yellow, orange, and intermediate shades). They are usually proteolytic, liquefying gelatine; they are not very active in fermenting sugars.

Staphylococcus. There are three species of the genus Staphylococcus which occur as parasites of the human body, especially the skin. They are *Staphylococcus aureus, Staphylococcus albus,* and *Staphylococcus citreus.* These are distinguished by their pigments — orange, white, and yellow, respectively. *Staphylococcus citreus* is never pathogenic. *Staphylococcus albus* may at times cause small localized abscesses, but practically never causes any extensive or severe infections. *Staphylococcus aureus* causes boils and carbuncles, osteomyelitis, and wound infections which may in some cases be very extensive and serious.

Boils. A boil is a localized abscess of the skin caused by *Staphylococcus aureus.* To the medical man a boil is a *furuncle,* and when these occur one after another, the disease is *furunculosis.* The bacteria invade the skin through a hair follicle, and with a single

333

boil the infected follicle may be seen at the center of the lesion. Sometimes several hair follicles become infected simultaneously, forming one large lesion which "comes to a head" at several points; this is a *carbuncle*.

Furunculosis is a disease which well illustrates the rôle of body resistance, or immunity, in the development of infection. The bacteria which cause the disease are normally present in the skin, and normally are prevented from invading the deeper tissues by the defense mechanisms. When a boil occurs the bacteria make their way into the tissues through the epithelium at the base of the hair follicle. A boil is usually followed by another, and many people have suffered, like Job, from continuous attacks of furunculosis over a considerable period of time. Just why the resistance of certain people to *S. aureus* should be lowered is not known. Attacks of furunculosis occur most frequently in adolescents or young adults. There is some evidence that the lowered immunity may be due to some dietetic deficiency, perhaps the lack of a vitamin; this idea is supported by the reputed value of yeast in treating the disease. Persons suffering from diabetes are likely to suffer from boils.

Opsonic Index. Whatever may be the cause, it can readily be demonstrated that the person suffering from boils has a lowered resistance to *S. aureus*. This organism is pyogenic; it gives rise to pus, and this indicates that one of the main factors in the body defense is the action of the phagocytes. We have seen previously that this action depends upon an antibody, the *opsonin*, in the blood, which must first act upon or sensitize the bacteria before they will be ingested by the pus cells. If one mixes in a tube some of the blood serum of a normal person with a suspension of *S. aureus* and some leucocytes, and after a time prepares a slide from this mixture, he will find that a certain number of bacteria have been taken up by the phagocytes. If, now, a similar experiment is performed with the serum of a person suffering from furunculosis, it will be found that the number of bacteria taken up by the phagocytes is less. This indicates a decreased amount of opsonin in the blood of the person suffering from boils. The ratio of the number of bacteria ingested after they have been sensitized by *patients'* serum, to the number ingested after sensitizing with *normal* serum is called the *opsonic index*.

Vaccine Treatment. Furunculosis presents an exception to the general rule that vaccines are of little value in the treatment of disease. If one cultures the *S. aureus* from a boil, suspends the bacteria in sterile physiologic salt solution, heats the suspension to 56° C. to kill the bacteria, and then reinjects the dead bacteria (in small doses, of course) into the patient, in many cases there occurs a rise in the opsonic index, and a cessation of the attacks. A vaccine so prepared from the patient's own strain of bacteria is an *autogenous vaccine.* Just why the patient will respond to an injection of the dead bacteria, and not to the invasion of his tissues by the living bacteria, is not clearly known. It is argued that in the boil the bacteria are walled off from the body tissues by the abscess wall. Whatever may be the explanation, vaccine treatment is of some value in certain cases of furunculosis.

Other Infections with S. aureus. Most localized abscesses following a cut, or running a splinter into the hand, or similar accidents, are due to *S. aureus.* Such infections usually tend to remain localized, and to heal when the abscess has been opened and the pus allowed to drain. Occasionally such infections may be followed by pyaemia, with secondary abscesses in other parts of the body, and still more rarely by septicaemia. *Osteomyelitis* is an acute infection of the bone marrow which may occur following blows or other injuries that do not expose the bone. It is to be assumed in such cases that the infection results from a localization of chance cocci floating in the blood stream.

Staphylococcus aureus may occasionally give rise to chronic infections in man and animals, quite different in their course from the acute diseases we have just considered. "Granuloma pyogenicum" is the medical name for a chronic ulcerative lesion of the skin in man, caused by the common *S. aureus*. In its chronic course and the character of the lesion it resembles tuberculosis, or a fungous disease, more than a pyogenic infection. There is a chronic infection of horses called "botryomycosis" which was at one time thought to be a mold disease. In the abscesses which form, the Staphylococci grow in compact colonies, which may be large enough to be seen with the naked eye as little granules in the pus. These are composed of a dense mass of cocci surrounded by an irregular capsule of hyaline material. A similar infection occurs more rarely in cattle, and very rarely in man. The granules resemble, at first glance, those which occur in actinomycosis.

Types of Staphylococcus aureus. It has recently been discovered that there are serological types of *Staphylococcus aureus* which, like the types of the pneumococcus, differ in the nature of the polysaccharide that occurs on the cell surface. They may be distinguished by agglutination, or better by precipitin tests carried out with extracts of the bacteria. There are several types, but all of the strains capable of causing disease appear to belong to one type, designated Type A.

Toxins of Staphylococcus aureus. Filtrates of broth cultures of pathogenic strains of *Staphylococcus aureus* exhibit, both in the test tube and the laboratory animal, effects which are attributed to exotoxins. Thus one may demonstrate a *haemolysin* which dissolves red blood cells suspended in salt solution. There is a *leucocidin* which kills white blood cells, or leucocytes. It may be demonstrated by adding the filtrate to leucocytes suspended in a dilute methylene blue solution. The living leucocytes quickly reduce methylene blue to a colorless base. But if they have been killed by the leucocidin, this decolorization fails to occur. There is a *necrotizing* toxin which kills tissue cells, and gives rise to an ulcer when injected into the skin of a rabbit; a *lethal* toxin which kills rabbits when injected into their blood stream; and an *enterotoxin* which is poisonous by mouth and affects the gastro-intestinal tract.

It is not yet certain whether these effects are due to five different substances or are different effects produced by a single substance or several. It is also not quite certain whether all of these substances, if there are several, are true toxins in the sense that they give rise to antitoxins.

Staphylococcus Food Poisoning. Of the toxic effects described, that attributed to the enterotoxin appears to be quite distinct from the others, and to be due to a distinct substance. The symptoms — diarrhoea, cramps, and vomiting — are due to a substance which is a strong irritant to the mucous membranes of the stomach and intestine. This substance was discovered in the investigation of outbreaks of food poisoning. The foods which gave rise to the symptoms contained large numbers of *Staphylococcus aureus*. It was found that when human volunteers drank filtrates of cultures of these strains, they developed the same symptoms as those who had consumed the food. Custards and pastries filled with custard are the foods which most frequently give rise to this kind of food poisoning.

The enterotoxin is very resistant to heat, withstanding boiling for a short time.

Gaffkya. *Gaffkya tetragena*, formerly known as *Micrococcus tetragenus*, is a Gram positive coccus occurring typically in groups of four, or tetrads. It is found in the throat and in sputum. It is highly virulent for mice, and very occasionally pathogenic to man.

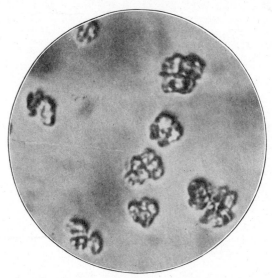

Fig. 79. *Sarcina lutea.* Photomicrograph of living, unstained organisms from broth, showing packets of cells.

The Sarcinae. The Sarcinae are undoubtedly very closely related to the Micrococci. They differ in occurring in regular packets of cells, due to cell division occurring in regular sequence in the three planes. But it is common experience that after rapid cultivation in the laboratory, the tendency to form packets is lost. Many cells will, however, still appear in pairs or tetrads.

The Sarcinae in general duplicate the cultural characters and pigment production of the Micrococci. Yellow, orange, red, and white species occur. They occur in cultures of milk and water, and appear most frequently as contaminations from the air. Their true natural habitat is unknown. A number of species have been described. The one most frequently found is the yellow *Sarcina lutea*.

Certain species of Sarcina are a cause of considerable trouble in breweries, giving rise to cloudiness, sourness, or ropiness in the beer. The amount of difficulty which they occasion may be indicated by the specific names, *damnosus* and *perniciosus*, which have been given to two such species.

A species decomposing urea has been described as *Sarcina ureae*, differing from the others in being motile and forming spores. The author has studied a culture of this organism and has concluded that it is not a coccus at all, but a spore-forming bacillus related to *B. megatherium*, which assumes a coccoid form in the resting phase. Young cultures, 6–8 hours old, were distinctly rod-shaped.

Neisseriaceae. This family is composed of Gram negative spherical bacteria. Aerobic species are contained in the genus *Neisseria*, anaerobic species in the genus *Veillonella*.

Neisseria. The group of Gram negative diplococci contains organisms which are essentially parasites of mucous membranes. It includes two pathogenic species, the organisms of epidemic meningitis and of gonorrhoea, and several harmless parasites, of which *N. catarrhalis* is the most common.

All of these organisms are alike in morphology and may be readily distinguished from other Coccaceae. They are Gram negative and occur very constantly in pairs. If more than two cells are associated, they form tetrads or irregular clusters, not chains. The individual cells of a pair usually appear as hemispheres, their opposing sides flattened. At times these surfaces are concave, and the individual cells of the pair appear as crescents. They are prone to develop involution forms in old cultures. Slides from such cultures will show a great irregularity in size and deepness of staining of the elements, certain ones appearing greatly swollen and staining very faintly.

In their cultural characters they must be separated into two groups. The pathogenic species (meningococcus and gonococcus) grow very poorly in artificial cultures, and must have blood or blood serum, at least when first isolated. Their growth is very thin and transparent on agar. The harmless species grow readily on ordinary media without blood or blood serum. Their growth is heavy and opaque, sometimes pigmented, on agar.

The Meningococcus. Meningitis is an inflammation of the meninges, or membranes covering the brain and spinal cord. It results in the formation of pus in the spinal fluid. Meningitis may be caused by a variety of bacteria — Streptococci, pneumococci, tubercle bacilli, etc. *Epidemic* meningitis is a form of the disease which is contagious, and which is caused by *Neisseria intracellularis*, commonly called the meningococcus.

Epidemic meningitis may be diagnosed by examining the spinal fluid which is obtained by a *lumbar puncture*. This operation consists of inserting a long hollow needle between two lumbar vertebrae into the spinal canal below the level of the spinal cord. The fluid is ordinarily clear and under moderate pressure, coming from the needle slowly, in drops. In meningitis the fluid is cloudy, due to the presence of pus cells, and is under increased pressure. If some of this cloudy fluid is spread on a slide, fixed and stained, the meningococci may be found as pairs of Gram negative coffee-bean-shaped organisms, *inside the white blood cells*. The bacteria are taken up by the phagocytes with great avidity, and it is usually rare to find many which are outside the pus cells. These characters are diagnostic.

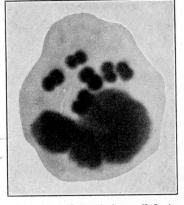

Fig. 80. *Neisseria intracellularis*, the Meningococcus. Photomicrograph of a leucocyte from spinal fluid, with phagocyted pairs of cocci.

The meningococcus invades the body through the nasopharynx, that part of the pharyngeal cavity which lies back of the nose. In many cases there may be a local inflammation of this mucous membrane, but this does not always occur. From the pharynx the bacteria invade the blood stream, and in some cases they may persist in the blood and give rise to local infections in joints or other parts of the body as well as the meninges. But usually they disappear from the blood soon after the onset of meningitis. The disease has a very high mortality rate, about 70% of the cases without serum treatment ending fatally.

Meningococcus Carriers. The disease occurs in sporadic cases in cities almost every winter; it is *endemic*. But it also occurs in outbreaks of epidemic proportions at times, especially in armies. The mode of spread of the disease was a mystery for a time because cases developed in individuals who had not in any way been in

contact with other cases. But it was found that the disease is spread
very largely by *carriers,* persons who are not at all ill, yet have the
meningococci growing in their throats. In talking or coughing or
sneezing such carriers discharge the bacteria into the air in droplets
of moisture which may be inhaled by others, and so the disease is
spread. This *droplet infection* is probably the common mode by
which all the infections of the respiratory tract are spread, such as
colds, influenza, etc.

Meningococcus carriers may be detected by making cultures from
the nasopharynx on serum agar plates. The minute transparent
colonies of the meningococcus must be carefully distinguished from
colonies of the harmless species of Neisseria normally present in the
nasopharynx. Surveys for the detection of meningococcus carriers
were conducted amongst the various troops during the World War.
It was found that over 20% of the men might be carriers in barracks
where an epidemic was occurring, whereas only about 2% proved
to harbor the germ in "normal" troops. Overcrowding in barracks
was found to be one of the main factors in causing epidemics. Merely
increasing the space between beds from one foot to three feet caused
a reduction of the carrier rate from 20% to less than 2%.

Types of Meningococci. Like the pneumococcus, the meningococcus occurs as a series of *types,* which can be distinguished by
agglutination tests. This is important because the serum against
one type will have no protective or curative action against infections
caused by another type. The actual number of types occurring is,
however, not yet completely worked out.

Serum Treatment. The use of antimeningococcus serum in the
treatment of epidemic meningitis was introduced by Flexner. The
serum is prepared by immunizing horses with suspensions of the dead
bacteria. It is, therefore, an antibacterial serum. The meningococcus does not secrete an exotoxin. But if the bacteria are suspended in water, they rapidly undergo self-digestion, or *autolysis,*
and such autolyzed cultures, free of the bacterial cells, prove toxic
to mice. It is therefore assumed that the meningococci form an
endotoxin which is liberated during their disintegration. This is
about the only evidence we have for the existence of endotoxins;
whether the curative value of the serum is due to an anti-endotoxin,
or to a direct action upon the bacteria themselves, is an unsettled
question.

To be of value the serum must be administered early in the disease, and must be given directly into the spinal canal in large doses. Since the discovery of the several different types of meningococci, the therapeutic serum now manufactured is *polyvalent*, i.e., the horses are immunized with representatives of as many different types as possible.

At present the drug sulfanilamide appears to be even more efficient than the serum in curing meningococcus meningitis.

The Gonococcus. Newborn infants may contract gonococcus infections of the eye from their passage through the birth canal, and at times in hospitals or other institutions there occur epidemics of gonorrhoeal disease of the vulva in children, transmitted by towels or other linen. But in adults gonorrhoea is a venereal disease, spread almost exclusively by sexual intercourse.

In both males and females the disease begins in the mucous membrane of the urethra, and is made manifest by a discharge of pus from the urethral orifice. It may in later stages extend to other parts of the genital tract — to the prostate, epididymis or seminal vesicles in the male, and to the cervix of the uterus or the Fallopian tubes in the female. Occasionally the gonococci may invade the blood stream and give rise to abscesses in distant parts. Acute in the beginning, the disease shows a pronounced tendency to become chronic, and to remain latent for months or even years.

Neisseria gonorrhoeae is almost identical with the meningococcus. In smears of pus from the urethra it appears precisely the same, as pairs of Gram negative coffee-bean-shaped diplococci inside the leucocytes. The diagnosis is established by such microscopic findings. In cultures, both the gonococcus and meningococcus appear exactly the same, showing at first a rather scant mucoid transparent growth, and growing only on blood media. The meningococcus may be cultivated a little more readily than the gonococcus. Both species ferment glucose with the production of acid only. But the meningococcus also ferments maltose, while the gonococcus does not. The two may also be distinguished by agglutination reactions.

Neisseria catarrhalis. This organism occurs normally in the throat or nasopharynx of most individuals. It derives its name from the fact that it was at one time suspected to be the cause of catarrhal inflammations of the upper respiratory passages. It is at present looked upon as a harmless parasite, important because it may be

342   THE BIOLOGY OF BACTERIA

confused with the meningococcus in searching for carriers of the latter organism.

It differs from the meningococcus in growing readily on media without blood or blood serum. Colonies on agar are firm and may

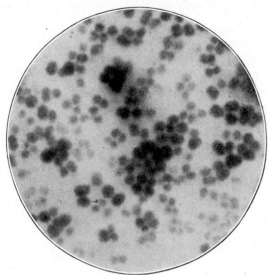

FIG. 81. *Neisseria catarrhalis.* Photomicrograph of a smear from an agar culture.

be removed in one mass, while the growth on agar slants is brittle. A sediment is formed in broth. On further cultivation growth becomes more abundant and buttery in consistency, while broth cultures show turbidity.

A number of other species of Neisseria from the throat and nasopharynx have been described or named. There is, however, some question whether these constitute distinct species, or lie within the limits of variability of *N. catarrhalis*.

Veillonella. This genus contains certain Gram negative spherical bacteria which do not occur in pairs as in Neisseria, but rather in irregular clusters as in Staphylococcus. They are *anaerobic*, and form gas from sugar media. They are found in the mouth and intestines. While not definitely pathogenic, they are at times found in abscesses or other lesions associated with pathogenic bacteria, and may contribute to the injury to tissues.

CHAPTER XXIII

EUBACTERIALES: STREPTOBACTERIACEAE

This family contains two tribes. The *Streptococceae* are spherical bacteria which occur in chains of cells. They were formerly included with the spherical bacteria described in the preceding chapter, in a family of Coccaceae. The *Lactobacilleae* are rod-shaped, and were formerly included in the family of Bacteriaceae. It was decided to form a new family from these two genera because they are so closely related in their physiological characters. They are all powerful fermenters of sugars, and with the majority of species lactic acid is the only product of fermentation. Being fermentative organisms, they can grow both aerobically and anaerobically; some species are definitely microaerophilic. Some species are thermophilic.

All are Gram positive. Both spherical and rod-shaped species tend to grow in chains. With the spherical Streptococceae one often finds cells which are elongated, rod-shaped; while the rod-shaped Lactobacilleae are often very short, tending toward the spherical form. With individual strains one is often at a loss to decide whether the cells should be called spherical or rod-shaped. It is obvious that the shape of the cells is not an important enough character to warrant placing these bacteria in separate families.

Streptococceae. This tribe contains three genera: *Diplococcus*, in which the cells occur often in pairs rather than long chains, with the pairs of cells surrounded by a capsule; *Streptococcus*, in which the cells tend to occur in long chains without a capsule; and *Leuconostoc*, in which the cells occur in long chains surrounded by a large amount of capsular material, to form zoögloeae. The last genus differs from the first two also in the way in which it ferments carbohydrates, producing, in addition to lactic acid, certain volatile acids and carbon dioxide.

The Pneumococcus. The organism known by the common name "pneumococcus" bears the scientific name *Diplococcus pneumoniae*. It is the only important member of the genus Diplococcus. It is called pneumococcus because it is the most common cause of acute

343

lobar pneumonia in man. But not all cases of lobar pneumonia are caused by the pneumococcus; a small proportion of cases is due to other microbes. Nor are all pneumococcus infections pneumonias. The pneumococcus may at times give rise to localized infections of the throat or ear, to meningitis, or to localized abscesses.

In smears of sputum from cases of pneumonia, the pneumococcus appears typically as pairs of cells. The cells are not spherical. The sides which are in contact are flattened, while the extremities of the pair are somewhat pointed. Each cell in the pair thus resembles somewhat the blade of an old-fashioned surgeons' lancet, and the organism was at one time called the *Diplococcus lanceolatus*. Each pair of cells is surrounded by a distinct capsule, which may be demonstrated by one of the capsule stains. The microscopic picture — the occurrence of lancet-shaped cells in pairs, surrounded by a capsule — is usually sufficiently characteristic to allow of positive identification. This morphology appears whenever the organism grows in body tissues or fluids. The pneumococcus is extraordinarily virulent for mice. The injection of even a small number of the bacteria into the peritoneal cavity will lead to an acute infection which is usually fatal within twenty-four hours. In the peritoneal fluid of the infected mouse the characteristic morphology may be demonstrated with great clearness. This is the most reliable method for detecting the presence of pneumococci — to inoculate the suspected material into a mouse, and on the next day look for encapsulated diplococci in smears of the peritoneal fluid.

But in artificial cultures the morphology is frequently quite different. When first cultured from sputum, or other material of similar nature, the morphology characteristic of the animal body may be maintained for a time, especially if the medium contains blood or blood serum. But after continued transfer in artificial cultures, the capsules disappear, the cells become rounded and no longer appear uniformly in pairs — they tend to form short chains of perhaps eight or ten or more elements. In artificial cultures they look much like Streptococci.

Differentiation from Streptococci. This resemblance to the Streptococci also includes the naked-eye appearance of the cultures. Like the Streptococci, the pneumococcus grows very poorly in artificial culture media. No growth occurs on potato and gelatine (at 20° C.). In broth the growth is scant, better in veal infusion broth, especially if sterile blood serum is added. Milk is made acid. On agar, growth appears as very fine transparent colonies, not as big as a pinhead. Now these are also the cultural characters common to the great group of Streptococci, and since in cultures the pneumococcus also appears in chains, it is often quite difficult to determine whether a given culture is a pneumococcus or one of the Streptococci. It is obvious that the pneumococci and Streptococci are very closely related. Indeed some bacteriologists would place the pneumococcus in the same genus with the Streptococci.

One way by which pneumococci may be differentiated from Streptococci is to add a little bile to a broth culture. The pneumococci are *bile soluble*. Under the influence of the bile salt, sodium taurocholate, the cells rapidly disintegrate, and the originally turbid broth becomes clear. It is not known precisely why the pneumococci dissolve in bile, but it is evidently due to a surface phenomenon, for the bile lowers the surface tension of the broth. And other substances which lower surface tension, certain soaps, will also cause the pneumococci to dissolve.

Pneumococci also ferment the polysaccharide *inulin*, forming acid, and most Streptococci will not. Most Streptococci are not sufficiently virulent to kill mice within twenty-four hours, and if they are, they appear in the peritoneal fluid in chains, not as encapsulated pairs.

Serum Treatment of Pneumonia. If rabbits are immunized with pneumococcus vaccine, they develop a protective immunity, i.e., they do not succumb to a dose of living pneumococci which would be fatal to a non-immunized rabbit. This immunity may be passively transferred. The serum of an immunized rabbit, injected into a mouse, will protect the latter from an inoculation of the living virulent pneumococci.

Based upon these experiments, serums have been developed for the treatment of lobar pneumonia in man. These serums are prepared by immunizing horses or rabbits; both kinds of immune serum are now being used in the treatment of pneumonia.

The therapeutic antiserum must be given early in the disease, directly into the blood stream, and in relatively large quantities. Such serum is now highly concentrated, i.e., the antibodies are separated from the rest of the serum proteins by chemical precipitation, and then redissolved in physiological saline solution.

The therapeutic serum is *type-specific*, i.e., it is efficient only against pneumococci of the same immunological type as that which was used to immunize the horse or rabbit. Since large doses of antibody are required, a polyvalent serum, i.e., a serum containing antibodies against all of the types, would not contain sufficient antibody against any one type to be efficient. It will be remembered that there are 32 different types.

Typing of Pneumococci. Before administering antipneumococcus serum it is necessary first to determine the type of pneumococcus causing the disease, so that the appropriate type therapeutic serum can be chosen. This may be done in several ways. The quickest, simplest, and most widely used is the Neufeld *quellungsreaktion.* Some of the patient's sputum, containing the pneumococci, is mixed with immune rabbit serum containing a little methylene blue, and observed under a coverslip with the oil immersion lens. Slides are prepared in this manner with each of the 32 type-specific immune serums. In the presence of the specific serum, the capsules of the pneumococci become greatly swollen, which may be readily seen by comparison with the other slides containing serums for different types.

Sometimes the pneumococci are not sufficiently abundant in the sputum for this test. In this case one inoculates a mouse, and performs a Neufeld test on the peritoneal fluid which will contain abundant organisms. Or one may do a precipitin test or an agglutination test with the peritoneal fluid.

By early typing of the pneumococci followed by prompt administration of the specific immune serum, the mortality from pneumonia has been greatly reduced in recent years.

The Streptococci. Perhaps no single genus of the bacteria is of such great concern to mankind as the Streptococci. They are the cause of a whole series of acute and serious infectious diseases in man, such as scarlet fever, erysipelas, "blood poisoning" from infected wounds, puerperal fever, etc. They are also a cause of severe disease in domestic animals. The souring of milk is caused by a Streptococcus, and Streptococci are used as "starters" in butter making, and play a part in the ripening of cheeses. In medicine and the dairy industry, the Streptococci are the most important bacteria.

As a class, the Streptococci are parasitic organisms. While they occur in milk and other dairy products, and to some extent upon

plants and in decomposing plant matter undergoing a lactic acid
fermentation, the great natural habitat is the mucous membranes
of animals — mouth, throat, and intestines. They grow but scantily
in artificial culture media in the laboratory. Upon agar slants they
grow either as minute pin-point colonies, or as a diffuse greyish veil
over the surface, which is not easily visible. In broth they may form
a sediment or turbidity, never a pellicle. Meat infusion media give
a better growth than meat extract. Most varieties grow well in
milk, which becomes acid and coagulated owing to the fermentation of lactose. No growth occurs on potato. As a group the Streptococci are fermentative organisms, producing acid from a variety
of carbohydrates. Most species show no proteolytic activities at all.

Morphology of Streptococci. The genus is defined as bacteria
occurring in chains of spherical cells. But the cells are not always
strictly spherical, and not always in chains. They may often appear
in pairs rather than chains, especially where growing well, as in the
body, in milk, or serum broth cultures. And they may frequently
be somewhat elongated, approaching the bacillary form. When the
growth is scraped from the surface of an agar slant culture, the chains
may be broken up and the cells artificially clumped. But normally
they never grow in clusters like the Staphylococci. Chain formation
is best observed in slides from liquid media. The Streptococci are
all Gram positive, non-motile, and without spores.

If a large number of strains of Streptococci are examined with
regard to their morphology, they tend to separate into two groups.
In one, the chains are long and the individual cells are either perfectly round or slightly compressed, i.e., longer in the diameter which
is at right angles to the axis of the chain. This type of morphology
is exhibited most frequently by those varieties which are highly
pathogenic, which are obtained from abscesses or blood cultures,
etc. They grow very poorly on artificial media, and may require
blood or blood serum for their growth. The other type grows in
short chains or pairs, and the cells tend to become elongated in the
diameter which coincides with the axis of the chain — as though they
had been stretched. This type of morphology is more frequently
encountered in strains occurring as harmless parasites in the mouth
or intestines, and from milk and dairy products. While these characters indicate a broad trend in the subdivision of the Streptococci,
they are too variable to be used in identifying unknown cultures.

Better procedures are available, as will be shown. The first type of morphology is, in general, characteristic of the great *haemolytic* group of Streptococci, the second of the non-haemolytic or *viridans* group. These groups will be discussed later.

Classification of Streptococci. Streptococci occur in a variety of habitats — the mucous membranes of man and animals, on plants, and in milk and dairy products. It was early suspected that several different species could cause disease in man. As our knowledge has extended to other fields of bacteriology, and as newer methods of study have developed, more and more species have been described and named. One could probably find several hundreds of scientific names applied to Streptococci in the literature of bacteriology. A number of bacteriologists have been concerned with the classification of this group, but until recently it has been most confused. With the introduction of immunological methods, especially by Lancefield, and careful studies of fermentation reactions and other physiological characters, especially by Sherman, we have arrived at a classification which, while undoubtedly not final, is clearly approaching its final form.

Changes Produced in Blood. The German bacteriologist, Schott-müller, was one of the first to diagnose disease by means of *blood cultures*. In cases of fever of unknown origin, he removed samples of blood from a vein in the arm with a sterile syringe, added this blood to melted agar at the bedside, and poured the agar into Petri dishes. In those diseases accompanied by a septicaemia he was then able to obtain colonies of the causative organisms, and so determine the nature of the disease. In the case of the Streptococci, he noted a characteristic change in the blood about the colonies, and recognized two distinct kinds of Streptococci.

From cases with acute infections, septicaemias from wounds, child-birth fever, etc., he obtained Streptococci which were *haemolytic*, i.e., which dissolved the red blood cells. About the colonies, the agar became quite clear and colorless, as contrasted with the opaque red of the medium where the blood cells were still intact. But from certain cases of disease in which there occurred a bacterial infection of the valves of the heart (acute vegetative endocarditis), he obtained colonies of a different character. They were *non-haemolytic*, i.e., did not dissolve the blood cells. But around the colony the blood turned a peculiar olive green color, best seen when the plate is examined by transmitted light, by looking *through* the plate toward a window. He recognized the first, or haemolytic type, as the Streptococcus which had been well known as a cause of acute infections and which was called *Streptococcus pyogenes.* The new type, which caused valvular heart disease, he called *Streptococcus viridans* because of the green color formed in blood agar. These two types are now generally accepted as two great groups of Streptococci — the *haemolytic* group and the *viridans* group.

To differentiate Streptococci by their action on blood it is necessary to pay some attention to the technique used. The method is not reliable unless the reaction is observed about *deep* colonies in a blood agar plate. The amount of blood must be sufficient and constant in quantity. Ten per cent of sterile human or rabbit's blood is added to the melted and sufficiently cooled agar which is then inoculated and poured into plates. The plates should be observed after twenty-four hours. The results with streak plates are not reliable.

Sugar Fermentations. Earlier workers tried to subdivide the Streptococci on the basis of sugar fermentations, which had proved so useful with the colon-typhoid group of bacteria. Lactose, mannitol, raffinose, salicin, and inulin were used; more recently, trehalose and sorbitol have been found to give significant results. Used alone the sugar fermentations are not sufficient, but together with the action on blood agar they are of diagnostic value. They do not serve to classify all of the Streptococci, but they do serve to help differentiate between certain closely related species.

Serum Reactions. Earlier attempts to subdivide the Streptococci by serum reactions were unsatisfactory, mainly because such studies were made by the agglutination method, and it is difficult to obtain stable suspensions of Streptococci for agglutination experiments. With the development of the precipitin technique, using extracts of the bacteria, better results were obtained. The use of cross-absorption tests has made possible an antigenic classification of the haemolytic Streptococci. Less progress has been made with the non-haemolytic Streptococci, because these are apparently more complex in their antigenic structure.

The haemolytic Streptococci fall into about eight *groups* as determined by precipitin tests with the polysaccharides extracted from them. These groups differ from each other in other characters, as habitat, sugar fermentations, etc. They show a sufficient number of different correlated characters to warrant considering them to be distinct species. Each of these species is made up of a number of serological *types*, which possess the same polysaccharide, but differ with regard to other antigens (nucleoproteins). Here then, we have a situation the reverse of that found in the pneumococci; the polysaccharide, probably a surface antigen, is common to all of the types, the latter differing as to their nucleoproteins (probably somatic).

The groups or species determined by precipitin tests with the extracted polysaccharides have been designated by letters, A, B, C, etc., by Lancefield.

Key to the Species of Streptococci. The key to the species of Streptococci on page 351 has been adapted from a paper by Sherman (*Bacteriological Reviews*, Vol. 1, No. 1, December, 1937) to which the student is referred for detailed information. The key is incomplete, certain less important species having been omitted.

Streptococcus pyogenes. While *S. pyogenes* may occur frequently in the throats of persons who are not ill, it is not a constant parasite. This Streptococcus is the cause of acute infections in man. It may invade the body through wounds, or through the mucous membranes of the respiratory tract.

Severe wound infections are usually caused by *S. pyogenes*. They may remain localized, causing a rapidly developing abscess, but they are more prone to invade the tissues widely and rapidly than other species of wound bacteria. *Erysipelas* is a rapidly spreading infection of the skin, resulting, not in localized abscesses, but in a diffuse inflammation. With virulent strains of *S. pyogenes*, invasion may occur through the apparently unbroken skin, and this is often the case in erysipelas. Erysipelas is to a certain degree contagious. *Puerperal fever*, an infectious disease following childbirth, is essentially a wound infection. The Streptococci invade the uterus, which has been denuded of its mucous membrane. In all Streptococcus wound infections, an invasion of the blood stream resulting in *septicaemia* is a sequel greatly to be feared. Acute *peritonitis*, following the rupture of an inflamed appendix, a perforation of an ulcer of the stomach, or a gunshot wound of the intestine is often caused by *S. pyogenes*.

S. pyogenes is the most common cause of *acute tonsillitis*. The infection begins at the base of the crypts of the tonsils, and results

KEY TO SPECIES OF STREPTOCOCCI

Mostly pathogenic and haemolytic, not surviving 60° C. for 30 minutes

PYOGENIC GROUP

Not fermenting lactose   *Streptococcus equi.*
Fermenting lactose
    Not hydrolyzing sodium hippurate   *Streptococcus pyogenes.*
    Hydrolyzing sodium hippurate   *Streptococcus mastitidis.*

Mostly non-pathogenic and non-haemolytic, surviving 60° C. for 30 minutes

Not growing at 10° C., not strongly reducing
  methylene blue   VIRIDANS GROUP
    Not fermenting lactose   *Streptococcus equinus.*
    Fermenting lactose
      Fermenting maltose
        Hydrolyzing starch   *Streptococcus bovis.*
        Not hydrolyzing starch   *Streptococcus salivarius.*
      Not fermenting maltose   *Streptococcus thermophilus.*
Growing at 10° C., strongly reducing methy-
  lene blue
    Not growing at 45° C., or in 6.5% NaCl,
      or at pH 9.6   LACTIC GROUP

      Forming ammonia from peptone   *Streptococcus lactis.*
      Not forming ammonia from peptone *Streptococcus cremoris.*
    Growing at 45° C., in 6.5% NaCl, and
      at pH 9.6   ENTEROCOCCUS GROUP

      Not haemolytic
        Not liquefying gelatine   *Streptococcus fecalis.*
        Liquefying gelatine   *Streptococcus liquefaciens.*
      Haemolytic
        Not fermenting glycerol or sor- *Streptococcus durans.*
          bitol
        Fermenting glycerol and sorbitol *Streptococcus zymogenes.*

in a series of small abscesses in the tonsillar tissues. Usually such throat infections clear up without further damage. But sometimes the infection extends up the Eustachian tubes to the middle ear, and gives rise to a very acute and painful inflammation, *otitis media.*

If the ear drum does not rupture, or is not lanced, the infection may be spread to the air cells in the mastoid process of the temporal bone, causing acute mastoiditis. This requires surgical treatment. From the temporal bone, the Streptococci may invade farther into the cranial cavity, causing *acute meningitis*.

S. pyogenes may invade the lungs, causing pneumonia. Such infections are not common as a primary disease, but may occur as a

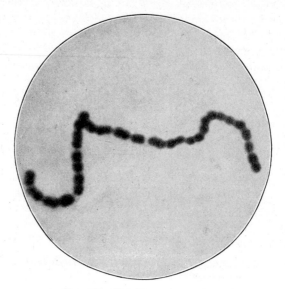

Fig. 82. *Streptococcus pyogenes.*

sequel to some other infection — measles, for instance. There were many Streptococcus pneumonias during the great influenza epidemic of 1918. These Streptococci do not cause the same sort of changes in the lung as are found in the lobar pneumonia caused by pneumococci. There is a greater tendency for *lung abscesses* to form, and for the infection to spread to the pleural cavity, which becomes filled with pus, a condition known as *empyema*.

This is a formidable list of acute and dangerous diseases. Physicians and surgeons alike fear the haemolytic Streptococcus more than any of the other bacteria which infect man.

Scarlet Fever. Although it was long known that haemolytic Streptococci are constantly present in the inflamed throat in cases of scarlet fever, until recently these Streptococci were looked upon as secondary organisms and not the true cause of the disease. It was not until 1923 that the experiments of the Dicks proved the causal relationship between the throat Streptococci and scarlet fever.

The rash and general illness of scarlet fever are due to an exotoxin secreted by the Streptococci in the throat and absorbed into the blood. While the filtrates of broth cultures may cause illness or death in laboratory animals, they do not give rise to the characteristic scarlatinal rash. It was not until experiments were performed upon susceptible human volunteers that it was possible to establish the relationship of the Streptococci to the disease.

The exotoxin of scarlet fever differs from other exotoxins in being more heat stable. It is not destroyed by heating to 75° C. for ten minutes, which treatment will render inactive other bacterial exotoxins.

If some of this toxin is injected into a susceptible person there may result a transient scarlet fever — general illness, fever, and rash. In much smaller quantities (the "skin test dose") the toxin, injected into the skin, gives rise to a temporary localized area of inflammation. This procedure, the *Dick test*, makes it possible to determine who are susceptible and who are immune to scarlet fever. If the area of inflammation fails to appear, the person inoculated is immune.

Scarlet fever, unlike other Streptococcus diseases, leaves a high degree of immunity upon recovery. This immunity is due to an antitoxin in the blood. It is possible to prepare an antitoxin by immunizing horses with the exotoxin. Such an antitoxic serum is used in the treatment of cases of scarlet fever, but owing to the fact that scarlet fever epidemics have been unusually mild since the discovery of this antitoxin, it is not possible at present to state its therapeutic value.

While not all haemolytic Streptococci of man will give rise to an exotoxin that will produce a scarlatinal rash in susceptible persons, strains from disease processes other than scarlet fever will do so. The toxins obtained from different strains of Streptococci are all neutralized by a single antitoxin. Streptococci from cases of scarlet fever do not differ in morphology and cultural characters from other haemolytic Streptococci. There is, therefore, no distinct species of Streptococcus which causes the diseases. Scarlet fever is due to certain strains of *Streptococcus pyogenes* which are capable of secreting the exotoxin.

Streptococcus mastitidis.   Also known as *Streptococcus agalactiae*, this organism causes a disease of cows known as "garget," an infection of the udder which gives rise to pus in the milk.   Milk from such cows will contain relatively long-chained Streptococci, and an abnormally large number of leucocytes.   Some strains of *S. mastitidis* are haemolytic, others are not.

S. mastitidis was at one time considered to be a cause of certain milk-borne epidemics of sore throat in man.   Such epidemics occur from time to time.   They occur suddenly, involving a number of people consuming milk from a single dairy, and the source of the infection can readily be traced to the milk.   It is now known that such epidemics are not due to the Streptococci of bovine mastitis, but are due to human Streptococci which have been implanted in the udder of the cow.   They do not cause disease in the udder, but do grow on the mucous membrane of the milk ducts and are shed into the milk in considerable numbers.

The Streptococci which cause milk-borne epidemics of sore throat are haemolytic strains which are said to differ from ordinary strains of *S. pyogenes* by the production of a capsule when grown in milk. The name *S. epidemicus* has been applied to such Streptococci. They may be differentiated from *S. mastitidis* by the fact that the latter organism will hydrolyze sodium hippurate in cultures, forming benzoic acid.

Streptococcus equi.   This haemolytic Streptococcus differs from the others in its failure to ferment lactose.   It is the cause of an acute infection of the throat and lymph glands of the neck in horses. The disease is called "strangles."

Other Haemolytic Streptococci.   *Streptococcus pyogenes* belongs to the serological group A, *S. mastitidis* to group B, and *S. equi* to group C.   There are some other group C haemolytic Streptococci derived from human and animal infections which are different from *S. equi* in fermentation reactions.   Group D belongs to the Enterococcus group, which will be described later.   Group F contains certain haemolytic Streptococci which are much smaller in size than other species; they have been obtained in throat cultures, especially from cases of rheumatic fever.   The remaining groups are represented by only a small number of strains from various sources.

Streptococcus salivarius. If one takes a clean microscope slide and scrapes the mucous membrane of the inside of the cheek with one end, he will remove many of the flattened superficial epithelial cells. If this material is spread in a thin film and stained, there will be found within many of the cells a number of Gram positive bacteria occurring in pairs. These bacteria are somewhat elongated,

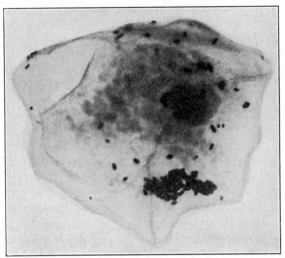

FIG. 83. *Streptococcus salivarius.* Photomicrograph of a squamous epithelial cell from the mucous membrane of the mouth. The Streptococci appear as oval or even rod forms, but grow as cocci in cultures.

their opposed sides flattened and the extremities rounded. They look somewhat like plump pneumococci, but may be even bacillus-like.

If some of the epithelial cells are mounted in a bit of agar as a hanging drop preparation and incubated under the microscope, the pairs of bacteria will be seen to grow out into the agar as chains of spherical cells. Transferred to ordinary cultures, they grow as typical short-chained Streptococci, giving green colonies on blood agar plates.

This bacterium is *S. salivarius,* the most constant and most abundant of the mouth bacteria. A loopful of saliva will yield hundreds of colonies. It appears in the mouth shortly after birth, and is always present in all persons. It is therefore to be looked upon as a normal mouth parasite. But there is evidence that it is also at times a cause of disease. It is usually present in pure cultures in the abscesses that develop at the roots of devitalized teeth, and is also present in the deepest tissues about the pus pockets that develop between the gums and the teeth — "pyorrhoea." And it may at times produce disease in distant parts.

Bacterial Endocarditis. The term "endocarditis" means an inflammation of the inner lining of the heart, but actually such a disease invariably develops on the heart valves. Endocarditis may be caused by various species of pathogenic bacteria, either as a primary disease or as a secondary infection following some other disease, especially rheumatic fever, sometimes scarlet fever. But the majority of cases are caused by non-haemolytic Streptococci which form green colonies on blood agar plates. As was first shown by Schottmüller, such Streptococci may often be isolated by blood cultures. The bacteria grow as "vegetations" upon the heart valves, and are shed into the blood in small numbers. The types most frequently encountered give the sugar fermentations characteristic of *S. salivarius*.

Rheumatism. "Rheumatism" is a collective name for diseases of an obscure nature involving the joints. Streptococci of the viridans group are suspected, but not proved, to be responsible for two distinct types of this disease — acute rheumatic fever and chronic deforming arthritis.

Acute rheumatic fever occurs most frequently in young people. It begins suddenly, and is accompanied by a very high fever. The infected joints become swollen, congested, and very painful, but pus is not formed and when recovery occurs there is no permanent damage to the joint. Bacterial endocarditis and an affection of the nervous system, chorea or "St. Vitus' dance," are frequent sequels of this disease.

Chronic deforming arthritis occurs most frequently in elderly people, begins slowly, and is very chronic in its course. The affected joints become deformed and crippled by an overgrowth of the tissues about the joint, and by changes in the bones.

In both of the above diseases it has been claimed that Streptococci of the viridans group are the causative agents, because they have frequently been obtained from blood cultures or from cultures of the inflamed joints. But such cultures are obtained from only a minor proportion of the cases. It has also been claimed that the lesions characteristic of rheumatic disease have been reproduced in rabbits by injecting the Streptococci into their blood. But the lesions in the heart and joints of such rabbits are not precisely like those of rheumatic fever in man, and similar lesions may be produced by other kinds of Streptococci, including *S. pyogenes* and *S. epidemicus*.

Recently haemolytic Streptococci, *S. pyogenes* and the minute Group F strains, have been considered as possible causes of acute rheumatic fever, because this disease so frequently follows attacks of acute Streptococcus sore throat, and because such Streptococci have been cultured from the throat (occasionally from the blood) of cases of acute rheumatic fever.

At present it must be admitted that the relationship of Streptococci to rheumatism is obscure, but there is evidence that some relationship exists. It has been suggested that the Streptococci secrete a soluble *toxin* which is responsible for the disease; or that the symptoms are due to a hypersensitiveness or *allergy* toward some product of the Streptococci. These theories suppose that the bacteria do not actually invade the joints, but are localized in some other part of the body, probably the mouth.

Other Viridans Group Streptococci. *Streptococcus equinus* occurs normally in the intestines of horses, *S. bovis* in cattle. *S. thermophilus* is somewhat thermophilic, growing at 50° C.

Streptococcus lactis. The normal souring of milk, as was described in an earlier chapter, is almost invariably caused by the rapid growth of *S. lactis*. This organism was formerly thought to be an intestinal parasite of cows, but is now known to be distinct from *S. bovis*. *S. lactis* has been found growing upon a number of plants — corn, cabbage, peas, beans — and is probably a plant parasite (or rather epiphyte), finding its way into the milk from dried plant matter in the barn.

Streptococcus fecalis. This species is a normal intestinal parasite, and may be usually isolated from the feces, though it is by no means as abundant as is *S. salivarius* in the saliva. It is slightly more heat resistant, and grows better on ordinary media, than the other Streptococci of human origin. *S. fecalis* regularly ferments mannite, and is usually differentiated from *S. salivarius* by this character, though occasional strains from the mouth also ferment mannite. Since some strains of non-haemolytic Streptococci isolated from blood cultures and infected joints will ferment mannite, it has been suggested that some cases of rheumatic disease may be caused by Streptococci of intestinal origin. *S. fecalis* is often referred to as the *enterococcus*.

Leuconostoc. *Nostoc* is the name of a genus of Blue-green Algae which grow in floating colonies of jelly-like consistency. The cells are arranged in chains, about which a gum is secreted to hold the colonies together. The name *Leuconostoc* ("white Nostoc") was given to certain Streptococcus-like bacteria which grow in sugar refineries in large gelatinous colonies or zoögloeae, and sometimes cause trouble by plugging up the pipes. They appear as ordinary chains of Streptococci, but secrete large masses of gum which may surround the individual chains like a voluminous capsule.

A recent study, by Hucker, of Leuconostoc species, and a comparison with certain organisms from dairy products and fermenting vegetables, indicate that members of this genus are widespread, and that several organisms formerly grouped with the Streptococci belong in this genus. The genus Leuconostoc differs from the genus Streptococcus in forming low amounts of acids from sugars, *in forming gas* (CO_2) as well as acid (levolactic acid) from glucose, and in forming volatile acids in addition; further, in the production of mannitol from fructose and sucrose, and the formation of the gums, levulan or dextran, from cane sugar.

Hucker recognizes three species. *L. mesenteroides* occurs in sugar solutions: it ferments the pentoses but not sucrose, and forms abundant gum in cane sugar solutions. *L. dextranicus* ferments cane sugar, but not the pentoses, forms less gum than the above, and occurs both in fermenting vegetables and dairy products. *L. citrovorus* ferments neither pentoses nor sucrose and forms no gum in sucrose solutions; it is found in milk and milk products.

Butter Starters. Sour cream butter is made from cream which has undergone a lactic acid fermentation. When the rôle of bacteria in the souring of milk was discovered, the hazards involved in depending upon a chance inoculation with lactic acid Streptococci were removed by first pasteurizing the cream and then inoculating it with cultures of the desirable organism. But it was found that butter made from cream inoculated with pure cultures of *S. lactis* was lacking in aroma. Investigation revealed that the desirable aroma was due to another organism, the *Leuconostoc citrovorus* mentioned above. This organism was formerly known as *Streptococcus citrovorus*. It produces volatile acids which give the aroma. It derives its name from the fact that it decomposes citric acid.

Kefir. Kefir is a fermented milk beverage. The fermentation is brought about by several associated organisms, which grow together in large firm zoögloeal masses, the *Kefir grains*. These grains contain a yeast, *Saccharomyces fragilis*, Lactobacilli, and, among others, a coccus growing in chains. Formerly known as *S. Kefir*, this coccus has since been recognized as *Leuconostoc dextranicus*. The fermentation of kefir is a complex process involving a simultaneous lactic acid fermentation and an alcoholic fermentation. Large amounts of carbon dioxide are formed.

Lactobacilleae. This Tribe contains two genera, *Lactobacillus* and *Propionibacterium*. Members of the former genus produce lactic acid from sugars, the latter propionic acid. The genus Lactobacillus is further subdivided into three subgenera — *Thermobacterium, Streptobacterium,* and *Betabacterium*. The subgenus Thermobacterium contains species which grow at high temperatures, like *Lactobacillus bulgaricus*. This subgenus, as well as Streptobacterium, produces a pure lactic acid fermentation, while Betabacterium ferments sugars like members of the genus Leuconostoc, producing carbon dioxide and volatile acids as well as lactic acid.

The Lactobacilli parallel the Streptococci in many features. They are found in similar habitats — the mucous membranes (especially the intestines) of animals, on plants, and in milk. They are Gram positive organisms typically occurring as slender rods in chains. As the Streptococci tend to become elongated, approaching the bacillary form, so the Lactobacilli tend to become shortened, approaching the Streptococcus form; and with a particular strain it is often difficult to decide offhand whether it is a Streptococcus or a Lactobacillus. Some species of Lactobacilli form prominent metachromatic granules, and such forms exhibit a strong resemblance to diphtheroid bacteria (Corynebacteria). Streptococci also show forms resembling the Corynebacteria.

Lactobacilli in the Human Body. While none of the Lactobacilli cause disease, certain of them are found frequently as parasites of the human body, occurring in the mouth, intestines, and vagina. If one makes smears of the feces of small infants, not yet weaned,

Gram positive bacilli are found to be the dominant bacteria. In breast-fed infants, *Lactobacillus bifidus* is found; this organism often forms branched, Y-shaped or X-shaped cells. It is anaerobic, or at least microaerophilic. In infants fed on cow's milk, *Lactobacillus acidophilus* is more commonly found. Species of Lactobacilli also occur in the mouth and there is some evidence that the production

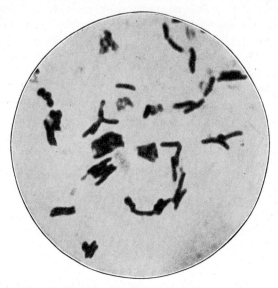

FIG. 84. Lactobacilli. Photomicrograph of a smear of infants' feces, showing mainly Lactobacilli. Some fecal Streptococci are also present.

of cavities in the teeth (dental caries) is due to the action of lactic acid formed by these bacteria. The acid dissolves the lime salts of the dentine and enamel. A species of Lactobacillus, *L. boasoppleri*, occurs quite constantly in the stomach contents in cases of gastric cancer. It is a large, conspicuous Gram positive rod, and has long been known to the medical profession, under the name of the "Boas-Oppler bacillus," as one of the diagnostic signs of cancer of the stomach. The reaction of the vaginal secretion is acid, and this acidity is due to the formation of lactic acid by one of the Lactobacilli commonly known as Doederlein's bacillus. This organism may be identical with *L. acidophilus*.

Lactobacilli in Dairy Products. As was described in a preceding chapter, when milk sours the initial fermentation is almost always due to *Streptococcus lactis*. This rapid-growing organism is, however, limited in growth by its own acidity. The milk may become still more acid, but this is due to the growth of Lactobacilli. Three species of Lactobacilli occur in milk, *L. casei*, *L. bulgaricus*, and *L. acidophilus*, but of these *L. casei* occurs much more commonly than the other two. It differs from the others in growing at lower temperatures. The Lactobacilli grow much more slowly than the other lactic acid bacteria in milk, but they form and tolerate higher degrees of acidity.

When Metchnikoff's theory was in vogue, Bulgarian buttermilk was much used. It is still marketed in some centers as a beverage. Acidophilus milk is sold more widely today. Since the Lactobacilli grow slowly they may be readily overgrown by other bacteria in the milk. This requires that the raw milk used must be produced carefully, and either sterilized, or pasteurized at higher temperatures than usual, before inoculating. It is difficult to keep the "starters" pure.

Lactobacilli also take part in the ripening of cheeses, especially Cheddar cheese. Cultures of *L. bulgaricus* are used in the manufacture of Swiss or Emmenthaler cheese to prevent "gassiness." The growth of Lactobacilli inhibits the growth of undesirable gas-forming bacteria.

Propionibacterium. The members of this genus are morphologically similar to the Lactobacilli, and are closely related to them. They differ in their fermentation, producing propionic acid, acetic acid, and CO_2.

Species of Propionibacterium are responsible in part for the ripening of Swiss or Emmenthaler cheese, and, by the production of CO_2, form the gas bubbles or "eyes" characteristic of that cheese. *Propionibacterium shermanii*, discovered by Sherman, is an important species.

CHAPTER XXIV

EUBACTERIALES: PARVOBACTERIACEAE, ENTEROBAC-TERIACEAE, AND BACTERIACEAE

The species of bacteria described in this chapter are all rod-shaped bacteria without spores, and with one or two unimportant exceptions, all are Gram negative. They include many important agents of disease in man and animals, as well as related saprophytic forms.

Parvobacteriaceae. This family is composed entirely of pathogenic species. Nearly all require complex culture media for their growth. The family contains the genera *Pasteurella, Malleomyces, Brucella, Haemophilus, Noguchia,* and *Dialister.*

Pasteurella. The genus Pasteurella comprises a group of pathogenic bacteria responsible for plague in man, and for a series of contagious or epizoötic diseases in both domestic and wild animals, which are known as the *haemorrhagic septicaemias.*

They are non-motile Gram negative rods, appearing mostly as short oval forms, and characterized by *bipolar staining.* The cells stain more deeply at the ends, and but faintly in the middle, as though there were a vacuole formed. This peculiar appearance of the stained cells may be due to plasmolysis.

They are aerobic organisms, rather inert in the biochemical activities, and with one exception (*P. tularensis*) growing fairly readily on routine culture media.

Plague. The species which causes bubonic plague in man is *Pasteurella pestis.* Plague is a disease which has occurred in great epidemics as far back as history goes. The last epidemic occurred at the close of the last century and was confined largely to Asiatic countries, where it is still endemic. The organism was discovered independently by Kitasato and by Yersin in 1894.

The plague bacillus infects not only man but also certain rodents, especially rats. An epidemic in man is always coincident with an epizoötic in rodents. The disease is spread from rat to rat, and from rats to men, by the bite of fleas. The bacteria multiply in the alimentary tract of the flea, and sucked blood may be regurgitated by the flea, thus infecting the man or rat.

Plague occurs in man in two forms — *bubonic* plague and *pneumonic* plague. The flea bites most frequently on the legs, and the infecting bacteria are carried to the nearest lymph nodes, which are located in the inguinal region. These glands suppurate. An abscess in the inguinal region is called a *bubo*. From this area the infection commonly spreads to the blood stream, and death results from septicaemia.

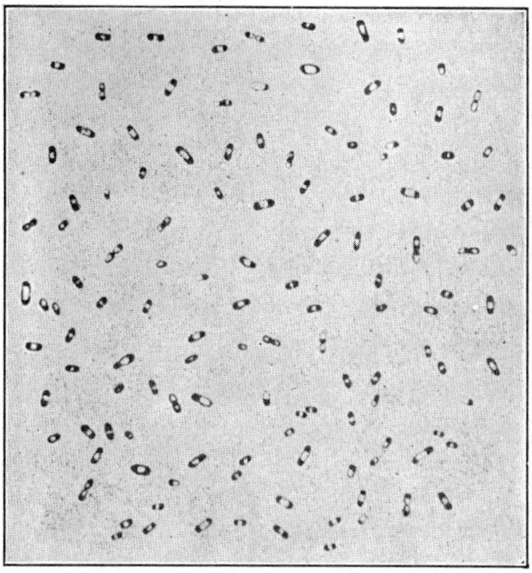

Pneumonic plague is contracted by direct contact with plague cases, and is transmitted, like other acute respiratory diseases, by droplet infection. It is almost certainly fatal.

The control of plague depends upon eradication of rats as far as possible, by preventing their access to dwellings and other buildings, and by personal hygiene and cleanliness to

Fig. 85. *Pasteurella pestis*. Drawing of a smear from a rat's liver. (After Ford, *Textbook of Bacteriology*, W. B. Saunders Co., Philadelphia.)

prevent flea bites. In the absence of the disease in man it may remain enzoötic in the rodent population.

Haemorrhagic Septicaemia. Bacteria resembling the plague bacillus have been recovered from a number of epidemics in lower animals — reindeer, cattle, swine, chickens, and at times in the laboratory animals, mice and rabbits. In severe epidemics the disease is acute and the mortality high. The occurrence of multiple haemorrhages throughout the body gives the disease its name. Intestinal and pulmonary forms of the disease may be recognized. In rabbits the infection may occur in chronic form involving the upper respiratory tract — "snuffles."

Different types of bacteria have been obtained from different epidemics, and several species have been described. These are distinguished largely by the species of animals they will infect.

Tularaemia. The rather absurd name of this disease is derived from the specific name of the causative organism, *Pasteurella tularensis*. This organism was first discovered as a cause of disease in rodents during a plague survey in Tulare County, California, and the organism was named for the locality. When later the disease was observed in man, it was called "tularaemia."

The disease occurs in a number of species of wild animals, especially in rabbits. It probably occurs continuously in small foci, and appears from time to time in large epizoötics. There is considerable evidence that cyclic variations in the population of snowshoe rabbits in the northern part of this continent are due to periodic recurrences of tularaemia. The disease is spread from animal to animal by biting insects, especially ticks.

The disease in man may be contracted through wounds (or possibly the unbroken skin) when dressing infected game animals, or from the bites of infected insects, woodticks or deer flies. Infection may also occur through the alimentary tract. The disease is extraordinarily infectious. Nearly all bacteriologists who have worked extensively with this bacterium have contracted the disease sooner or later.

There occurs a suppurative inflammation leading to the formation of an ulcer at the site of inoculation. The infection spreads by way of the lymph vessels, and abscesses may form along the course of these, or more commonly in the regional lymph nodes. If infection occurs by way of the alimentary tract, the disease runs a course similar to typhoid fever, without localized lesions.

P. tularensis differs from the other Pasteurellae in growing rather poorly in artificial media. Growth occurs only in special media containing egg yolk or cystine, with blood or blood serum. While the disease in rodents somewhat resembles plague, immunological studies indicate that the organism is more closely related to the agents of contagious abortion (*Brucella abortus*) and of Malta fever (*Brucella melitensis*).

Brucella. This genus contains certain minute Gram negative rod-shaped bacteria which cause diseases in lower animals (goats, swine, and cattle) that are transmitted to man.

Malta Fever. Malta fever, or undulant fever, is a disease endemic on the island of Malta, but occurs also in other localities about the Mediterranean, and to a lesser extent in other parts of the world. The disease is a long-drawn-out affection with attacks of fever and inflammations of the joints. The organism also affects goats, and in man the disease is contracted by drinking goats' milk. The organisms may be shed into the milk in large numbers.

Brucella melitensis is a very minute oval Gram negative rod. It was at one time classified as a Micrococcus because it is so small that it approaches the coccoid form. It grows rather slowly on culture media, and is practically inert as far as biochemical activities are concerned, being neither putrefactive nor fermentative.

Contagious Abortion. This is a disease of cattle which occasions considerable economic loss. The organism invades the mucous membrane of the uterus and causes abortion. The disease may spread extensively through a herd, and is very difficult to eradicate.

Brucella abortus is morphologically and culturally identical with the organism of Malta fever, but the two may be distinguished by agglutination reactions. *Brucella abortus* may infect man, producing a disease very closely resembling Malta fever. A number of such cases have been observed in America. The disease may be contracted by drinking unpasteurized milk from infected herds. Some cases have occurred in packing-house workers.

The Brucella species, like *Pasteurella tularensis*, are extraordinarily dangerous to work with. There have been a number of accidental laboratory infections.

Malleomyces. The organism of glanders, *Malleomyces mallei*, was formerly called *Pfeifferella mallei*, but the generic name *Malleomyces* has the right of priority.

Glanders is mainly a disease of horses. The name "glanders" is applied properly only to the pulmonary form of the disease. It also attacks the subcutaneous lymph vessels and glands, in which form the disease is called "farcy." The pulmonary type may be chronic, with the formation of nodules somewhat resembling tubercles, or acute, with consolidation of the lungs, as in pneumonia. The lymphatic form gives rise to a characteristic swelling of the lymph vessels and glands.

Malleomyces mallei is a slender Gram negative rod, not motile, and without spores or capsules. It is not acidfast. It is aerobic and grows moderately well on ordinary culture media.

The glanders bacillus is pathogenic to guinea pigs. If inoculated into the peritoneal cavity of male guinea pigs, there occurs a characteristic inflammatory reaction of the testicles. This is called the "Strauss reaction."

The disease in horses gives rise to an allergic state similar to that of tuberculosis. *Mallein* is prepared from glanders bacilli in the

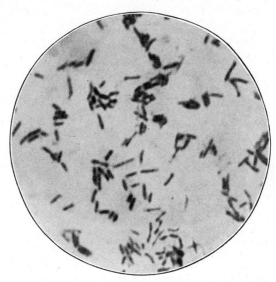

FIG. 86. *Malleomyces mallei.* Photomicrograph of a smear from an agar culture.

same way that tuberculin is made from tubercle bacilli. The mallein test is used to detect glandered horses, so that they may be destroyed, and so prevent the spread of the disease.

The glanders bacillus also infects man. It is a very dangerous organism to work with in the laboratory. A number of laboratory infections have occurred.

Haemophilus. Several species of aerobic bacteria pathogenic to man and animals will grow, at least when first isolated, only in the presence of blood. The haemoglobin of the blood appears to be the essential ingredient. These bacteria are grouped together in the genus *Haemophilus.* Important species are *H. influenzae, H. pertussis, H. conjunctivitidis,* and *H. ducreyi.*

Haemophilus influenzae. The so-called influenza bacillus was discovered by Pfeiffer in 1890 during an extensive epidemic of influenza. Generally accepted as the cause of that disease for a number of years, its relationship became doubtful as a result of investigations begun during the great pandemic of 1918, and it is now known that influenza is caused by a filterable virus, *H. influenzae* being merely a frequent secondary invader.

H. influenzae has become important in recent years as a cause of cerebrospinal meningitis, especially in children.

Haemophilus pertussis. Whooping cough, or pertussis, is another contagious disease of the respiratory tract. It is one of the most common and most serious diseases of childhood. The causative organism, *H. pertussis*, was discovered by Bordet and Gengou in 1906.

It is a small oval rod, and, like Pfeiffer's bacillus, somewhat irregular in its morphology. When first isolated it grows very poorly — a complex medium made of potato, glycerine broth, and blood is necessary. But on continued cultivation, it may be gradually adapted to grow on ordinary media.

The bacteria grow in enormous numbers on the mucous membrane of the bronchi, and cause an exudation of very tenacious sputum, which causes the characteristic paroxysms of coughing.

Haemophilus conjunctivitidis. The conjunctiva is the moist membrane that covers the eyeball and the inner surface of the eyelids. An inflammation of this membrane is "conjunctivitis," and a common, contagious form of this disease ("pink eye") is caused by an organism very similar to the influenza bacillus. *H. conjunctivitidis* is frequently called the Koch-Weeks bacillus, for its two discoverers.

Haemophilus ducreyi. Ducrey's bacillus causes an ulcerative disease of the external genital organs. This disease is often referred to as the third venereal disease, the first two being gonorrhoea and syphilis. The lesion is called a "soft chancre" to distinguish it from the "hard chancre" which is the lesion characteristic of primary syphilis.

Ducrey's bacillus differs from the others of this genus in growing characteristically in chains. It grows only on blood media.

Dialister. This genus was created to include a single species, *Dialister pneumosintes*. It is a very minute Gram negative rod, strictly anaerobic, and growing only in media containing unheated fresh tissue or blood serum. It was first isolated from the nasal secretions of influenza cases, but has since been found in normal persons.

Noguchia. This genus contains certain very slender, small Gram negative bacteria which have been found in the inflamed tissues of the eyelids in *trachoma*, a chronic destructive infectious disease of the eyes in humans, and in similar diseases in monkeys and rabbits. It is not certain that the bacteria included in the genus Noguchia are the true cause of these diseases.

Enterobacteriaceae. This family includes an important group of species to which we have had occasion to refer in previous pages as the "colon-typhoid" group. They form a very homogeneous group, quite similar in morphology and in their fundamental biochemical characters, occurring mostly either as normal intestinal parasites or as causes of intestinal diseases, the "enteric" fevers. They are of great importance in medicine, both human and veterinary, and also in the sanitary control of water supplies, and have therefore been studied very intensively, probably more so than any other group of bacteria. It is in this group particularly that much "splitting" has occurred in recent taxonomy — former species have been elevated to the rank of genera.

The Enterobacteriaceae are all Gram negative rods, usually with numerous peritrichous flagella. The family is subdivided into five Tribes, as follows: Tribe I, the *Eschericheae,* contains certain normal intestinal parasites of the genus *Escherichia*, related species of the genus *Aerobacter,* and pathogenic species of the genus *Klebsiella*. Tribe II, the *Erwineae,* includes species clearly related to the first tribe, which are plant parasites. Tribe III, the *Serrateae,* contains pigment-forming species. Tribe IV, the *Proteae*, includes certain putrefactive bacteria. Tribe V, the *Salmonelleae,* contains the important disease-producing bacteria of the intestines — the causes of typhoid and paratyphoid fevers, and of dysentery.

Escherichia and Aerobacter. These two genera are very closely related, and their classification is still in some confusion. Both are Gram negative rods without spores. The size and form of the cells are subject to some variation, according to the strain, medium, and age of the culture. The cells vary from short ovals to long filamentous forms, but typically they occur as straight rods, rather short, say about 0.5×2 microns. In a single preparation, however, one may find considerable variation in length.

Members of the genus *Escherichia* are typically intestinal parasites, and while they may persist in a viable form for some time in
water or soil, do not usually multiply to any great extent free in
nature. Members of the genus *Aerobacter* also occur in the intestines,
but are typically saprophytic organisms associated with plant matter,

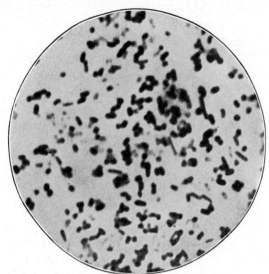

FIG. 87. *Escherichia coli.* Photomicrograph of a smear
from an agar slant culture several days old.

occurring naturally in water, soil, and frequently in milk. The most
common and important species of Escherichia is *E. coli;* the most
common and important species of Aerobacter is *A. aerogenes.*

Escherichia coli. The colon bacillus occurs normally in the intestines, not only of man, but also of all the higher animals. There
is apparently some difference in strains from different animals, but
this has not been extensively investigated. This organism is the
most numerous of the bacteria in feces (except infants') which can
be cultivated aerobically on agar plates.

While normally a harmless parasite, it may at times become
pathogenic. Occasionally newborn infants may develop a rapidly
fatal septicaemia or meningitis in which this organism is present in
pure culture. It is to be assumed in such cases that the child has
been completely lacking in natural immunity. The colon bacillus

is a common cause of ascending infections of the urinary apparatus. Most commonly the infection is restricted to the bladder (cystitis) but it may ascend the ureters to the pelvis of the kidney (pyelonephritis). Strains of colon bacilli isolated from such infections are usually more motile and ferment lactose more slowly than strains from feces.

Aerobacter aerogenes. This organism was formerly called *Bacillus lactis aerogenes*. Its normal habitat is soil and grains. It occurs commonly in milk, and may take part in the souring of milk. Members of this group are undesirable in milk since they give rise to disagreeable flavors.

In morphology and cultural characters, *A. aerogenes* bears a very close resemblance to *Klebsiella pneumoniae*, and there is no certain method of differentiation save by animal inoculation. Klebsiella is very pathogenic to guinea pigs, which usually die within 24 hours. Distinct capsules appear about the cells in smears of the peritoneal fluid.

Differentiation of Escherichia and Aerobacter. Species of Escherichia are typically sluggishly motile and show peritrichous flagella. Species of Aerobacter are typically non-motile and tend to form capsules, especially in milk. The growth of Escherichia on agar is pasty or buttery in consistency; the growth of Aerobacter is sticky or mucoid. These two groups are, however, differentiated by their biochemical reactions.

Both groups ferment the common sugars with the production of acid and gas. The different species are distinguished largely by their ability to ferment different carbohydrates. *Escherichia coli* ferments glucose, lactose, maltose, and mannitol, while *Escherichia communior* ferments sucrose in addition. *Aerobacter aerogenes* produces acid and gas from all five of these carbohydrates.

But the two groups ferment the carbohydrates in different ways. From glucose *Escherichia coli* produces more acid than does *Aerobacter aerogenes;* it produces both carbon dioxide and hydrogen, usually in about equal proportion; and it does *not* produce the organic compound, acetyl-methyl-carbinol. Aerogenes bacilli produce a lower acidity, produce more carbon dioxide than hydrogen, and *do* produce acetyl-methyl-carbinol. There are certain other biochemical differences; indeed, new ones are being discovered right along. For instance, colon bacilli cannot utilize citrates as the sole source of carbon, while aerogenes types can. But the products from glucose provide the most important differential characters.

Aside from the sugar fermentations the cultural characters of the two genera are much alike. They grow readily on artificial media, even on those of very simple composition. Neither liquefies gelatine nor peptonizes milk. Both, fermenting lactose, produce an acid coagulation of milk. Some strains form indol from peptone, others do not.

Sanitary Water Analysis. The bacterial diseases which affect the intestines — cholera, typhoid, paratyphoid, and dysentery — are transmitted by drinking water. Water may be heavily contaminated by sewage containing these bacteria in large numbers. Other diseases are not transmitted by water because the causative organisms do not gain access to water in any great numbers. Most of the other pathogenic bacteria would die very shortly in water.

The prevention of water-borne epidemics of the enteric diseases is accomplished by preventing the consumption of polluted water. This depends upon water purification by filtration and chlorine treatment, and upon bacteriological examination to check the purity of the water consumed.

The bacteriological examination serves to determine the presence or absence of intestinal bacteria in the water. Chemical analysis or a count of the total bacteria present may give some clue as to the occurrence of sewage pollution, but these are not so important as the direct demonstration of the presence of intestinal bacteria. In a case of typhoid fever, the typhoid bacilli in the feces are usually outnumbered by the normal intestinal bacteria, especially the colon bacilli. When the feces from such cases become mixed with the excreta of all the normal people in a community, in the sewage, this disproportion becomes greater. It may readily be seen then that the direct finding of typhoid (or other pathogenic) bacteria in the water is an almost hopeless task, because they are so few, even in a dangerous water supply, compared with the other bacteria. But it is not necessary to show the presence of typhoid bacilli in water to condemn it. The mere presence of intestinal bacteria shows that the water is potentially dangerous and should not be consumed. The colon bacilli are the most abundant of intestinal bacteria, and are easily detected by culture methods. The sanitary examination of a water supply therefore narrows down to a search for colon bacilli. If present, the water is dangerous. If absent, it is safe as far as the intestinal infections are concerned.

The Presumptive Test. In preliminary tests of the water, advantage is taken of the fact that colon bacilli produce gas from lactose, a property not exhibited by many other species of bacteria. Some of the water is inoculated into tubes of lactose broth containing gas traps. If *no* gas is formed after a suitable incubation period, colon bacilli are absent and the water is presumably safe. If gas *is* formed, this may be due to colon bacilli or to some other organism, and further studies must be carried out.

The bacteria other than colon bacilli occurring in water which may form gas from lactose are aerogenes bacilli and certain spore-forming anaerobes, particularly the Welch bacillus. If the presumptive test is positive it is necessary to determine which of these bacteria is forming the gas.

Isolation of the Gas Formers. The lactose broth tubes were inoculated with the water before any plating; therefore they contain a *mixed* culture, since of course other bacteria than the lactose fermenters will also grow in the broth. It is therefore necessary to isolate the lactose-fermenting organisms *in pure culture* before they may be identified. This is done by the use of a selective medium. We have referred in previous chapters to Endo's medium, a medium containing lactose and decolorized basic fuchsin, for the detection of lactose-fermenting bacteria. But in water analysis a better medium for this purpose is Levine's eosin-methylene blue agar. This medium contains peptone, dibasic potassium phosphate, lactose, agar, and the dyes eosin and methylene blue.

Broth from positive presumptive tests is streaked upon this medium in Petri plates. If the gas was due to anaerobes, these will, of course, not grow on the aerobic plates, and there will be no signs of lactose-fermenting colonies. Colon and aerogenes bacilli form very characteristic colonies on this medium, the colony type being due to the way they ferment lactose. Typical colonies of *colon bacilli* will be smaller than those of aerogenes, rather flat, and of a deep blue-black color with a metallic sheen on the surface. This color reaction is due to the large amount of acid formed from lactose. Typical colonies of *A. aerogenes* will be larger, elevated, convex, of a pinkish or lavender color, and mucoid in texture, without metallic luster.

Atypical colonies are often encountered, and in any case it is best to isolate the colonies most resembling colon bacilli in pure culture. Pure cultures should show Gram negative rods without spores, and should again ferment lactose with the production of acid or gas.

Final Identification. Final identification requires a clear differentiation between colon and aerogenes types, i.e., between intestinal and soil types. The gas-forming organism, now isolated in pure culture, is subjected to the *methyl red* test and the *Voges-Proskauer* test.

The methyl red test depends upon the fact that colon bacilli produce higher acidities than aerogenes types. The organism is inoculated into a medium containing peptone, phosphate, and glucose. After incubation an indicator, methyl red, is added. This indicator changes color at a hydrogen ion concentration between that produced by colon bacilli and that formed with aerogenes types. After testing, the medium will be red with *E. coli*, and yellow with *A. aerogenes*.

The Voges-Proskauer test is a test for the acetyl-methyl-carbinol which is formed from glucose by aerogenes types, but not by colon bacilli. To a glucose broth culture, after incubation, some strong sodium hydroxide solution is added. If acetyl-methyl-carbinol has been formed, an eosin-red color appears in the liquid and the organism is of the aerogenes types, and is said to be Voges-Proskauer positive. If no red color appears the organism is Voges-Proskauer negative, and therefore of the colon bacillus type.

Correlated Characters. We have gone into these methods of differentiation in some detail because, aside from their practical importance in water analysis, they illustrate so beautifully the value of biochemical studies in identification, and of correlated characters in classification, of bacteria. While exceptions occur, the great majority of lactose-fermenting bacteria which give a negative methyl red test will give a positive Voges-Proskauer test, and conversely. The table below shows at a glance the various correlated characters which serve to distinguish the two genera, Escherichia and Aerobacter.

	Habitat	Ratio of CO_2 to H_2	Methyl red test	Voges-Proskauer	Utilization of citrates
Escherichia	Parasitic	Low	Positive	Negative	Negative
Aerobacter	Saprophytic	High	Negative	Positive	Positive

Intermediate Types. Not all lactose-fermenting Gram negative rod forms isolated from water will fall sharply into these two groups. A number of intermediate forms have been encountered which give some of the characters of Escherichia and some of Aerobacter. While Aerobacter species are found in soil and other places, they are also common enough in the intestines. For these reasons at present there is a tendency to minimize the importance of differentiating between Aerobacter species and Escherichia species in water analysis, and to condemn any sample which gives gas in lactose broth.

Klebsiella. This genus contains Gram negative rods which form distinct *capsules*. Two species, *K. pneumoniae* and *K. rhinoscleromatis*, are occasionally pathogenic to man.

Klebsiella pneumoniae was formerly known as *Bacillus mucosus capsulatus*, and is frequently called "Friedländer's bacillus." It occasionally gives rise to lobar pneumonia in man, and may also produce a rapidly fatal septicaemia. It was early confused with the pneumococcus, but is quite distinct. It is a rather plump Gram negative rod which grows readily in artificial media. It forms distinct capsules in the animal body, and is very pathogenic for guinea pigs. In cultures growth is slimy or mucoid, due to the formation of gum which does not, however, appear as discrete capsules. It actively ferments glucose, lactose, sucrose, usually also maltose and glycerine, with the production of acid and gas.

Rhinoscleroma is a peculiar disease of the nose occurring in eastern Europe characterized by a marked overgrowth of the tissues, producing considerable deformity. Great numbers of rod-shaped bacteria are found inside large macrophages that crowd the tissues. An encapsulated Gram negative rod has been isolated from such lesions. Whether it is the true cause of the disease is, however, uncertain.

The encapsulated Gram negative rods resemble very closely bacteria of the genus *Aerobacter*. Without any knowledge of animal pathogenicity or true capsule formation (as occurs with old laboratory cultures) it is impossible to distinguish them.

Erwinia. This genus contains a number of species of Gram negative rod-shaped bacteria which exhibit peritrichous flagella, and which cause disease in plants. Some of them are fermentative bacteria and resemble very closely the genera Escherichia and Aerobacter in their cultural characters. Several species have been mentioned in the chapter on plant diseases.

Serratia. Twenty-seven species of red pigmented bacteria are described, but only one is at all well known. This is *Serratia marcescens*, formerly known as *Bacillus prodigiosus*. It forms a deep red pigment, especially on potato and other starchy substances. It is sometimes referred to as the "miraculous" organism, for it occurs occasionally upon bread, and in olden times the red color was looked upon as blood; occurring upon the bread used at the Sacrament, it was believed that a miracle had occurred. *Serratia indica* is another species, and was isolated by Koch from a monkey in India during his studies of cholera.

Proteus. *Proteus vulgaris* is one of the most common of the aerobic putrefactive bacteria. It is found in soil and water, in the feces, in decomposing carcasses, in fact wherever protein material is undergoing decomposition.

It is a slender Gram negative rod varying markedly in length. It is actively motile, with numerous peritrichous flagella. On agar plates the surface colonies are very striking. The growth is moist, the colonies are flat and only slightly elevated. From the margin of the colony, due to the active motility of the cells, irregular lobes or streamers extend over the surface of the agar. Gelatine is liquefied, milk peptonized, and acid and gas are formed from glucose, maltose, sucrose and mannitol, but not from lactose.

Proteus occurs frequently in suppurating wounds, and may at times invade the deeper tissues. A variety known as "Proteus X 19" was isolated from the blood in a case of typhus fever. While it probably has nothing to do with the causation of that disease, this strain is regularly agglutinated by the blood of typhus fever cases.

Salmonelleae. The Tribe of pathogenic intestinal bacteria forms a compact group of obviously related species of Gram negative rods. They are similar to the colon bacilli, i.e., members of the genus Escherichia, but differ sharply from these harmless intestinal parasites in *their inability to ferment lactose*. This important biochemical character is a great aid in isolating typhoid and paratyphoid and dysentery bacilli from the feces. The paratyphoid group, genus *Salmonella*, produce gas from sugars, while the typhoids (*Eberthella*) and dysenteries (*Shigella*) form only acid. The typhoids and paratyphoids are motile, while the dysentery bacilli are non-motile.

Typhoid Fever. The cause of typhoid fever is *Eberthella typhi*, discovered by Eberth in 1880 and first cultivated by Gaffky in 1884.

The control of typhoid fever is probably the greatest achievement of practical bacteriology. The disease was at one time the most common of the serious infectious diseases and one of the principal causes of death. Today it is rare, occurring only in small localized epidemics traceable to carriers. This great change has been accomplished by making application of the following facts: The disease may be contracted only by swallowing the bacteria. The bacteria are discharged from the body (almost exclusively) in the urine and feces. Preventing contamination of food and water by urine and feces of carriers and cases will completely eradicate the disease.

After an incubation period of about a week, the disease begins with fever and rather vague symptoms of illness that increase in intensity. When fully developed there occurs a characteristic enlargement of the spleen, and small areas of inflammation, the "rose spots," appear on the skin. In the early stages the bacteria invade the blood stream, and during the first weeks may be readily detected by blood cultures. Later the infection becomes localized in the intestines, characteristic ulcers developing in the lower part of the small intestine.

Eberthella typhi. The typhoid germ is a Gram negative rod appearing under the microscope much like the colon bacillus. It is, however, very actively motile. It grows readily on artificial media, but does not grow so abundantly as the colon bacillus. Acid, but no gas, is formed from glucose, maltose, and mannitol. Lactose and sucrose are not fermented. Milk shows a slight initial acidity, but later becomes alkaline. No indol is formed.

Diagnosis of Typhoid Fever. Bacteriology has provided three procedures for the diagnosis of typhoid fever — the blood culture, the Widal test, and the stool culture.

Blood cultures are made by withdrawing some blood by means of a sterile syringe from a vein at the bend of the elbow. It may be placed in a flask of broth. After incubation, if the broth becomes cloudy and shows motile Gram negative rods, these may be transferred to routine media and sugar broths, or may be identified immediately by agglutination, if typhoid immune serum is available. The blood culture is often positive at the very beginning of the disease, and makes it possible to establish the diagnosis before any definite signs or symptoms have developed.

The *Widal test* is a test for the presence of agglutinins in the patient's blood. A small amount of blood is collected either by means of a syringe, or from a prick of the finger. The serum is properly diluted, say 1–50, with physiologic salt solution, and added to a suspension of living motile typhoid germs. If agglutinins have developed, the bacteria will be observed to form clumps under the microscope, or if the macroscopic method is followed, they will form a sediment at the bottom of the tube. Since agglutinins do not develop until some time after the blood or body tissues have been invaded, the Widal test will not prove positive until the second week of the disease, or later.

The *cultivation* of the typhoid bacilli from the *feces* is rather difficult, since the organism resembles closely the colon bacilli normal to the intestines. Here again advantage is taken of the fact that the colon bacilli will ferment lactose. The sample of feces, somewhat diluted, is streaked upon plates of Endo agar or eosin-methylene blue agar. The former is preferable. Upon Endo agar the colonies of the colon bacillus appear deep red in color, while the somewhat smaller typhoid colonies are colorless and rather transparent. The stool culture is positive during the later stages of the disease, and in general is used in diagnosis only when for some reason or other the former two methods have failed.

The stool culture is, however, an important procedure in the detection of typhoid carriers. Such cultures are also performed in the case of convalescent cases to determine when they may be released from quarantine.

Protective Vaccination. While water purification and the detection of carriers serve to check the occurrence of typhoid fever in cities, the conditions of life with troops in the field are such that this disease is an important factor in warfare. In the Franco-Prussian War, the Boer War, and the Spanish-American War, typhoid fever was the principal medical problem. During the World War the incidence of typhoid fever was strikingly less. Thus with American troops in the Spanish-American War, approximately one soldier out of five contracted typhoid, while in the World War the ratio was approximately one to four thousand. This was undoubtedly due in part to improvements in field hygiene, particularly in provision for the chlorination of drinking water, but probably in the main was the result of *vaccination* of the troops before they took to the field.

Typhoid vaccine is composed of typhoid bacilli suspended in physiologic salt solution, and killed by heating to 55° C. for one hour. Since the danger from paratyphoid infections is as great as from typhoid, the vaccine now prepared is a "triple" vaccine containing, in addition to the typhoid germs, two different kinds of paratyphoid bacilli. Three injections are given, a week apart. Some temporary fever and headache may result from the inoculations.

Salmonella. The genus Salmonella includes the organisms of paratyphoid fever, as well as a large number of other bacteria pathogenic to man and to various lower animals. Collectively they are referred to as the "paratyphoids."

These bacteria are intermediary in characters between the typhoid bacillus and the colon bacilli. Some strains produce a disease in man similar to typhoid fever, but milder. This is paratyphoid fever. Other strains cause food poisoning. Of the common sugars, they ferment the same ones as typhoid germs, viz., glucose, maltose, and mannitol; but, like the colon bacilli, they form gas as well as acid from these carbohydrates. The different species and strains vary among themselves, some approaching more closely the colon bacilli, others the typhoid bacilli. They are all motile. Save for the production of gas in carbohydrates, their cultural characters are essentially those of the typhoid bacillus.

Paratyphoid Fever. Two species of Salmonella may give rise to a typhoid-like disease in man — *S. paratyphi* and *S. schottmülleri.* These were formerly referred to as "Paratyphoid A" and "Paratyphoid B," respectively. They were first distinguished by agglutination reactions, but later studies showed that they could be distinguished by certain biochemical reactions. *S. paratyphi* does not form sulphides in meat extract media, while *S. schottmülleri* does. This may be demonstrated by adding a minute quantity of lead acetate to the medium. In the presence of sulphides, a dark brown precipitate of lead sulphide is formed. *Salmonella schottmülleri* ferments the sugar *xylose*, with the production of acid and gas, while *S. paratyphi* does not.

The diagnostic procedures and preventive measures which are applicable to typhoid fever will also serve for paratyphoid fever; food poisoning is a different type of disease.

Food Poisoning. The term "bacterial food poisoning" has been applied to a variety of conditions arising from the ingestion of food in which bacteria have grown, or have been suspected to have grown. Formerly one heard frequently of cases of ptomaine poisoning, supposedly due to eating food in which poisonous basic substances, the ptomaines, had been formed by the action of putrefactive bacteria. It is doubtful that true ptomaine poisoning occurs in man.

Cases of bacterial food poisoning nearly all fall into three groups: those caused by the enterotoxin of *Staphylococcus aureus*, those caused by the exotoxin of *Clostridium botulinum*, and those which are actual infections with members of the genus *Salmonella*.

This type of paratyphoid infection is quite different from typhoid fever. The incubation period is very short, perhaps but a few hours, the onset is sudden, and the symptoms are those of a severe digestive disturbance rather than of an infectious disease — diarrhoea, vomiting, abdominal cramps. Fever may be slight. Fortunately, in most cases there is a rapid recovery.

These acute symptoms generally arise from eating food which is rather heavily contaminated with the paratyphoid-like bacteria. There are two general sources of infection. The food at fault may be meat from an animal which was suffering from a paratyphoid infection at the time it was slaughtered. Or the food may have become contaminated through handling by a human carrier, or from contact with rats or mice, which are known to be carriers. From the standpoint of prevention, it is important to know that such attacks may arise from eating food which does not show any signs of spoilage. The causative organisms are readily killed by heat, and thorough cooking should make food perfectly safe.

There are two species of Salmonella causing outbreaks of food poisoning in man, *S. aertrycke* and *S. enteriditis.* The latter is often called "Gaertner's bacillus." Both resemble *S. schottmülleri* in cultural characters.

Paratyphoids in Lower Animals. The paratyphoids form a great group like the haemorrhagic septicaemia group, producing infections in a variety of animals. To what extent the strains isolated from different animals constitute distinct species or varieties is still uncertain. *S. suipestifer* occurs in hogs, and was at one time thought to be the cause of hog cholera. It is now known that that disease is caused by a filterable virus, and that the paratyphoid organism is merely a frequent secondary invader. *S. psittacosis* bears a similar relation to the disease, psittacosis, which occurs in parrots and is transmissible to man. *S. pullorum* is a cause of bacillary white diarrhoea in chicks, *S. gallinarum* of fowl typhoid. Several species occur in natural epidemics in rats and mice.

Shigella. The *dysentery bacilli* form a natural group of species or strains which are included in the genus Shigella.

Bacillary dysentery, caused by these bacteria, is to be distinguished from amoebic dysentery, caused by *Entamoeba histolytica*, which will be discussed in a later chapter.

The dysentery bacilli are *non-motile*. They do not form gas from carbohydrates. Lactose is not fermented. They grow rather more poorly on artificial media than other members of the colon-typhoid group. There are several species or types which are distinguished in part by sugar fermentations, and in part by agglutination reactions. The two most common are the Shiga type, or *Shigella dysenteriae*, and the Flexner type, or *Shigella paradysenteriae*. Of the five common sugars, the former ferments glucose only, the latter ferments maltose and mannitol as well. The Flexner type forms indol, while the Shiga type does not.

Bacillary dysentery is a very acute intestinal infection, characterized by severe diarrhoea and symptoms of severe intoxication. It occurs in extensive epidemics in Oriental countries, but in this country is seen in institutional epidemics.

The dysentery bacilli are extremely toxic to lower animals, especially rabbits. The dead bacteria are just as injurious as living cultures. There is some question concerning the formation of exotoxins, but it appears that the toxicity is mainly bound in the bacteria themselves.

Bacteriaceae. This is a miscellaneous group of rod-shaped bacteria which cannot be readily fitted elsewhere in the classification of bacteria. Undoubtedly many of the species included here are thus placed only temporarily; when better known they will be more properly classified. We shall note briefly the characters of the various genera.

Listerella. This genus contains an organism pathogenic for rabbits which is noteworthy in that it gives rise to a great increase in the large mononuclear leucocytes, or *monocytes*.

Microbacterium. These are minute Gram positive rod-shaped organisms, perhaps better classified with the Lactobacilli.

Kurthia. This genus contains two little-known species of Gram positive bacteria without spores, which are putrefactive rather than fermentative.

Cellulomonas. This genus includes species (mostly described by Kellerman and McBeth) of aerobic non-sporogenous rods which may decompose cellulose. They are soil bacteria. Some of them form yellow pigments.

Flavobacterium. This is a large genus, with 67 described species. Yellow chromogens appear to be characteristic water bacteria. Most of the species have been obtained from cultures of water, either fresh or sea water.

Achromobacter. The genus Achromobacter is a large "waste basket" group, containing a long list of species of Gram negative rods without spores, which are rather indefinite in their characters. They do not form pigments, or cause disease, or produce important chemical reactions. Their most important group character is that they do not attract attention to themselves! They are encountered in routine examinations of water and soil and other materials. Undoubtedly some day these bacteria will be more thoroughly studied and will then be further classified.

Actinobacillus. *Actinobacillus ligniersi* is the cause of a disease of cattle very similar to actinomycosis. This disease is called "actinobacillosis." Like actinomycosis, it begins usually in the mouth parts, but involves the soft tissues rather than the jaw bones. It produces a chronic infection of the tongue with the production of scar tissue, called "woody tongue." The disease is more frequent than is actinomycosis. A large proportion of the cases formerly diagnosed actinomycosis were actually cases of this disease.

The organism is found in the pus as colonies, or granules, closely resembling those of actinomycosis. The granules are composed of slender rod-shaped or filamentous elements, which are not branched. These may be radially arranged, and show "clubs" of hyaline material at the periphery, so that they imitate very closely the granules of *Actinomyces bovis.*

Actinobacillus ligniersi grows aerobically on ordinary culture media, and is a non-motile Gram negative rod, in no way resembling an Actinomyces. It has recently been suggested that it is very similar to the glanders organism, *Malleomyces mallei,* in morphology and cultural characters, and has been found to give cross-immunity reactions with that organism.

Bacteroides. A number of anaerobic rods without spores have been described. Most of them have not been extensively investigated. A large proportion of them are Gram positive. Undoubtedly some of these are related to the Lactobacilli.

Fusobacterium. In the crevices between the gums and the teeth, and in the crypts of the tonsils, one may often find certain straight or slightly curved rod-shaped bacteria with distinctly pointed ends. These are members of the genus Fusobacterium. There are probably several species found in man, and similar bacteria are found in lower animals. They are Gram doubtful, i.e., with the usual techinque some cells are decolorized, others are not. Some species contain within the cells granules which, like the nuclei of Protozoa, stain red with Giemsa's stain; these granules are probably not volutin, and may be chromatin. Some strains are motile, others are not.

All of the species are strict anaerobes, and most strains produce a very foul odor in cultures. They are cultivated with difficulty.

While often found in the normal mouth or tonsils, species of Fusobacterium have been isolated from a number of disease processes, all of which are characterized by ulceration or gangrene of the tissues. In these diseases the fusiform bacilli are always associated with spirochaetes of the genus Borrelia. The relations of these bacteria to each other and to the diseases in which they occur will be discussed in the chapter on spirochaetes.

Bacterium. This generic name has been used in several different senses — for instance, to include all non-motile rod-shaped bacteria, or all non-spore-forming rods, etc. It has been retained "as a temporary generic term with an admittedly unrecognizable type species, *Bacterium triloculare* Ehrenberg, to include those species of non-spore-forming, rod-shaped, motile or non-motile bacteria whose relationships to other bacteria are not clear."

CHAPTER XXV

EUBACTERIALES: THE BACILLACEAE

This family contains all of the true bacteria which form spores. They are all Gram positive, at least when actively growing. The majority of species are motile, with peritrichous flagella. They are mainly saprophytic organisms whose natural habitat is the soil. There are but two genera, the aerobic genus *Bacillus* and the anaerobic genus *Clostridium*.

Bacillus. The aerobic spore-forming bacteria form a homogeneous natural group. They are mostly soil saprophytes, but their light, resistant spores are everywhere. To the bacteriologist they are known as troublesome contaminants which are not destroyed by any save the most drastic methods of sterilization.

They are very active in attacking complex organic compounds, but are proteolytic rather than fermentative. Most species liquefy gelatine and peptonize milk. In soil their function is mainly ammonification. Some species are active in digesting starch.

The spore-forming bacteria exhibit a definite cytomorphosis. In the young, actively growing cultures the cells are large and elongated, relatively slender. With most species the cells occur in chains. Probably all species are Gram positive in this phase of their growth. As growth slows up the cells become shorter and more oval in form. The previously homogeneous protoplasm now begins to show granules and vacuoles of various reserve materials, and spore formation commences. With some species the cells now appear Gram negative. With increasing age of the culture, spores become more and more numerous, and vegetative cells relatively less abundant. Those cells which do not form spores may show marked involution changes — branching, budding, etc.

A number of species of aerobic spore-formers have been described. Ford, who has studied this genus intensively, lists forty-two species and varieties which he arranges in ten groups of saprophytic forms, and one of pathogenic species. Important characters in identifying spore-formers are the size of the cells, the size, shape, and position of the spores, the presence or absence of motility, and the various cultural characters.   We shall consider but a few representative species.

Bacillus anthracis.   The organism of anthrax has had an important part in the history of bacteriology.   It is one of the largest of pathogenic bacteria, and occurs in the blood and tissues of infected animals in enormous numbers.   It was, therefore, one of the first disease-producing bacteria to be observed.   It was with this organism that Koch performed his first experiments which conclusively proved that bacteria cause disease.   And Pasteur's spectacular public demonstration of the value of protective vaccination against anthrax had a great deal to do with stimulating interest in immunity.

B. anthracis is a Gram positive rod occurring in chains.   It is non-motile.   In the animal tissues or fluids it is encapsulated.   It forms spores readily in cultures, not in the infected animal.   In blood withdrawn from the animal, spores appear on standing.   Exposure to air is probably necessary for spore formation.

The organism grows luxuriantly on artificial culture media.   Colonies on agar are characteristic, the edges showing striking curled parallel chains of cells under the microscope.   A pellicle is formed on broth.   Gelatine and coagulated blood serum are liquefied; milk is peptonized.

Anthrax.   The disease, anthrax, occurs in a variety of animals, both wild and domestic, and occasionally in man.   Cattle and sheep are most commonly affected.   The disease is usually contracted by swallowing the organisms, but may result from wound infections. The bacteria invade the blood stream and death results from septicaemia.   The spores from dead animals infest the soil, and may remain alive for years.

In man the disease occurs usually as a localized abscess, the "malignant pustule," resulting from spores being introduced into the skin.   Such infections occur in butchers and handlers of hides. A number of cases have been due to the use of shaving brushes made of bristles from infected animals.   A respiratory form of the disease, called "woolsorters' disease," is due to inhalation of spores.   An intestinal form may also occur in man, but is rarer.

Pasteur's vaccine consists of two inoculations of bacteria partially attenuated by heat, the second dose of greater virulence than the first. Since the vaccine contains living organisms, it is not perfectly safe, and some serious epidemics have resulted from its use. But in general the inoculation of domestic animals with this vaccine in districts which are badly infested appears to reduce the mortality.

Bacillus subtilis. This name was applied by Cohn to an actively motile, spore-forming bacterium obtained from hay infusions. It has sometimes been called the "hay bacillus."

There is some confusion regarding the identity of this organism. Earlier medical bacteriologists used the name rather indiscriminately for any saprophytic aerobic spore-former. Two distinct types of spore-formers have been described as *Bacillus subtilis* in textbooks of bacteriology, a large species and a much smaller one. The larger one was probably the species observed by Cohn. It is described as being very similar to *B. anthracis*, but differs in being actively motile, and possessing peritrichous flagella. The cells occur in chains, and the whole chain moves, bending at the connections between the cells, with a very characteristic "waddling" motion. It is a pellicle-forming proteolytic type.

Bacillus cereus. This is probably the most common species, encountered frequently as a contaminating organism in all sorts of bacteriological work. It is a large organism (0.75 × 2.5 to 4 μ), actively motile.

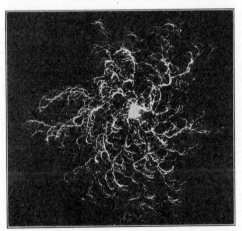

FIG. 88. Colony of *Bacillus mycoides*.

The spores are central. A heavy pellicle is formed in broth. Gelatine is liquefied, and milk undergoes alkaline peptonization.

Bacillus mycoides. This is one of the most abundant and striking of the spore-formers in soil. It derives its name (mycoides = "mold-like") from the characteristic appearance of the surface colonies. From the central portion long narrow streamers extend over the surface of the agar, looking much like the filaments of mycelium of a mold. These streamers are made up of parallel chains of cells. As they extend outward they branch and also curl, all curling in the same direction, usually clockwise.

The cells are square-ended, and grow in chains. They are actively motile. Spores are central. A pellicle is formed on broth, and the organism is very actively proteolytic.

Bacillus vulgatus. Formerly known as *B. mesentericus vulgatus*, this bacterium is commonly called the "potato bacillus," because it occurs so frequently in potato tubes prepared as culture media, the spores resisting sterilization. This bacillus is somewhat smaller than the preceding species ($0.5 \times 2 \mu$). The cells are more rounded at the ends, and do not tend to form long chains. Active motility is produced by peritrichous flagella. A pellicle is formed on broth, gelatine is liquefied, and milk slowly peptonized. A heavy wrinkled growth, brown in color, spreads over the plug of potato.

Ropy Bread. Species of spore-formers very similar to *B. vulgatus* are responsible for a type of spoilage of bread known as "ropiness." The spores get in the flour, and are not destroyed by baking temperatures. They grow within the loaf during storage, and secrete a gum which produces the ropiness.

Bacillus megatherium. This is quite the largest of the bacteria which may be readily cultivated on artificial media, and has therefore been a favorite subject for morphologic study. The cells measure 0.75 to 1.25×3 to 9μ in 24-hour cultures, but in young cultures during the actively growing period the author has observed individual cells 4μ in diameter and as much as 50μ in length. Young cultures are actively motile. Spores are central.

B. megatherium differs from most of the common aerobic spore-formers in failing to form a pellicle on broth. The medium may show some turbidity, but generally the bacteria sink to the bottom and do not grow vigorously unless the medium is agitated. On solid media the growth is moist and glistening, not dull or wrinkled, as is true of most species of Bacillus. The growth on solid media is often yellowish in color.

Bacillus terminalis. This species is mentioned as an example of a Bacillus with terminal spores. The cells are long and slender. The spores appear at the very end, and are oval or cylindrical in form.

Clostridium. Our knowledge of the strictly anaerobic bacteria has been rather slow in developing and is still undoubtedly very incomplete. It is much more difficult and laborious to cultivate the anaerobes, and the earlier workers in bacteriology naturally turned to the more facile aerobes, especially as the anaerobes appeared to be of minor importance. It is particularly difficult to *isolate* the anaerobes in pure culture, and this led to some serious errors in earlier descriptions.

The large number of wounded who developed gas gangrene or tetanus during the World War led to a greatly increased interest in this group of bacteria, and this interest was intensified by the occur-

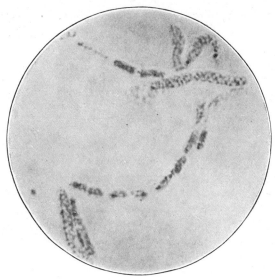

Fig. 89. *Bacillus megatherium.* Photomicrograph of a smear from a young agar culture, stained with iron haematoxyline.

rence of several serious outbreaks of botulism, and also by the discovery of a method for utilizing commercially the fermentative powers of an anaerobic bacillus in the production of acetone and butyl alcohol, solvents for lacquers. Within the past twenty years our knowledge of the anaerobic bacteria has been very greatly extended.

The natural habitat of the anaerobes is the soil. Some species occur frequently in the feces. *Clostridium welchii* is constantly present in the human intestine. But these species also occur in the soil. Even the pathogenic species are normally soil saprophytes, and only accidentally pathogens, as was indicated in Chapter XVI. The Clostridia play a varied rôle in the soil economy. All are heterotrophic. *Cl. pastorianum* can fix nitrogen. Several species decompose cellulose, and these are important in the decomposition of plant matter in poorly aerated soil, or in bogs and marshes. The remaining species are either putrefactive or fermentative organisms.

Classification of Anaerobes. The anaerobes have been subdivided by some authorities on the basis of their biochemical activities, whether predominantly proteolytic or fermentative, and by others on the position of their spores, whether central, subterminal, or terminal. Both sets of characters are useful.

While with the majority of the aerobic bacilli the spores are only slightly, if at all, greater in diameter than the cells, the reverse is true of the anaerobes. The spores usually produce a distinct bulging, which gives the cell a form characteristic for the species, according to the position within the cell.

Most of the culture media used routinely in the study of aerobic bacteria are not suitable for the study of anaerobes because of the difficulty involved in maintaining anaerobic conditions. The most useful are the deep glucose-agar shake cultures, for observing colony form and gas production, litmus milk, and *cooked meat* medium. The latter consists of a broth or peptone solution to which is added ground muscle, liver, or brain. Liver seems most useful since it is rich in carbohydrate, which will favor the growth of fermentative species. The medium is tubed so that a number of particles of the ground meat are present in each tube, forming a layer one or two centimeters deep at the bottom of the tube. The meat particles absorb oxygen, thus tending to maintain anaerobic conditions, but they further serve as an indicator of the activities of the organism. If it is predominantly putrefactive, it will usually form sulphides that darken the meat, and the latter may be ultimately digested. If it is predominantly fermentative, the acids formed will turn the meat particles red.

Clostridium butyricum. Bacteria producing butyric acid from carbohydrates were the first anaerobic bacteria to be discovered, by Pasteur. In the years that have intervened, such organisms have been repeatedly described and studied under one name or another. They have attracted attention as agents fixing nitrogen, and as industrial ferments producing acetone and butyl alcohol.

It is probable that a rather large group of closely related species is included under the name *Clostridium butyricum*, but their classification is confused. *Cl. butyricum, Cl. pastorianum,* and *Cl. acetobutylicum* are considered to be distinct species by some authorities, to be synonyms by others.

The butyric acid bacteria are large rod forms, actively motile in young cultures. As the period of spore formation is approached, the cells become distinctly larger, bulge markedly in the middle, and become rather pointed at the extremities, appearing somewhat diamond-shaped. Such cells store carbohydrate in the form of a starch-like substance, which has been called *granulose*. The generic names Amylobacter and Granulobacter, which have been applied to these bacteria, are based upon this peculiarity. The large oval spores are subterminal in position.

The most striking of the cultural characters is the vigorous fermentation of carbohydrates. A variety of such substances, from starch and gums down to the hexose sugars, are fermented with the production of acid and gas. The fermentation is a complex one yielding several acids, of which *butyric* is most abundant; alcohols, mainly butyl alcohol; acetone, carbon dioxide, and hydrogen. The organism is not proteolytic.

Anaerobic Nitrogen Fixation. Anaerobic bacteria which fix atmospheric nitrogen were discovered by Winogradsky, who applied the name *Clostridium pastorianum*. It is probable, however, that the ability to fix nitrogen is common to the butyric acid group of anaerobes. Such organisms are widespread in soil, and may be readily cultivated in impure form by inoculating a little soil into a sugar solution with no nitrogenous constituents, kept under anaerobic conditions. Such organisms are more numerous in soil than is Azotobacter.

In the soil these organisms exist, of course, together with many other species of microbes, among them many aerobic forms. Presumably the latter use up much of the oxygen, which diffuses into the soil from the atmosphere, allowing the anaerobic forms to grow.

Commercial Solvents. During the War an increased demand for acetone as a solvent for nitrocellulose in the manufacture of smokeless powder, and of "dope" for airplanes, led to a search for cheaper methods of obtaining this substance. Such a method was found in the fermentation of starch by butyric acid anaerobes. The development of cheap solvents made it possible to use solutions of cellulose derivatives as artificial quick-drying lacquers, which has greatly increased the demand for the solvents.

The organism used is called *Clostridium acetobutylicum.* It is very similar to, if not identical with, *Cl. butyricum.* The industrial fermentation utilizes a corn mash which is inoculated with a pure culture starter. The solvents are recovered, after fermentation, by distilling.

Anaerobic Cellulose Decomposition. The decomposition of cellulose by microörganisms was first observed by Omeliansky. When soil was inoculated into a solution containing various mineral salts, but with no organic matter save cellulose in the form of filter paper, the latter was found to decompose slowly, with the formation of gas. Omeliansky believed that this decomposition was due to the action of two species of anaerobes, one of which liberated hydrogen, the other forming marsh gas, or methane. But he did not succeed in obtaining pure cultures.

Later workers have considered certain aerobic bacteria of the genus Cellulomonas as more important in breaking up cellulose in the soil. But anaerobic bacteria which can decompose cellulose have been found abundant in the digestive tracts of herbivorous animals and of wood-boring insects. Such organisms are perhaps essential in the utilization of cellulose by the animals which harbor them.

Putrefactive Anaerobes. The decomposition of proteins by anaerobic bacteria is accompanied by the development of particularly foul odors. Several species of harmless anaerobes which are predominantly putrefactive have been described. *Clostridium sporogenes* is the most common. It is a very frequent contaminating organism in anaerobic cultures. It possesses central spores. *Cl. putrificum* differs in developing terminal spores. While predominantly putrefactive, these bacteria also ferment sugars with the production of acid and gas.

Gas Gangrene. Well known before the days of aseptic surgery, this disease was almost unknown to surgeons at the time of the War, but became one of the most serious medical problems of the armies. This disease is prone to occur as a sequel to badly lacerated wounds which become contaminated with soil. Such wounds are likely to occur under conditions of modern warfare. As the name implies, the disease is characterized by rapid death and sloughing of the tissues, and by the formation of gas within the tissues.

Bacteriological studies of cases of gas gangrene indicate that in most cases a mixed flora is present. There are both aerobes and anaerobes of several kinds, and it is very difficult to ascribe the whole process to any one species. Three species of pathogenic anaerobes appear to be most important. They are *Clostridium welchii*, *Clostridium oedematis-maligni*, and *Clostridium oedematiens*. Each of these, in pure culture, is capable of producing a disease resembling gas gangrene when injected into guinea pigs. But in the natural disease they are often accompanied by Streptococci which may help prepare the way for their invasion, and by putrefactive bacteria which take part in the process by decomposing the tissues which have been killed by the toxins of the anaerobes.

The anaerobes of gas gangrene all secrete exotoxins which are very potent in destroying tissues with which they come in contact. If one inoculates a guinea pig with a culture of *Cl. welchii* there will result a typical gas gangrene. But if, instead of the whole culture, one injects the bacteria washed free of culture medium, no infection occurs. The bacteria alone cannot multiply in the living tissues. But if some of the toxin accompanies them, cells are killed, and in the dead tissue the bacteria may grow, secrete more toxin to kill more cells, and so rapidly extend the process.

This experiment explains why gas gangrene occurs following extensively lacerated wounds. Such wounds frequently have on their walls tags of tissue detached from their blood supply, and therefore dead, which provide a culture medium for the essentially saprophytic anaerobes. Bits of dirt forced into the wound may serve the same purpose. Surgeons found that the incidence of gas gangrene could be greatly reduced by carefully cutting away the ragged surface of wounds. Gas gangrene bacteria were frequently cultivated from wounds where the gas gangrene did not occur.

While the bacteria of gas gangrene all produce potent toxins, it is probable that, with the Welch bacillus at least, further damage to tissues results from the large amount of acid and gas produced as a result of the fermentation of muscle sugars.

Antitoxins against these bacteria were developed at the end of the War. They were not used extensively enough to determine their value, but there is every indication that they are successful, at least when used as a preventive before the development of symptoms.

Clostridium welchii is the most common of the gas gangrene bacteria. It is widespread, constantly present in the human intestine, and apparently universally distributed in soil. It is a large, square-ended rod, without motility. Spores are central. Spores are not formed in acid media; therefore they will fail to appear in cultures containing sugars which are fermented. In infected tissues the cells are encapsulated. This organism produces a violent fermentation of carbohydrates, forming large quantities of both acid and gas. In litmus milk it gives rise to a characteristic *stormy fermentation*, coag-

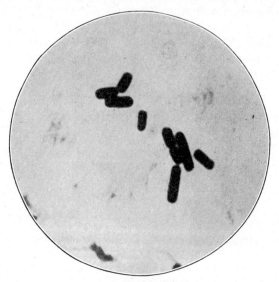

Fig. 90.   *Clostridium welchii.*

ulating the caseinogen, and often blowing the curd entirely out of the whey by gas formation.

Clostridium oedematis-maligni, called the *vibrion septique* by Pasteur, differs from the bacillus of Welch in being motile and without capsules. It is less vigorous than the former in fermenting carbohydrates. Spores are subterminal.

Clostridium oedematiens is somewhat similar to the preceding, but is still less active in fermentation.

The three gas gangrene organisms can be further differentiated by the characteristic tissue changes which result when they are inoculated into guinea pigs.

Blackleg. Blackleg is a disease of cattle and sheep essentially similar to gas gangrene in man. The disease in cattle is caused by *Clostridium chauvoei*, but in sheep is usually due to *Cl. oedomatis-maligni*. The disease may be prevented by vaccination.

Tetanus. Tetanus, or lockjaw, is also a wound infection. The organism is widespread, present in the intestines of man and herbivorous animals, and almost universally distributed in soil. The disease is, however, rare in civilian life. The conditions which favor the occurrence of gas gangrene equally favor the development of tetanus. Spores of tetanus bacilli, freed of toxin, cannot germinate and multiply when inoculated into healthy tissue. A previous injury with death of some of the cells is necessary for their development.

Tetanus differs markedly from gas gangrene, however, in the nature of the toxin and the symptoms which it produces. The toxins of the gas gangrene bacteria have a *general* action, killing cells of all kinds with which they come in contact in sufficient concentration. The toxin of the tetanus bacillus has a *specific* action upon *motor nerve cells*.

The incubation period of tetanus is quite variable, but is longer with wounds of the lower extremities than with wounds of the head and neck. This is due to the fact that the symptoms result from an absorption of toxin through the peripheral nerves rather than by way of the blood stream. Toxin secreted by the bacteria in a wound travels by way of the nerve trunks to the spinal cord, and symptoms develop only when the toxin has become bound to the motor nerve cells. These symptoms consist of spasmodic contractions of the muscles. At first those muscles nearest the wound are involved, but as the toxin spreads through the nervous system, more of the muscles go into spasms, until finally general convulsions develop. Spasms of the muscles which close the jaws give rise to the popular name "lockjaw."

A potent specific antitoxin has been obtained against the exotoxin of the tetanus bacillus. When used as a *preventive*, inoculated shortly after the occurrence of a wound, this antitoxin greatly diminishes the chances of tetanus developing. The antitoxin injections should be repeated at weekly intervals if conditions of the wound indicate a possibility of tetanus bacilli developing. Used in *treatment*, after symptoms have developed, the antitoxin is not of such great value, probably because the toxin in the body has a greater affinity for nerve tissue than for the antitoxin.

Clostridium tetani. The tetanus bacillus is a slender, actively motile rod. The spherical spores appear at the very end of the rods, giving them a characteristic "drum-stick" appearance.

In gelatine stab cultures the bacteria grow out from the line of the stab into the gelatine in fine streamers, giving the culture the appearance of a fir tree. Gelatine is slowly liquefied. Sugars are not fermented. It is rather inert with regard to biochemical activities, as compared with the other anaerobes.

Botulism. Botulism is another disease of the nervous system caused by the toxin of an anaerobic bacillus. But *Clostridium botu-*

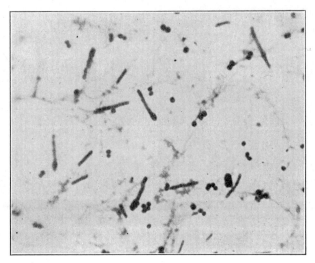

Fig. 91. *Clostridium tetani.* Photomicrograph of a smear of pus from a wound. Note the terminal spores. Cocci are also present.

linum cannot multiply in the tissues; it is purely a saprophytic organism. The disease results from eating food in which the bacterium has been growing, the toxin being absorbed through the digestive tract. Botulism is therefore strictly a food poisoning, not a true infection.

Botulism differs markedly from the so-called food poisoning, caused by species of Salmonella, which was described in the preceding chapter. The disease is much more serious, and the symptoms are mainly due to involvement of the nervous system rather than the gastro-intestinal tract. As with tetanus, the toxin affects motor

nerve cells, but produces *paralysis* rather than spasms. The muscles
of the tongue and throat are often involved first, causing difficulty in
speech and swallowing. Muscles of the eyes are also paralyzed, producing double vision. Death may result from paralysis of the
diaphragm.

The exotoxin of *Cl. botulinum* is the most powerful poison known.
It has been estimated that 0.00001 gm. would be fatal to man. It

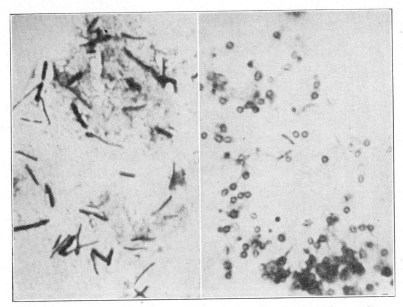

FIG. 92.   *Clostridium botulinum.*   Photomicrographs of smears from cultures.
At the left, a young culture just forming spores; at the right, an old culture containing mostly free spores.

differs from other known exotoxins in its ability to pass through the
mucous membrane of the alimentary tract. There are three types
of the species, designated A, B, and C. These differ in their toxins;
antitoxin against type A will not neutralize the toxins of types B
and C, and so on. They also differ with regard to their toxicity for
different species of animals. Type C causes a disease of poultry
called "limberneck," and a similar disease of wild ducks occurring
in great epidemics in certain alkaline lakes of western America.
There is no evidence that type C affects man.

Clostridium botulinum is also apparently widely distributed in soil, but its distribution appears to be more irregular than that of the other anaerobes. The disease results from eating food in which the organism has grown and secreted toxin. Preserved foods which present anaerobic conditions will allow the bacterium to grow. Outbreaks of the disease have been traced to ham and sausages ("botulus" = sausage), but recent epidemics have been caused in most cases by the consumption of canned goods, olives, and particularly home-canned vegetables. The heat-resistant spores are usually destroyed by the autoclave temperatures used in commercial processing of canned goods, but not by the temperatures attained in the "cold pack" method of home processing. The organism is both putrefactive and fermentative, and canned goods containing *Cl. botulinum* may give warning by a weak odor of butyric acid or of putrefaction on opening. But this is not always true. While the spores are heat resistant, this is not true of the toxin, which is quickly destroyed at the temperature of boiling water. The best way to prevent this disease is to heat canned vegetables or meats to the boiling point before serving.

The antitoxins which have been developed against the three toxins will protect experimental animals. There are no data available as yet by which their value in the treatment of human cases may be determined.

Clostridium botulinum is a rather large rod with oval subterminal spores which bulge the cells. It is motile. Gelatine is liquefied, cooked meat medium is blackened, coagulated egg and blood serum are digested. Acid and gas are formed in sugar media. Litmus milk shows reduction and peptonization.

CHAPTER XXVI

THE ACTINOMYCETALES

We have already considered in an earlier chapter the division of this order into two families, the more bacteria-like *Mycobacteriaceae*, and the mold-like *Actinomycetaceae*.

Mycobacteriaceae. There are three genera, *Mycobacterium*, *Corynebacterium*, and *Proactinomyces*.

Mycobacterium. The acidfast bacteria comprise an important group, containing the pathogenic species which cause tuberculosis and leprosy, and a number of saprophytic species. In addition to the property of acidfastness, they exhibit other peculiarities of morphology and cultural characters in common, which indicate that this genus is a homogeneous group of related species.

Mostly they are rather slender rods, sometimes tending to be slightly curved. They frequently occur in a characteristic grouping, not precisely parallel, but tending to bunch together like a bundle of fagots. They often exhibit deeply stained intracellular granules, the nature of which is not precisely known. They are not motile and without spores or capsules. They are all Gram positive.

In artificial cultures they grow slowly but abundantly. The growth is often pigmented — shades of buff or orange, occasionally almost red. Some species show a smooth, pasty growth in solid media, but the tendency is to form a wrinkled growth of friable consistency, with a rather dull surface. Usually a pellicle is formed in liquid media. They are neither fermentative nor putrefactive in the usual sense of the words.

The property of acidfastness varies within the genus, some species being much more tenacious in their staining than others. This property tends to disappear after prolonged cultivation, more rapidly with some species than with others. The group tends to form fats and waxy substances, which may be demonstrated by extraction with appropriate solvents.

The Tubercle Bacilli. There are four kinds of tubercle bacilli, affecting different groups of animals. Although sufficiently distinct to warrant considering them different species, they are usually referred to as types — a human type, a bovine type, an avian type, and a cold-blooded type.

The *human type* appears in sputum or other material from the body as very slender, slightly curved rods, frequently showing here and there in the cell deep-staining granules which bulge the cell somewhat, and give it a characteristic beaded appearance. When first isolated it grows very slowly, requiring several weeks to produce visible growth. Growth is best in media containing glycerine. On agar there occurs a characteristic buff to orange colored friable, wrinkled, tenacious growth. A wrinkled pellicle is formed on broth. On glycerine potato the growth is similar to that on agar, usually deeper in color. In glycerine broth, after prolonged incubation, the medium becomes acid in reaction.

Injected subcutaneously into guinea pigs, the human type of tubercle bacilli produces a progressive disease which is generally fatal within two months. When inoculated into rabbits disease may result, but it is usually not progressive and fatal, tending to remain localized and eventually to heal; similar results occur in cats and calves.

The *bovine type* is usually shorter, plumper, and straighter than the human type. Growth in artificial cultures is in general similar to that of the human type, but is less luxuriant, and only faintly pigmented. Glycerine broth does not tend to become acid. The bovine type is somewhat more pathogenic to guinea pigs, and distinctly more pathogenic to rabbits, cats, and calves, producing a progressive and fatal disease in these animals.

The *avian type* resembles the bovine type in morphology. It grows more rapidly in artificial culture media than either of the preceding, and tends to produce a soft, flat growth on solid media, as distinguished from the friable wrinkled growth of the mammalian types. The growth is often of a pinkish color. The avian type is pathogenic for pigeons and rabbits, but not for guinea pigs.

These three types are of medical and veterinary importance. They are differentiated best by their pathogenicity for laboratory animals, summarized in the following table:

	Human	Bovine	Avian
Guinea pigs	+	+	−
Rabbits	−	+	+
Pigeons	−	−	+

The *cold-blooded* types (there may be several) produce a disease resembling tuberculosis in various species of lower animals — fish, snakes, turtles, and frogs. In general they resemble the avian type, growing rapidly in artificial cultures, and forming a rather smooth, pasty growth on solid media. They differ mainly in their optimum temperatures — 40° C. for the avian, 25° C. for the cold-blooded types. Cold-blooded types are not pathogenic for warm-blooded animals.

The tubercle bacilli are usually given the scientific name *Mycobacterium tuberculosis*, with the type in parenthesis after, as *M. tuberculosis* (human).

Tuberculosis. While definitely decreasing in frequency, tuberculosis is still one of the most important of the infectious diseases, not only taking a great toll of human life, but causing tremendous losses of domestic animals — cattle, swine, and poultry.

Man is subject to infection by both human and bovine types. Swine are susceptible to both avian and bovine types. Cattle and fowls are susceptible to their own types alone.

Tuberculosis is a chronic but progressive disease. In the vast majority of cases the disease begins in the lungs, and may remain localized in those organs. But it may also extend to other parts of the body, and no tissue is immune. In man, adults practically never contract an infection with the bovine type. The disease results almost invariably from the inhalation of the human type bacilli, discharged in sputum or droplets of moisture from other cases of pulmonary tuberculosis. But in children a proportion of cases are due to bovine type bacilli. Here the portal of entry is the intestinal tract; the bacteria are ingested in milk from tuberculous cows. Practically all cases of primary abdominal tuberculosis are due to bovine type bacilli, while a large proportion of infections of the bones and joints, and of lymph glands of the neck (scrofula), are also due to bovine type bacilli.

The growth of the tubercle bacilli within the tissues gives rise to a very characteristic reaction, the formation of *tubercles*. These are small white nodules of new-formed tissues, composed mainly of large phagocytic cells (macrophages). As the disease progresses, these nodules enlarge, and in the central portion the tissue dies and undergoes a peculiar transformation, appearing somewhat like cheese when cut into (*caseation necrosis*). If the process heals, lime salts are deposited in this cheesy material, while a firm wall of scar tissue is deposited about the tubercle. Post-mortem examinations reveal such calcified or walled-off tubercles in a large proportion of adults, many of whom have never known that they had suffered from a tuberculous infection. These healed tubercles are found most frequently in the lymph glands about the bronchi. The frequent occurrence of these evidences of an old tuberculous infection explains why such a large proportion of adults give positive tuberculin reactions.

Diagnosis of Tuberculosis. The bacteriologist may aid in the diagnosis of tuberculosis by demonstrating the presence of tubercle bacilli in sputum, or pus from abscesses, or other materials from the body of the patient. Tubercle bacilli are not discharged from the body except in cases of active tuberculosis, i.e., there is no evidence that tubercle bacillus carriers occur. Therefore the finding of tubercle bacilli is proof of the existence of active tuberculosis.

In the early stages of the disease the bacteria are not discharged. It is only after the tubercles begin to break down that the bacteria appear in the sputum or other material. Failure to find tubercle bacilli does not mean that tuberculosis is absent, but their demonstration is positive evidence of presence of the disease. At first the organisms appear in sputum only in small numbers, and as the sputum always contains a number of other bacteria (saprophytes and parasites from the mouth), it is often a difficult matter to detect the tubercle bacilli. Three procedures are used — animal inoculation, cultures, and microscopic examination of the sputum.

Microscopic Examination of the Sputum. One may often find the bacteria by looking at smears of sputum stained by the Ziehl-Neelsen method (described on page 97). Since other acidfast bacteria do not occur in sputum, the finding of acidfast rods is conclusive evidence of the existence of active tuberculosis. It is obvious that on a single slide one may examine only a very small quantity of sputum, and that to examine thoroughly a large sample would be too tedious and time-consuming to be practical. Therefore it is desirable in some cases to concentrate the tubercle bacilli from a large volume of sputum in a small volume of liquid. This is done by first treating the sputum with *antiformin,* an alkaline solution of sodium hypochlorite. This digests the mucus and thus reduces the viscosity of the sputum. The thin liquid may now be whirled in a centrifuge, and the tubercle bacilli are thrown to the bottom of the tube. A smear made from the sediment may show abundant tubercle bacilli, when direct smears of the sputum showed few or none.

Cultivation. *M. tuberculosis* grows very slowly on artificial media, and when one tries to cultivate it directly from sputum, it is found that other bacteria in the sputum grow so much more rapidly that the tubercle bacilli are crowded out. One may, however, take advantage of the fact that the tubercle bacilli are more resistant to the disinfectant action of acids and alkalies than are other bacteria. It has been found that if sputum is treated with a rather strong acid solution (3% H_2SO_4), then neutralized with an alkali, that other bacteria will be killed, and pure cultures may be readily obtained. The sputum so treated is inoculated on glycerine potato, or on a special glycerinated egg medium. A small amount of crystal violet may be added to these media, to further help in inhibiting the growth of other bacteria. No visible growth appears until after two or three weeks' incubation.

Animal Inoculation. The guinea pig is so very susceptible to tuberculosis that the inoculation of even a very small number of bacilli will give rise to a progressive, fatal infection. The inoculation is made into the thigh, just beneath the skin. If tubercle bacilli were present in the inoculated sputum, after three to four weeks there will be noticeable an enlargement of the lymph glands in the fold between the thigh and abdomen. If these lymph nodes are removed, they will show tubercles forming in the interior of the gland, and smears of these tubercles will show acidfast bacilli. This is the most reliable method for diagnosing tuberculosis.

Tuberculin Reaction. The tuberculin reaction may also be used as an aid in diagnosing tuberculosis. In man this reaction is not of great value, since it is positive in such a large proportion of people who have had tuberculosis, but in whom the disease is arrested. A positive reaction is therefore not of much significance, but a *negative* reaction is of value in excluding tuberculosis. The tuberculin test is an important means of detecting tuberculous cattle in dairy herds. The tuberculin reaction has been described on pages 297–298.

Johne's Disease of Cattle. Johne's disease affects cattle, and less frequently sheep. It is caused by an acidfast rod called *Mycobacterium paratuberculosis*. This disease affects the small intestine, which is greatly thickened, but not ulcerated. The bacteria are present in large numbers in the diseased tissue.

M. paratuberculosis is a short, thick rod with rounded ends, strongly acidfast. It is cultivated with difficulty only on special media. It may be grown on coagulated egg medium to which has been added tuberculin, or other extracts of acidfast bacteria, or the dead bacteria themselves. The timothy hay bacillus, *M. phlei*, is usually used to provide the special nutrients required.

Leprosy. Leprosy is a chronic infectious disease caused by acidfast bacteria. The disease occurs in greatest extent in Oriental countries, Japan, India, and Malaysia, but in isolated foci in other parts of the world. There are two types of the disease, a *nodular* form involving mainly the skin, and an *anaesthetic* type in which the bacteria grow in the nerves.

The leprosy bacilli (*Mycobacterium leprae*) are found in enormous numbers within the cells of the nodules. They are slender, slightly curved rods, often granular, occurring in dense bundles of parallel cells. They stain and decolorize a little more readily than tubercle bacilli.

Although a number of different types of acidfast or diphtheroid bacteria have been cultivated from lesions of leprosy, it is probable that all of these are saprophytic forms, and unless some very recent claims are substantiated, it is probable that the true leprosy bacilli have never been grown in artificial cultures. It is not possible to transmit the disease to lower animals.

Rat leprosy is a disease occurring spontaneously in wild rats. It resembles human leprosy in the formation of nodules, which, however, occur in lymph glands or the muscles. Within the cells of the nodules acidfast bacilli occur. These also have not been cultivated.

Saprophytic Acidfast Bacilli. A variety of saprophytic acidfast bacteria have been isolated from various sources. Some of these resemble the tubercle bacilli very closely.

Mycobacterium smegmatis occurs in the smegma, material that accumulates in the folds of mucous membrane of the external genital organs. It is important in that it may be confused with tubercle bacilli in examining urine for the diagnosis of tuberculosis of the kidneys. It is not so strongly acidfast as the tubercle bacillus.

M. phlei is often called the "timothy hay bacillus," because it was isolated from that grass. It is a slender rod, rather resembling the tubercle bacillus, but grows luxuriantly in a few days on artificial media, producing a heavy, dry, wrinkled growth of buff to orange color.

M. stercoris, the "mist bacillus," was isolated from cow manure. *M. butyricum* has been found repeatedly in butter. Acidfast bacteria occur in the ear wax of man and animals, but have not been precisely described.

Acidfast Bacteria in the Soil. A variety of Mycobacteria have recently been isolated from soil. They may be cultivated by taking advantage of a peculiarity of their nutrition. They can utilize such hydrocarbons as paraffin, benzene, or petroleum. They utilize inorganic sources of nitrogen. By inoculating soil into agar plates containing no organic matter, and placing these under a bell jar containing a vessel of benzene or gasoline, the soil Mycobacteria will grow. A number of species have been isolated. It is not certain that all of these are acidfast.

Corynebacterium. The best known species of this genus is the organism of diphtheria. Other species are usually referred to as *diphtheroid* bacteria. While a great variety of species have been observed, for the most part they have been inadequately studied, and the saprophytic species are but little known.

The genus is characterized by the peculiar morphology of the cells. This is readily recognized under the microscope, once it has been learned, but a little difficult to describe. The cells are *Gram positive* and *non-motile*. They vary in form from plump ovals to slender rods. The peculiar "whipping" post-fission movements give rise to characteristic arrangements of cells, often in V or L formation, sometimes in parallel rows (the *palisade* arrangement). The cells are sometimes swollen at one or both ends. Such *clubbed* cells give rise to the scientific name of the genus. Occasionally the cells are *branched*, and the occurrence of such branched cells was for a long time unknown save in the diphtheroid group. It was for this reason that the genus was first considered related to the Actinomycetes, and placed with the "higher" bacteria. However, such branched forms have since been found in nearly all genera of rod-shaped bacteria, and have lost their original significance. The cells are often quite varied in form and size in a single preparation, and this *pleomorphism* is one of the distinguishing characters of the group. The cells show a great tendency to irregularity in staining, due in part to the development of vacuoles, producing *barring;* in part to the accumulation of volutin, appearing as *metachromatic granules.*

All the morphologic characters which have been italicized in the preceding paragraph serve to define the genus, but in a given species several of these characters may be lacking. With a few exceptions (Kurthia, Bacteroides), any Gram positive rod without spores which is not acidfast must be a Corynebacterium or a Lactobacillus. The Lactobacilli may resemble the Corynebacteria very closely, particularly in forming metachromatic granules. They tend to grow in chains rather than in the palisade arrangement. They tend to be microaerophilic, thermophilic, and very active in fermentation; while the Corynebacteria are mostly aerobic, grow at body temperature or less, and are not active biochemically. But the Lactobacilli show sufficient resemblance to the Corynebacteria to warrant a belief in their relationship.

There is also some evidence of a relationship between Corynebacteria and Streptococci. A number of organisms have been described which have appeared like Streptococci in one phase of their observation, and like Corynebacteria in another, and some of the pleomorphists, particularly Mellon, have assumed that these organisms go through a complicated cycle of development, in which coccoid and bacillary forms alternate. As was noted in the section on Lactobacilli, one can trace a fairly continuous transition between Streptococci and Lactobacilli. It would thus seem that these three genera might be considered as part of a natural group.

But the Corynebacteria also show strong affinities with the Mycobacteria. Aside from acidfastness they are very much alike in morphology. Old laboratory strains of Mycobacteria which have lost their acidfastness may hardly be distinguished from certain saprophytic Corynebacteria. Some of the latter produce wrinkled growths of a buff to orange color very similar to cultures of tubercle bacilli. In short, one may find every transition between Corynebacteria and Mycobacteria.

Corynebacteria a Key Group. The genus *Proactinomyces*, to be described shortly, contains organisms which show close similarities to both the Corynebacteria and the Mycobacteria. A culture of *Proactinomyces bovis* which has undergone fragmentation into rod-shaped segments can hardly be distinguished from a diphtheroid bacillus; and a culture of the acidfast *Proactinomyces asteroides*, similarly fragmented, appears precisely like tubercle bacilli.

It will thus be seen that the various similarities and relationships of the Corynebacteria serve to tie together a large series of microorganisms in one taxonomic group which includes all of the Actino-mycetales, and the Streptobacteriaceae of the Eubacteriales. *All of these organisms are Gram positive,* and include practically all of the Gram positive bacteria save the Micrococcaceae and the spore-forming Bacillaceae. There have been found some rare transitional forms between the Micrococcaceae and the Actinomycetales, but the relationships of the Bacillaceae are quite unknown.

The complex interrelationships of the Corynebacteria may be in-dicated by the following diagram:

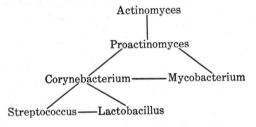

Diphtheria. Diphtheria is an acute infectious disease of the throat accompanied by a severe toxaemia. The disease is usually contracted from healthy carriers. The symptoms are due solely to the exotoxin of the diphtheria bacilli. This toxin gives rise to an antitoxic im-munity. Recognition of these facts has provided means for combating the disease. By the detection and isolation of carriers, by early diag-nosis of cases and their treatment with antitoxin, and finally by pre-ventive vaccination of children with detoxified toxin, the incidence of the disease has been reduced, and the mortality has been greatly decreased.

Diagnosis of Diphtheria. The growth of diphtheria bacilli in the throat gives rise to a characteristic reaction. Fibrin is exuded from the tissues and forms a rather adherent white coagulum on the surface of the mucous membrane. This "false membrane" is characteristic of the disease, and contains the diphtheria bacilli. However, such a false membrane may at times appear in other infections, and if possible the diagnosis should be established earlier than the time of appearance of a typical membrane. It should, therefore, be a rule to look for diph-theria bacilli in every case of acute sore throat, especially in children.

While the bacteria may often be found in direct smears from the throat, they are frequently so few in number that they may be easily overlooked. Since the organism grows rapidly in cultures it is best to seek for the bacilli in slides made from such cultures. For this purpose, a special medium called Loeffler's blood serum (see p. 226) is used. Upon this medium the diphtheria bacilli will grow more rapidly than most of the bacteria of the throat. A sterile cotton swab is rubbed over the surface of the tonsils, or the mucous membrane of the nose, and then over the surface of the coagulated blood serum. This will serve as an enrichment culture. After a short incubation period (12 hours or less) the diphtheria bacilli, if present, will have multiplied to such an extent that they may be readily found on microscopic examination. This is, of course, not a pure culture. Other species of bacteria are also present, especially various cocci from the throat, but the diphtheria germs are increased proportionally more than the others, and therefore are easily found.

Corynebacterium diphtheriae shows in general the morphologic characters of the genus. The cells are usually somewhat more slender than other Corynebacteria which may be present in the throat, and they usually exhibit more pronounced metachromatic granules. A number of different special stains are used for detecting diphtheria bacilli in throat cultures. All are based upon the intense affinities of the granules for basic dyes. Loeffler's methylene blue is most widely used. This is a weakly alkaline aqueous solution of methylene blue. The granules appear dark blue, the remainder of the cell a lighter blue.

The mere finding of such bacteria showing the morphologic characters of the diphtheria bacillus is sufficient evidence to warrant considering the case one of diphtheria, and instituting serum treatment. But such a diagnosis is not definitive, for harmless diphtheroid bacteria may occur in the throat, which at times cannot be distinguished from true diphtheria bacilli by microscopic examination. There is but one reliable method for definitely identifying *Corynebacterium diphtheriae*, and that is to determine its toxin-forming power *by inoculating guinea pigs*. If a small portion of the culture is injected subcutaneously the animal will die within 24 to 48 hours, with characteristic lesions at the site of inoculation, and haemorrhage in the adrenal glands. To make assurance doubly sure, a second animal may be inoculated in the same manner, and simultaneously given a preventive injection of diphtheria antitoxin; this guinea pig should survive.

In a suspected case of diphtheria one should not wait for animal inoculation to confirm the microscopic diagnosis, but should administer antitoxin to the patient at once. But in detecting diphtheria carriers, cultures showing morphologic diphtheria bacilli should be checked by animal inoculation. Otherwise individuals harboring harmless diphtheroid bacilli will be needlessly quarantined.

Diphtheria Antitoxin. To prepare diphtheria antitoxin one must first obtain the toxin. This is done by growing diphtheria bacilli in broth. Not all strains are equally potent in secreting toxin. A particular strain called the "Park No. 8" is universally used for this purpose. The bacteria are inoculated into large shallow flasks of veal broth. The medium must be slightly alkaline, and must contain the right kind of peptone. Some brands of the latter substance will not serve as a medium for toxin production. The bacteria are strictly aerobic and grow mainly at the surface of the medium.

The toxin is a very unstable compound, losing its toxicity rapidly on standing. It is inoculated into horses, at first in very minute doses. But the injections are repeated at intervals of a few days, and the dosage is gradually increased. The immunization is continued for six months or longer, and the final injections will contain several thousands of the initial dose.

When preliminary tests show that a satisfactory antitoxin has formed, the horse is bled aseptically from the jugular vein, removing as much blood as can be obtained without endangering the now valuable animal. The blood is allowed to clot, and the serum is separated. The antitoxin is contained in that fraction of the serum proteins called the "pseudoglobulins" which are precipitated by half-saturation with ammonium sulphate, but which dissolve again in saturated sodium chloride solution. The purified antitoxin is finally dissolved in physiologic salt solution and filtered through Berkefeld filters to make it sterile.

Before it may be issued to physicians this antitoxin must be standardized, i.e., its potency must be measured. Since the toxin is very unstable, the more permanent antitoxin is used as a standard. Such a standard antitoxin is preserved in Washington and issued to manufacturers of serum for comparison with their own products. It is kept at a low temperature, in a dried form, sealed in dark glass. A certain amount of this antitoxin is given an arbitrary value, called 1 unit. To one unit of standard antitoxin, freshly prepared toxin is added in increasing quantities until an amount is found which will completely neutralize the antitoxin and still have enough toxin in excess to kill a guinea pig of 250 gms. weight in just 4 days. This is called the L+ dose of toxin. This quantity of fresh toxin is then taken as a standard against which the new antitoxin is titrated. An amount of antitoxin which, when mixed with the L+ dose of toxin, will delay the death of a 250 gm. guinea pig for 4 days, will contain one unit. In this way the dosage of the serum may be accurately determined. From 3000 to 20,000 units or more must be inoculated to treat diphtheria successfully.

Preventive Vaccination. A large proportion of adults are immune to diphtheria. This may be demonstrated by the *Schick test*, by inoculating into the skin a minute quantity of diphtheria toxin. In people who are immune, the toxin is neutralized, and no reaction occurs. But in susceptible individuals a characteristic area of local inflammation occurs at the site of injection. By the widespread use of this test it has been found that the largest proportion of susceptibles occurs in the pre-school age (4 to 5 years).

This observation led to the proposal to *actively* immunize school children against diphtheria. The pure toxin is too dangerous to use in immunizing doses. At first a neutralized mixture of toxin and antitoxin (popularly known as "T.A.T.") was used. At present this has been replaced by *toxoid*, i.e., toxin which has been detoxified by treatment with dilute formaldehyde. It has been found that such treatment does not destroy the immunizing power of the toxin.

Other Corynebacteria. There are no other species of Corynebacteria of any great practical importance. Bacteriologists have been interested in diphtheroid bacteria merely to distinguish them from true diphtheria bacilli. A few other species have been sufficiently studied to warrant their recognition, but the genus needs extensive systematic work.

Diphtheroid bacilli occur frequently as contaminations from the air, but their true habitat is not known. They do not appear to be abundant in soil or water. Most of the forms which have been described have been derived from the human or animal body.

Corynebacterium pseudodiphthericum, commonly called "Hoffman's bacillus," occurs occasionally as a parasite of the human throat. It is harmless, but important in that it may be confused with true diphtheria bacilli. The cells show a greater tendency to solid staining, and do not so regularly show metachromatic granules.

Corynebacterium xerosis occurs frequently in smears from the conjunctiva (the mucous membrane of the eye) and may also appear occasionally in throat cultures. The cells are usually shorter than the preceding.

These two species may be distinguished from true diphtheria bacilli by sugar fermentations. Where carbohydrates are fermented, acid is formed without gas.

	Glucose	Sucrose
C. pseudodiphthericum	−	−
C. diphtheriae	+	−
C. xerosis	+	+

Corynebacterium acnes is probably the cause of pimples. It is usually much smaller than the preceding species. The cells are often clubbed, but usually solid in their staining. It is semianaerobic. This organism occurs together with *Staphylococcus albus* in pimples. Vaccines prepared from the Corynebacterium usually give pronounced improvement in chronic cases of acne.

Proactinomyces. Members of this genus, until recently included in the genus *Actinomyces*, are characterized by an initial growth in the form of fine branched mycelium, which is followed by fragmentation into bacillus-like fragments. The latter may continue to grow as such, multiplying by transverse fission. Although saprophytic species from soil are known, pathogenic species have received the most attention. The diseases known as *actinomycoses* are all caused by members of this genus. There are several of these diseases. The most important are those caused by the anaerobic non-acidfast *Proactinomyces bovis*, the aerobic non-acidfast *Proactinomyces madurae*, and the aerobic acidfast *Proactinomyces asteroides*.

Proactinomyces bovis. When the term "actinomycosis" without further qualification is used, it means a disease of man or cattle caused by the anaerobic *Proactinomyces bovis*. It is by far the most common type of infection in this group.

The common form of actinomycosis occurs frequently in cattle, much more rarely in man. The disease is a chronic infection resulting in the formation of abscesses which break through the skin, discharging pus for long periods. About the abscesses dense walls of scar tissue are formed. The organism appears in the pus as little masses or colonies, often visible to the naked eye. These are called *sulphur granules* because of their yellow color. The granules are composed of a central mass of tangled branched filaments, and a peripheral zone of *clubs*, i.e., club-shaped refractile bodies attached to the free tips of the filaments. The substance forming these clubs is probably something similar to the material which forms capsules about certain bacteria. It may serve to protect the parasite from the action of body fluids. The appearance of the granules is sufficiently striking and characteristic to diagnose the disease.

These sulphur granules must be distinguished from similar granules of *Actinobacillus ligniersi* and also from granules of Staphylococci, such as occur in botryomycosis. This may be done by crushing the granules between two slides, and staining the smears so obtained. In the case of *actinomycosis* the slide will show long Gram positive branched filaments; in the case of *actinobacillosis*, slender Gram negative rods will be found; while in *botryomycosis* the typical Gram positive Staphylococci will appear.

Actinomycosis in both man and cattle occurs most frequently in the tissues about the mouth — in the jaw bone in cattle, in the soft tissues of the face and neck in man. The disease is also sometimes primary in the lungs or abdomen. There is no evidence that the disease is transmitted from cattle to man, or indeed that it spreads from one animal to another.

Until recently it was believed that this disease is contracted from bits of vegetable matter (awns of grains, for instance) being forced into the tissues in chewing, or being inhaled or swallowed. It was thought that the organism lived as a saprophyte on such vegetable matter. There is still much circumstantial evidence to indicate that this is the case, but it has been demonstrated that microörganisms having the morphology and cultural characters of *Proactinomyces bovis* may be found in the crypts of the tonsils and in other parts of the mouth of healthy individuals, and it has been suggested that the disease is caused by these normal mouth parasites getting into the tissues and multiplying there.

Proactinomyces bovis is cultivated with some difficulty. When first isolated it is a fairly strict anaerobe, but after a few transfers it will grow in the presence of air. It will not grow readily on most media. Deep veal infusion agar shake cultures and veal infusion broth appear to be favorable media. In broth cultures it grows as characteristic pearly white granules at the bottom of the tube.

Microscopic examination of colonies in agar shows that these grow as radiating branched filaments. But after a time the filaments break up into oidia. These become separated by post-fission movements similar to those of the Corynebacteria. The granules in veal broth appear to be composed entirely of fragments resembling diphtheroid bacilli. After continued cultivation they may cease forming mycelium and grow entirely like a diphtheroid bacillus. This organism clearly presents a transition between Corynebacteria and the Actinomycetes.

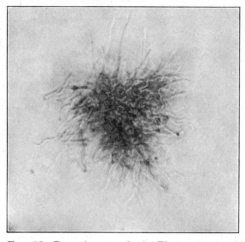

FIG. 93. *Proactinomyces bovis.* Photomicrograph of a deep colony in agar.

Proactinomyces madurae. "Madura foot" is a disease of tropical countries, a chronic infection of the feet leading to great deformity, with abscesses involving the bones and discharging pus through a number of openings. The disease has a multiple etiology, i.e., a number of different parasites may cause the same kind of tissue changes. Many cases are caused by higher fungi. But a considerable proportion are due to *Proactinomyces madurae.* The organism appears in the pus as granules looking much like those of ordinary actinomycosis. But the organism grows readily in the presence of air, forming a buff-colored, wrinkled growth of mealy consistency. Young cultures show branched mycelium, but later this breaks up into fragments resembling diphtheroid bacilli.

Proactinomyces asteroides. There are several *acidfast* species of the genus which are pathogenic to man and animals — dogs, cattle, and goats. Some have also been found in soil. The species most commonly encountered is *Proactinomyces asteroides.* In man this species causes a primary disease of the lungs which resembles tuberculosis very closely in symptoms and in the character of the lesions. The organism appears in the sputum in the form of long, slender, acidfast branched filaments. These filaments undergo frag-

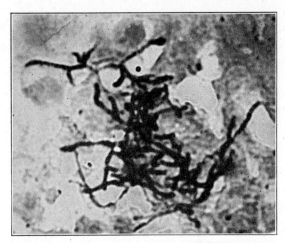

FIG. 94.   *Proactinomyces bovis.*   Photomicrograph of a smear of pus from a case of actinomycosis, showing the branched filaments.

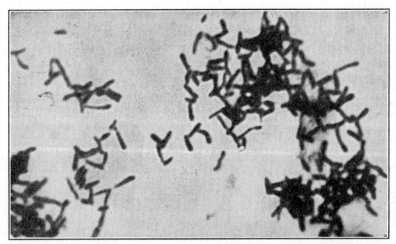

FIG. 95.   *Proactinomyces bovis.*   Photomicrograph of a smear from a broth culture, showing fragmentation of the mycelium into bacillus-like oidia.

mentation, and the slender fragments show some resemblance to tubercle bacilli.   *Proactinomyces asteroides* may be readily cultivated. It is aerobic.   On solid media a characteristic wrinkled orange-colored growth appears.   On liquid media a wrinkled pellicle is formed.

The naked eye appearance of the culture is very similar to that of the human type tubercle bacilli. Occasionally aerial mycelium with conidia develops, and then the surface of the growth appears white and powdery.

The acidfast species of Proactinomyces, unlike *Pr. bovis* and *Pr. madurae*, are very pathogenic to laboratory animals, especially guinea pigs. In such animals they produce an infection which is more acute than tuberculosis, generally killing the animals within a week. But with small doses one obtains a more chronic type of disease. It has been claimed that inoculated guinea pigs give a positive tuberculin test, but the author has been unable to confirm this.

Actinomycetaceae. The Actinomycetaceae comprise the more definitely filamentous species. There are three genera: *Actinomyces*, with much-branched filaments, and *Leptotrichia* and *Erysipelothrix* with unbranched filaments. The systematic relations of the latter two genera are quite obscure; they are placed in this family only for convenience.

The genus *Actinomyces* is a large one, with many species, most of which are saprophytic in the soil. It is doubtful that any members of this genus are pathogenic. They are such common contaminants that they occur frequently in cultures of pus or sputum, and have been repeatedly described as causes of diseases without sufficient evidence. The genus is differentiated from *Proactinomyces* by the fact that the mycelium does not readily fragment into rod-like segments; instead, *aerial* filaments project into the air and form conidia. This gives a characteristic powdery appearance to the surface of the colonies. In liquid media, species of *Actinomyces* usually form a fluffy growth at the bottom of the tube, species of *Proactinomyces* form a wrinkled pellicle.

Soil Actinomycetes. Actinomycetes form a large proportion of the soil flora. They are abundant in all soils which are rich in organic matter and which are not too acid in reaction. As a group they prefer an alkaline or neutral medium, and are sharply inhibited if the reaction goes far on the acid side. They are important in the decomposition of organic matter.

Soil Actinomycetes grow slowly and are not readily isolated on common culture media, because they are overgrown by colonies of the more rapidly developing bacteria. But they can multiply with extraordinarily minute amounts of nutrient. Special very weak culture media are used for their isolation. One such medium is Conn's, containing glycerine and sodium asparaginate; another is Czapek's, containing sucrose and sodium nitrate. On these media the colonies of the soil Actinomycetes develop, looking much like miniature mold colonies, the surface powdery or velvety because of the conidia. Often brilliant pigments are formed, either in the colony or in the medium beneath.

Soil Actinomycetes may be divided into two groups by a characteristic reaction in protein media caused by some species. This is a darkening of the medium due to the production of a pigment from the amino-acid, tyrosine, through the action of the enzyme, *tyrosinase*. This is the same reaction which occurs when potatoes darken (after peeling) on exposure to the air. The reaction may be readily observed in peptone solution or gelatine, or on potato. The medium gradually darkens, to become finally almost black. This reaction is produced by a number of different species, which are designated as the *chromogenus* group of Actinomycetes.

Other characters by which species of Actinomycetes may be identified are the formation of more specific pigments — yellow, orange, red, blue — which may develop on any medium; the branching of the spore-bearing stalks, and the spiral twisting of the chains of conidia, and such cultural characters as the liquefaction of gelatine, digestion of coagulated egg, hydrolysis of starch, etc.

Many species of soil Actinomycetes give rise to a very characteristic odor, which is best described as musty or moldy. The odor of freshly turned loam, or of a damp cellar or potato bin, is due to the Actinomycetes.

Activities of Soil Actinomycetes. The Actinomycetes are heterotrophic organisms, important in the decomposition of organic matter. They are aerobic, not fermentative, and utilize the simple sugars without producing acid. Many species can hydrolyze starch, and some can digest cellulose. Mostly they are putrefactive, digesting various proteins readily. These are decomposed rapidly to amino acids, but with many species the nitrogen finally appears as ammonia. They may reduce nitrates to nitrites.

Actinomycetes are not abundant in acid soils, and the imperfect decomposition of organic matter which occurs in bogs may be due in part to the failure of Actinomycetes to develop in such acid environments.

Leptotrichia. This genus is not to be confused with *Leptothrix*, a filamentous iron bacterium of the Chlamydobacteriales.

Leptotrichia buccalis is a normal parasite of the human mouth. It may be found frequently in the white scum which develops on the teeth, and also on the surface of the tongue. It occurs as long, slender, unbranched filaments, Gram positive and non-motile. It has been cultivated, but with great difficulty. It is anaerobic.

Leptotrichia buccalis has been considered a possible factor in causing decay of the teeth. It is claimed that the organism may grow as adherent colonies, forming "plaques" on the surface of the enamel, and that under these adherent plaques other bacteria may grow and dissolve the lime salts by acid production.

Erysipelothrix. Swine erysipelas is a disease common in Europe, but considered rare in America. It occurs in an acute form, a septicaemia with a rash occurring in patches resembling erysipelas in man; and a more chronic form, in which the microbes grow as vegetations on the heart valves.

Erysipelothrix rhusiopathiae occurs in the blood, and in vegetations on the heart valves, as long, slender, unbranched Gram positive filaments. It grows scantily on artificial media under semianaerobic conditions as small Gram positive rods, often in chains.

Erysipelothrix murisepticae is a similar organism causing an acute spontaneous disease in mice.

CHAPTER XXVII

THE MOLDS

The term "mold" is a common name having no taxonomic significance. It is applied to a variety of Fungi which grow as semi-microscopic organisms, and whose mycelium tends to form a loose meshwork rather than a dense tissue. Thus molds are distinguished from the large fleshy Fungi, the mushrooms, etc. Molds may belong to any of the classes of Fungi, but actually the great majority of species are either Phycomycetes or Fungi imperfecti.

Molds are heterotrophic organisms which must depend upon other creatures for their nutrition. A great many species are parasitic on plants, a few upon animals, but mostly they are saprophytic organisms occurring principally in soil. Thus they occur in the same sorts of habitats as the bacteria, and like the bacteria they are agents of disease and decay. Their spores are widely distributed and frequently get into cultures of bacteria, causing annoying contaminations. Whatever may be the field in which he is working, the bacteriologist is constantly forced to pay some attention to molds.

Biochemical Characters. While in general the nutrition of molds is the same as that of heterotrophic bacteria, there are some characteristic differences in the conditions of their growth. Molds as a group may tolerate *high acidities*, and it is possible to adjust the hydrogen ion concentration of media to a point which will suppress most species of bacteria, and permit a growth of most molds. Molds will also grow in media of high *osmotic pressure*, media which will usually suppress bacteria.

Molds are mostly strictly aerobic. A few will grow under semi-anaerobic conditions, but probably none can multiply to any extent in the complete absence of oxygen. This is correlated with their carbohydrate metabolism. While a few species may produce a feeble alcoholic fermentation, mostly they are not fermentative organisms. It is true that many species produce acid from sugars, but the acids formed are mainly oxalic, citric, or gluconic, rather than the lactic, acetic, or butyric acids produced by bacterial fermenta-

416

tions. These acids result from a partial oxidation of the sugar, not from fermentation in the sense of Pasteur, i.e., intramolecular respiration. Many molds may utilize organic acids as sources of carbon and energy, oxidizing them to CO_2 and water.

A knowledge of the above facts makes it possible to understand the relations of molds to the spoilage of foods. Molds may grow upon foods which are preserved from bacterial decomposition by their acidity — pickles, fruit juices, sour milk, etc. — or by their high osmotic pressure — jellies, fruits in syrup, salted meats, etc. But they will not grow upon such foods if the latter are completely sealed from the air. Molds growing upon acid foodstuffs may oxidize the acid and so reduce the hydrogen ion concentration to a point where bacteria can grow.

Molds are active in the hydrolysis of the complex polysaccharides, starch and cellulose, and also in the decomposition of proteins. They may grow with surprisingly small amounts of moisture, upon such substrates as cloth, paper, and leather, if only these are somewhat damp. They may frequently appear in the laboratory in solutions of reagents in which it would seem impossible for growth to occur.

Molds in the Soil. As with the bacteria, the soil is to be looked upon as the great natural habitat of the molds. They are abundant in almost all sorts of soils, but relatively more so in soils rich in organic matter, and in acid soils.

Soil molds are active, in the same manner as soil Actinomycetes, in decomposing starch and cellulose and proteins. But where the Actinomycetes are inhibited by the acidity of the soil, here the molds are most active. In well-aerated soils the *decomposition of cellulose* is due more to the activities of molds than of bacteria. With many molds, the *liberation of ammonia* from proteins is more active than with ammonifying bacteria.

Molds perform another function in maintaining soil fertility. They may themselves utilize the products of decomposed organic matter to build up mycelium. When soluble nitrogenous matter is present in excess of the needs of green plants, it may be absorbed by molds and stored up in the mycelium, and thus prevented from leaching out. Upon the death and disintegration of the mold such material is again available to green plants. And so the soil Fungi perform a stabilizing function, tending to maintain the food supply at a constant level.

Molds in Foodstuffs. In the household molds may be a cause of spoilage of almost any sort of foodstuff if it is held for a sufficient length of time and is sufficiently damp. Molds may grow even at ice-box temperatures. Starchy foods, bread, and fruits are most commonly affected.

Commercial packers of foodstuffs are also greatly troubled by molds. Meat packers, dairymen, bakers, and dealers in fruits all have mold problems to solve. Molds are prone to develop upon cured and smoked meats — sausages, hams, and bacon. Here the humidity of the storage rooms appears to be an important factor. Butter may become contaminated from many sources, but mainly from the cream itself. The growth of mold produces patches of discoloration in the butter. Bread will support the growth of a variety of molds. Species of Mucor and Rhizopus are commonly called the "bread molds" because they occur so frequently upon bread in the household. But another mold, *Monilia sitophila*, which can grow with extreme rapidity, is sometimes a cause of serious outbreaks in bakeries. It is salmon pink in color. Fruits are largely protected from mold growth by their outer coverings, and if unbruised fruit is packed with care, it is not nearly so liable to mold spoilage as injured fruit. Certain species of molds occur characteristically upon certain fruits, as *Penicillium digitatum* upon oranges.

Industrial Uses of Molds. While man is largely concerned with combating the destructive activities of molds, he has learned to make use of their chemical activities in some instances.

The characteristic flavor of *Roquefort* cheese is due to a mold, *Penicillium roqueforti*, which produces caproic acid from the butter fat. Similarly the flavor of *Camembert* cheese is produced by the proteolytic enzymes of *Penicillium camemberti* acting upon the casein. *Gallic acid*, used in making ink, is obtained from the action of *Aspergillus niger* upon the tannic acid in oak galls. *Soya sauce*, the dark brown salty sauce served in Chinese restaurants, is the result of a fermentation of soy beans by the mold *Aspergillus oryzae*.

The above processes were all developed empirically long ago. Science has shown how to control them, but did not originate them. More recently, however, industrial applications of molds have resulted from scientific investigations. The enzymes, particularly diastase, of *Aspergillus oryzae*, are extracted and marketed under the name "Taka-diastase." This substance is used as a remedy for certain types of indigestion, and also commercially in the production of sugar from starch. From a study of the biochemistry of *Aspergillus niger*, it was possible to develop a commercial process for producing *citric acid* from cane sugar. And it is proposed to utilize certain species of Penicillium in the same manner to make *gluconic acid*.

Fungous Diseases. The fungous diseases of plants are legion. Fungi are the most important agents of plant disease. Their study properly belongs in the domain of plant pathology, and will not be considered here.

Fungous diseases of man and animals are rarer than bacterial diseases, but none the less important and interesting. Fungous diseases are called *mycoses*, often with a prefix signifying the part affected, as *dermatomycosis*, a fungous infection of the skin. Fungous diseases may be well discussed in two groups, those due to the ringworm Fungi, or *dermatophytes*, and those due to other Fungi.

Ringworms. The dermatophytes are probably essentially parasitic Fungi, living upon the skin and its append-

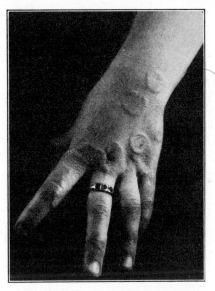

Fig. 96. Lesions of Ringworm, a Fungous Disease.

ages, and not occurring to any great extent free in nature. They produce very superficial skin diseases in man and the higher animals. These diseases are contagious, from man to man or from animals to man. The lesions vary from a mere scaling of the epidermis or loss of hair to the formation of abscesses in the skin, but the disease never invades the deeper tissues of the body, and while very annoying is not serious.

The name "ringworm" is derived from a peculiarity of the disease. The inflammatory reaction tends to spread from the initial focus of infection, and as it does so, to heal in the center, so that there results a gradually increasing circle of reddened, scaling skin. Sometimes the disease may again become active in the center, starting a new ring, so that several concentric circles of inflammation result.

The disease may occur upon the scalp or upon the smooth skin. Upon the scalp the infection is made manifest by a loss of hair in patches, the hairs breaking off at or near the skin surface. This is due to the growth of the Fungus within the shaft of the hair. The skin itself may be but little involved, showing merely a little redness or scaling of the epidermis. But in some cases minute abscesses form at the roots of the hairs. Such cases are more commonly caused by dermatophytes of animal origin.

In recent times dermatophyte infections of the smooth skin have been more prevalent. Such an infection occurring upon the feet, and popularly known as "athlete's foot," is said to be the most common infectious disease in America. It has spread widely during the years since the War, particularly among college students and athletes. The disease is probably spread mainly by the wet floors of shower baths. The disease is characterized by the formation of blisters between the toes and on the soles, which burst and leave raw patches that are slow in healing. The disease is chronic, prone to recur, and very resistant to treatment. Dermatophyte infections of the smooth skin are also prone to occur on other parts of the body, especially those parts where the skin is moist, as the inner surfaces of the thighs, the folds of the buttocks, or the armpits.

A number of species of ringworm Fungi are known. Most of them belong in the genus *Trichophyton*. The infections may be diagnosed by the microscopic examination of diseased hairs or scales of epidermis. These are mounted in a strong solution of sodium hydroxide which softens the hair or scale, and also makes it transparent. The Fungi are resistant to the solvent action of the alkali and will appear as filaments of septate mycelium and as spores.

Other Mycoses. The remaining fungous diseases differ from those we have just considered. Although they often involve the skin, the infection tends to go deeper, to spread, and if untreated, to involve the inner viscera and eventually endanger life. These serious fungous diseases are, however, much rarer. They are, for the most part, not contagious. In many cases there is every indication that, like actinomycosis, the disease has resulted from contact with vegetable matter upon which the Fungus has grown. The infections

are always chronic, but progressive, in character, simulating tuberculosis very closely. Most commonly they are primary in the
subcutaneous tissues, resulting from a wound in many cases. But
primary infections of the lungs occur, and such cases develop much
like cases of pulmonary tuberculosis. In rare cases the disease may
begin in the abdominal cavity. A number of these diseases are
known, but we shall take space merely to describe briefly a few of
the more important ones.

Aspergillosis. This disease is quite common in birds. The
causative organism, *Aspergillus fumigatus*, is a very common green
mold. The disease occurs both in wild birds and domestic ones.
In all cases it probably results from feeding upon moldy grain. The
disease usually involves primarily the air sacs, the surfaces of which
are found to be coated with grey-green mold upon autopsy.

Aspergillosis also occurs in man, but is very rare indeed. In most
cases the infection is secondary to pulmonary tuberculosis, the mold
growing upon cavities in the lung much as in the air sacs of birds.

Sporotrichosis. Sporotrichosis is a disease affecting man and
horses. It is usually a wound infection, in the majority of cases
involving an arm. From the initial lesion on the hand there occurs
a characteristic extension up the arm by way of the lymph vessels,
with the production of a series of inflammatory nodules extending
to the shoulder.

The Fungus, *Sporotrichum schenckii-beurmanni*, occurs in infected
tissues as a *unicellular* organism. It is generally found within the
pus cells as a cigar-shaped body resembling a large bacillus. Sometimes it appears as a rounded, yeast-like cell. But in artificial media
it grows out as a mold, forming large numbers of pear-shaped conidia
attached to all parts of the mycelium.

Blastomycosis. This name is applied, in America, to a disease
peculiar to this continent. It is usually described as a yeast infection, but this is erroneous, for the parasite grows in cultures as a
mold.

The disease is usually primary in the skin, especially of the
hand or face, but occasionally begins in the lungs. The lesions
on the skin are elevated, ulcerated patches resembling in some
cases a tuberculous ulcer, in others a cancer. The disease in the
lungs runs a course similar to a rapidly developing pulmonary tuberculosis.

In the pus the parasite, *Zymonema dermatitidis*, appears as a one-celled, yeast-like body, reproducing by budding. The cells have a thick wall. But in cultures these cells grow out to form a white mold composed of septate mycelium, which, however, usually fails to form spores.

Coccidioidal Granuloma.   This is another disease peculiar to America.   Most of the cases have occurred in the San Joaquin Valley

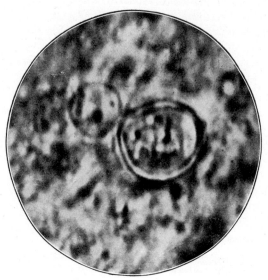

Fig. 97.   *Zymonema dermatitidis.*   Photomicrograph of a preparation of pus mounted in sodium hydroxide, showing the parasite of blastomycosis. In pus it appears as a budding yeast, but in cultures it grows as a mycelial mold.

in California. The reason for this restricted geographic distribution is not known, but the organism is thought to be parasitic upon plants restricted to these areas.

The disease resembles blastomycosis very closely, but has a much higher mortality. In artificial cultures the causative Fungus, *Coccidioides immitis*, also appears as a white mold without spores, but in the infected tissues it differs from the organism of blastomycosis. It is a round, thick-walled cell, but never reproduces by budding. Instead it produces a large number of smaller cells by division of the protoplasm. These smaller cells are then liberated by a rupture of the cell wall.

Methods for Studying Molds. In general one studies molds in the same manner as bacteria, isolating them in pure culture, examining them under the microscope, and observing their reactions on various types of media.

For isolating molds special media are desirable. Most species may be readily separated from bacteria by the use of a strongly acid medium. Such a medium may be prepared by adding dextrose and tartaric acid to ordinary nutrient agar. A solution of 50% dextrose and 5% tartaric acid is sterilized separately. This solution is added to melted agar in the proportion of 1 part to 10 parts of agar, just before use. Some Fungi will not tolerate strong acidities, and for their isolation a medium rich in sugar but only slightly acid in reaction is desirable. *Sabouraud's agar* originally contained 4% of crude maltose and 1% peptone. Glucose is generally substituted for maltose in this formula. Sabouraud's agar is especially useful in isolating and identifying pathogenic Fungi, particularly the dermatophytes.

The microscopic examination of molds is best carried out with Petri plate cultures and with slide cultures. A Petri dish may be placed on the stage of the microscope, and the characters of the spore heads observed with the low power objective. Slide cultures may be prepared in several ways. Perhaps the simplest procedure is to inoculate the mold into a tube of melted agar, a little of which is then spread in a thin film on sterilized microscope slides, which may then be incubated in Petri dishes containing moistened blotting paper to prevent drying of the agar. After growth has occurred one may place a coverglass over the mold and examine it unstained, or the slide may be dried, fixed, and stained. In this manner one may study the mold with high-power lenses, with the various parts in their natural arrangement.

Identifying Molds. A preliminary examination should give some idea as to the general type of mold. If the colony is *woolly* in texture, the coarse mycelium being loosely meshed, and is grey or smoky brown in color, the mold probably belongs to the Phycomycetes. If the colony is *velvety* in appearance, the finer mycelium being more closely interwoven, and particularly if the spores are brightly colored — green, yellowish, etc. — the mold probably belongs to the Fungi imperfecti. Observation with the low-power lens will show whether the spores are contained within sporangia (Phycomycetes) or are free conidia (Fungi imperfecti).

Species of Molds. The species of molds are legion. Any detailed account of them would take us too far afield. The student is referred

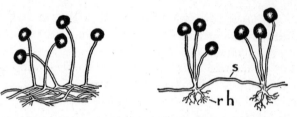

FIG. 98. Mucor and Rhizopus. *Left*, the formation of sporangiophores in Mucor; *right*, in Rhizopus. *s* is a stolon, or runner; *rh* is a rhizoid, or holdfast.

to works dealing more specifically with this phase of microbiology for more information. We can take space to discuss but briefly four groups of molds which are so common that they will include the majority of cultures encountered in bacteriological work. These are

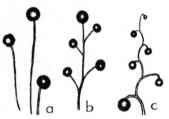

FIG. 99. Types of Sporangiophores of Mucors. *a* is Monomucor; *b* is Racemomucor; *c* is Cymomucor.

the genera *Mucor* and *Rhizopus* of the Phycomycetes; and *Aspergillus* and *Penicillium* of the Fungi imperfecti.

Mucor and Rhizopus. Molds belonging to the Phycomycetes are characterized by the formation of non-septate mycelium (there are exceptions) and by forming nonsexual spores in sporangia. Mucor and Rhizopus are representatives of a subclass of the Phycomycetes called Zygomycetes. These form sexual zygospores by the conjugation of filaments which are not differentiated into sexes by size or other distinguishing characters.

Rhizopus may be distinguished from *Mucor* by the formation of "runners," or *stolons*, by members of the former genus. These runners are filaments of mycelium which, extending into the air, come down again to the substrate and form a "holdfast" or *rhizoid* by which the filament becomes anchored. This holdfast consists of a tuft of fine branches of mycelium. From the holdfast another runner arises to extend the growth, and also several sporangiophores, or stalks which will bear sporangia. In Mucor no stolons or rhizoids are formed; the sporangiophores arise from any part of the plant. Because of the runners, Rhizopus cultures extend rapidly over the surface of the agar and fill the Petri dish with aerial mycelium. Runners with holdfasts may be seen on the under side of the dish. The aerial mycelium of Mucor is also abundant but does not fill the dish so rapidly, and does not adhere to the lid.

Mucor. A number of species of Mucor are known. These are divided, according to the character of their sporangiophores, into three groups: *Monomucors* bear sporangia on unbranched stalks; *Racemomucors* show racemose branching of the sporangiophore; *Cymomucors* exhibit cymose branching (see Fig. 99). Species of Mucor are further identified by the size and shape of the *columella*, the expanded tip of the sporangiophore which extends into the sporangium; and by the size and shape of the spores themselves.

M. mucedo is a Monomucor readily cultivated from horse manure. It is often considered as a type of the genus. *M. racemosus* is the most common Racemomucor. It is abundant in soil. This species produces a slight alcoholic fermentation of sugar, but *M. rouxianus* is more active in this respect, and has been used in the production of alcohol directly from starch, since it forms diastase as well as zymase. *M. corymbifer* is pathogenic to man and animals, but is very rare.

Rhizopus. The most common and best known species is *Rhizopus nigricans*, which is ubiquitous. It is a particularly annoying contaminant because it spreads so rapidly over plate cultures by means of its runners.

It is a common cause of spoilage of foodstuffs, especially bread and other starchy foods. It gives rise to a soft rot of stored potatoes, and produces a spoilage of strawberries called "leak."

Aspergillus and Penicillium. The common green molds that appear so frequently upon fruits, jellies, and similar foodstuffs are almost always species of Aspergillus and Penicillium. Species producing spores of other colors are common. These are molds which reproduce by free spores, or conidia, and are distinguished by the characters of their spore-bearing stalks, or *conidiophores*.

In *Aspergillus* the conidiophore arises from a specialized cell in the vegetative mycelium called a *foot-cell*. This is somewhat larger than the filament of mycelium, and when the spores are ripe, it is often empty, i.e., contains no protoplasm. The stalk itself is *non-septate*, without cross-walls. It ends in a swollen portion, the *vesicle*. From this expanded tip the conidia are formed in chains from the

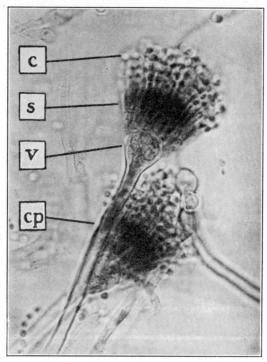

Fig. 100. Spore Heads of an Aspergillus. *cp*, conid-iophore; *v*, vesicle; *s*, sterigmata; *c*, chains of conidia.

ends of a large number of little stalks, the *sterigmata*. In some cases the sterigmata are branched, the spores arising from the branches, or *secondary sterigmata*.

In *Penicillium* there is no foot-cell, the stalk arising from an undifferentiated cell of the mycelium. The conidiophore is *septate*, and ends in a whorl of short branches, the *metulae*, each of which bears a whorl of little stalks, or *sterigmata*, which form the conidia. Because of the branching at the tip of the conidiophore, the spore heads of Penicillium appear looser than those of Aspergillus. They are brush-like in appearance, as compared with the compact globular or cylindrical spore heads of Aspergillus.

Aspergillus. Aspergillus species are widespread. They occur in soil, and also upon straw and grain and vegetable matter. Aspergillus species in general grow best at rather high temperatures, 35–40° C.

A. niger is probably the most common species. It is widespread, and is one of the most troublesome contaminating molds in the laboratory. It forms very large striking *black* globular spore heads. The sterigmata are branched. The conidia are round, black, and prickly on the surface. *A. glaucus* is a common *green* species which may produce ascospores as well as conidia. The ascospores are formed in globular bodies called *perithecia*, which are bright yellow in color. *A. fumigatus* is similar to *A. glaucus* but has smaller spores, and does not form perithecia. It grows on grain and causes aspergillosis in birds. *A. flavus* forms conidia which are yellowish-green in color, and very large.

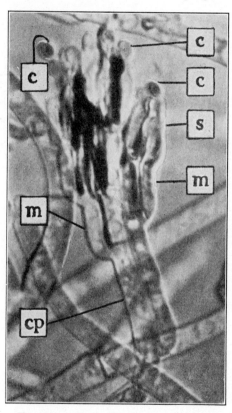

Fig. 101.   Spore Head of a Penicillium. *cp,* conidiophore;   *m,* metula;   *s,* sterigma; *c,* conidia.

A. oryzae, the species used in making Soya sauce, is very similar to *A. flavus*. *A. wentii* produces conidia which are at first white, but gradually turn brown.

Penicillium. Species of Penicillium are perhaps more common than those of Aspergillus, but grow more slowly, and have a lower optimum temperature (25–30° C.).   They are therefore not so troublesome as bacteriological contaminants.   They are very abundant in soil.

Many species form green conidia.   The name *Penicillium glaucum* has been applied so indiscriminately to a variety of green Penicillia that it has lost all specific meaning, and should not be used.   *P. expansum* is one of the most common of the green Penicillia, causing a rot of apples.   It may readily be obtained from bruised apples by keeping these in a moist chamber.   The green spores will appear in little tufts of conidiophores (*coremia*) on the brown rotted surface. *P. roqueforti* is also a green species forming the mold spots in Roquefort cheese.   *P. camemberti* forms a woolly white aerial mycelium, with conidia which are of a light grey-green color.   On lemons and oranges one may often find *P. italicum* (blue-green) and *P. digitatum* (olive-green).

CHAPTER XXVIII

YEASTS AND YEAST-LIKE FUNGI

The term "yeast," like "mold," is a common name having no taxonomic significance. Yeasts are Fungi which do not form mycelium. Mostly they reproduce by budding. Often the buds do not immediately separate from the parent cell, but themselves give rise to new cells by budding while still attached. In this manner characteristic clusters of cells are formed, and if the yeast cells are elongated, there may be formed long chains of cylindrical cells resembling mycelium. One finds all sorts of transitions between this *pseudomycelium* and true mycelium.

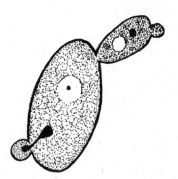

And so it is often difficult to decide whether a given organism is a yeast or a mold. In some cases the organism may completely change from one type to another with a change of environment. We have seen in the preceding chapter that the parasites of sporotrichosis, blastomycosis, and coccidioidal granuloma are unicellular in the infected tissues, but grow as filamentous molds in cultures.

Fig. 102. Diagram of a Budding Yeast Cell. The nucleus is seen dividing to form a nucleus for the lower bud.

We have considered these parasites with the molds because, to the author, they seem more mold-like than yeast-like. But some authorities would classify the organism of blastomycosis with the yeasts, because in the body it is so like an ordinary budding yeast.

Yeast-like Fungi. But in addition to these dimorphic types we find certain other Fungi which may be both unicellular and mycelial in the same environment. Growing first as filamentous molds, they give rise to one-celled growth forms either by a fragmentation of the mycelium into its component cells, or by budding off rounded cells

429

from the sides of the filaments. In the first case, the free cells broken off (called "oidia") are cylindrical or oval in form, and produce new cells by fission. A common mold which forms free cells in this manner is the milk mold, *Geotrichum lactis*. If free cells are formed by budding, they are usually globular in form, and produce new free cells by budding. The free cells are thus precisely like common yeasts. Fungi of this type are classified in another genus of the Fungi imperfecti, *Monilia*. *Monilia albicans* is a well-known species.

Geotrichum lactis. If a bottle of milk is allowed to stand exposed to the air, it will first sour, due to the lactic acid fermentation brought about by *Streptococcus lactis*, by bacteria of the colon-aerogenes type, and by Lactobacilli. But after a time there will appear on the surface a white coating of mold. This mold is *Geotrichum lactis*. It grows upon the lactic acid which has been formed by the fermentative bacteria, oxidizing it, and so reduces the acidity of the milk. When the milk has returned to a neutral reaction, putrefactive bacteria may grow, digesting the casein, and so completing the decomposition of the milk.

Geotrichum lactis is a common Fungus, occurring wherever lactic acid is available. It is a white mold forming conidia in single chains at the tips of aerial hyphae. If one makes a slide culture, the spores are seen to form at first radiating filaments of mycelium. After a time these begin to undergo fragmentation, beginning at the center of the colony and proceeding toward the periphery. The cells are separated by rather sudden snapping movements similar to the post-fission movements of diphtheria bacilli. These give the oidia a characteristic zigzag arrangement before they become completely separated.

Monilia albicans. This is an organism very close to the yeasts. It is a parasite of mucous membranes, and produces a mild, localized infection of the mucous membrane of the mouth, called *thrush*. The disease occurs most frequently in undernourished nursing infants, and appears as whitish patches on the mucous membrane of the cheek or gums, sometimes in the throat. These patches are composed of branched filaments of true mycelium, with budding yeast cells tangled in the meshes.

It was at first thought that the disease is caused by two organisms, a mold and a yeast, growing together. But such is not the case. The two are but different growth forms of the same organism. The thrush parasite may be readily isolated in pure culture by plating on the dextrose tartaric acid agar described in the preceding chapter. The surface colonies are composed entirely of round budding yeasts. But from the deep colonies, after a time, filaments of branched mycelium radiate into the agar. From these filaments yeast cells are budded off in little clusters. Mycelium is produced abundantly in gelatine stab cultures where the filaments may be seen radiating

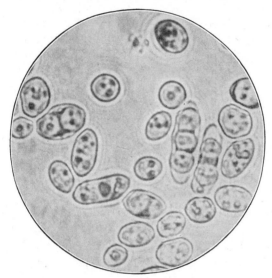

Fig. 103. Yeast Spores. *Saccharomyces ellipsoideus*, photomicrograph of unstained cells.

at right angles to the line of the stab; but only yeast cells are formed at the surface. It is obvious that aerobic conditions favor the unicellular form, anaerobic conditions the mycelial form.

Species of Monilia are also found causing other types of disease — chronic bronchitis and skin lesions. They occur in the mouth and intestines in a tropical disease, sprue, but probably play a secondary rôle in its causation.

Classification of Yeasts. Yeasts proper, i.e., those forms which do not produce true mycelium, are divided into three classes — yeasts with *endogenous* spores, yeasts with *exogenous* spores, and yeasts with *no* spores.

Yeasts with Endogenous Spores. The industrial yeasts, and a considerable number of "wild" yeasts form spores within the cells. These appear somewhat like the spores of bacteria, but usually more than one spore is formed within a cell — the number varies from one to eight, four occurring in most species. Yeast spores are not nearly so heat-resistant as bacterial spores.

Endogenous spores may result from a conjugation of two cells, or may be formed by a single cell without conjugation. In the latter cases spores are said to be formed by *parthenogenesis*. Since they result from a sexual process in some cases, and are eight in number in some cases, they are looked upon as ascospores, and yeasts with endogenous spores are classed as a family, *Saccharomycetaceae*, in the Ascomycetes.

There are a number of genera in this family. Some of the more important are *Zygosaccharomyces* (spores formed by conjugation), *Schizosaccharomyces* (multiplying by fission instead of budding), *Willia* (with hat-shaped spores), and *Saccharomyces* (round spores, parthenogenetic). The latter genus contains the important industrial yeasts.

Industrial Yeasts. The brewing and baking yeast, *Saccharomyces cerevisiae*, is not known in the "wild" state. It has been handed down in crude cultures since antiquity. It forms large globular cells which, in some strains, tend to remain attached in characteristic clusters. Generally four spores are formed.

Brewing yeasts are divided into *top* yeasts, which form gas so abundantly that it tends to carry the yeasts to the top of the fermenting liquid; and *bottom* yeasts, which do not produce so vigorous a fermentation, and tend to form a sediment. Ordinary baking yeast is a top brewing yeast.

Compressed yeast is manufactured by inoculating a pure culture of yeast into a sterilized nutrient solution composed of molasses and ammonium sulphate. Air is bubbled through the culture to obtain maximum growth. The yeast is collected by centrifuging, and the sediment so obtained is mixed with starch and pressed into cakes. This may be run as a continuous process.

Saccharomyces ellipsoideus is the scientific name of the wine yeast, which can tolerate larger amounts of alcohol than *S. cerevisiae*. This yeast occurs naturally on grapes. The cells are elliptical in form. There is evidence that *Saccharomyces cerevisiae* is a cultivated variety of *Saccharomyces ellipsoideus*.

Yeasts with Exogenous Spores. These are rare and but little known.

Sporobolomyces is the generic name of a group of yeasts which give rise to spores on little stalks, or sterigmata, formed by those cells on the surface of the colony. When mature these spores are forcibly discharged into the air. If one grows this yeast in an inverted Petri plate culture, the pattern of the colony will be faintly reproduced on the lid by the discharged spores. The shape of the spores, and the mode of their formation and discharge, is identical with that of the basidiospores of the mushrooms, and therefore these yeasts are classified with the Basidiomycetes.

Certain peculiar yeasts are found in the nectar of flowers, which are given the name *Nectaromyces*. They also form exogenous spores on little stalks, but their systematic relations are obscure.

Yeasts without Spores. The great majority of the "wild" yeasts which occur frequently in bacteriological investigations do not form spores of any sort. They are classified in the Fungi imperfecti. The majority of species fall in the genus Torulopsis, composed of round or oval budding yeasts without spores. Another genus, Mycoderma, includes species with elongated, sausage-shaped cells that form a scum or pellicle on liquid media.

Yeasts without spores are widespread, and are generally undesirable organisms in industrial fermentations, since they use up the sugar without yielding much, if any, alcohol. Some species produce pigments. A species which forms a coral red or pink color is a common contaminating organism in the laboratory.

Methods for Studying Yeasts. Like the molds, yeasts can generally tolerate high acidities and osmotic pressures. They are best isolated in pure culture by plating on dextrose tartaric acid agar. The morphologic characters are more easily determined from wet preparations than from fixed smears, since the cells shrink and become distorted on drying.

In identifying yeasts, important characters to note are the size and form (globular, elliptical, sausage-shaped) of the cells; the formation of spores; if ascospores are formed, whether by conjugation or by parthenogenesis; the mode of multiplication, by budding or fission. Of cultural characters, the most significant are the ability to ferment sugars (glucose, fructose, galactose, sucrose, maltose, and lactose) and the character of the growth in liquids (pellicle or turbidity).

Most yeasts with endogenous spores do not form these spores readily in artificial cultures. A stimulus appears to be necessary for spore formation. This stimulus may be supplied by a sudden change from favorable conditions to adverse conditions. The usual procedure is to transfer actively growing cells from a glucose agar culture to blocks of plaster moistened with a dilute peptone solution. These plaster blocks must be incubated at a temperature proper for the species, which is not always the optimum temperature for growth.

Activities of Yeasts. Yeasts occur in nature wherever there is sugar. Their scientific name (Saccharomyces = "sugar fungi") is most appropriate. While they occur occasionally in small numbers in soil, there is no evidence that this is their natural habitat. The nectar of flowers, the sweet sap exuding from trees, and above all, fruits, are the habitats where yeasts may be found. They are also present in the alimentary tracts of many insects, and are probably distributed and winter over in this manner. Yeasts occur as symbiotic organisms within the body cavity of certain insects.

Yeasts may be a cause of spoilage of food products, especially fruits. They are like the molds in this respect, but differ in that many yeasts may grow in semianaerobic conditions, and thus spoil canned fruits or bottled fruit juices. Recently there have been discovered a series of *osmophilic* yeasts which can tolerate enormous osmotic pressures, and which have produced fermentations of honey and syrups.

Aside from their use as leavening agents, and in the production of alcohol and alcoholic beverages, yeasts have been used in the commercial production of *glycerine* from sugar. It has been proposed to use yeasts as food, and yeast has been widely used as a source of *vitamins*. Yeast has also been widely recommended as a therapeutic agent for various conditions, without much justification. It has also been proposed to use certain species of yeasts as a source of fats.

Some yeasts are pathogenic. *Debaromyces neoformans* is a yeast which produces a disease of the nervous system called "torula meningitis," and may also cause subcutaneous abscesses, or abscesses in internal organs. It is quite rare.

CHAPTER XXIX

THE PATHOGENIC PROTOZOA

A great variety of Protozoa are parasitic upon man and animals, and some of these are pathogenic. Protozoan diseases of man are not so important as bacterial diseases in the temperate zones, but in tropical countries they are frequent and important infectious diseases. The study of pathogenic Protozoa constitutes a highly specialized branch of microbiology, with a technique quite different from that of bacteriology. We shall present merely a brief sketch of the subject. For more information the student must consult one of the special texts dealing with this phase of microbiology.

Geographic Distribution. Most of the bacterial diseases have a world-wide distribution. It is true that plague and cholera are practically restricted to Asiatic countries, but this is due to quarantine and hygienic measures. Leprosy, for some unknown reason, is restricted to certain localities. But in general bacterial diseases do not favor one locality more than another. Protozoan diseases, on the other hand, show a definitely limited geographic distribution. Protozoan diseases are rare in northern countries, and when observed are usually found in individuals who have returned from the tropics. Not only are they essentially tropical diseases, but the diseases and parasites found in one part of the world are often different from those occurring elsewhere. South America has protozoan diseases which are unknown in Africa, and conversely.

This restricted geographic distribution is due in large part to the fact that many of these diseases are caused by protozoan parasites which must of necessity spend part of their life cycle in the body of some insect which serves as an alternative host. The rôle of the anopheline mosquito in malaria and that of the tsetse fly in African sleeping sickness are well-known examples. The geographic distribution of the disease is determined by the distribution of the insect host. But this does not explain the limited distribution of all the protozoan diseases. Amoebic dysentery is an intestinal disease transmitted in the same manner as typhoid fever or cholera, yet the disease is mainly tropical in its distribution, although in recent years increasing numbers of cases have appeared in the United States.

Modes of Transmission. Protozoan diseases may be transmitted by biting insects. In such cases the parasites live within the blood stream, and produce a generalized disease. Blood containing the Protozoa is withdrawn by a blood-sucking insect in whose body the parasites undergo a cyclic development. Upon biting another person the insect introduces the microörganisms into the blood, and so starts a new infection. In other cases the protozoan parasites invade the body by way of the digestive tract, and the disease is contracted by the ingestion of infected food or water. In these diseases the organisms are discharged in the feces in an encysted or resting form, in which form they may remain dormant in soil or water for considerable periods of time. In the intestinal diseases the infection tends to remain localized in the digestive tract or the liver. A third type of protozoan disease may be transmitted by direct contact, producing at first a localized infection, with later a generalized disease.

Recurrent Character of Protozoan Diseases. Bacterial diseases for the most part tend to run a "self-limited" course. One may predict for the patient with lobar pneumonia that within ten days he will have recovered or succumbed, and the same is true of typhoid fever if one extends the time to five or six weeks. In other cases the duration of the disease is not so precise. Chronic bacterial infections may run a very indefinite course. But, although the patient may have his ups and downs, such infections are usually progressive. It is rare for signs of the disease to disappear and to reappear again without reinfection.

But protozoan diseases show a pronounced tendency to recurrence. In malaria the disease recurs in regularly spaced exacerbations, most commonly every other day. This is due to a regular developmental cycle of the parasite in the blood. But it is common with most of the protozoan diseases to note a marked improvement or even complete disappearance of the symptoms, to be followed by a recurrence of the disease at a later period without reinfection. The Protozoa may disappear from the blood or intestines, but remain latent in some part of the body. In some cases the disease may progress in distinct stages — a primary phase with local lesions, a period of quiescence, and then secondary and tertiary stages with general distribution. Such recurrent infections are also very characteristic of the diseases caused by the protozoa-like Spirochaetes.

Immunity in Protozoan Diseases. Although various antibodies — agglutinins, precipitins, lysins, and complement-fixing substances — have been demonstrated in protozoan diseases, for the most part these appear in small quantities or irregularly, or they have been incompletely investigated, so that practical diagnostic serum tests have not been developed.

But some interesting facts have been learned regarding protective immunity, which throw some light upon the recurrent character of protozoan infections. When certain species of Trypanosoma are inoculated into guinea pigs, the infection proceeds until the parasites are quite numerous in the blood; then there occurs a "crisis" and the organisms suddenly disappear from the blood stream. Now, following a period of apparent freedom from infection, a "relapse" develops, and the Trypanosomes may once more be found in blood smears.

It can be shown that the crisis is due to the development of lysins in the blood, antibodies which completely destroy most but not quite all of the parasites. The relapse is due to the further growth of those few resistant Trypanosomes which were not destroyed by the lysins. If such "relapse" strains are tested with serum obtained from the animal at the time of the crisis, they are found to be refractory, i.e., they do not undergo lysis. They are said to be *"serum fast."*

In addition to this lysin, Taliaferro has shown that in trypanosome infections there may occur another type of antibody which does not destroy, nor apparently injure, the Protozoa, but which inhibits their reproduction. The Protozoa persist in the blood as active adult forms, but do not divide.

Methods for Studying Protozoa. The pathogenic Protozoa cannot be studied by the same techniques that are used for bacteria. Many of them cannot be grown in artificial culture media. Those which are cultivable are grown only with difficulty on special media. For the diagnosis of protozoan diseases the bacteriologist must depend upon morphologic examinations.

Protozoan parasites may be searched for either in wet preparations, in which one looks for the characteristic locomotion, or in stained slides, where details of morphology are seen to better advantage. Thus one may look for the dysentery amoebae in wet preparations of fecal material from the patient, seeking cells which show the characteristic movement by means of pseudopodia. But the positive identification of the amoeba often requires study of the structure of the nucleus, which may be observed only in slides carefully fixed and stained with iron haematoxyline.

The presence of blood-inhabiting Trypanosomes may often be detected by examining a drop of blood under a coverglass. The almost colorless Protozoa are hard to see, but their active lashing movements knock the red blood cells about, and so reveal their presence. But in general the blood Protozoa are best observed in thin smears of the blood, stained by a special method. The stains most useful are those which are used in staining blood cells — certain mixtures of eosin and methylene blue, which are called "polychrome" stains. Of these, Wright's stain and Giemsa's stain are most widely used. The protoplasm of the Protozoa takes on a characteristic pale blue tint, while their nuclei stain an equally characteristic red color.

Types of Pathogenic Protozoa. There are species representative of three of the classes of Protozoa included in the list of those pathogenic to man, possibly also one member of a fourth class. The organism of amoebic dysentery belongs to the Sarcodina. The species of Trypanosoma and Leishmania are representatives of the Mastigophora. The malarial parasites are Sporozoa. *Balantidium coli*, of the Ciliata, is an intestinal parasite which may be pathogenic.

Parasitic Amoebae. The parasitic amoebae differ from free-living forms, like *Amoeba proteus*, in several respects. Perhaps the most important distinguishing character is the lack of a contractile vacuole in the parasitic forms. The parasitic amoebae are included in a genus, *Entamoeba*. There are three species of Entamoeba which occur in man. *E. gingivalis* is a normal parasite of the mouth. It may usually be found in the crevices between the gums and teeth. *E. coli* is a harmless intestinal parasite. *E. histolytica* is the cause of amoebic dysentery.

Amoebic Dysentery. Amoebic dysentery is to be distinguished from bacillary dysentery caused by species of Shigella, which has been considered in a preceding chapter. Amoebic dysentery runs a more chronic course. It is an infection of the large intestine, characterized by gradually increasing diarrhoea with blood and mucus in the stools. Remissions and relapses are common. At times the parasites are carried to the liver by way of the portal blood vessels and give rise to abscesses in that organ.

Entamoeba histolytica. The parasite is found in the stools as active forms and as encysted forms. The active forms are larger (20–30 μ), and are usually elongated or irregular in form because of their pseudopodia. When actively moving usually but one pseudopod is apparent, extending in the direction of the motion. Within the amoeba will be found red blood cells which have been phagocyted by the parasite. The tissues of the intestine or liver about the amoeba are destroyed and digested. The specific name *histolytica* means "tissue-dissolving." In the encysted form the cells are smaller and round, and show a thick cell wall. The protoplasm of the cyst contains no ingested food particles. The mature cyst contains four nuclei, whereas the active forms have but one.

In diagnosing amoebic dysentery by examination of the feces, *E. histolytica* must be differentiated from *E. coli,* which is a harmless intestinal parasite. *E. coli* does not ingest blood cells. Its nucleus is larger, and shows structural differences from that of *E. histolytica.* The mature cyst contains eight nuclei.

Transmission of Amoebic Dysentery. The active forms of *E. histolytica* cannot remain alive outside the body. During the acute stages of the disease the amoebae are discharged as active forms, not as cysts. Therefore active cases of the disease are not important in its spread. But during convalescence or remissions the parasites are encysted, and the cysts may remain dormant outside the body to develop into active forms whenever swallowed by a susceptible individual. Cysts may be discharged from the bowel for a long time after symptoms disappear. Moreover, where amoebic dysentery is endemic there may be found many individuals who have not had the disease, yet harbor the parasite in their intestines and discharge cysts in their feces. Such *carriers* are the most important agents in spreading the disease. It has been estimated that about 10% of the population are carriers of *Entamoeba histolytica.*

Amoebic dysentery was formerly treated empirically with the drug ipecac. Later it was found that the alkaloid from this drug, emetine, was more efficient, and that it has a specific inhibitory effect upon the parasite. An organic iodine compound, chiniofon, is now used for the same purpose, since it is less toxic than emetine.

The Trypanosomes.   The blood-inhabiting flagellates of the genus Trypanosoma are the most important parasitic representatives of the Mastigophora.   A large number of species are known, infecting various species of animals.   *Tr. lewisi* is found frequently in wild rats.   Although it multiplies extensively in the blood, it does not produce disease.   The organism is transmitted by fleas.   Several species are a source of serious losses in horses in different parts of the world.   *Surra* is the name of a disease of horses in India, caused by

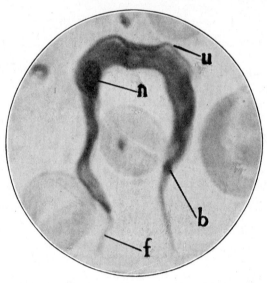

Fig. 104.   *Trypanosoma lewisi.*   Photomicrograph of a smear of blood from a rat.   *b,* blepharoplast; *u,* undulating membrane; *n,* nucleus; *f,* flagellum.

Tr. evansi.   *Nagana,* affecting various domestic animals in Africa, is due to *Tr. brucei;* this disease is transmitted by the tsetse fly, *Glossina morsitans.*   The *mal de caderas* is a disease of horses in South America, caused by *Tr. equinum.*

Dourine, a disease of horses in Algeria, is remarkable in its resemblance to human syphilis.   Whereas the other trypanosome diseases are transmitted by biting insects of one sort or another, *dourine* is transmitted by contact — by sexual intercourse.   It produces first a local lesion of the genital organs, then a stage of generalized eruption with lesions on the skin, and finally a third stage with ulcers, paralysis, and loss of weight. The causative organism is called *Tr. equiperdum.*

African Sleeping Sickness. This disease is a trypanosome infection of man which has taken a tremendous toll of life in Africa. Like *nagana*, it is spread by the bite of a species of tsetse fly, *Glossina palpalis.* Two species of Trypanosoma, *Tr. gambiense* and *Tr. rhodesiense* may cause sleeping sickness in man.

The disease runs a rather chronic course, beginning with fever, weakness, and emaciation, and terminating in a comatose condition. It is treated with a variety of organic compounds of arsenic and antimony, with favorable results in early cases. But relapses are of frequent occurrence.

Morphology of the Trypanosomes. The Trypanosomes appear in the blood as elongated fish-like bodies. From the anterior end of the cell there extends a single flagellum, but this flagellum arises from the *blepharoplast* at the posterior end. From this origin it extends forward as the free border of the *undulating membrane.* In most species the body is long and slender. Motility is very active. A single nucleus is present in the anterior portion of the cell.

The various species are distinguished by (often slight) peculiarities of morphology, as the size and position of the nucleus, and the relative slenderness of the cell body; also by the species of animals which may be successfully inoculated.

Life Cycles. Within the blood the Trypanosomes multiply by simple longitudinal fission, a division of the nucleus preceding cell division. Biting insects may transmit the parasites directly from one animal or person to another, if the bitings occur a short interval apart. But in the case of the tsetse flies, the insects after a short time become non-infectious, to again become capable of infecting after a period of some days. It is assumed that during this period the Trypanosomes undergo some sort of cyclic development within the body of the insect. But although the organisms are seen to undergo various morphologic changes within the body of the insect, there is no evidence of sexual reproduction in the cycle.

Leishmania Infection: Kala-azar. Kala-azar is a serious disease in Asia and northern Africa, with fever, anemia, and marked enlargement of the spleen as important symptoms. Within the cells of the spleen, and also in other parts of the body, there occur enormous numbers of small oval bodies within which may be distinguished two structures, a nucleus and another rod-shaped body, the *kinetoplast*. These bodies, the parasites of the disease, were long known as Leishman-Donovan bodies. But it was found possible to cultivate them in a special blood medium, and in this medium they develop into

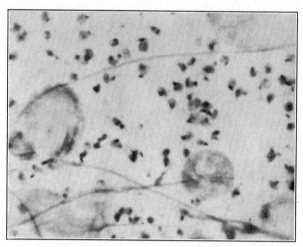

Fig. 105. *Leishmania donovani*. Photomicrograph of a smear of splenic pulp from a case of kala-azar.

elongated cells with a flagellum, somewhat resembling a Trypanosome without an undulating membrane. This parasite is now called *Leishmania donovani*.

Several other species of Leishmania pathogenic to man are known: *Leishmania tropica* causes a disease of the skin called tropical ulcer, or Delhi boil. *L. braziliensis* also infects the skin, especially involving the nose; the disease occurs in South America. *L. infantum* causes a disease similar to Kala-azar in children in Mediterranean countries.

Insect hosts are suspected to transmit these diseases, but are not known with certainty.

Sporozoa. The Sporozoa are obligate parasites, never free-living, with complex life cycles in which asexual reproduction alternates with a sexual phase. There are many species parasitic upon different animals, but the only ones important as a cause of disease in man are the parasites of malaria.

Malaria. Malaria is probably the most important of the diseases affecting mankind, occurring in tropical and semitropical countries throughout the world. It is said to cause over a million deaths a year in India alone.

The disease is characterized by recurrent attacks of chills and fever, with enlargement of the spleen in cases of some duration. There are three kinds of malaria, each caused by a different para-

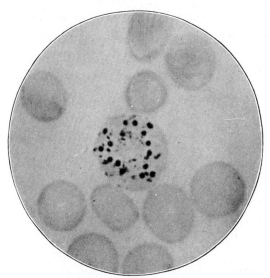

FIG. 106. *Plasmodium vivax.* Large blood cell in center of field contains a parasite in process of segmentation.

site: *tertian* fever, caused by *Plasmodium vivax; quartan* fever by *Plasmodium malariae;* and *aestivo-autumnal* fever by *Plasmodium falciparum.*

In tertian fever, chills with fever recur every 48 hours, the temperature being normal on the day intervening. In quartan fever the chills recur every 72 hours, while in the aestivo-autumnal form the fever is more irregular, but tends to recur daily. The chill and fever occur at the time of cell division of the parasites, and the interval is therefore determined by the time required for the developmental cycle in the blood. The various species of Plasmodium differ in structural details. Tertian fever is the most common form. We shall consider the life cycle of *Plasmodium vivax* as illustrative of the group.

Life Cycle of the Malaria Parasite. The asexual phase, *schizog-*

ony, occurs in the blood of the individual suffering from malaria; the sexual phase, *sporogony*, occurs in the body of the mosquito.

Schizogony. If a susceptible person is bitten by an anopheline mosquito infested with *Plasmodium vivax*, the parasites are introduced into the blood as *sporozoites*. A sporozoite is a long, slender

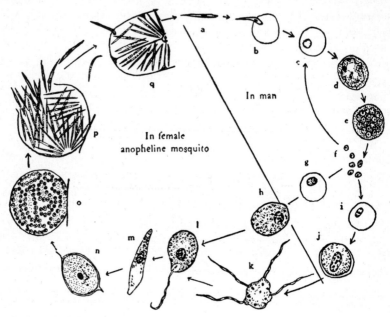

FIG. 107. Life Cycle of *Plasmodium vivax*. *a–c*, sporozoite entering red blood cell and developing into "signet ring" form; *d*, large trophozoite; *e*, segmentation; *f*, merozoites set free from red blood cell; *g*, *h*, macrogametocytes; *i*, *j*, microgametocytes; *k*, microgamete; *l*, conjugation; *m*, *n*, development of oökinete; *o*, oöcyst with developing sporozoites; *p*, sporozoites emerging from oöcyst; *q*, sporozoites entering salivary gland of mosquito. (After Kudo, *Handbook of Protozoölogy*, C. C. Thomas, Springfield, Ill.)

cell with a gliding motion. It burrows into the interior of a red blood cell. Here it undergoes a transformation, becoming rounded with a large vacuole that distends the cell, pushes the nucleus to one side, and gives the cell a characteristic "signet ring" form. Within the red blood cell the parasite now grows, increasing in size to eventually completely fill the blood cells. Such growing forms inside the red blood cells are called *trophozoites*.

Trophozoites may develop further in two different ways. Most of them undergo division, forming new small cells which will invade new red blood cells, and so continue the infection. But some develop into special cells capable of infesting the mosquito. Those trophozoites which are destined to division are called *schizonts*.

The division of the malarial parasite is multiple rather than binary, i.e., the cell divides into a number of smaller cells rather than merely two. It is *segmentation* rather than fission. When the schizont has reached a sufficient size, the nucleus divides into a number of daughter nuclei; then the cytoplasm divides, forming a number of smaller cells with one nucleus each. These small cells, the *merozoites*, now escape from the cell into the blood plasma. The paroxysms of chills and fever correspond with the liberation of merozoites from the red blood cells. It is probable that toxic material is set free in the blood at the same time. The newly liberated merozoites next proceed to invade the new blood cells, and so continue the process. It requires 48 hours for the development of the trophozoite from a merozoite until segmentation, in the case of *Pl. vivax.*

Sporogony. Those trophozoites which are destined to continue the cycle within the mosquito develop into gametocytes. The gametocytes do not go through the signet ring stage, as do the schizonts. There are two kinds, the *microgametocytes*, which develop into male cells, and the *macrogametocytes*, which develop into female cells. The macrogametocytes are the larger of the two, and also stain more deeply.

Cycle in the Mosquito. The gametocytes are unable to develop further in the human body. But if blood containing gametocytes is taken by an anopheline mosquito, the cyclic development is continued. The macrogametocyte undergoes nuclear changes, part of the chromatin being extruded, and so is converted to a *macrogamete*, corresponding to the ovum of a higher organism. The microgametocyte undergoes nuclear division, and gives off several long narrow whip-like processes, which break free. These are the *microgametes*, corresponding to the sperm cells of higher organisms. These changes occur in the digestive tract of the mosquito. The microgametes are actively motile, and swimming about, arrive at a macrogamete, with which they fuse.

The fertilized macrogamete is also motile, and is known as an *oökinete*. By a gliding motion it penetrates the stomach wall, and comes to rest in the outer muscular layer of that organ. Here it becomes rounded and enlarged, and is called an *oöcyst*. The nucleus of the fertilized oöcyst now divides, forming a number of smaller cells, the *sporoblasts*, which continue to divide, forming more and more cells. From these sporoblasts another type of cells, slender and pointed at the ends, is formed — the *sporozoite*. These are the end result of sporogony. They may be produced in thousands from the oöcysts. They are liberated into the body cavity of the mosquito, and are carried to all parts of its body, but are attracted especially to the salivary glands, to be injected with the saliva into the next victim of malaria.

The life cycle of the malarial parasite is recapitulated below in diagrammatic form. The stages printed in bold-face type occur in the mosquito, the others in the blood of man.

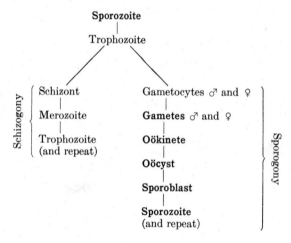

Transmission of Malaria. The malarial parasite exhibits a high degree of host specificity. Schizogony occurs only in the blood of man, sporogony only in certain species of mosquitoes belonging to the genus Anopheles. The disease may be artificially transferred from man to man by inoculation of blood. But, naturally, there is no way for one person to contract the disease from another save through the agency of the mosquitoes. The bearing of this fact upon the geographic distribution of the disease and upon modes of prevention is obvious.

CHAPTER XXX

THE SPIROCHAETALES

Although included as an order of bacteria, many authorities believe that the Spirochaetales are really more closely related to the Protozoa than to the Schizomycetes. They are characterized by very slender, *flexible* spiral cells. All are motile and Gram negative. Some species are saprophytic, living in water, but the majority are parasitic in animals and man.

There is but one family, the *Spirochaetaceae*, containing the following genera: *Cytophaga, Spirochaeta, Saprospira, Cristispira, Borrelia, Treponema*, and *Leptospira*. These genera can be distinguished only by a detailed consideration of their morphology.

Our knowledge of the Spirochaetes is very incomplete. Many of the species are very small, especially very narrow. They stain with difficulty, and faintly. Therefore it is not easy to study their morphology. A number of species have not been cultivated, and those which are cultivable grow slowly, and may be grown only on special media. In fact the study of the Spirochaetes requires a rather highly specialized technique. It is largely for this reason that only a few bacteriologists have concerned themselves with a detailed study of this group of microbes. Our knowledge of the Spirochaetes was greatly extended by a Japanese bacteriologist, Noguchi, who worked in America.

Spirochaetes and Spirilla. The Spirochaetes were first separated from the Spirilla because of the flexibility of their cells. The apparent absence of flagella, and the sinuous, snake-like motion by contraction of the protoplasm itself, are characters quite foreign to the bacteria proper, but are characteristic of some Protozoa. This similarity to Protozoa was strengthened by the discovery of the "crest" in the genus Cristispira, a structure superficially resembling the undulating membrane of Trypanosoma, and by the observation that some Spirochaetes multiply by longitudinal fission (as with the Trypanosomes) rather than by transverse division, which is characteristic of the bacteria.

447

More recent observations have, however, thrown some doubt on the validity of these differentiations. The crest of Cristispira is not a membrane, properly speaking, but results from the fusion of a number of fine, flagella-like filaments. The supposed longitudinal fission is claimed by some authors to be erroneous, the appearance being due to agglutination of cells which have already divided. While the Spirochaetes do not have flagella of the same sort as bacteria, many exhibit a fine filament at one or both ends of the cell which may be related to true flagella. The contractility of the protoplasm remains, however, undoubted.

Spirochaetes and Protozoa. The opinion that the Spirochaetes are related to the Protozoa can be more strongly supported by a consideration of their pathogenicity. Syphilis in man, caused by *Treponema pallidum*, is transmitted, like dourine in horses, by sexual contact; and, like dourine, occurs in three stages: a primary localized lesion, a secondary general eruption, and a tertiary stage. In the relapsing fevers, caused by species of *Borrelia*, the Spirochaetes are found in the blood like the Trypanosomes in sleeping sickness. The relapsing character of these diseases is due to a disappearance of the organism in crises, and recurrence following the growth of "serum fast" individuals which have survived the crises, very evidently due to some peculiar mechanism which governs the crises and recurrences in Trypanosome diseases. The Borrelias are transmitted by insects which are essential intermediate hosts. Within the bodies of these insects the organisms probably undergo some sort of cyclic development. Finally, the similarity to the Trypanosomes is strengthened by the fact that Spirochaete diseases may be successfully treated with the same sort of chemotherapy (arsenicals) that is used in the Trypanosome diseases.

Structure of the Spirochaetes. According to Noguchi, the finer structure of the Spirochaetes is best observed in dead, disintegrating cells. Such studies indicate that the cell is built up about a fine, central *axial filament* which is rigid but becomes plastic at the time of cell division. The axial filament extends beyond the cell at the ends as a finely tapered structure which was referred to previously as resembling the flagella of bacteria. But they do not move. The *protoplasm* surrounds the axial filament, and is, in turn, covered by the cell membrane, or *periplast*.

While rigid, the axial filament is elastic, or spring-like. By contraction of the protoplasm, the coils may be brought closer together, to spring apart again when the contraction ceases. By rhythmic contractions, the coils are alternately tightened and released, and this gives the cell a rotary motion, which, because of the spiral coiling, moves the cell forward or back according to the direction of rotation.

Life Cycles: Filterability. The relapsing fevers are transmitted by biting arthropods (ticks and lice). When blood containing the Spirochaetes is ingested by such vectors, the organisms almost completely disappear after a few days. Such insects remain infective for a long time, and have been found infective in some cases after the Spirochaetes have disappeared. These facts, considered with the well-known cyclic development of the malarial parasite in the mosquito, have led to the supposition that the organisms of relapsing fever undergo some sort of development in the louse or tick, which leads to a different morphologic type that cannot be recognized. Certain minute granules found within the bodies of the arthropod hosts are looked upon as reproductive bodies of the Spirochaetes.

One may often find granules within the protoplasm of various Spirochaetes, especially in cultures. Sometimes an entire cell is seen to break up into granular bodies. These granules are considered to be reproductive bodies by some authorities, to be evidences of degeneration by others. A number of workers have claimed to have separated the minute granular forms by filtration. It has been shown, however, that with many Spirochaetes, the spiral forms themselves will pass through Berkefeld filters. Even without suction, such organisms may worm their way through the pores of the filter by their own motility.

Cytophaga. This genus includes certain microbes not definitely related to the other Spirochaetales, but resembling them in certain characters. They occur as slender filamentous cells which vary from almost straight, rod-like forms through different degrees of curvature to distinctly corkscrew-shaped cells. They also occur as small globular coccoid bodies. The latter appear in older cultures and are thought to be a spore-like structure, but not resistant like the endospores of the Bacillaceae. The cells are sluggishly motile, not actively vibrating like the true Spirochaetales. They have no flagella, but move by the contractility of their protoplasm.

Members of this genus have been particularly studied by Winogradsky. They are obligate cellulose bacteria, found in soil. They

—

grow on a simple mineral medium containing no organic matter except cellulose, which is decomposed to form a gummy material. They are cultivated on plates of silica gel instead of agar, where they form round mucoid colonies, yellow to red in color.

Spirochaeta. The term "Spirochaeta" was first applied by Ehrenberg (1833) to a saprophytic spiral organism found in water. When, later, the pathogenic spiral organisms were discovered, they were at first referred to the same genus, and for a number of years the organisms of syphilis and relapsing fever, etc., were called "Spirochaeta." As these have been studied further, however, it has been found that they are quite different from Ehrenberg's organisms and therefore they have been given different generic names.

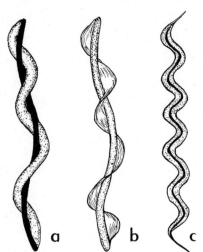

Fig. 108. Diagram Showing the Structure of Several Types of Spirochaetales. *a,* Spirochaeta; *b,* Cristispira; *c,* Treponema.

Meanwhile, however, the name "Spirochaete" has become firmly established as a common name for the group, and has been perpetuated in the names of the family and order. One must therefore distinguish between *Spirochaete,* used as a common name for the group, and *Spirochaeta,* the scientific name of one genus in the group.

Spirochaeta plicatilis is the full name of the organism discovered by Ehrenberg. The organism is composed of an axial filament which is flexible, about which the protoplast is spirally wound. There are no tapering ends. The cell shows a creeping motion quite different from that of the parasitic species. Volutin granules are present in the protoplasm.

Several other species of Spirochaeta have been found. All are saprophytic aquatic organisms. There is some evidence that hydrogen sulphide is necessary for their growth.

Cristispira. In certain molluscs, as oysters, clams, and fresh-water mussels, there is found within the oesophagus a peculiar elongated body of glassy appearance and cartilaginous consistency called the "crystalline style." Within this body certain spiral organisms are constantly found. If the style is removed and placed in water, it will shortly dissolve, liberating the microbes. These organisms move by means of a peculiar structure, the *crista*, or crest. This is a sort of membrane, spirally twisted about the protoplast, attached at one border and free at the other. The spiral character of the organism is due largely to the twisting of this membrane, the cell itself being relatively straight.

Upon death of the organism the crista may become detached, and on disintegrating is found to be composed of a number of parallel fibrils. The organism moves apparently by a wave-like motion of the fibrils composing the crista. According to Noguchi, these fibrils are homologous with the flagella of bacteria.

Several species of Cristispira are known, found in different species of molluscs.

Saprospira. The genus Saprospira is described as resembling Cristispira but lacking the crista. The cells are quite large, the spirals are irregular and shallow. There is no axial filament. Several species are recorded, found in the intestinal tract of oysters and in sea water.

Treponema. The most important species is *Treponema pallidum*, the cause of syphilis. Others are *Tr. pertenuis*, the cause of yaws, and several species occurring as normal parasites in the mouth.

The Treponemata are smaller than the types of Spirochaetes which we have considered so far. They do not have a crista, and the protoplast is evenly disposed about the axial filament, not spirally twisted upon it. The ends of the cells taper.

Syphilis. Syphilis is a chronic infectious disease which may be *acquired* by contact, or which may be *congenital*. Syphilis is perhaps the only infectious disease known to be transmitted directly from parent to offspring, i.e., to be hereditary.

Acquired syphilis develops in three stages. The *primary* lesion is called a *chancre*. It develops as an ulcer with sharply punched-out margins, and a rather firm base. In most cases the disease is transmitted through sexual intercourse, and the chancre appears on the external genital organs. But the organism may invade the skin of other parts of the body, and extragenital chancres have occurred accidentally, for instance on the hands of physicians. After several weeks, a *secondary* stage appears, characterized by a skin rash or eruption, and often by shallow ulcers in the mouth, called *mucous patches*. This stage indicates a generalized distribution of the organisms by way of the blood stream. The *tertiary* stage may appear at an indefinite period after the secondary lesions. In this stage nodular masses of inflammatory tissue, or *gummas*, develop in vari-

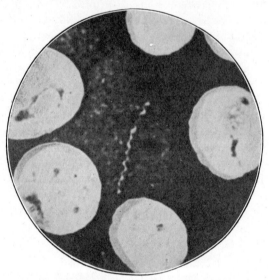

Fig. 109. *Treponema pallidum*. Photomicrograph of a smear from a syphilitic chancre, negatively stained with India ink.

ous parts of the body. Finally an invasion of the central nervous system may result in *locomotor ataxia* if the spinal cord is involved, or *paresis* if the brain is attacked. These diseases are sometimes referred to as a fourth stage, or as *parasyphilis*.

Treponema pallidum. The organism of syphilis is a very slender Spirochaete, varying somewhat in length, but averaging about 7 μ. It is not over 0.5 μ in diameter, often less than that. The cells are usually rather straight, and show a varying number of closely set spiral turns, which are very steep in their pitch. The cells stain very faintly or not at all with the ordinary aniline dyes.

The syphilis Spirochaete may be cultivated (with some difficulty) in a special medium containing pieces of sterile unheated tissue (such as rabbit kidney) together with blood serum. It is strictly anaerobic.

The disease may be produced experimentally in monkeys and in rabbits by inoculation of material from syphilitic lesions, and of cultures.

Diagnosis of Syphilis. In the primary stage the diagnosis is best established by demonstration of the Treponemata in the chancre. Since the organisms do not stain readily, they are most easily detected by examination with *dark-field* illumination. A drop or two of serum is squeezed from the chancre and mounted under a cover-slip, and is examined immediately. The Treponemata reveal their presence by their characteristic motion. They are to be distinguished from another Spirochaete, *Borrelia refringens*, which occurs normally on the external genitalia. The latter organism is coarser, and has fewer, more shallow turns than the organism of syphilis. If a dark-field condenser is not available, the Treponemata may be detected by *negative staining* with India ink, or better by the use of Congo red.

In secondary syphilis the organism may be demonstrated in a similar manner in the mucous patches. With the lesions of tertiary syphilis and of "parasyphilis," and in congenital syphilis, the Spirochaetes are demonstrated in sections of the affected tissues by *silver impregnation*. This procedure involves treating the tissues with silver nitrate, followed by a photographic developer, which deposits metallic silver in the parasites. The Spirochaetes are black, the tissues a pale brown.

The Wassermann Reaction. Syphilis, especially in the late stages, is a disease so protean in its manifestations, so varied in its signs and symptoms, that often the diagnosis is very difficult. In the late lesions it is not possible to demonstrate the organisms with any certainty, and if internal organs are involved, it is quite impossible. It is, however, possible to diagnose syphilis by a blood test, the Wassermann reaction.

The Wassermann reaction is a sort of complement-fixation test. As originally planned by Wassermann it was to be a true complement-fixation reaction, in which an antigen (extract of the *Treponema pallidum*,) in the presence of antibody, combines with complement so that the latter will no longer dissolve red blood cells in the presence of an antibody against red blood cells (see p. 290). When Wassermann first worked on this test, it was not possible to grow the organism of syphilis in artificial cultures. To obtain the antigen, he therefore made a watery extract of the liver of a still-born syphilitic fetus. In such tissue the Treponemata are present in enormous numbers, and he believed it would be possible to extract materials from the organisms which would combine with antibodies in the patient's blood, and so fix the complement.

Actually the test so planned worked, i.e., a mixture of the extract of syphilitic liver and patient's serum fixed complement with cases known to be syphilitic, and did not with cases known not to be syphilitic. But later it was found first, that an *alcoholic* extract gave better results than an aqueous extract, and second, that *normal* liver would serve as well as syphilitic liver. This required a complete revision of the theory upon which the test is based.

Briefly, an emulsion of certain fat-like substances or *lipoids*, present in various tissues but especially in heart muscle, serves as an antigen in the Wassermann test. These lipoids have nothing to do with the *Treponema pallidum*. In the blood of patients with syphilis there is produced some sort of change (not connected with antibody production) such that, when this blood is mixed with the emulsion of lipoids, there results a colloidal complex capable of absorbing complement.

To perform the Wassermann test one mixes in a little test tube

Antigen (alcoholic extract of heart),
Patient's serum,
Complement (fresh guinea pig serum).

These are incubated for a time. If the case is syphilitic, the complement will become inactive. Next,

Sheep's red blood cells,
Rabbit serum immunized to sheep's r.b.c.,

are added. If the case is syphilitic, the complement, being inactive, will be unable to dissolve the blood cells and the tube will remain cloudy. If the case is not syphilitic, the complement will be free, the blood cells will dissolve, and the tube will clear.

While not a true complement-fixation test in the sense that a specific antigen combines with its antibody, the Wassermann test is nevertheless specific for syphilis. Long experience has shown that when carefully performed and properly controlled, this test is positive with the great majority of syphilitic bloods, and negative with the great majority of non-syphilitic bloods.

The *Kahn* test is a sort of precipitation reaction used to diagnose syphilis. If syphilitic blood serum is added to a fine emulsion of lipoids in salt solution, the lipoid particles flocculate to form a coarser emulsion. The Kahn test apparently depends upon the same mechanism as the Wassermann test, and the two tests check well.

Yaws. Yaws is a disease occurring in certain tropical countries which resembles syphilis in many respects. It is caused by a Spirochaete, *Tr. pertenuis*, which resembles *Tr. pallidum* very closely. Yaws is transmitted by direct contact; it is not a venereal disease.

Mouth Spirochaetes. If the student will run a toothpick along the margins of his gums, removing some of the soft white material that collects in the gingival crevice, and examine some of this material under the microscope, he will almost certainly find some Spirochaetes. They may be demonstrated by dark-field illumination, by negative staining with Congo red, or by staining deeply with carbol fuchsin. Numerous other organisms will, of course, also be present, including probably some fusiform bacilli.

There are probably several species of mouth Spirochaetes, which are distinguished by their size, and the number and steepness of their coils. Noguchi divides them into two groups — the larger species, of which *Treponema macrodentium* and *Borrelia vincenti* are examples; and the smaller species of which *Tr. microdentium* and *Tr. mucosum* are examples.

Vincent's Angina. This is a disease believed to be caused by mouth Spirochaetes associated with fusiform bacilli (see p. 382). The disease occurs in the mouth, often on the tonsils, but also frequently involves the gums. It begins acutely with the development of painful, punched-out ulcers. It is often accompanied by a peculiar fetid odor of the breath. The disease may become chronic, and may relapse. It sometimes occurs in epidemics, but is not clearly contagious. Most of the epidemics have been observed in institutions, in prison camps, or in troops at the front (where the disease was called "trench mouth"). In these cases a dietetic deficiency or some other factor might explain the epidemic occurrence.

Smears from the lesions of Vincent's angina show an abundance of fusiform bacilli and mouth Spirochaetes, and either or both of these organisms have long been considered to be the causative agents of the disease. The predominating spiral organism is a large, readily staining Spirochaete with but a few shallow, irregular turns. It seems to resemble the Spirochaetes of relapsing fever closely, and is now called *Borrelia vincenti*.

The constant association of the fusiform bacilli with the Spirochaetes has not been explained, but several theories have been offered: 1. The two organisms are different phases in the life cycle of a single species. 2. The association is a true symbiosis, the organisms living together to the mutual advantage of both. 3. The two organisms are similar in their growth requirements. The latter appears to be the most probable explanation. Both organisms are anaerobic and putrefactive, producing foul odors in cultures.

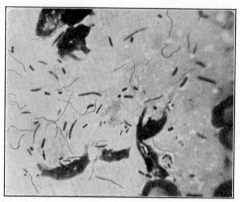

FIG. 110.   *Borrelia vincenti*. Photomicrograph of a smear from Vincent's angina, showing fusiform bacilli and *Borrelia vincenti*. The latter are faintly stained.

The supposed etiologic relationship of the Spirochaete and fusiform bacilli is based solely upon constantly finding the organisms in smears from the lesions. But we have seen that they are nearly always also present in the normal mouth, though fewer in number. Neither alone nor together will they produce infections when inoculated into lower animals. Both organisms are found in a variety of other disease processes — gangrene due to obstruction of the blood supply, gangrenous appendicitis, various types of ulcerative lesions of the skin, gangrene of the lung, and in certain forms of chronic bronchitis. They are found in conditions where dead tissue occurs, and their true rôle is probably that of mere saprophytes growing upon such dead tissues. There is evidence that the disease called "trench mouth" is a form of scurvy, due to a lack of vitamin C.

Borrelia. The Spirochaetes of this genus are not sharply differentiated from the Treponemata, but in general they are larger, coarser, and stain more deeply. Their spiral turns are fewer, shallower, and more irregular.

Vincent's organism is included in this genus, but the majority of species are blood parasites. The most important are those causing relapsing fever in man, but a number of others are known, occurring in the blood of various animals, sometimes causing a disease resembling relapsing fever.

The Relapsing Fevers. One of the first microbes shown to be specifically associated with an infectious disease of man was the spiral organism discovered by Obermeier in 1873 in the blood of patients suffering from relapsing fever.

Relapsing fever is a disease which begins suddenly with a chill and fever, runs an acute course for several days, and then ends by a crisis, to be followed by recurrence after a week or more. Several such attacks occur, the recurrences being usually milder than the initial fever. During the attacks the Spirochaetes are present in the blood in large numbers, and may be demonstrated by direct microscopic examination of stained blood smears.

It is now apparent that there are several different relapsing fevers of man, caused by morphologically similar and closely related species of Borrelia. The various types of the disease differ in their geographic distribution and in the species of insect which serves to transmit the disease. The European type, caused by *Borrelia recurrentis*, is transmitted by lice and bedbugs. An African type, caused by *B. duttoni*, is transmitted by a tick.

A North American form of the disease is caused by *Borrelia novyi*. This disease has been known for some time in foci in the South. Recently it has appeared in the western states, especially California, where it is transmitted to man from chipmunks, by ticks of the genus Ornithodorus.

It is not yet certain that these various types are caused by distinct species, but there is some evidence that immunity to one type does not protect against another.

The relapsing fever Spirochaetes may be cultivated in sterile blood serum to which is added some sterile tissue. They differ from the Treponemata in being aerobic. They are more easily grown in rats. If blood from a case of relapsing fever is inoculated into a rat, the animal is parasitized i.e., the organisms may be found in the blood, but no disease results.

Leptospira. The Leptospiras differ from the other Spirochaetes in being very small, with numerous very closely set spiral turns. According to Noguchi the axial filament is very fine, and not spirally wound. It terminates at one or both ends in a *hooked* extremity. The end of the filament turns over like a letter J. The organisms are very active, showing a rapid rotary movement, so that the spirals are not readily seen, and the rapidly rotating hook looks like a swollen extremity to the cell, which appears hollow in the center.

The Leptospiras are apparently primarily aquatic organisms found living free in stagnant water, especially upon slime that accumulates on submerged surfaces. A disease of man, infectious jaundice, is caused by a Leptospira, as is also a disease occurring in Japan, called "seven-day fever." It is possible that this genus contains a number of pathogenic or parasitic species.

Infectious Jaundice. This disease is also called "Weil's disease." It occurs in widely distant parts of the world, and has been observed almost exclusively in coal miners and in soldiers in the trenches. Two factors are apparently involved in the transmission of the disease — the presence of standing water and of rats. Wild rats, particularly Norway rats, are often found to be infected with the parasite. The organisms are discharged in the urine of the rats, and apparently can live as saprophytes in water. It is supposed that they invade through abrasions of the skin or through the conjunctiva.

The disease begins with fever, and after a few days jaundice and haemorrhages in the skin appear. In the early stages the organisms are present in the blood, but later disappear. In the later stages they are found in the urine.

Leptospira icterohaemorrhagiae, the causative organism, agrees in morphology with the description of the genus given above. It may be grown, aerobically, in complex media containing blood or blood serum. It is very pathogenic to guinea pigs, producing jaundice as in man.

The Leptospira disease differs from other Spirochaete infections in failing to respond to treatment with arsenic compounds.

Rat-bite Fever. This is a rather rare disease that sometimes follows the bite of a rat. It is interesting in that the causative organism resembles a Spirillum rather than a Spirochaete, yet the disease shows all the earmarks of a Spirochaete infection.

The causative organism is called *Spirillum minus*. It is very small, shows several regular spirals, and exhibits lophotrichous flagella. The disease is manifested by paroxysms of fever, with intermissions, as in relapsing fever. During the attacks the organisms are found in the blood. The disease may be successfully treated with arsenical compounds.

CHAPTER XXXI

THE RICKETTSIA AND VIRUS DISEASES

We have considered so far the activities of microbes which are tangible, visible things, which for the most part may be grown in artificial cultures free from all other living material, and therefore may be subjected to critical experimentation. We must now step into less certain territory, and inquire into the nature of certain diseases which are known to be *infectious*, often *contagious*, and therefore probably due to living parasites, but in which the nature of the parasite is as yet unknown.

Following the principles laid down by Koch, the majority of the microbes pathogenic to man were discovered in a relatively short period of time. While new organisms are added to the list from time to time, these discoveries become progressively rarer, and largely concern localized or uncommon diseases. As the years have gone by it has become more and more apparent that there is left a large residue of infectious disease in which microbes have not been found, and in which it appears more and more probable that microbes of the sort already known will *not* be found. This residue of unsolved problems includes some of the most important and most common of the ailments of man, such as chickenpox, measles, mumps, and smallpox.

The list of infectious diseases of unknown origin is a fairly long one, and undoubtedly includes several distinct groups. Some of these have very probably been incompletely investigated by bacteriological methods, and may yet be included in the group of diseases caused by bacteria or protozoa or other more tangible parasites. It was only recently, for instance, that scarlet fever was removed from the list and placed with the bacterial diseases.

But with ever continued research, two groups of diseases are emerging from this heterogeneous list, two groups which are evidently distinct from each other, but with diseases in each group which are evidently very similar to each other. One group comprises certain insect-borne diseases — typhus fever, trench fever, and Rocky

460

Mountain spotted fever. In the insects which transmit these diseases may be found certain very minute, rather indefinite, bacteria-like bodies, known as *Rickettsiae;* the same bodies, in smaller numbers, may be found in the tissues of the diseased individual. The second group, a larger one, contains a more varied assortment of diseases, in which no visible parasite has been found, and in which in most cases it has been found that the infectious agent will pass through bacteria-proof filters. These diseases are said to be caused by *filterable viruses*, and are commonly referred to as "virus" diseases. While no visible parasites can be detected in the majority of virus diseases, it has been possible to demonstrate in the cells of affected tissues certain peculiar structures of unknown nature, called *inclusion bodies*, and it is coming to be recognized that the inclusion bodies provide a better criterion of a virus disease than does filterability of the infectious agent.

Rickettsiae. Some years ago (1909) an American bacteriologist, Ricketts, observed certain minute bacteria-like bodies in the intestines of the ticks which transmit Rocky Mountain spotted fever. Similar bodies were seen in 1916 by Rocha-Lima in lice taken from cases of typhus fever. Believing these to be living organisms, the cause of the disease, he named them *Rickettsia prowazekii*, honoring Ricketts and Prowazek, both of whom died of typhus fever during the course of their investigations. Since then a number of other Rickettsiae have been observed, not only in biting insects which transmit disease, but also in other species.

The Rickettsiae appear like minute bacteria, 0.3 to 0.5 μ in length and about 0.3 μ in thickness. They stain faintly with the ordinary dyes, but are more deeply colored with a complex mixture called Giemsa's stain. This is a polychrome stain of the type used in studying blood smears. They are coccoid, oval, occasionally bacillary in form, and often appear in pairs, or show bipolar staining.

They occur in large numbers in the lumen of the intestine in insects, and also within the epithelial cells which line the intestine. They have been found in the blood in some cases of Rickettsia disease of man, but are evidently present only in small numbers. They have been observed to increase in number when grown with living cells in "tissue cultures," and they have been cultivated on special blood media, but they cannot be grown like ordinary bacteria. They do not pass through bacteria-proof filters.

There seems to be but little doubt that the Rickettsiae are minute living organisms of some sort. Their etiologic relationship to the so-called rickettsia diseases has now been definitely proved by inoculating animals with cultures.

Typhus Fever. This is a disease which formerly occurred in great epidemics. The disease is transmitted by the body louse, and has become epidemic only under those circumstances of overcrowding and lack of morale which make for lousiness — great poverty, catastrophes, and wars. During the World War the disease reached epidemic proportions in central Europe, especially Serbia.

In earlier days the disease was confused with typhoid fever. It usually begins more abruptly, with fever and chills. An eruption appears on the skin after a few days, composed of red to purplish spots which gradually turn brown.

Various bacteria have been brought forward from time to time as the cause of typhus, but with none of these was it possible to fulfill Koch's postulates. It is a curious fact that the blood serum of typhus cases will usually agglutinate a particular strain of *Proteus vulgaris*, known as "Proteus X19," although this organism is not constantly present in the disease and probably has nothing to do with its causation.

If guinea pigs are inoculated with blood from a case of typhus fever they develop a febrile disease, and upon recovery are immune to a second inoculation. It was formerly claimed that filtered blood would transmit the disease, but this is now not accepted. The finding of Rickettsia bodies regularly in the lice which have fed on typhus cases, and at times in the blood and tissues from human cases of the disease, indicates that these bodies probably are the causative organisms.

Trench Fever. Trench fever appeared as an apparently new disease among troops on nearly all fronts during the War. It begins suddenly with fever which is very irregular, showing marked remissions and recurrences. Like typhus, the disease is transmitted by lice.

Rickettsia bodies may be found in the intestines of lice which have fed on cases of trench fever. They are somewhat plumper than those of typhus, and are not found within the epithelial cells. These Rickettsiae (called *R. quintana*) have not been found in man, but it has been shown in human experiments that the infectivity of the lice runs parallel with the occurrence of Rickettsiae in their intestines.

Rocky Mountain Spotted Fever. This is an interesting disease resembling typhus in many respects. It is endemic in the Bitter-root Valley but also occurs in other parts of the Rocky Mountain region. The same or a very similar disease has recently been reported from the eastern part of the United States.

The disease is characterized by fever and a skin rash resembling the eruption of typhus. It is transmitted by the bite of a wood tick, *Dermacentor andersoni*.

Ricketts found small coccoid bodies in the blood of patients suffering from this disease. Later these bodies were also found in ticks (by Wolbach). In the ticks the Rickettsia bodies (*R. rickettsi*) are present not only in the epithelial cells of the intestine, but also in the cells of other tissues, including the salivary glands. They are present in the eggs, and the progeny of infective females are also infective.

The disease may be transmitted to guinea pigs, which frequently develop a fatal infection. Guinea pigs which recover are immune. It has been found that in some cases the inoculation of guinea pigs with wild ticks may not produce infection, but that such guinea pigs are later found to be immune when inoculated with virulent material. This indicates that the causative organism may exist in wild ticks in varying degrees of virulence. The fact that Rickettsiae occur in wild ticks which are found to be non-infective may be explained on this basis.

Virus Diseases. Our conception of filterable viruses dates from the end of the last century, when Beijerinck expressed the idea of a "contagium fluidum" as the cause of *mosaic disease* in plants, and Loeffler and Frosch discovered the filterability of the virus of foot and mouth disease in cattle. Since then a great variety of diseases of man, domestic and wild animals, insects and plants have been referred to this category. It is rather difficult to decide just what should be included in a list of the virus diseases. In the past, *filterability* of the infectious agent through Berkefeld or Chamberland filters has been a criterion. But we do not yet clearly understand what determines filterability. We have noted that probably some visible bacteria will pass through such filters under certain conditions. We know that some of the Spirochaetes are thus filterable. One of the diseases which was formerly grouped with those due to filterable viruses, infectious pleuro-pneumonia of cattle, is caused by a very minute but visible organism which may be cultivated in artificial media. It is probably a minute bacterium.

On the other hand, there are diseases of both animals and plants which resemble those due to filterable viruses in many characters, in which no visible microbes have been found, but in which so far filterability of the infectious agent has not been shown. Such diseases have been included as "virus diseases" by many authorities even though the virus is not filterable.

Inclusion Bodies. In many of the virus diseases, at least of man and the higher animals, the virus shows a predilection for certain

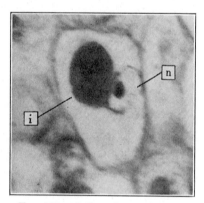

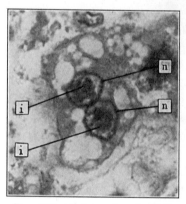

FIG. 111.   A Cytoplasmic Inclusion Body. Photomicrograph of an epidermal cell from fowl pox. *i*, inclusion body; *n*, nucleus.

FIG. 112.   Intranuclear Inclusion Bodies. Section of liver from yellow fever. *n*, nuclei; *i*, inclusion bodies.

tissues. Thus, in the poxes it is the skin which bears the brunt of the attack; while in rabies, anterior poliomyelitis, and epidemic encephalitis, the nervous system is attacked. In cells of the affected tissues one may often find peculiar, indefinite structures, which are not present in normal cells. They are given the rather noncommittal name, "inclusion bodies."

Inclusion bodies vary widely in appearance. In some diseases they occur only in the cytoplasm, not in the nucleus; in other diseases they are typically intranuclear, not appearing in the cytoplasm; while in a few cases they may be either intranuclear or cytoplasmic. They vary in size from minute granules to bodies that nearly fill the cell. While in general they tend to take the acid dyes rather than the basic stains, there are many exceptions, and in some cases basophilic granules may be found in an acidophilic matrix.

From observations of experimental lesions, made at intervals, it appears that the inclusion bodies appear first as a number of minute granules, which increase in size and coalesce to eventually form one rather large body. At first they appear homogeneous, but the larger bodies often show some differentiation in staining or refractility, as though approaching a definite cell structure. This led some of the earlier workers to the opinion that the inclusion bodies are protozoan parasites, of which the virus is but a filterable phase in the life history. But it has been necessary, with further study, to abandon this theory.

Three theories regarding the nature of the inclusion bodies are currently supported:

1. They are the parasite. While we no longer believe that these bodies are Protozoa, it is possible that they represent masses of the virus particles. Although we may not be able to see the cells of the virus, we may be able to see *colonies* of them. It has been possible, by digestion and centrifuging, to obtain inclusion bodies free of cells in some cases, and such bodies, inoculated into susceptible animals, have proved infectious. This proves that the virus is present in the inclusion, but does not prove that the inclusion is composed entirely of virus.

2. They are composed of both the virus particles and cellular constituents. This theory was especially supported by Prowazek, who was impressed by differential staining and apparent heterogeneity in some inclusions. He believed that the inclusion body is composed of minute parasites which are enclosed within a sheath of substance derived from the cell. He called such organisms *Chlamydozoa*.

3. The inclusion body is derived entirely from the cell, and is composed of material produced by a degeneration of the protoplasm, or by a chemical reaction induced by the parasite. This theory has perhaps been most widely accepted.

Whatever may be the nature of inclusion bodies, we cannot doubt their specificity. They have been demonstrated in a great variety of virus diseases in plants, insects, birds, and mammals. In certain diseases they appear in such characteristic form that they may be relied upon for diagnosis.

Transmission of Virus Diseases.   There is apparently no single mode of transmission peculiar to the virus diseases.   Certain of them, the eruptive fevers in man (smallpox and chickenpox, for example), are extraordinarily contagious.   Smallpox spreads like wildfire in an unvaccinated community.   Actual contact, direct or indirect, does not appear to be necessary to spread the disease from one person to another.   While it is not known precisely how these diseases are spread, the most plausible theory postulates that the virus is present in the throat and is discharged into the air in droplets of moisture which are inhaled by others who become infected.   Carriers may be responsible for the spread of such diseases.   Influenza is a virus disease certainly transmitted by droplet infection, and the common cold is possibly another one.   The mode of transmission of anterior poliomyelitis is not definitely known, but there is strong experimental evidence to indicate that infection occurs through the nose.   Yellow fever and encephalitis of horses are transmitted by biting insects, and insect vectors are also important agents concerned in the spreading of virus diseases of plants.

Immunity in Virus Diseases.   In most cases recovery from virus diseases leaves a high degree of permanent immunity.   This is true to a much greater degree than in bacterial diseases.   This immunity is of such a degree that it may be passively transferred by inoculations of serum.   Thus the blood serum of a person who has recovered from yellow fever will protect monkeys inoculated with the virus of that disease, even in small doses.

Protective vaccination with attenuated virus seems to be the most promising method of preventing such diseases.   It has almost completely eliminated smallpox as an epidemic scourge in civilized countries.   Recent experiments indicate that such vaccination may prevent canine distemper and yellow fever.   Preventive vaccination is effective in rabies if started immediately after exposure, i.e., after the patient has been bitten by a mad dog.

Convalescent serum, i.e., serum of patients who have recently recovered from the disease, has recently been used in the treatment of measles and anterior poliomyelitis.   The immunity appears to be due to a substance in the serum, an *antivirus*, which acts much like an antitoxin.   It neutralizes the infectivity of the virus but does not actually destroy it.   The virus may be separated from the antibody by certain methods, and is again found to be infectious.

Mosaic Disease. The very first demonstration of a filterable virus was made in 1892 by a Russian scientist, Ivanovsky, who found that the filtered juice of tobacco plants suffering from *mosaic disease* would give rise to that disease when inoculated into healthy plants. He believed that this disease was due to a bacterium which could pass through his filters.

Since then a wide variety of virus diseases of plants have been observed in many species. They do not tend to destroy the plant outright, as is often the case with bacterial diseases, but rather lead to abnormalities in development or pigmentation, and are of economic importance in reducing crop yields. The name "mosaic disease" was applied because of a characteristic mottling of the leaves, pale areas alternating with dark green areas. Other types of virus diseases of plants are indicated by their names, as "curly top" of beets, peach "yellows," "bunchy top" of bananas, etc.

In general virus diseases of plants are not transmitted by the seeds, but may be transmitted by grafting. In this manner it has been discovered that some of the variegated foliages considered desirable in certain ornamental plants are due to a virus disease; the same variegated foliage may appear in a solidly colored plant after a branch from a variegated plant has been grafted on it.

Smallpox. Smallpox (*variola*), cowpox (*vaccinia*), and alastrim are three diseases of man very probably caused by the same virus.

Smallpox is a very severe disease with a high mortality. It is continuously endemic in some localities, and from time to time gives rise to extensive epidemics. Such epidemics, widespread and destructive in the past, have become less and less frequent and extensive in recent times. This is due mainly to general vaccination, compulsory to many communities, but in part to the occurrence in certain parts of the world of a mild form of the disease, alastrim, which confers immunity to the severe form.

Smallpox begins with fever, chills, and severe muscular pains. The eruption appears first as reddish spots which soon develop into blisters. Eventually pus collects in these blisters, they become little abscesses, which on healing leave scars in the skin. The mortality varies from 10 to 30 per cent in different epidemics.

Alastrim appears much like smallpox, but is milder, with a mortality of but 0.5 to 2 per cent. Originally described as a disease peculiar to the West Indies and certain parts of the world, it is now generally agreed that the same disease is widely distributed and was formerly diagnosed as smallpox. Both types of the disease may occur in the same area.

Vaccinia is the disease which results from inoculation with vaccine virus. It is strictly localized at the site of inoculation, produces only a mild constitutional reaction, and has no mortality. We know that vaccinia is due to the same virus as smallpox, because smallpox virus has been inoculated into cattle, and after several generations in calves, produces typical cowpox, which when inoculated into man, gives rise to only the localized vaccinia. We believe that alastrim is due to the same virus that causes smallpox because recovery from alastrim leaves an immunity to smallpox and because vaccination gives rise to immunity to both diseases.

These facts are important because they indicate that a single virus may exist in three forms, each having a distinct and fairly constant degree of virulence. This is possibly another peculiarity of the viruses. Something approaching this "step" phenomenon in virulence is observed in other virus diseases, as rabies, and in Rocky Mountain spotted fever, a Rickettsia infection.

While typical smallpox, as it appears in man, cannot be reproduced in lower animals, the virus is transmissible to several species producing a somewhat similar disease. Calves, rabbits, and monkeys are susceptible. In the skin of man and experimentally inoculated animals, with both smallpox and vaccine virus, there appear characteristic inclusion bodies in the epithelial cells. They are cytoplasmic, and very irregular in form. They are called *Guarnieri bodies*.

Chickenpox. Chickenpox, or *varicella*, is a mild disease of children with an eruption somewhat resembling that of smallpox, which does not leave scars. It is not certainly known that the causative agent is filterable, but inclusion bodies have been reported. In contagiousness, character of the lesions, and the high degree of immunity which develops, it resembles smallpox sufficiently to warrant considering it a disease in the same category.

Herpes. The common "cold sore" is an infectious disease caused by a filterable virus. This disease usually accompanies some other infection, as a common cold or pneumonia. To the physician the disease is known as *herpes simplex* or *herpes febrilis*. The lesions are little blisters that form on the lips or edge of the nostrils. One attack does not confer immunity. In fact, certain individuals are annoyed by repeated attacks which may recur without a cold or other pre-disposing cause.

If fluid from a herpetic blister is inoculated into the cornea of a rabbit's eye, there develops a characteristic inflammation of the cornea (*keratitis*) and this may be transmitted through rabbits in an indefinite series. If the virus is inoculated directly into the brain of a rabbit, there develops an inflammation of the brain (*encephalitis*) which proves fatal. Intranuclear inclusion bodies are found in the epithelial cells of man, and in cells of the cornea and brain in inoculated rabbits.

Shingles, or *herpes zoster*, is another disease which may or may not be related to herpes simplex. It is characterized by an eruption of blisters which usually develops upon one side of the trunk, the distribution of the eruption corresponds to the terminal distribution of one of the nerves, and there can be no doubt that the disease is intimately associated with the nervous system.

Experiments with herpes zoster have been somewhat confusing, and it is not certain that it is caused by a filterable virus, but there is evidence that it is, and that it is caused by a virus similar to (perhaps identical with) that of herpes simplex, but that the virus is distributed to the skin by way of the nerves. It has also been claimed that herpes zoster is but a special form of chickenpox, one disease giving rise to immunity to the other.

Rabies. Rabies or hydrophobia is an infectious disease of the central nervous system caused by a filterable virus. The disease occurs in a variety of animal species, but particularly in carnivorous animals — dogs, cats, coyotes, skunks, etc. It is transmitted from animal to animal, and from animal to man by biting. The virus is present in the saliva, and its effect upon the brain of the animal is such as to make it "go mad," biting other animals or man without provocation.

The disease in man has a long incubation period which varies considerably from case to case, but is usually longer than six weeks. The duration of the incubation period varies with the severity of the wound and other factors, but more particularly with the site of the wound. Thus with a wound on the leg, it will be longer than with a wound on the face or shoulder. This is due to the fact that the virus is not disseminated through the blood stream, but is absorbed by the peripheral nerves, and travels along that route to the

---

central nervous system. It is not until the virus attacks the nerve cells of the brain that symptoms of the disease develop. This has been proved by various experiments.

The symptoms resemble somewhat those of tetanus or strychnine poisoning. There are spasmodic contractions of various muscles. Often at first the muscles of the throat and tongue are involved, leading to difficulty in swallowing. Later the spasms become generalized, and an attempt at swallowing may throw the patient into a convulsion. This has given rise to the popular name "hydrophobia" (= fear of water). The disease is almost invariably fatal. Rabies is a very real and very terrible disease, certain dog lovers to the contrary notwithstanding.

In the nerve cells there are found characteristic inclusion bodies, called *Negri bodies.* They are cytoplasmic inclusions, and vary considerably in appearance and staining reactions, often showing an acidophilic ground substance containing basophilic granules. They are so constant and characteristic that they may be relied upon to diagnose the disease. By examining smears or sections of the brain of a dog which has bitten people we may determine whether the dog was rabid or not.

The Pasteur Treatment. It was Pasteur who realized that the long incubation period of rabies might make it possible to *immunize* the victim of a mad dog before the symptoms could develop. He had reproduced the disease experimentally, first in dogs, then in rabbits, by inoculating brain from a mad dog into the brain of his experimental animals. Although he could not find the germ, he could experiment with the disease by growing the virus in the nervous system of rabbits. He had found that if he took the brain of a dog which had "gone mad" (*street virus*) and injected some of it into the brain of a rabbit, the rabbit would die after about three weeks. But if the rabbit brain was inoculated into another rabbit, and so on in series, the rabbits died in shorter and shorter periods, until finally after 40 to 50 such passages, the virus regularly killed the rabbits in seven days. This he called the *fixed virus,* constant in its virulence. Fixed virus differs from street virus in other respects. It will not, for instance, produce the disease in rabbits if inoculated under the skin, as will the street virus.

Further experiments showed that the disease might be transmitted by bits of the spinal cord of the rabbit, as well as by brain tissue, and that if the spinal cord was *dried* for a time, it lost its infectiousness, but was capable of producing immunity. Dogs vaccinated with fixed virus (rabbit spinal cord) which had been dried 14 days, then with some dried 13 days, and so on, finally tolerated fresh fully virulent material, even when this was inoculated directly into the brain.

It was a nine-year-old boy, a Joseph Meister from a town in Alsace, who made history by being the first to receive Pasteur's vaccine. He had been bitten in fourteen places by a mad dog. The injections of the dried spinal cord were begun sixty hours after the accident, and were continued, as in the dogs, for 14 days, the final injection being spinal cord which had dried but one day. His wounds healed, and no hydrophobia developed. This was in 1885, and Pasteur's treatment has been used, in modified form, ever since in the prevention of rabies, with striking success. Very rarely has a vaccinated case died, and then usually when the treatment was begun too late. Although only a proportion of people who are bitten by mad dogs develop rabies, once the symptoms appear the outcome is almost certainly fatal.

Anterior Poliomyelitis. Infantile paralysis is another name for this disease. It affects children, mainly. Beginning suddenly with vague symptoms somewhat resembling influenza, there develops in a day or two paralysis of various muscles. The mortality is low, death resulting in most cases from paralysis of the diaphragm. Lives have been saved by the use of artificial respiration kept up by a mechanical respirator. In children that recover from the disease, a large proportion show more or less permanent paralysis of some part of the body.

The mode of spread of this disease is still obscure. The virus is present in the nose and throat, and presumably the disease is disseminated by droplet infection. But the distribution of cases is erratic, and many cases occur which have clearly not been in contact with other cases. This may be due to spread by carriers. A peculiarity of the disease is its seasonal incidence. Epidemics usually occur in the summer, increase in the fall, and stop sharply with the first freezing weather. This is quite different from most other epidemic diseases, which tend to increase in the winter because of the closer association of people in houses and schools. It has been suggested that "polio" is spread by insects prevalent in the summer, and actually the stable fly was suspected for a time. But experimental proof of insect transmission is lacking.

Anterior poliomyelitis may be experimentally transmitted to monkeys, which develop the typical disease. The infectious agent is definitely filterable, but inclusion bodies have not been found. The serum of convalescent cases has a protective effect on monkeys, and there is some evidence that it is of value in treatment if given in the early (pre-paralytic) stages.

Encephalitis. Epidemic encephalitis, or lethargic encephalitis, has been popularly called "sleeping sickness." It must be distinguished from African sleeping sickness due to Trypanosomes. Epidemic encephalitis appeared in Europe during the War and spread rapidly through the United States (from east to west) just after the great influenza epidemic of 1918. The disease usually begins gradually, but there may be an acute stage with fever. It is characterized by a gradually increasing lethargy which progresses to coma.

It was not definitely proved that the post-war encephalitis was caused by a virus, but there have since occurred several localized epidemics which are now known to have been caused by a filterable agent. One of these, occurring in St. Louis, was distributed in such a manner that there is strong presumptive evidence that mosquitoes were responsible for its spread.

Influenza. Influenza is an acute infectious disease attacking the respiratory organs. It has occurred in several great *pandemics*, i.e., epidemics that spread over the whole world. In uncomplicated cases the disease resembles the common cold, but is more severe, with greater prostration. There is a great tendency for the primary disease to be followed by secondary infections with bacteria, especially Streptococci, and the high mortality is largely due to these secondary infections.

For many years this disease was thought to be due to Pfeiffer's bacillus, *Haemophilus influenzae*, but this bacterium is now known to be merely a frequent secondary organism. The disease is due to a filterable virus, which may be found in the nasal mucus. This virus will reproduce the disease when instilled into the noses of ferrets. Influenza differs from the majority of virus diseases in failing to give rise to a lasting immunity. Swine are subject to a very similar disease, swine influenza, and it has been suggested that this is the same as human influenza; the disease may remain latent in swine between epidemics.

The *common cold* is probably also caused by a filterable virus similar to that of influenza.

Viruses and Tumors. The common wart, a tumor-like growth of the skin, is caused by a virus; it may be transmitted by inoculating the filtered fluid from the warts. Similar growths caused by viruses may be found on lower animals, and one, occurring on wild rabbits, has been extensively studied experimentally. It has been found that under certain circumstances the virus of rabbit warts may give rise to extensive tumors of internal viscera, resembling a cancerous growth. A disease of fowls, the Rous chicken sarcoma, is caused by a virus, and also resembles cancer in many respects. These discoveries have given rise to investigations of the possibility that human cancer is caused by a filterable virus.

Virus Diseases in Lower Animals. A variety of domestic animals are subject to a *pox* showing some similarity to smallpox in man. We have seen that cowpox is due to the same virus. Whether the other poxes are but manifestations of the smallpox virus adapted to different animals has not yet been determined.

Fowl pox is a disease of chickens (having no relation to chickenpox in man) which appears to be different from the other poxes. Very striking inclusion bodies appear in the epithelial cells.

Borna disease is a disease of horses which has occurred in extensive epizoötics. It also occurs in cattle and sheep. The disease is a form of encephalitis, but the virus extends to the spinal cord and peripheral nerves. It is definitely caused by a filterable virus and can be transmitted to lower animals. Intranuclear inclusions are found in the brain cells.

Another disease of horses, *equine encephalitis*, has caused great losses in America. There are two forms of the disease, caused by two distinct viruses. The eastern form is apparently spread by mosquitoes. The western form has been experimentally transmitted to guinea pigs by ticks. Ground squirrels have been found to be susceptible to the western virus, and the eastern form of the disease has been found occurring naturally in pheasants. It is probable that the disease occurs naturally in various wild animals and is transmitted to horses by biting insects. The disease occurs only in the summer, stopping sharply with the first frost, as does anterior poliomyelitis. There have been several human infections with equine encephalitis virus.

Distemper of dogs is a disease well known by every dog lover, which has recently been added to the virus diseases. It is characterized by an inflammation of the upper air passages somewhat similar to an acute cold in man, and by symptoms referable to the central nervous system. It has been proved to be due to a filterable virus, and cytoplasmic inclusion bodies occur in various epithelial tissues. It is claimed that this disease may be prevented by vaccination with attenuated virus.

Encephalitis of foxes occurs in epizoötics of considerable extent in fur farms in America. This disease has been extensively studied by Green. In some cases the foxes go into a lethargic state somewhat resembling the symptoms of epidemic encephalitis in man. A respiratory condition resembling a cold also occurs. The disease is caused by a filterable virus, and inclusion bodies are present.

Interrelationships of the Viruses. Long before the bacteriological era, physicians had not only clearly distinguished between diseases, but had learned to group together similar diseases much as naturalists had grouped plants and animals into families. It was a fundamental principle of Koch that each disease is due to a specific microbe, and that the specific characters of the disease depend upon the specific characters of the microbe.

With the virus diseases we cannot study the organism in the laboratory, and are forced to direct our attention entirely to the diseases themselves. With these diseases it becomes doubly important to differentiate between different kinds and to determine group relationships. This may be done by observation of patients and by experiments on animals.

The virus diseases present certain characters which serve to distinguish them from diseases caused by bacteria and protozoa. But when we come to subdivide them, we run into a whole series of intertangling alliances that make the subject rather confusing and that indicate that a great deal more must be learned about these diseases before we may understand them clearly.

At first glance it would seem that we might recognize two great divisions — one attacking primarily the skin (the poxes and herpes), the other the nervous system (rabies, poliomyelitis, encephalitis). But we have seen that the herpes virus may produce encephalitis in rabbits. With virulent strains, inoculation of the cornea of rabbits will give rise to encephalitis, the virus probably traveling by way of nerves to the brain, as in rabies. And in herpes zoster, the virus is apparently distributed to the skin by the nerves. There is some evidence that the viruses of herpes zoster and chickenpox are the same. It has been claimed that some cases of human encephalitis have followed vaccination, that they may be due to the vaccine virus!

Influenza, and probably the common cold, are virus diseases which attack primarily the nose and throat and bronchi. Herpes is definitely associated with colds, and the encephalitis epidemic followed so closely upon the influenza epidemic that many physicians considered them to be causally related. Distemper in dogs and encephalitis in foxes are diseases resembling encephalitis in man which begin with symptoms resembling an acute cold in man.

All of these considerations lead one to wonder whether the various diseases described in the preceding pages are due to different causes, or are rather varying manifestations of virulence of but a few distinct viruses. We have seen how, by animal passages, viruses may be "fixed" at different degrees of virulence, and may be caused to form different types of disease. Perhaps something of this sort also occurs naturally.

Yellow Fever. Yellow fever occupies an anomalous position among the infectious diseases. Like protozoan and Rickettsia diseases, it is transmitted by an insect host necessary to the developmental cycles of the agent, i.e., the disease is spread in no other manner. Yet it is caused by an invisible filterable agent which gives rise to inclusion bodies in the affected tissues.

The story of yellow fever is as thrilling as anything history can offer, a story of cold-blooded heroisms and martyrdoms; cold-blooded because these heroes deliberately exposed themselves to almost certain death, not in the hurly-burly of war, but in the quiet calm of carefully planned experiments. Yellow fever, not so long ago, was a scourge that periodically wiped out thousands in South America, the West Indies, and the southernmost parts of North America. Communities were terrorized by its appearance. All sorts of theories were rife regarding the cause and mode of spread, but nothing was definitely known. It was hoped to stop the contagion by quarantine and fumigation, but these proved futile.

During the Spanish-American War the disease attacked American troops, and during the occupation of Cuba an American commission was sent to investigate, aiming to discover the cause and mode of spread. This commission was composed of Walter Reed, James Carroll, Jesse Lazear, and Aristides Agramonte, the latter a Cuban who had already contracted yellow fever and had recovered (and was therefore immune). Acting upon a theory proposed by a Cuban doctor, Carlos Finlay, they *proved* that the disease was transmitted by a certain species of mosquito, then called *Stegomeiya fasciata*, now known as *Aedes aegypti*.

This proof was obtained by a series of well-planned and well-controlled experiments upon themselves and upon other human volunteers, soldiers and civilians. The first evidence was obtained when Carroll allowed himself to be bitten by a mosquito which had fed upon a yellow fever patient. He contracted the disease and nearly died. Then Lazear, noting a Stegomeiya alight upon his arm while in a yellow fever hospital ward, deliberately allowed it to fill with blood. He died of yellow fever.

Now with a group of volunteers a crucial experiment was performed. These men were first kept in quarantine in screened houses for a time, to be sure that none of them had accidentally contracted yellow fever. In a special house kept warm and humid, but thoroughly screened, volunteers exposed themselves to infection by the popularly supposed method of contagion. They slept with bedclothing from beds in which yellow fever cases had slept. They even wore the pajamas in which patients had died. Clothing, bedding, and eating utensils were soiled with vomitus, urine, and feces of yellow fever patients. They lived in the house thus for twenty days without developing the disease. Next these volunteers were proved to be non-immune. When bitten by infectious mosquitoes, they contracted the disease.

In another house, again thoroughly screened, a second experiment was performed. Here things were all clean and hygienic. The house was divided by a mosquito-proof screen. On one side, infectious mosquitoes were liberated. Volunteers who stayed here and were bitten contracted the disease. On the other side of the screen, two non-immunes slept for thirteen nights without results.

And so it was known that the disease is transmitted only by the mosquito. The mosquito becomes infectious only when it feeds upon the blood of a case during the first four or five days, and does not become infectious until at least twelve days after it has so fed. This was precious information, bought with the life of Lazear, and with desperate illness in a number of others.

Control of Yellow Fever. The prevention of yellow fever depends upon preventing the spread of the disease by *Aedes aegypti*, and this involved a study of the life history and habits of this mosquito. It is something like the English sparrow; it lives about dwellings and does not travel far. Its larvae live in cisterns or tin cans or little puddles, not in swamps and ponds like other mosquitoes. How, by screening and cleaning up breeding places, Gorgas eradicated the disease from Havana and later from the Panama Canal Zone, is now history. Similarly it has disappeared from New Orleans and Rio de Janeiro and other places where it was rampant, because of the use of the information bought at such a price by Reed's associates and volunteers.

Noguchi and the Leptospira. But still the nature of the infectious agent was unknown. Reed and his associates had found that the disease could be transmitted to humans by inoculation of the blood, if this was taken in the early stages of the disease. And then, following up the possibilities of the newly discovered filterable virus theory, they found that they could transmit the disease with *filtered* blood, and on this basis the disease was listed for a time with the virus diseases.

But this part of the problem was by no means considered settled, and in 1918 a Japanese bacteriologist, Noguchi, began researches looking for the causative organism. We noted in the preceding chapter that Noguchi had greatly extended our knowledge of the Spirochaetes — he was a specialist on Spirochaetes. He had just returned to the Rockefeller Institute from Japan, where he had studied infectious jaundice and its causative organism, the *Leptospira icterohaemorrhagiae*. He was impressed by the similarity between yellow fever and Weil's disease, and by the known filterability of Spirochaetes. He went to South America to look for Spirochaetes in yellow fever.

And he found them. By injecting blood or urine from yellow fever cases into guinea pigs he reproduced a disease resembling yellow fever, and in these guinea pigs he found an organism closely resembling the Leptospira of Weil's disease, which he called *Lepto-*

spira icteroides. He found them occasionally in the blood of patients, and he grew them in cultures from both patients and guinea pigs. He transmitted the infection from patients to guinea pigs with mosquitoes, and again found the spiral microbes in the guinea pigs. These experiments were repeated in several parts of South America and in Mexico with cases which the native physicians assured him were typical cases of yellow fever.

But Noguchi's results were not generally accepted; they were opposed especially by people who had known yellow fever, like Agramonte who had pioneered with Walter Reed. No one before had produced yellow fever in guinea pigs. No one but Noguchi could distinguish his Leptospira from the organism of infectious jaundice, and it was claimed that he had been studying that disease, not yellow fever at all.

Yellow Fever in Africa. Yellow fever increases in severity with the age of the individual attacked. A deadly disease in adults, it may be very mild in children. In certain parts of Africa, notably Nigeria, the disease is endemic. It does not exterminate the natives because, for the most part, they contract it when children, recover, and are immune. But to outsiders who come into the territory, it is a deadly menace — how deadly will be shortly disclosed.

Here the International Health Board has maintained new researches, and here new history has been made. Here Stokes, Bauer, and Hudson made the important discovery that yellow fever (the real thing, this time) could be transmitted to certain monkeys. No more human volunteers! More precious information, for Adrian Stokes contracted yellow fever and died during his investigations. Precious information because it has made possible a whole new series of experiments on monkeys, which indicate more and more clearly that this disease is truly caused by an invisible filterable virus. That it is a virus disease is further indicated by the finding of definite intranuclear inclusion bodies, similar to but distinct from the intranuclear inclusions of herpes, in the liver cells of diseased monkeys.

It has been further discovered that the virus may be transmitted from monkeys to mice by inoculation of the monkey's blood serum directly into the mouse's brain. The virus may then be transmitted directly from mouse to mouse in an indefinite series. But within the mouse the virus becomes modified, attacking only the nervous system and producing encephalitis. Although guinea pigs are refractory to direct inoculations of the virus from human cases, they are susceptible to the virus after it has been altered by passage through mice, and also develop encephalitis. These newer observations very definitely bring yellow fever into relationship with the other virus diseases.

With the experimental disease established in monkeys, it now became possible to study the problem of immunity. This work is still too new to evaluate, but sounds promising. It has long been known that people who have recovered from yellow fever are highly immune — another characteristic of virus diseases. It was found by Stokes and his associates that the blood of convalescent cases would protect monkeys from a fatal infection, and more recently Hindle, in England, has found that monkeys may be successfully vaccinated with a vaccine made from infectious monkey liver treated with formaldehyde.

The Rockefeller commission found no Leptospiras in African yellow fever, and Noguchi himself began to doubt his work, and went to Africa to make sure. He, too, found no Leptospiras there, but found — death from yellow fever.

INDEX

Abortion, contagious, 365.
Abscess, 278; dental root, 356; lung, 352.
Acceptor, hydrogen, 180.
Accommodation, 20.
Acetic acid, 183, 179; production of, 326.
Acetobacter, 326; *aceti*, 327; *industrium*, 327; *oxydans*, 327; *xylinum*, 327.
Acetobacteriaceae, 99, 326.
Acetone, 183, 389.
Acetyl-methyl-carbinol, 370.
Achromobacter, 381.
Acidfast bacteria, 97, 397; in soil, 403; saprophytic, 402.
Acidfastness, 97.
Acidobacteriaceae, 317.
Acne, 409.
Acquired characters, 151.
Actinobacillosis, 381, 410.
Actinobacillus, 381; *ligniersi*, 381.
Actinomyces, 315, 413.
Actinomycetaceae, 95, 316, 397, 413.
Actinomycetales, 94, 397.
Actinomycetes, 94, 176; conidia of, 95; mycelium of, 95; soil, 413.
Actinomycosis, 381, 409.
Actinophrys sol, 107, 108.
Actinopoda, 49.
Actinosphaerium eichhorni, 107.
Activation, of hydrogen, 180.
Adaptation, 154.
ADOLPH, 107.
Adsorption, 34, 110, 172, 204, 292.
Aedes aegypti, 476.
Aerobacter, 368; *aerogenes*, 241, 370.
Aestivo-autumnal fever, 443.
Agar, 15, 219; blood, 226; deeps, 219; preparation of, 219; Sabouraud's, 423; serum, 226; slants, 219; tartaric acid, 423.
Agglutination, 204, 281; tests, 287.
Agglutinins, 281.
AGRAMONTE, 476, 478.
Air, microbes in, 8, 229.
Alastrim, 467.
Albumose, 187.
Alcohol, as disinfectant, 254; oxidation of, 326.
Alcoholic fermentation, 183, 425.
Aldehyde, 216.
Alexin, 289.

Algae, 58; blue-green, 63; green, 59; relationships of, 65.
Alkalibacteriaceae, 317.
Alkaligenes, 321.
Alkylamines, 332.
Allergy, 297; in rheumatism, 357.
ALMQUIST, 145.
Amines, 188.
Amino acids, 187.
Amitosis, 54; of yeast cells, 78.
Ammonia, 187.
Ammonification, 188, 417.
Amoeba, 40; nutrition of, 42; *proteus*, 41, 107, 438; reproduction of, 42.
Amphoteric compounds, 33.
Amylobacter, 389.
Amylopsin, 174.
Anaerobic bacteria, 177, 201, 386; classification of, 388; putrefactive, 390.
Anaerobic cultures, 217.
Anaphylaxis, 295.
Animalcules, 2.
Anopheline mosquitoes, 444.
Anterior poliomyelitis, 110, 471.
Antheridium, 68.
Anthrax, 13, 384.
Antibiosis, 209.
Antibodies, 281.
Antiformin, 400.
Antigens, 282, 454; somatic, 286; surface, 286.
Antitoxin, 265, 273, 281; botulism, 395; diphtheria, 407; gas gangrene, 391; scarlet fever, 353; tetanus, 393.
Antivirus, 466.
APPERT, 4.
Arabinose, 224.
Arcella dentata, 107.
Archimycetes, 80.
Arnold sterilizer, 227.
Arsenic, 101, 441, 448.
Arteries, hardening of, 246.
Arthritis, chronic, 356.
ARTHUR, 301.
Artificial selection, 152.
Ascomycetes, 69, 73, 80.
Ascospores, 73, 146, 432.
Ascus, 73.
Aspergillosis, 421.
Aspergillus, 425, 427; *flavus*, 427; *fumi-*

481

gatus, 421, 427; *glaucus*, 74, 427; *niger*, 179, 184, 418, 427; *oryzae*, 418, 427; *wentii*, 427.
Assimilation, 168.
Asthma, 295.
Athlete's foot, 420.
Atopy, 295.
Autoclave, 227.
Autolysis, 340.
Autotrophic bacteria, 85, 165, 169, 319.
Autotrophic metabolism, 168.
Avian tubercle bacilli, 398.
Axial filament, 48, 448.
Axopodia, 48.
Azotobacter, 192; *agile*, 237, 325; *beijerincki*, 325; *chroöcoccum*, 121, 210, 233, 325; *vinelandi*, 325.
Azotobacteriaceae, 99, 324.

Bacillaceae, 100, 129, 383.
Bacillarieae, 61.
Bacillus, 98, 314, 315; *anthracis*, 157, 384; *cereus*, 385; *lactis aerogenes*, 370; *megatherium*, 131, 140, 139, 386; *mesentericus vulgatis*, 386; *mucosus capsulatus*, 374; *mycoides*, 136, 188, 385; *prodigiosus*, 375; *ramosus*, 108; *subtilis*, 385; *terminalis*, 100, 386; *vulgatus*, 386.
Bacteraemia, 263.
Bacteria, acidfast, 97, 397; acidophilic, 199; aciduric, 199; antigenic structure of, 285; atrichous, 126; autotrophic, 85, 165, 319; cells of, 118; chemical analysis of, 126; chromogenic, 207; classification of, 306; colonies of, 212, 214; counting of, 214; cultivation of, 212; cytoplasm of, 126; death of, 248; definition of, 82; diphtheroid, 403; discovery of, 3; evolution of, 103; exotoxin-forming, 264; growth of, 138; halophilic, 207; heredity in, 151; intestinal, 245, 368; invasive power of, 261, 268; iron, 84; isolation of, 212, 215; lake, 236; life-cycles of, 145; marine, 238; mesophilic, 198; metabolism of, 165; microaerophilic, 178; milk, 239; motility of, 126; mouth, 244; nitrifying, 319; nuclei of, 133; nutrient requirements of, 194; oligocarbophilic, 197; orders of, 83; origin of, 103; parasitic, 208, 259; pathogenic, 208, 260; photosynthetic, 91; plant-disease, 301; prototrophic, 165; psychrophilic, 197; pyogenic, 278; relationships of, 102; reproduction of, 138; respiration of, 177; staining of, 35, 142; structure of, 83, 117; sulphur,

89; symbiotic, 208; temperature relations of, 197; thermophilic, 198; toxins of, 263; true, 98; variations of, 151, 152; wax in, 120.
Bacteriaceae, 100, 314, 380.
Bactericidal antibodies, 281; disinfectants, 256.
Bacteriolysin, 265.
Bacteriophage, 111, 159.
Bacteriopurpurin, 91.
Bacteriostasis, 255, 258.
Bacterioviridin, 91.
Bacterium, 314, 315, 382; *coli mutabile*, 156; *denitrificans*, 191; *radicicola*, 192; *triloculare*, 382.
Bacteroides, 382.
Bacteroids, 322.
Balantidium coli, 438.
BARBER, 215.
Barred cells, 403.
DE BARY, 12.
Basidiomycetes, 69, 73, 433.
Basidiospores, 74, 433.
Basidium, 74.
BAUER, 478.
Bedbugs, 457.
BEEBE, 229.
Beer, 11, 17, 338, 432.
Beggiatoa alba, 90.
VON BEHRING, 273.
BEIJERINCK, 18, 192, 463.
BERGEY, 317.
Berkefeld filters, 109.
Betabacterium, 359.
Bichloride of mercury, 254.
Bile solubility, 345.
Biochemistry, 167.
Biological oxygen demand, 204.
Blackleg, 393.
Blastomycosis, 421.
Blepharoplast, 44, 441.
Blights, 304.
Blood, agar, 226, 348; cultures, 348, 376; invasion of, 263; media, 226; stains, identification of, 287.
Blue-green algae, 63, 102.
Boas-Oppler bacillus, 360.
B.O.D., 204.
Boils, 333.
BORDET, 290, 292, 367.
Borna disease, 473.
Borrelia, 244, 382, 447, 456; *duttoni*, 457; *novyi*, 102, 457; *recurrentis*, 457; *refringens*, 453; *vincenti*, 455, 456.
Botryomycosis, 335, 410.
Botulism, 264, 267, 394.
Bougies, 61.
Bovine tubercle bacilli, 398.

Branching of bacteria, 96, 146; false, 87.
Bread molds, 418.
Bread, ropy, 386.
BREED, 317.
Broth, 218.
Brown algae, 59.
Brucella, 362, 364; *abortus*, 196, 242, 364, 365; *melitensis*, 364, 365.
Bubo, 363.
Bubonic plague, 363.
BUCHANAN, 317.
BUCHNER, 171, 266.
Budding, 56, 72, 76, 77, 146, 432.
Bulgarian buttermilk, 361.
Bunchy top of bananas, 467.
BURRILL, 17, 301.
Butter starters, 358.
Butyribacteriaceae, 317.
Butyric acid, 8, 183, 388; bacteria, 388.

CAGNIARD-LATOUR, 5.
Cancer, 305, 473.
Canning, 4, 253, 396.
Caproic acid, 418.
Capsules, 120, 344.
Carbohydrates, decomposition of, 175; in milk, 222.
Carbol fuchsin, 97.
Carbolic acid, 254.
Carbon cycle, 184.
Carbon dioxide, 196.
Carbon monoxide, oxidation of, 320.
Carboxydomonas, 320.
Carbuncle, 334.
Carriers, of amoebic dysentery, 439; of diphtheria, 407; of disease, 260; of enzymes, 172; of hydrogen, 181; of meningitis, 339; of typhoid, 376, 377.
CARROLL, 476.
Caseation necrosis, 399.
Casein, 223.
Caseinogen, 223.
CASTELLANI, 317.
Catalase, 174, 202.
Catalyst, 171.
Cattle, disease of, 335, 354, 365, 393, 398, 401.
Caulobacteriales, 84, 88.
Cellfalcicula, 328.
Cellobiase, 177.
Cellobiose, 176.
Cellulase, 176.
Cellulomonas, 381.
Cellulose, 47, 176; decomposition of, 176, 390, 417, 450.
Cellvibrio, 328.
Central body, 64.
Cephalotrichinae, 316.

CHALMERS, 317.
Chamberland filters, 109.
Chancre, 367, 451.
Cheese, Camembert, 418; Cheddar, 361; Roquefort, 418; Swiss, 361.
Chemosynthesis, 169.
Chemotaxis, 277.
Chemotherapy, 257.
CHICK, 250, 251.
Chickenpox, 468.
Chilomonas paramecium, 108.
Chiniofon, 439.
Chitin, 47, 70, 94, 120.
Chlamydobacteriaceae, 316.
Chlamydobacteriales, 84, 86.
Chlamydospores, 72.
Chlamydothrix, 316.
Chlamydozoa, 465.
Chlorine, 254.
Chlorophyceae, 58, 59.
Chlorophyll, 44.
Chloroplasts, 44, 60.
Cholera, 328.
Cholera red reaction, 331.
Cholera vibrio, 329.
CHOLODNY, 231.
Chromatin, 128, 132, 136.
Chromatium, 91.
Chromobacterium, 321.
Chromogenus actinomycetes, 414.
Chromosomes, 152.
Chrysophyceae, 59, 61.
CHURCHMAN, 119.
Ciliata, 43, 52.
Cirri, 56.
Citric acid, 182, 419.
CLARK, 198, 199.
Classification of bacteria, 306; LEHMANN and NEUMANN, 314; MIGULA, 315; ORLA-JENSEN, 316; S.A.B., 317.
Clostridium, 383, 386, 387, 392; *acetobutylicum*, 389, 390; *botulinum*, 183, 267, 379, 396; *butyricum*, 183, 388; *chauvoei*, 393; *oedematiens*, 391, 392; *oedematis-maligni*, 391, 392; *pastorianum*, 192, 389; *putrificum*, 188, 390; *sporogenes*, 390; *welchii*, 387, 391, 392.
Clubbed cells, 403.
Clubs, 410.
Coagulants as disinfectants, 254.
Coccaceae, 314, 315.
Cocci, 98.
Coccidioidal granuloma, 422.
Coccidioides immitis, 422.
Coccogoneae, 65.
Coenocyte, 60.
Coenocytic mycelium, 67.
Co-enzyme, 183.

Cohn, 18, 145, 314, 385.
Cohn-Koch dogma, 19, 145.
Cold, common, 473.
Cold sore, 468.
Colloids, 204.
Colon bacillus, 155, 369.
Colonies of bacteria, 14, 212; deep, 212; giant, 156; rough, 159; satellite, 209; secondary, 156; smooth, 159; surface, 212.
Colonies of protozoa, 46.
Colonies of viruses, 465.
Colon-typhoid group, 368.
Colpidium, 251; *colpoda*, 107.
Colpoda cucullus, 107.
Columella, 71, 425.
Comma bacillus, 329.
Complement, 288; fixation, 289; test, 290, 453.
Condenser, 28.
Congo red, 36, 39, 143, 453.
Conidia, 71, 95.
Conidiophore, 425.
Conjugation, 54.
Conjunctivitis, 367.
Conn's agar, 414.
Constitutive enzymes, 174.
Contagium fluidum, 463; vivum, 6.
Coprinus, 75.
Corynebacterium, 95, 96, 243, 315, 397, 403; *acnes*, 409; *diphtheriae*, 406; *pseudodiphthericum*, 408; *xerosis*, 409.
Cowpox, 271, 467.
Crenothrix polyspora, 86, 316.
Cresol, 187, 254.
Crista, 451.
Cristispira, 447, 450.
Crown gall, 304.
Crystal violet, 37.
Crystalline style, 451.
Cucumber wilt, 304.
Cultural characters, 218.
Cultures, anaerobic, 217; enrichment, 216; pure, 12, 13, 15, 212; pure line, 215.
Curdling of milk, 223.
Curly top of beets, 467.
Cyanophyceae, 59.
Cycle, carbon, 184; nitrogen, 190.
Cyclogeny, 162.
Cyclostages, 162.
Cymomucor, 424.
Cystitis, 370.
Cysts of bacteria, 93, 319; of protozoa, 42, 439.
Cytase, 176.
Cytodes, 133.
Cytomorphosis, 143, 383.

Cytophaga, 447, 449.
Cytoplasm of bacteria, 126.
Czapek's agar, 414.

Dancing body, 78.
Daphnia, 276.
Dark-field illumination, 29, 30, 453.
Davaine, 13.
Deaminization, 187.
Death of bacteria, 248; order of, 249.
Debaromyces neoformans, 434.
Decarboxylation, 188.
Decay of teeth, 360.
Deer flies, 364.
Dehydrogenation, 180.
Denitrification, 190, 233.
Dental bacteriology, 17.
Dental caries, 360.
Dermacentor andersoni, 463.
Dermatomycosis, 419.
Dermatophytes, 419.
Desmolase, 175.
Dextran, 121, 358.
Dialister, 362, 367; *pneumosintes*, 367.
Diastase, 174, 176.
Diatoms, 61, 109.
Dick and Dick, 353.
Dick test, 353.
Differentiation, 47, 105, 144.
Difflugia corona, 107.
Dilution, extinction, 215.
Dinoflagellates, 46.
Diphtheria, 264, 405; diagnosis of, 405.
Diphtheria antitoxin, 407.
Diphtheroid bacteria, 96, 403.
Diplococcus lanceolatus, 344; *pneumoniae*, 343.
Diploid nuclei, 55, 75, 151.
Disaccharides, 176; hydrolysis of, 177.
Disinfectants, 253; standardization of, 256.
Disinfection, 248.
Dissimilation, 168.
Dissociation, microbic, 159.
Distemper, 474.
Doederlein's bacillus, 360.
Donator, hydrogen, 180.
Donker, 183.
Dourine, 440.
Droplet infections, 340.
Drug idiosyncrasies, 295.
Drum-stick bacillus, 394.
Drying, death by, 252.
Ducrey's bacillus, 367.
Dulcite, dulcitol, 224.
Durham, 279.
Dusch, 4.
Dyes, acid, 33, 36, 143; aniline, 33;

bacteriostatic action of, 255; basic, 33, 36.
Dysentery, amoebic, 438; bacillary, 380.
Dystrophic lakes, 234.

EBERTH, 375.
Eberthella typhi, 125, 183, 306, 375.
Ecology, 194.
Ectoplasm, 41, 119.
Eh, 201.
EHRENBERG, 3, 314.
EHRLICH, 291.
Electrolytes, 293.
Electrophoresis, 204.
Emetine, 439.
EMMERICH, 329.
Empyema, 352.
Encephalitis, 469, 472; of foxes, 474; of horses, 473.
ENDERLEIN, 145.
Endo's medium, 216.
Endocarditis, 356.
Endoenzyme, 174.
Endoplasm, 41.
Endospores, 129.
Endotoxins, 264, 265.
Entamoeba, 438; *buccalis*, 244; *coli*, 245, 438, 439; *gingivalis*, 438; *histolytica*, 438, 439.
Enteric fevers, 368.
Enterobacteriaceae, 100, 368.
Enterococcus, 358.
Enterotoxin, 336.
Environmental factors, 194.
Enzymes, 170; adaptive, 174; amylolytic, 174; constitutive, 174; lipolytic, 174; nomenclature of, 173; proteolytic, 173; specificity of, 172.
Eosin, 33.
Eosin-methylene blue agar, 372.
Erwineae, 368.
Erwinia, 302, 307, 374; *amylovora*, 304; *carotovora*, 304; *tracheiphila*, 304.
Erysipelas, 350.
Erysipelothrix, 415; *murisepticae*, 415; *rhusiopathiae*, 415.
Eschericheae, 368.
Escherichia, 368; *coli*, 241, 245, 369.
Eubacteriales, 84, 98; families of, 99.
Euglena viridis, 45.
Eumycetes, 68.
Eustachian tubes, 351.
Eutrophic lakes, 234.
Eversporting races, 158.
Evolution, 47, 152, 306; of algae, 65; of bacteria, 102; of fungi, 80; of protozoa, 57.
Exoenzyme, 174.

Exotoxins, 263, 264, 265.
Extinction dilution, 215.
Eye, accommodation of, 20; infections of, 367.
Eyepiece, 23; Huygens, 24.

Facultative anaerobes, 178; autotrophs, 169.
False branching, 87; membrane, 405.
Farcy, 365.
Fat in bacteria, 127; in fungi, 69; in yeasts, 78, 434; metabolism, 193.
Fermentation, 5, 7, 181; alcoholic, 183, 432; induced reactions in, 181; stormy, 223; types of, 182.
Feulgen reaction, 136.
Filterability of bacteria, 149; of spirochaetes, 449.
Filterable viruses, 109, 110.
Filters, bacterial, 109.
Filtration of water, 204.
FINLAY, 476.
Fire blight, 304.
Fission, binary, 42; longitudinal, 46; transverse, 54; yeasts, 432.
Fixed virus, 470.
Flagella, 44, 124; staining of, 124.
Flagellates, 44, 45, 46.
Flavines, 255.
Flavobacterium, 381.
FLEXNER, 340; type of dysentery bacilli, 380.
Food poisoning, 336, 378, 394.
Foraminifera, 49.
FORD, 383.
Foot, athlete's, 420; Madura, 411.
Foot-cell, 426.
Formaldehyde, 91, 254.
Fowl pox, 473.
Foxes, encephalitis of, 474.
Frequency distribution, 310.
Friedländer's bacillus, 374.
FROSCH, 463.
Fruits, molds in, 418.
Fungi, 67; classes of, 68; nutrition of, 79; relationships of, 80.
Fungi imperfecti, 69, 75.
Fungous diseases, 419.
Furuncle, furunculosis, 333.
Fusiform bacilli, 382, 456.
Fusobacterium, 244, 382.

Gaertner's bacillus, 379.
GAFFKY, 16, 375.
Gaffkya tetragena, 337.
Galactan, 121.
Galactose, 177, 222, 224, 433.
Gallic acid, 418.

Gallionella ferruginea, 88.
Galls, 304.
Gametes, 52, 445.
Gametocytes, 445.
Gammarus, 134.
Gangrene, gas, 264, 390.
GANGULEE, 147.
GARDNER, 146.
Garget, 354.
Gas gangrene, 264, 390.
Gas trap, 223–225.
GAY-LUSSAC, 5.
Gelatinase, 220.
Gelatine, 220; liquefaction of, 220.
Generation time, 140.
Genes, 115, 152, 163, 251.
GENGOU, 290, 367.
Geotrichum lactis, 140, 200, 430.
GERLACH, 33.
Giant colonies, 156.
Giardia, 3.
Giemsa's stain, 438.
Glanders, 365.
Globigerina ooze, 49.
Globulin, 282.
Glossina morsitans, 440; *palpalis*, 441.
Gluconic acid, 419.
Glucose, 177, 222, 224.
Glutathione, 181.
Glycerine, 434.
Glycogen, 69, 127.
Gonidia, 65, 147.
Gonococcus, 196, 341.
Gonorrhoea, 341.
GORGAS, 477.
GORTNER, 115.
Gram's stain, 36.
Granulation tissue, 262.
Granuloma pyogenicum, 335.
Granulose, 127.
GREEN, 115, 474.
Green algae, 59.
GREW, 2.
Group reactions, 284.
Growth, 138; curve of, 141, 144; law of, 141.
GRUBER, 279.
Guarnieri bodies, 468.
GUILLIERMOND, 135.
Gumma, 452.
Gums, 121, 244.
GUTSTEIN, 119.

HAAG, 157.
HADLEY, 150, 162.
HAECKEL, 133.
Haemoglobin, 226.
Haemolysin, 288, 336, 349.

Haemophilus, 362, 366; *conjunctivitidis*, 367; *ducreyi*, 367; *influenzae*, 190, 208, 366; *pertussis*, 367.
HALVORSON, 85.
Hanging drop preparations, 32.
HANSEN, 17.
Haploid nuclei, 55, 75, 151.
Haptens, 283, 285.
HARDEN, 183.
Hay bacillus, 385.
Hay fever, 295.
Heart disease, 356.
Heat, death of bacteria by, 252.
HELLRIEGEL, 18.
Hemicellulose, 176.
Heredity, 151.
Herpes, 468; febrilis, 468; simplex, 468; zoster, 469.
HESSE, Frau, 15.
Heterocysts, 65.
Heterogamy, 72.
Heterothallism, 72.
Heterotrophic nutrition, 99, 170.
Hexose, 175.
Hexylresorcinol, 255.
Higher bacteria, 403.
HINDLE, 479.
Hiss's stain, 122.
Hives, 297.
Hoffman's bacillus, 408.
Hog cholera, 379.
Holdfasts, 87, 88, 424.
Holophytic nutrition, 45.
Holozoic nutrition, 42.
Homothallism, 72.
HOOKE, 2, 24.
Hormogone, 65.
Hormogoneae, 65.
Horses, disease of, 335, 354, 365, 440, 473.
HORT, 145.
Host specificity, 260.
Hucker's stain, 36.
HUDSON, 478.
Human tubercle bacilli, 398.
Hybrids, 151.
Hydrogen, acceptor, 180; activation of, 180; donator, 180; ion concentration, 198; oxidation of, 320; peroxide, 202, 254; sulphide, 89, 91, 187.
Hydrogenomonas, 320.
Hydrolase, 175.
Hydrophobia, 469.
Hypersensitivity, 294, 299.
Hyphae, 67; ascogenous, 73.

Immunity, 271; active, 273; cellular, 280; humoral, 280; passive, 275; of plants, 303.

Immunology, 280.
Inclusion bodies, 464.
Incubation period, 265, 269.
Incubators, 216.
Indicator, Andrade's, 225; Eh, 201; pH, 199.
Individuation, 105.
Indol, 187, 221, 246.
Induced reactions, 172, 181.
Infantile paralysis, 110, 471.
Infection, 259; allergy of, 297; local, 262; metastatic, 263; spreading, 262.
Infectious jaundice, 458.
Influenza, 366, 472; swine, 472.
Ink, manufacture of, 418.
Insects, disease transmission by, 52, 101, 303, 363, 364, 436, 440, 441, 446, 449, 457, 460, 462, 463, 466, 471, 473, 476; yeasts in, 434.
Intermolecular respiration, 170, 178.
Intestines, bacteria in, 245.
Intramolecular respiration, 178.
Inulin, 345.
Invasive power of bacteria, 261.
Invertase, invertin, 177.
Involution forms, 143.
Iodine, 254.
Ipecac, 439.
Iron bacteria, 84.
Isoelectric point, 33.
Isogamy, 72.
IVANOVSKY, 467.
Ivy poisoning, 295.

JANSEN, 23.
Jaundice, infectious, 458.
JENNER, 271.
Johne's disease, 401.
JORDAN, 106.

Kahn test, 455.
Kala-azar, 441.
Kefir, 359.
KELLERMAN, 381.
Keratitis, 469.
Kieselguhr, 109.
Kinetoplast, 442.
KITASATO, 16, 362.
Klebsiella, 368, 374; pneumoniae, 374; rhinoscleromatis, 374.
KLUYVER, 180, 181–183.
KNIGHT, 194.
KOCH, 13, 143.
Koch's postulates, 16.
Koch-Weeks bacillus, 367.
KRAUS, 279.
Kurthia, 380.

L+ dose of toxin, 408.
Lab ferment, 223.
Lacquers, 390.
Lactalbumen, 222.
Lactase, 177.
Lactic acid, 7, 179, 183, 430.
Lactobacilleae, 100, 359.
Lactobacilli, in dairy products, 360; in human body, 359.
Lactobacillus, 359; acidophilus, 241, 245, 246, 360, 361; bifidus, 245, 360; boasoppleri, 360; bulgaricus, 241, 246, 361; casei, 241, 361.
Lactose, 177, 222.
Lag phase, 141.
Lake bottoms, bacteria in, 235.
Lakes, 234; bacteria in, 235, 236.
LANCEFIELD, 350.
LARSON, 255.
LAURENT, 192.
LAZEAR, 476.
Lead acetate medium, 378.
Leaf spots, 304.
Leak of strawberries, 425.
VAN LEEUWENHOEK, 1; microscopes of, 22.
Legumes, 192, 321.
LEHMANN, 314.
Leishmania, 441; braziliensis, 442; donovani, 442; infantum, 442; tropica, 442.
Lenses, 20–25.
Leprosy, 402; rat, 402.
Leptospira, 447, 458; icterohaemorrhagiae, 458, 477; icteroides, 478.
Leptothrix, 84; crassa, 85; ochracea, 84.
Leptotrichia buccalis, 244, 415.
Leucocidin, 336.
Leucocytes, 277.
Leucocytosis, 278.
Leuconostoc, 358; citrovorus, 358; dextranicus, 358; mesenteroides, 358.
LEVINE, 372.
Lice, 457, 462.
LIEBIG, 5.
Life-cycles of bacteria, 146.
Light, effect on bacteria, 207, 252.
Limberneck, 395.
LISTER, 11.
Listerella, 380.
Litmus, reduction of, 224.
Lockjaw, 393.
Locomotor ataxia, 452.
LOEFFLER, 15, 463.
Loeffler's blood serum, 226.
LÖHNIS, 145.
Lophotrichous flagella, 124, 126.
LUBS, 199.
Lumbar puncture, 339.

Luminibacteriaceae, 316.
Lumpy jaw, 96, 410.
Lymph glands, 247, 263, 363, 401.
Lyngbya, 64.
Lysins, 281.
Lysol, 254.

McBETH, 381.
McIntosh-Fildes jar, 218.
Macrogamete, 445.
Macrogametocyte, 445.
Macronucleus, 54.
Macrophages, 278.
MADSEN, 250.
Madura foot, 411.
Magnification, 21, 25; useful, 27.
Mal de caderas, 440.
Malachite green, 255.
Malaria, 442; transmission of, 446.
Malignant pustule, 384.
Mallein test, 366.
Malleomyces, 362; *mallei*, 365, 381.
Malta fever, 364.
Maltase, 174, 177.
Maltose, 176.
Mannitol, 224.
Mannose, 224.
Mantoux test, 299.
MASSINI, 155.
Mastigophora, 43.
Mastitis, 354.
Mastoiditis, 352.
Media, blood, 225; differential, 216; nutrient, 218; routine, 218; selective, 231; special, 225; sterilization of, 227; sugar, 224; synthetic, 226.
MEISTER, 471.
MELLON, 145, 148.
Meningitis, 339, 340, 352, 434.
Meningococcus, 338.
Mercaptan, 187.
Merozoite, 445.
Metabolism, 168; autotrophic, 169; carbohydrate, 175; fat, 193; heterotrophic, 170; protein, 186.
Metachromatic granules, 129, 403.
METCHNIKOFF, 246, 276, 279.
Methane, oxidation of, 320.
Methanomonas, 320.
Methyl red test, 373.
Metula, 426.
MEYER, 128, 135.
Microbacterium, 380.
Micrococcaceae, 99, 333.
Micrococcus, 314, 315, 333; *progrediens*, 106.
Microgamete, 445.
Microgametocyte, 445.

Micromanipulator, 215.
Micronucleus, 54.
Microphage, 249.
Microscopes, 20; compound, 23; electronic, 29; van Leeuwenhoek's, 22; simple, 21.
Microspira, 315.
MIGULA, 315.
Milk, 221, 239; acidophilus, 246; bacteria in, 239; carbohydrates in, 222; coagulation of, 223; diseases spread by, 241; fermentations of, 240; grades of, 240; litmus, 221; molds in, 430; peptonization of, 223; proteins of, 222; reduction of, 224.
MILLER, 17.
MINOT, 144.
Miraculous organism, 375.
Mist bacillus, 403.
Mitosis, 42, 54.
Mode, 311.
Molds, 416; biochemical characters of, 416; identification of, 423; industrial uses of, 418; in soil, 417; methods for studying, 423; species of, 424.
Molluscs, 450.
Monilia albicans, 77, 430; *sitophila*, 418.
Monocytes, 380.
Monomolecular reaction, 250.
Monomorphism, 18, 145.
Monomucor, 424, 425.
Monosaccharides, 177; fermentation of, 182.
Monotrichous flagella, 124, 126.
Mordants, 36, 124.
Morphologic characters, 308.
Mosaic disease, 463, 467.
Mosquitoes, transmission of disease by, 444, 445, 446, 472, 473, 476.
Motility of bacteria, 33, 124.
Mouth bacteria, 244; spirochaetes, 455.
Mucor, 424, 425; *corymbifer*, 425; *mucedo*, 425; *racemosus*, 173, 425; *rouxianus*, 425.
Mucous patches, 452.
MUDD, 110.
MUELLER, 314.
MÜLLER, 3.
MÜNTZ, 189.
MURRAY, 317.
Mushrooms, 74.
Mutations, 151, 152, 155, 163.
Mycelium, 67.
Mycetozoa, 51.
Mycobacteriaceae, 95, 397.
Mycobacterium, 95, 96, 315, 397; *butyricum*, 403; *leprae*, 402; *paratuberculo-*

sis, 401; *phlei*, 402; *smegmatis*, 402; *stercoris*, 403; *tuberculosis*, 397.
Mycoderma, 433.
Mycoplana, 332.
Mycoses, 419.
Myxobacteriales, 84, 92.
Myxomycetes, 51, 69.

NAEGELI, 12, 150.
Nagana, 440.
NAKANISHI, 134.
Nasopharynx, 339.
Nectaries, 303.
Nectaromyces, 433.
NEEDHAM, 4.
Negri bodies, 470.
NEISSER, 155.
Neisseria, 244, 338; *catarrhalis*, 160, 341; *flava*, 160; *gonorrhoeae*, 341; *intracellularis*, 339.
Neisseriaceae, 100, 338.
NEUBERG, 184.
Neufeld test, 346.
Neutral red, 32, 129.
Niches, 210.
VAN NIEL, 90.
Nigrosin, 36, 39.
Nitrate formers, 190.
Nitrates, reduction of, 170, 190.
Nitrification, 189, 233, 319.
Nitrifying bacteria, 319.
Nitrobacter, 190, 320.
Nitrobacteriaceae, 99, 319.
Nitrobacterieae, 319.
Nitrogen cycle, 190.
Nitrogen fixation, 191, 233, 322–324.
Nitrosococcus, 190, 319.
Nitrosocystis, 320.
Nitrosomonas, 190, 210, 319.
Nodule bacteria, 147, 192, 321.
NOGUCHI, 447, 479.
Noguchia, 362, 368.
Nose, bacteria of, 244.
Nostoc, 358.
Nucleic acid, 64, 128.
Nucleoprotein, 128.
Nucleus, 132; diffuse, 135; incipient, 64.
NUTTALL, 279.
NYMAN, 250.

OBERMEIER, 457.
Objective, achromatic, 24; immersion, 28.
Oidia, 76, 95, 430.
Oil, immersion, 28.
Oligocarbophilic bacteria, 197.
Oligotrophic lakes, 234.
OMELIANSKY, 390.

Oöcyst, 445.
Oögonium, 68.
Oökinete, 445.
Oömycetes, 72.
Oöspore, 68.
Opsonic index, 334.
Opsonin, 280, 281.
Oral groove, 53.
Organelle, 52.
Orla-Jensen's classification, 316.
Ornithodorus, 457.
Oscillatoria, 89, 102.
Osmophilic yeasts, 207, 434.
Osmotic pressure, 206.
Osteomyelitis, 335.
Otitis media, 351.
Oxalic acid, 179, 416.
Oxidation-reduction, 180, 200, 202.
Oxidizing agents, effect on bacteria, 254.
Oxydobacteriaceae, 316.
Oxygen demand, biological, 204.

Palisade arrangement, 140, 403.
Palmella, 59.
Paracasein, 223.
Paraffin, 210, 332, 403.
Paralysis, infantile, 471.
Paramecium, 52; *caudatum*, 107.
Parasitic bacteria, 243.
Parasyphilis, 452.
Paratyphoid bacilli, 378; fever, 378.
Paresis, 452.
Parthenogenesis, 78, 432.
Parvobacteriaceae, 100, 362.
PASTEUR, 6, 179, 272; treatment, 470.
Pasteurella, 362; *pestis*, 362, 363; *tularensis*, 364.
Pasteurization, 10, 240, 253.
Peach yellows, 467.
PEARL, 141.
Pébrine, 10.
Pellicle, 219.
Penicillium, 418, 426–428; *camemberti*, 418, 428; *digitatum*, 418, 428; *expansum*, 428; *glaucum*, 428; *italicum*, 428; *roqueforti*, 418, 428.
Pentoses, 176, 224.
Peptone, 187, 220.
Peptonization, 223.
Periplast, 448.
Perithecium, 73, 427.
Peritonitis, 350.
Peritrichinae, 316.
Peritrichous flagella, 125, 126.
Peroxide, 202, 254.
Pertussis, 290, 367.
Petri plates, 213.
PETTENKOFER, 329.

PFEIFFER, 16, 265, 279, 367.
pH, 199.
Phaeophyceae, 59.
Phagocytosis, 276.
Phenol, 187, 246, 254; coefficient, 256.
Photosynthesis, 44, 79, 90, 91, 207.
Phototaxis, 207.
Phragmidiothrix, 316.
Phycocyanin, 64.
Phycomycetes, 68, 72, 424.
Phyla, 43, 306.
Phytomastigina, 45.
Phytomonas, 302, 307, 332; *malvaceara*, 304; *phaseoli*, 304; *stewarti*, 304; *tumefaciens*, 305.
PIETSCHMANN, 136.
Pigments of bacteria, 207.
Pimples, 409.
Pink eye, 367.
Plague, 362; bubonic, 363; pneumonic, 363.
Planococcus, 315.
Planosarcina, 315.
Plants, bacterial disease of, 301.
Plasmodesmids, 139.
Plasmodium, 51.
Plasmodium, 443; *falciparum*, 443; *malariae*, 443; *vivax*, 443.
Plasmolysis, 120, 206.
Plasmoptysis, 206.
Plates, Petri, 213; pour, 212, 213; streak, 213.
Plating, 15, 212; quantitative, 214.
PLENCIZ, 6.
Pleomorphism, 12, 145, 403.
Pleuro-pneumonia of cattle, 463.
Pleurosigma, 62.
Pneumococcus, 120, 343.
Pneumonia, 344, 374; serum treatment of, 345; Streptococcus, 352.
Poisoning, food, 336, 378, 394.
Poison oak, 295.
Polar groups, 292.
Poliomyelitis, anterior, 471.
Pollen, 295.
Polysaccharides, 121, 175, 283, 285; hydrolysis of, 176.
Polyvalent serum, 341.
Portal of entry, 261, 303.
Post-fission movements, 139.
Postulates, Koch's, 16.
Potato, bacillus, 386; medium, 221; rot of, 425.
Pour plates, 212, 213.
Precipitin, 281; test, 287.
Presumptive test, 372.
Proactinomyces, 95, 397, 409; *asteroides*, 411; *bovis*, 409, 412; *madurae*, 411.

Producing organisms, 46.
Prontosil, 257.
Propionibacterium, 359, 361; *shermanii*, 361.
Propionic acid, 183, 361.
Prosthetic group, 172.
Protaminobacter, 332.
Proteae, 368.
Proteins, 186, 282, 285.
Proteose, 187.
Proteus, 188, 375; *vulgaris*, 188, 375; X 19, 375, 462.
Protobacterieae, 319.
Protoplasm, 167.
Protozoa, 40; classes of, 43; relations of, 57.
Protozoa, pathogenic, 435; methods for studying, 437; types of, 438.
Protozoan diseases, 435; geographic distribution of, 435; immunity in, 437; recurrent character of, 436; transmission of, 436.
PROWAZEK, 461, 465.
Pseudoglobulin, 407.
Pseudomonadaceae, 99, 328.
Pseudomonadeae, 99, 328, 332.
Pseudomonas, 91, 315, 332; *aeruginosa*, 188, 209, 332; *cyanogenes*, 241, 332; *fluorescens*, 332; *syncyanea*, 332.
Pseudomycelium, 429.
Pseudopodia, 40, 48, 276.
Ptomaines, 188.
Puerperal fever, 350.
Pure cultures, 12, 212.
Pure line cultures, 215.
Pus, 278; blue, 332.
Putrefaction, 5, 187, 199.
Putribacteriaceae, 317.
Pyaemia, 263.
Pyelonephritis, 370.
Pyocyanase, 209.
Pyocyanin, 332.
Pyogenic bacteria, 278.
Pyorrhoea, 244.
Pyrenoids, 60.
Pyruvic acid, 184.

Quartan fever, 443.
Quellungsreaktion, 346.
Quinine, 257.

Rabbits, snuffles of, 363; tularaemia of, 364.
Rabies, 272, 469.
Racemomucor, 424, 425.
Radiating canals, 54.
Radium, 252.
RAHN, 248, 249, 250, 251.

Rat-bite fever, 458.
Rat leprosy, 402.
Rats, transmission of plague by, 362; infectious jaundice, 458.
Reaction of media, 198.
Red sulphur bacteria, 90.
REDI, 3.
Reducibacteriaceae, 316.
Reductase, 174.
REED, 476.
Relapsing fever, 457.
Rennin, 223.
Reproduction of bacteria, 138.
Resolving power, 26.
Respiration, 168, 177; intermolecular, 170, 178; intramolecular, 178.
Retrograde evolution, 82, 115.
Rheumatism, 356.
Rhinoscleroma, 374.
Rhizobacteriaceae, 99, 321.
Rhizobium, 321; leguminosarum, 147, 148, 192, 304.
Rhizoid, 424.
Rhizopoda, 49.
Rhizopus, 424, 425; nigricans, 73, 425.
Rhodobacteriaceae, 316.
Rhodophyceae, 59.
Ricin, 274.
RICKETTS, 461.
Rickettsia, 460, 461; prowazekii, 461; quintana, 462; rickettsi, 463.
Ringworm, 419.
RIPPEL, 136.
RIVERS, 114.
ROCHA-LIMA, 461.
Rocky Mountain spotted fever, 463.
Roentgen rays, 152, 252.
Ropy bread, 386.
Rots, 304.
ROUX, 273.
Royal Society, 2.
Rusts, 75.

Sabouraud's agar, 423.
Saccharomyces, 78, 432; cerevisiae, 432; ellipsoideus, 431, 432; fragilis, 359.
Saccharomycetaceae, 432.
Safranin, 37.
Salmonella, 378; aertrycke, 379; enteriditis, 379; gallinarum, 380; paratyphi, 378; psittacosis, 379; pullorum, 380.
Salmonelleae, 368, 375.
San Joaquin Valley, 422.
Saponin, 255.
Saprolegnia, 67.
Saprophyte, 165.
Saprospira, 447, 451.
Saprozoic nutrition, 45.

Sarcina, 314, 315, 337; damnosus, 338; lutea, 337; perniciosus, 338; ureae, 338.
Sarcodina, 43, 48.
Satellite colonies, 209.
Sauerkraut, 200.
Scarlet fever, 264, 352; serum treatment of, 353.
Schick test, 300, 408.
Schizogony, 52, 444.
Schizomycetes, 69, 83.
Schizont, 445.
Schizosaccharomyces, 432.
SCHLOESING, 189, 192.
SCHOTTMÜLLER, 348.
SCHROEDER, 4.
SCHULTZE, 4.
SCHUMACHER, 128.
SCHWANN, 4.
Scrofula, 399.
Scurvy, 456.
Sea, bacteria in, 238.
Secondary colonies, 156.
Sectors, 157.
Segmentation, 445.
Seitz filters, 109.
Selection, artificial, 152.
Self-purification of streams, 237.
Sensitization, 295.
Septa, 69.
Septic tank, 203.
Septicaemia, 263, 350; haemorrhagic, 362.
Serrateae, 368.
Serratia, 375; indica, 375; marcescens, 375.
Serum, antibacterial, 275; antitoxic, 275; convalescent, 466; immune, 159, 273, 279; polyvalent, 341.
Serum-fast organisms, 437.
Serum media, 225.
Serum sickness, 296.
Serum treatment, 274; of diphtheria, 407; of gas gangrene, 391; of meningitis, 340; of pneumonia, 345; of scarlet fever, 353; of tetanus, 393.
Seven-day fever, 458.
Sewage, purification of, 202.
Sex in bacteria, 148, 161.
SHERMAN, 350, 361.
SHIGA, 380.
Shigella, 380; dysenteriae, 380; paradysenteriae, 380.
Shingles, 469.
Shock, anaphylactic, 295.
Side-chain theory, 291.
Signet-ring forms, 444.
Silage, 200.
Silkworms, disease of, 10.

Silver nitrate, 254.
Skin, bacteria of, 243.
Skin tests, 299.
Sleeping sickness, 472; African, 441.
Slime bacteria, 84, 92.
Slime molds, 51.
Smallpox, 467.
SMITH, ERWIN, 18, 301.
Smuts, 74.
Snuffles, 363.
Soaps, 255.
Soil, actinomycetes in, 413; bacteria in, 203, 205, 229; environmental factors of, 232; molds in, 417; structure of, 229.
Sore throat, 350, 354.
Soya sauce, 418.
SPALLANZANI, 4.
Species, 309.
Specificity, of enzymes, 172; of infections, 260; of serum reactions, 284.
Sphaerotilus, 87, 316; dichotomus, 87, 139.
Spinal fluid, 339.
Spirillaceae, 314, 315.
Spirilleae, 99, 328.
Spirillum, 314; minus, 459; volutans, 101, 120, 331.
Spirochaeta, 314, 447; plicatilis, 450.
Spirochaetaceae, 447.
Spirochaetales, 84, 100, 447.
Spirochaetes, 447; and Spirilla, 447; and Protozoa, 448; life-cycles of, 449; structure of, 448.
Spirodiscus, 314.
Spirogyra, 61.
Spirosoma, 315.
Spirostomum ambiguum, 106.
Spontaneous generation, 3, 8.
Sporangiophore, 424, 425.
Sporangiospore, 71.
Sporangium, 51, 70, 424.
Spores of bacteria, 18, 100, 129, 153; of fungi, 70, 72; of yeasts, 78, 432.
Sporoblast, 446.
Sporobolomyces, 433.
Sporogenous granule, 130.
Sporogony, 52, 444, 445.
Sporotrichosis, 421.
Sporotrichum schenckii-beurmanni, 421.
Sporozoa, 43, 442.
Sporozoite, 52, 444, 446.
Sputum, examination of, for pneumonia, 344, 346; for tuberculosis, 400.
Stain, Giemsa's, 438; Gram's, 36; Hiss's, 122; Welch's, 122; Wright's, 438; Ziehl-Neelsen's, 97.
Staining, 33; bacteria, 35, 142; capsules, 122; flagella, 124; negative, 39; spores,

131; theory of, 34; vital, 32; volutin, 128.
Stains, acid and basic, 33.
Stalked bacteria, 88.
Staphylococcus, 243, 333; albus, 333; aureus, 312, 333, 336, 379; citreus, 333.
Starch, 176.
Starters, butter, 358.
STEARN and STEARN, 38.
Stegomeiya fasciata, 476.
Sterigmata, 74, 426.
Sterilization, 251; fractional, 228; of media, 227.
Sterilizers, 227.
Stewart's disease of sweet corn, 304.
Stigma, 45.
STOKES, 478.
Stolon, 424.
Stomach, bacteria in, 244.
Stomata, 303.
Stormy fermentation, 223.
Strangles, 354.
Strauss reaction, 366.
Streak plates, 213.
Streams, bacteria in, 237.
Street virus, 470.
Streptobacteriaceae, 100, 343.
Streptobacterium, 359.
Streptococceae, 100, 343.
Streptococci, 346; classification of, 348; differentiation from pneumococci, 344; haemolytic, 348; morphology of, 347; serum reactions of, 349; species of, 351; types of, 350.
Streptococcus, 314, 315, 346; agalactiae, 354; bovis, 351, 357; cremoris, 351; durans, 351; epidemicus, 354, 357; equi, 351, 354; equinus, 351, 357; fecalis, 245, 351, 357; lactis, 179, 240, 241, 351, 357, 358; liquefaciens, 351; mastitidis, 351, 354; pyogenes, 258, 349, 351, 354, 357; salivarius, 244, 351, 355; thermophilus, 351, 357; viridans, 349; zymogenes, 351.
Stylonichia pustulata, 107.
Sucrase, 177.
Sucrose, 177, 224.
Suctoria, 43, 56.
Sugar media, 224.
Sulfanilamide, 257.
Sulphur, oxidation of, 320.
Sulphur bacteria, 89, 90, 320.
Sulphur granules, 410.
Surface tension, 255.
Surfaces, effect on bacteria, 204.
Surgery, antiseptic, 11; aseptic, 11.
Surra, 440.
Swarmers, 319.

Swine erysipelas, 415; influenza, 472.
Symbiosis, 56, 192, 208, 456.
Symplasm, 149.
Synergism, 208.
Syphilis, 208, 451; diagnosis of, 453.

Taka-diastase, 418.
TALIAFERRO, 437.
Tartaric acid agar, 423.
T.A.T., 408.
Taxonomy, 288, 306.
Teeth, bacteria on, 244; decay of, 415.
Temperature, effect on bacteria, 197.
Tentacles, 43, 56.
Tertian fever, 443.
Test, agglutination, 287; complement fixation, 290; Dick, 300; Mantoux, 299; precipitin, 287; Schick, 300.
Tests of Protozoa, 49.
Tetanus, 264, 393.
Thallophytes, 58.
Thallus, 58.
Thermal death point, 253.
Thermal death time, 253.
Thermobacterium, 359.
Thiobacilleae, 319.
Thiobacillus, 321; denitrificans, 170, 191, 321; thioxidans, 321.
Thiobacteriaceae, 316.
Thiobacteriales, 84, 89, 320.
Thiocystis, 91.
Thiophysa, 90.
Thiothrix, 90.
THORNTON, 147.
Three-point multiplication, 146.
Thrush, 430.
Thymonucleic acid, 64, 128, 136.
Ticks, transmission of disease by, 364, 457, 463.
Timothy hay bacillus, 402.
Toluidin blue, 129.
Tongue, bacteria on, 244.
Tonsillitis, 350; epidemic, 354.
Tonsils, bacteria of, 244.
Torula meningitis, 434.
Torulopsis, 433.
Toxaemia, 264.
Toxins, 263, 405, 408.
Toxoid, 408.
Trachoma, 368.
Trench fever, 462; mouth, 455.
Treponema, 447, 451; macrodentium, 455; microdentium, 455; mucosum, 455; pallidum, 451, 452; pertenuis, 451, 455.
Trichobacteriaceae, 316.
Trichocyst, 54.
Trichophyton, 420.
Tripoli, 61.

Trophozoite, 52, 444.
Trypanosoma, 46, 440; brucei, 440; equiperdum, 441; evansi, 440; gambiense, 441; lewisi, 46, 440; rhodesiense, 441.
Trypsin, 174, 278.
Tryptophane, 221.
Tsetse fly, 440.
Tubercle, 399.
Tubercle bacilli, 397; cultivation of, 401; staining of, 97.
Tuberculin, 297; reaction, 297, 401.
Tuberculosis, 399; diagnosis of, 400.
Tularaemia, 364.
Tumors, 304, 473.
Turbidity, 219.
Types, antigenic, 123, 285, 286; of Clostridium botulinum, 395; of meningococci, 340; of pneumococci, 346; of Staphylococci, 336; of Streptococci, 350; of tubercle bacilli, 397.
Typhoid fever, 375; diagnosis of, 376; vaccination for, 377.
Typhus fever, 462.
Tyrosinase reaction, 414.

Ultramicrobes, 105.
Ultramicroscope, 29.
Ultraviolet light, 27, 252.
Undulating membrane, 441.
Urea, 188.

Vaccination, 271; against anthrax, 384; against blackleg, 393; against diphtheria, 408; against typhoid, 377.
Vaccine, 271, 275; treatment, 334.
Vaccinia, 271, 467.
Vacuole, contractile, 41, 53; digestive, 42, 53.
Variation, 151; discontinuous, 311.
Varicella, 468.
Variola, 467.
Veillonella, 338, 342.
Vibrio, 314, 328; comma, 328; danubicus, 331; metchnikovi, 331; schuylkiliensis, 331.
Vibrion septique, 392.
Vincent's angina, 455.
Vinegar eels, 184.
Vinegar, manufacture of, 326.
Virulence, 260, 302; attenuated, 272; variations in, 269.
Virus diseases, 463; immunity in, 466; transmission of, 466.
Viruses, attenuated, 272; cultivation of, 112; enzyme theory of, 113; filterable, 110; no free-living, 112; interrelationships of, 474; nature of, 113; size of, 114, 115.

494 INDEX

Vitamins, 434.
Voges-Proskauer test, 373.
Volutin, 64, 79, 127.
Volvox, 47.
Vorticella, 56.

Warts, 473.
Wassermann reaction, 453.
Water, bacteria in, 233; bloom, 64;
purification of, 204; sanitary analysis
of, 371; spread of disease by, 371.
Weil's disease, 458.
WELCH, 16; bacillus of, 391.
Wet preparations, 31.
Whooping cough, 367.
Widal test, 287, 376.
WIELAND, 180.
WILFARTH, 18.
Willia, 432.
Wilts, 304.
Wine, disease of, 10; acetic bacteria, 327;
yeasts, 432.
WINOGRADSKY, 18, 189, 231, 449.
WINSLOW, 313.
Woody tongue, 381.

Woolsorter's disease, 384.
Wright's stain, 438.

Yaws, 455.
Yeast-like fungi, 429.
Yeasts, 77, 429; activities of, 434; classification of, 431; industrial, 432; osmophilic, 207; methods for studying, 433; wild, 433.
Yellow fever, 475.
YERSIN, 362.
YOUNG, 183.

ZETTNOW, 135.
Ziehl-Neelsen stain, 97.
Zoögloea, 122.
Zoömastigina, 45.
Zoösporangium, 68.
Zoöspore, 68.
Zygomycetes, 72.
Zygosaccharomyces, 78, 432.
Zygospores, 72, 146, 148.
Zymase, 174.
Zymonema dermatitidis, 422.